# Introductory 1
# ALGEBRA

*Third Edition*

Russell F. Jacobs

**Harcourt Brace Jovanovich, Publishers**

New York   Chicago   San Francisco   Atlanta   Dallas   *and*   London

## ABOUT THE AUTHOR

### RUSSELL F. JACOBS

*Author and Consultant in Mathematics*
*Harcourt Brace Jovanovich, Inc.*
*Formerly Mathematics Supervisor for the*
*Phoenix Union High School System*
*Phoenix, Arizona*

### PICTURE CREDITS

Printed in the United States of America

Regular Edition: **ISBN 0-15-357790-8**
With Alternate Answers: **ISBN 0-15-357791-6**

# Preface

INTRODUCTORY ALGEBRA 1 is the first book of a two-volume series designed to extend the regular one-year algebra course over a period of two years. Both this book and its companion volume, INTRODUCTORY ALGEBRA 2, are written in a semiprogrammed style that has proven to be pedagogically sound. The pivotal questions labeled **P-1, P-2, P-3,** and so forth, have been popular with both students and teachers in previous editions. These pivotal questions encourage student involvement and help students discover key relationships as they progress through each lesson. Answers to the pivotal questions are provided in the back of the student editions of both texts.

Concepts are presented by means of the pivotal questions, by framed generalizations usually accompanied by one or more examples of the generalization, by one or more examples of typical problems or exercises that are set off by a unique design feature, and by a minimal amount of formal discourse. As an additional feature, chevroned side comments are used to clarify or emphasize important points or occasionally to introduce a term.

Both *Oral* and *Written Exercises* are provided for each section. The *Oral Exercises* help reinforce students' understanding of the concepts presented in the section and prepare them to do the *Written Exercises* successfully. The items of the *Written Exercises* labeled "A" are paired by type and degree of difficulty. The "B" exercises are considered more difficult than the "A" exercises but are related to the topics covered in the accompanying section. The "C" exercises are either supplemental in nature or will help students discover relationships to be presented later.

There is a statement of the main goal of each section just before the first group of items in the *Written Exercises*. A sample problem related to the goal is given followed by the answer to the problem. Each group of items in the *Oral Exercises* and the "A" portion of the *Written Exercises* is referenced to specific examples and pivotal questions of the section wherever it is possible. This feature enables students to refer readily to a worked example or a pivotal question.

A *Chapter Summary* consisting of *Important Terms* and *Important Ideas* is included at the end of each chapter. Each important term is referenced to a page in the chapter, and many concepts that are shown as framed generalizations are stated as important ideas. A set of *Chapter Review* exercises is also included for each chapter. Each group of these review exercises is referenced to the appropriate section of the chapter. Three groups of cumulative review exercises are also included.

There are nine two-page spreads, each concerning a specific career in today's world. These appear after each even-numbered chapter of both INTRODUCTORY ALGEBRA 1 and INTRODUCTORY ALGEBRA 2. In each spread relevant information about a career is included as well as some examples of mathematical concepts and skills needed to pursue the career. Exercises related to these career spreads are included in the *Teacher's Manual* of the *Teacher's Edition* and can be used as optional assignments.

Three sections of INTRODUCTORY ALGEBRA 1 deal specifically with an introduction and discussion of metric units of measure: 1.2 Metric Units of Length, 1.4 Metric Units of Area, 8.6 Metric Units of

Volume, Capacity, and Mass. Metric units of measure are emphasized throughout both volumes of INTRODUCTORY ALGEBRA.

Several satellite publications are available to use in conjunction with the INTRODUCTORY ALGEBRA books. These publications include Teacher's Editions, Skills Practice Books, Form A and Form B tests, and Pupil's Editions with alternate answers. All of these satellites are described in detail in the *Teacher's Manual* of the *Teacher's Edition* starting on page M-1.

## ACKNOWLEDGEMENTS

The author wishes to thank the following persons who assisted in the piloting of INTRODUCTORY ALGEBRA 1 and INTRODUCTORY ALGEBRA 2 in junior and senior high school classes. The information gained from these classes has been extremely valuable in shaping both the final form of this book and the ancillary materials that accompany it.

Mrs. Mary Ann Smith
*Mathematics Teacher*
*Surrattsville Junior High*
  *School*
*Clinton, Maryland*

Mr. Edwin Burnham
*Mathematics Teacher*
*Temple City High School*
*Temple City, California*

Mr. Gerhard Plessinger
*Mathematics Teacher*
*Goodyear Junior High School*
*Akron, Ohio*

Mr. John Brannon
*Mathematics Teacher*
*Buchtel High School*
*Akron, Ohio*

Mr. Michael De Groff
*Mathematics Teacher*
*Trevor Browne High School*
*Phoenix, Arizona*

Mr. William Hutcherson
*Mathematics Teacher*
*West High School*
*Phoenix, Arizona*

Mr. Abraham L. Stanfield
*Mathematics Teacher*
*West High School*
*Phoenix, Arizona*

Mr. Conrad Seeboth
*Supervisor of Mathematics*
*Prince George's County Board of*
  *Education*
*Upper Marlboro, Maryland*

Mr. Harold Onderdonk
*Mathematics Chairman*
*Temple City High School*
*Temple City, California*

Mr. James Wortham
*Mathematics Curriculum Specialist*
*Akron Public Schools*
*Akron, Ohio*

Dr. Scott Bull
*Mathematics Chairman*
*Camelback High School*
*Phoenix, Arizona*

Mr. Gerald Hickman
*Mathematics Chairman*
*Trevor Browne High School*
*Phoenix, Arizona*

Mr. Hugh Hackett
*Mathematics Chairman*
*West High School*
*Phoenix, Arizona*

Miss Margaret Doyle
*Mathematics Teacher*
*West High School*
*Phoenix, Arizona*

# Contents

# 1

# Metric Units and Formulas

# 1.1 Measurement

Persons in many careers use algebra to solve problems. These problems often involve numbers obtained by measurement.

Nurses measure doses of medicine in milliliters.

Biologists measure substances in grams.

Opticians measure lengths for fitting eyeglasses in millimeters.

Dress-pattern designers measure lengths in centimeters.

**P-1**  **How many units long is the nail in Figure 1?**

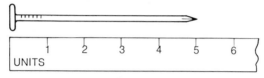

**Figure 1**

▷ *The number that describes the size of the nail is its* **measure.**

Figure 1 shows one way to find the length of an object. The object is compared with a **unit of measure.** The unit of measure of Figure 1 is the **centimeter.** It is a unit of the **metric system.**

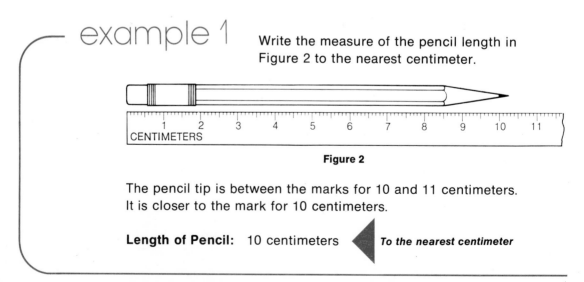

## example 1

Write the measure of the pencil length in Figure 2 to the nearest centimeter.

**Figure 2**

The pencil tip is between the marks for 10 and 11 centimeters. It is closer to the mark for 10 centimeters.

**Length of Pencil:** 10 centimeters  ◀ *To the nearest centimeter*

The **millimeter** is also a unit of the metric system.

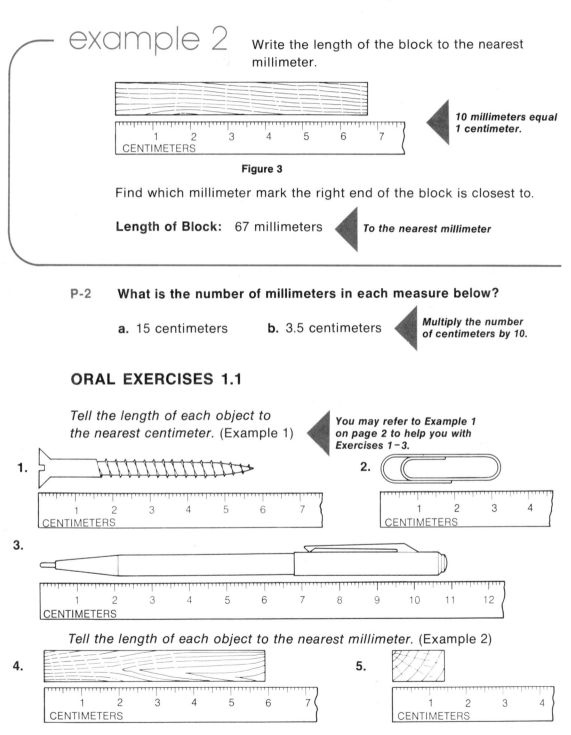

example 2 Write the length of the block to the nearest millimeter.

10 millimeters equal 1 centimeter.

**Figure 3**

Find which millimeter mark the right end of the block is closest to.

**Length of Block:** 67 millimeters

To the nearest millimeter

P-2 **What is the number of millimeters in each measure below?**

**a.** 15 centimeters **b.** 3.5 centimeters

Multiply the number of centimeters by 10.

## ORAL EXERCISES 1.1

*Tell the length of each object to the nearest centimeter.* (Example 1)

You may refer to Example 1 on page 2 to help you with Exercises 1–3.

**1.**

**2.**

**3.**

*Tell the length of each object to the nearest millimeter.* (Example 2)

**4.**

**5.**

*Tell the number of millimeters in each measure.* (P-2)

**6.** 3 centimeters    **7.** 18 centimeters    **8.** 27 centimeters

## WRITTEN EXERCISES 1.1

**A**  **Goal:** To measure a length to the nearest centimeter or millimeter
**Sample Problem:** Write the length of the block to the nearest centimeter and to the nearest millimeter.
**Answer:** 5 centimeters; 47 millimeters

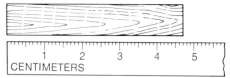

*Write the length of each object to the nearest centimeter.* (Example 1)

**1.**    **2.**

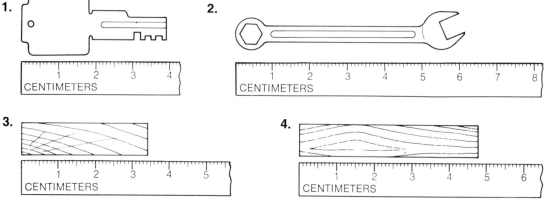

**3.**    **4.**

*Write the length of each block to the nearest millimeter.* (Example 2)

**5.**    **6.**

*Use a centimeter ruler to find each measure to the nearest centimeter.* (Example 1)

**7.** Length of line segment *AB*    **8.** Length of line segment *CD*

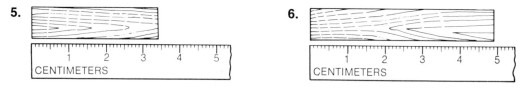

*Write the number of millimeters in each measure.* (P-2)

**9.** 14 centimeters    **10.** 23 centimeters    **11.** 9.6 centimeters    **12.** 34.5 centimeters

## 1.2   Metric Units of Length

The basic unit of length in the metric system is the *meter.*

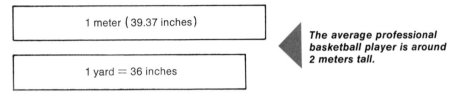

1 meter (39.37 inches)

1 yard = 36 inches

*The average professional basketball player is around 2 meters tall.*

The meter is related to other metric units of length (linear metric units). The relationships are shown below. The abbreviation for each unit is given in parentheses.

| Less Than a Meter | Greater Than a Meter |
|---|---|
| Millimeter (mm) = $\frac{1}{1000}$ of a meter (m) | Decameter (dkm) = 10 meters (m) |
| Centimeter (cm) = $\frac{1}{100}$ of a meter (m) | Hectometer (hm) = 100 meters (m) |
| Decimeter (dm) = $\frac{1}{10}$ of a meter (m) | Kilometer (km) = 1000 meters (m) |

**P-1**   **Which is the greater unit, a centimeter or a decimeter?**

1 decimeter (dm)

10 centimeters (cm)

100 millimeters (mm)

**P-2**   **How many times as great as a centimeter is a decimeter?**

In the chart below, the linear metric units are arranged in order of size. The largest unit, the kilometer, comes first.

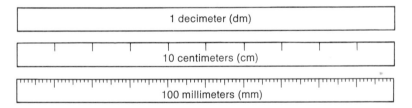

| km | hm | dkm | m | dm | cm | mm |
|---|---|---|---|---|---|---|

0.0028 km = 0.028 hm = 0.28 dkm = 2.8 m = 28. dm = 280. cm = 2800. mm

When you move one unit to the right, <u>multiply</u> by 10.————▶ 28 dm = 10 × 28 cm   or   280 cm

When you move one unit to the left, <u>divide</u> by 10.————▶ 0.028 hm = $\frac{0.028}{10}$ km   or   0.0028 km

> To change to the next smaller metric unit, multiply by 10.
> To change to the next larger metric unit, divide by 10.

## example 1    $0.35 \text{ m} = \underline{\quad?\quad} \text{ mm}$

| | GIVEN | | | UNKNOWN |
|---|---|---|---|---|
| | m | dm | cm | mm |

1  Write the needed columns of units in order.———►0.35                    ?

2  The unknown is 3 columns (places) to the right.

   Multiply by $10 \times 10 \times 10$  or  1000.————————►$0.35 \text{ m} = 1000 \times 0.35 \text{ mm}$
                                                                            $= 350 \text{ mm}$

## example 2    $2430 \text{ dm} = \underline{\quad?\quad} \text{ km}$

| UNKNOWN | | | | GIVEN |
|---|---|---|---|---|
| km | hm | dkm | m | dm |

1  Write the needed columns of units in order.———►  ?                        2430

2  The unknown is 4 columns to the left.

   Divide by $10 \times 10 \times 10 \times 10$  or  10,000. ————————►$2430 \text{ dm} = \dfrac{2430}{10,000} \text{ km}$
                                                                             $= 0.243 \text{ km}$

## ORAL EXERCISES 1.2

*Complete each sentence.*

**1.** To change a measure from meters to centimeters __?__ by 100.

**2.** To change a measure from centimeters to decimeters __?__ by 10.

**3.** To change a measure from millimeters to meters divide by __?__.

**4.** To change a measure from kilometers to meters multiply by __?__.

*Express each measure in millimeters.* (Example 1)

**5.** 12 centimeters

**6.** 3 meters

**7.** 2.5 centimeters

**8.** 2.7 meters

**9.** 0.23 m

**10.** 0.8 cm

*Express each measure in meters.* (Example 1, Example 2)

**11.** 15,000 millimeters      **12.** 1200 centimeters      **13.** 6 kilometers

**14.** 183 cm      **15.** 145,000 m      **16.** 9.4 km

*Express each measure in centimeters.* (Example 1, Example 2)

**17.** 35 m     **18.** 7.8 m     **19.** 75 mm     **20.** 3.8 mm

**21.** 5 km     **22.** 15 km     **23.** 830 dm     **24.** 96 dm

## WRITTEN EXERCISES 1.2

**A**     **Goal:** To change from one linear metric unit to another
**Sample Problem:** 2.3 cm = __?__ m
**Answer:** 0.023

**1.** How would you change a measure in decimeters to a measure in meters?

**2.** How would you change a measure in meters to a measure in decimeters?

**3.** How would you change a measure in centimeters to a measure in kilometers?

**4.** How would you change a measure in kilometers to a measure in centimeters?

*Write each missing numeral.* (Example 1, Example 2)

**5.** 5.2 m = __?__ mm     **6.** 7.6 m = __?__ mm     **7.** 3.4 m = __?__ cm

**8.** 9.5 m = __?__ cm     **9.** 1800 mm = __?__ m     **10.** 2700 mm = __?__ m

**11.** 173 mm = __?__ m     **12.** 244 mm = __?__ m     **13.** 3.4 m = __?__ dm

**14.** 7.8 m = __?__ dm     **15.** 13.5 dm = __?__ m     **16.** 22.9 dm = __?__ m

**17.** 178 dm = __?__ m     **18.** 5280 dm = __?__ m     **19.** 83 mm = __?__ cm

**20.** 127 mm = __?__ cm     **21.** 5.8 cm = __?__ mm     **22.** 0.9 cm = __?__ mm

**23.** 0.37 cm = __?__ mm     **24.** 43.9 cm = __?__ mm     **25.** 5.3 mm = __?__ cm

**26.** 17 m = __?__ cm     **27.** 75 km = __?__ m     **28.** 36 km = __?__ m

**29.** 3.8 km = __?__ m     **30.** 9.1 km = __?__ m     **31.** 1400 m = __?__ km

**32.** 6300 m = __?__ km     **33.** 13.6 hm = __?__ dkm     **34.** 6.8 hm = __?__ dkm

# 1.3 Variables and Open Phrases

To find a **perimeter** add the lengths of the sides.

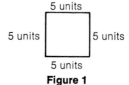

**Figure 1**

**P-1** **What is the perimeter of the square in Figure 1?**

**P-2** **How can you write 5 + 5 + 5 + 5 as a product?**

The perimeter of a square can also be found by multiplying the length of one side by 4.

A **variable** is a letter representing one or more numbers.

**Figure 2**

**P-3** **What variable represents the length of a side of the square in Figure 2?**

**P-4** **In Figure 2, how can you write the perimeter as a sum? as a product?**

---

A **phrase** is formed by
1. numerals or variables (or both), and
2. at least one of the operations of addition, subtraction, multiplication, or division.

$$5 + 5 + 5 + 5$$
$$4 \cdot 5$$
$$n + n + n + n$$

---

$4 \times 5$ can be written as $4 \cdot 5$ or $(4)(5)$. Notice that $4 \cdot 5$ and $4.5$ are not the same number. "$4 \cdot 5$" is "four times five." "$4.5$" is "four and five tenths."

---

An **open phrase** contains a variable. $4 \times n$ or $4n$

---

**P-5** **Which of these are open phrases?**

    **a.** $5y$    **b.** $15 \div 3$    **c.** $5.8 - 3$    **d.** $3.1 + 2n$

The **value** of $15 \div 3$ is 5. ◄ *The value is usually the simplest name. Thus, you simplify $15 \div 3$ to get 5.*

**P-6** **What is the value of $5.8 - 3$?**

## example 1

Find the value of 5*y* if *y* is replaced by 12.

Notice that the operation in 5*y* is multiplication.

1. Replace the variable. ⟶ $5y = 5 \cdot 12$
2. Multiply. ⟶ $= 60$

> If you forget to use "·", then "5 12" might be mistaken for "five hundred twelve."

**P-7** **What number would you get if you first multiplied and then added in 3 + 2 · 5? if you first added and then multiplied?**

A rule is necessary to avoid different answers.

> Mathematicians agree to multiply or divide before adding or subtracting unless parentheses indicate otherwise.
>
> $3 + 2 \cdot 5 = 3 + 10$
> $= 13$

**P-8** **What is the value of 6 · 8 − 2? of 6(8 − 2)?**

## example 2

Simplify $14 - 6 \div 3 + 2 \cdot 5$.

> Here "simplify" means "find the value of."

1. Multiply and divide (from left to right). ⟶ $14 - 6 \div 3 + 2 \cdot 5 = 14 - 2 + 10$
2. Add and subtract (from left to right). ⟶ $= 22$

**P-9** **What is the value of each of these phrases?**

    **a.** $5 + 7 \cdot 2$      **b.** $4 \cdot 6 \div 3$      **c.** $12 \div 3 \cdot 3 - 1$

## example 3

Find the value of 3 + 2*n* if *n* is replaced by 5.

1. Replace the variable. ⟶ $3 + 2n = 3 + 2 \cdot 5$
2. Multiply. ⟶ $= 3 + 10$
3. Add. ⟶ $= 13$

**P-10** **Which of these open phrases have the same value if x is 5?**

    **a.** $x + 2$      **b.** $2x$      **c.** $6x \div 3$      **d.** $3x + 5$

## ORAL EXERCISES 1.3

*Simplify.* (Example 2)

1. $4 \cdot 9 \div 12$
2. $2 \cdot 7 + 4$
3. $3(8) - 5$
4. $6 + 8 \cdot 2$

5. $12 - 3 \cdot 3$
6. $4 + 18 \div 2$
7. $30 - 12 \div 3$
8. $32 \div 8 \cdot 2$

*Replace the variable by 2. Then simplify.* (Example 1, Example 3)

9. $8 - 3n$
10. $x + x$
11. $4y \div 2$
12. $7 - y + 2$
13. $3a + a$

14. $4 + 2y$
15. $6n \div 3$
16. $8 - t \div 2$
17. $27 - y \cdot y$
18. $x - x + 5x$

## WRITTEN EXERCISES 1.3

**A**

**Goal:** To find the value of a phrase
**Sample Problem:** $8 + 4a - 6$ if $a$ is replaced by 3
**Answer:** 14

*Simplify.* (Example 2)

1. $19 + 6 - 8$
2. $23 - 9 + 14$
3. $3 \cdot 6 \div 9$
4. $4 \cdot 9 \div 6$

5. $3 \cdot 8 + 7$
6. $7 \cdot 8 + 13$
7. $15 - 8 \div 2$
8. $23 - 18 \div 6$

9. $45 \div 5 \cdot 3$
10. $63 \div 7 \cdot 3$
11. $112 - 9 \cdot 6 + 5$
12. $92 + 7 - 11 \cdot 8$

13. $20 + 28 \div 7 - 1$
14. $33 - 9 + 21 \div 7$
15. $45 - 2 + 51 \div 3$
16. $29 - 42 \div 3 + 7$

*Replace the variable by 3. Then simplify.* (Example 1, Example 3)

17. $2a - 1$
18. $4n - 2$
19. $2 + 2y$
20. $1 + 4c$

21. $2 + g - 1$
22. $5 - k - \frac{1}{2}$
23. $2 + 6 \div x$
24. $1 + 12 \div x$

**C**

*Replace each variable by 5. Then write* <u>Yes</u> *or* <u>No</u> *to show whether the two phrases have the same value.*

**EXAMPLE:** $3y + y$ and $4y$     **SOLUTION:** $3y + y = 3 \cdot 5 + 5$         $4y = 4 \cdot 5$
$= 15 + 5$   or   $20$         $= 20$
**ANSWER:** Yes.

25. $x + 2$ and $2 + x$
26. $3x + 2$ and $2 + 3x$
27. $x + x$ and $x \cdot x$

28. $x \cdot x$ and $2 \cdot x$
29. $3a + a$ and $4a$
30. $3a - a$ and $2a$

# 1.4   Metric Units of Area

The square at the right is called a **square centimeter.** Each side has a length of one centimeter.

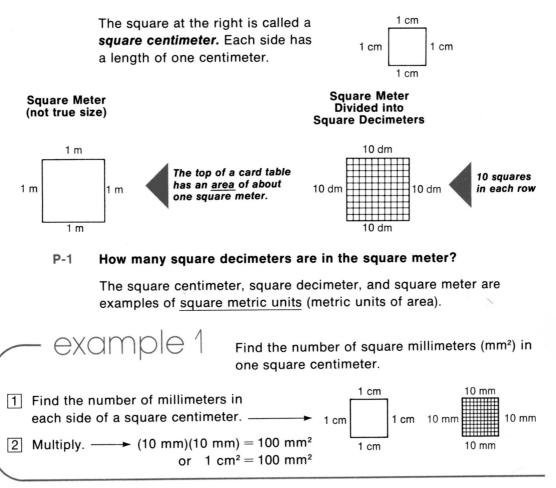

**Square Meter (not true size)**

The top of a card table has an <u>area</u> of about one square meter.

**Square Meter Divided into Square Decimeters**

10 squares in each row

**P-1**   **How many square decimeters are in the square meter?**

The square centimeter, square decimeter, and square meter are examples of <u>square metric units</u> (metric units of area).

## example 1

Find the number of square millimeters (mm²) in one square centimeter.

1. Find the number of millimeters in each side of a square centimeter. ────▶

2. Multiply. ────▶ (10 mm)(10 mm) = 100 mm²
      or   1 cm² = 100 mm²

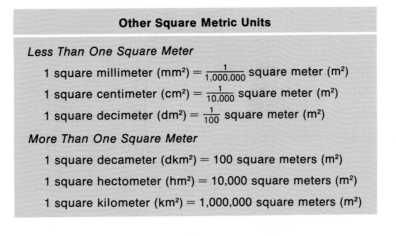

**Other Square Metric Units**

*Less Than One Square Meter*

1 square millimeter (mm²) = $\frac{1}{1,000,000}$ square meter (m²)

1 square centimeter (cm²) = $\frac{1}{10,000}$ square meter (m²)

1 square decimeter (dm²) = $\frac{1}{100}$ square meter (m²)

*More Than One Square Meter*

1 square decameter (dkm²) = 100 square meters (m²)

1 square hectometer (hm²) = 10,000 square meters (m²)

1 square kilometer (km²) = 1,000,000 square meters (m²)

## example 2

The floor area of Moe's kitchen is 16.2 m². Find the area of his kitchen in square centimeters.

|  | GIVEN | | UNKNOWN |
|---|---|---|---|
|  | m² | dm² | cm² |

1 Write the columns of units in order. ⟶ 16.2      ?

2 The unknown is 2 columns to the <u>right</u>.

<u>Multiply</u> by 100 × 100   or   10,000. ⟶ 16.2 × 10,000 = 162,000 cm²

The area of Moe's kitchen is shown below in terms of seven different square metric units.

| km² | hm² | dkm² | m² | dm² | cm² | mm² |
|---|---|---|---|---|---|---|
| 0.0000162 | 0.00162 | 0.162 | 16.2 | 1620. | 162,000. | 16,200,000. |

Start with any measure in this table.

When you move one unit to the <u>right</u>, <u>multiply</u> by 100. ⟶ 1620 dm² = 100 × 1620   or   162,000 cm²

When you move one unit to the <u>left</u>, <u>divide</u> by 100. ⟶ 16.2 m² = $\dfrac{16.2}{100}$   or   0.162 dkm²

> To change from one square metric unit to the next smaller unit, multiply by 100.
> To change from one square metric unit to the next larger unit, divide by 100.

## example 3

387 mm² = __?__ m²

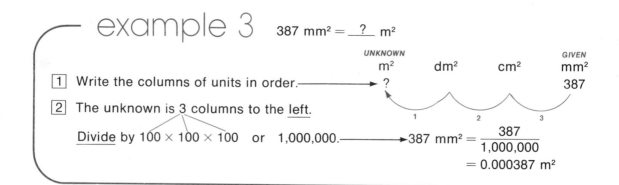

|  | UNKNOWN | | | GIVEN |
|---|---|---|---|---|
|  | m² | dm² | cm² | mm² |

1 Write the columns of units in order. ⟶ ?            387

2 The unknown is 3 columns to the <u>left</u>.

Divide by 100 × 100 × 100   or   1,000,000. ⟶ 387 mm² = $\dfrac{387}{1,000,000}$

= 0.000387 m²

## ORAL EXERCISES 1.4

*Tell each unknown number of square metric units.* (Example 1)

1. The number of square millimeters in 1 square decimeter

2. The number of square centimeters in 1 square decimeter

3. The number of square meters in 1 square kilometer

4. The number of square centimeters in 1 square meter

*Tell each missing numeral.* (Example 2, Example 3)

5. $3 \text{ m}^2 = \underline{\ ?\ } \text{ cm}^2$

6. $12 \text{ dm}^2 = \underline{\ ?\ } \text{ cm}^2$

7. $35 \text{ cm}^2 = \underline{\ ?\ } \text{ mm}^2$

8. $14 \text{ dm}^2 = \underline{\ ?\ } \text{ mm}^2$

9. $8 \text{ km}^2 = \underline{\ ?\ } \text{ m}^2$

10. $18 \text{ m}^2 = \underline{\ ?\ } \text{ mm}^2$

11. $75 \text{ m}^2 = \underline{\ ?\ } \text{ dm}^2$

12. $5600 \text{ dm}^2 = \underline{\ ?\ } \text{ m}^2$

13. $80,000 \text{ cm}^2 = \underline{\ ?\ } \text{ m}^2$

14. $700 \text{ mm}^2 = \underline{\ ?\ } \text{ cm}^2$

15. $2300 \text{ cm}^2 = \underline{\ ?\ } \text{ dm}^2$

16. $90,000 \text{ mm}^2 = \underline{\ ?\ } \text{ dm}^2$

## WRITTEN EXERCISES 1.4

**A**

**Goal:** To change one square metric measure to another
**Sample Problem:** $50.92 \text{ cm}^2 = \underline{\ ?\ } \text{ dm}^2$
**Answer:** $0.5092 \text{ dm}^2$

*Write each missing numeral.* (Example 2, Example 3)

1. $53 \text{ m}^2 = \underline{\ ?\ } \text{ dm}^2$

2. $95 \text{ cm}^2 = \underline{\ ?\ } \text{ mm}^2$

3. $4 \text{ km}^2 = \underline{\ ?\ } \text{ m}^2$

4. $6 \text{ m}^2 = \underline{\ ?\ } \text{ mm}^2$

5. $37 \text{ dm}^2 = \underline{\ ?\ } \text{ mm}^2$

6. $69 \text{ m}^2 = \underline{\ ?\ } \text{ cm}^2$

7. $1.8 \text{ dm}^2 = \underline{\ ?\ } \text{ cm}^2$

8. $0.39 \text{ dm}^2 = \underline{\ ?\ } \text{ cm}^2$

9. $3400 \text{ dm}^2 = \underline{\ ?\ } \text{ m}^2$

10. $6700 \text{ mm}^2 = \underline{\ ?\ } \text{ cm}^2$

11. $62,000 \text{ cm}^2 = \underline{\ ?\ } \text{ m}^2$

12. $870 \text{ mm}^2 = \underline{\ ?\ } \text{ dm}^2$

13. $258 \text{ cm}^2 = \underline{\ ?\ } \text{ dm}^2$

14. $153.7 \text{ cm}^2 = \underline{\ ?\ } \text{ dm}^2$

15. $5.23 \text{ cm}^2 = \underline{\ ?\ } \text{ mm}^2$

16. $0.726 \text{ m}^2 = \underline{\ ?\ } \text{ dm}^2$

17. $7624 \text{ m}^2 = \underline{\ ?\ } \text{ mm}^2$

18. $0.0053 \text{ km}^2 = \underline{\ ?\ } \text{ m}^2$

19. $0.139 \text{ m}^2 = \underline{\ ?\ } \text{ cm}^2$

20. $53.9 \text{ dm}^2 = \underline{\ ?\ } \text{ cm}^2$

21. $7.208 \text{ hm}^2 = \underline{\ ?\ } \text{ m}^2$

22. $0.1873 \text{ km}^2 = \underline{\ ?\ } \text{ dkm}^2$

23. $9.47 \text{ dkm}^2 = \underline{\ ?\ } \text{ hm}^2$

24. $6280 \text{ hm}^2 = \underline{\ ?\ } \text{ km}^2$

25. $4800 \text{ dm}^2 = \underline{\ ?\ } \text{ dkm}^2$

26. $96,230 \text{ dkm}^2 = \underline{\ ?\ } \text{ km}^2$

27. $95,700 \text{ m}^2 = \underline{\ ?\ } \text{ km}^2$

28. $6249.8 \text{ mm}^2 = \underline{\ ?\ } \text{ m}^2$

29. $17,283 \text{ cm}^2 = \underline{\ ?\ } \text{ dm}^2$

30. $0.5092 \text{ cm}^2 = \underline{\ ?\ } \text{ dm}^2$

# 1.5 Perimeter and Area Formulas

A sentence may be true, false, or neither true nor false.

**P-1** **Which of these sentences is true? Which is false? Which is neither true nor false?**

**a.** $2 + 3 = 5$    **b.** $4 + 7 = 10$    **c.** $x + 5 = 13$

**P-2** **What number in place of x will make sentence c true?**

An **equation** is a sentence that contains the equality symbol "=".

$$x + 5 = 13$$
$$8 \cdot 2 - 6 = 7 + 3$$

Sometimes an equation describes a commonly used rule and is called a **formula.**

**P-3** **What open phrase describes the perimeter of the rectangle at the right?**

You can write a formula for the perimeter as $p = 2l + 2w$.

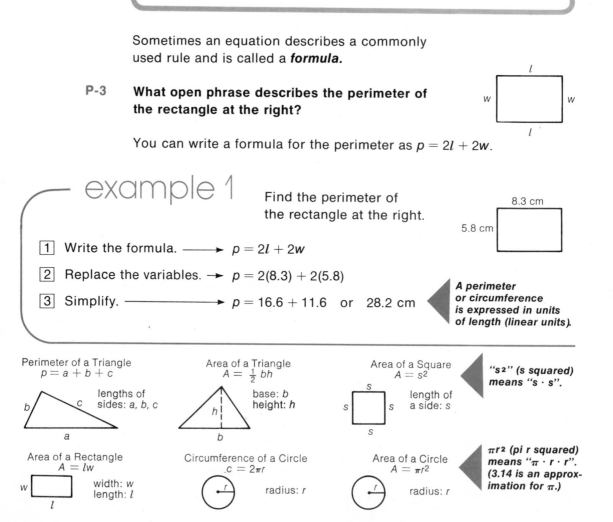

## example 1

Find the perimeter of the rectangle at the right.

8.3 cm

5.8 cm

1. Write the formula. ⟶ $p = 2l + 2w$
2. Replace the variables. ⟶ $p = 2(8.3) + 2(5.8)$
3. Simplify. ⟶ $p = 16.6 + 11.6$   or   28.2 cm

A perimeter or circumference is expressed in units of length (linear units).

Perimeter of a Triangle
$p = a + b + c$

lengths of sides: $a$, $b$, $c$

Area of a Triangle
$A = \frac{1}{2} bh$

base: $b$
height: $h$

Area of a Square
$A = s^2$

length of a side: $s$

"$s^2$" ($s$ squared) means "$s \cdot s$".

Area of a Rectangle
$A = lw$

width: $w$
length: $l$

Circumference of a Circle
$c = 2\pi r$

radius: $r$

Area of a Circle
$A = \pi r^2$

radius: $r$

$\pi r^2$ (pi r squared) means "$\pi \cdot r \cdot r$". (3.14 is an approximation for $\pi$.)

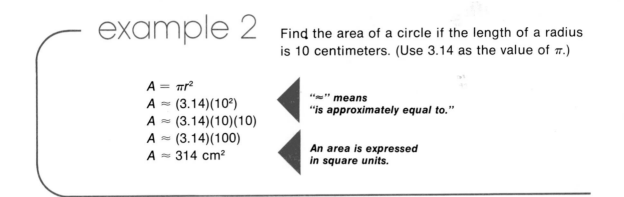

example 2　Find the area of a circle if the length of a radius is 10 centimeters. (Use 3.14 as the value of $\pi$.)

$A = \pi r^2$
$A \approx (3.14)(10^2)$
$A \approx (3.14)(10)(10)$
$A \approx (3.14)(100)$
$A \approx 314 \text{ cm}^2$

◀ "$\approx$" means
"is approximately equal to."

◀ An area is expressed
in square units.

## ORAL EXERCISES 1.5

*Tell the perimeter of each rectangle. Use $p = 2l + 2w$. (Example 1)*

1. $l = 10$ cm; $w = 5$ cm
2. $l = 5$ m; $w = 3$ m
3. $l = 8$ dm; $w = 6$ dm
4. $l = 15$ mm; $w = 12$ mm
5. $l = 2.5$ cm; $w = 1.5$ cm
6. $l = 1.2$ km; $w = 0.3$ km

*Tell the area of each rectangle. Use $A = lw$.*

7. $l = 5$ m; $w = 3$ m
8. $l = 12$ dm; $w = 4$ dm
9. $l = 6$ cm; $w = 3.5$ cm
10. $l = 24$ mm; $w = 0.5$ mm
11. $l = 7.5$ km; $w = 2$ km
12. $l = 3$ cm; $w = 25$ mm

*Simplify.*

13. $9^2$
14. $(12)^2$
15. $(0.5)^2$
16. $(1.2)^2$
17. $2 \cdot 3^2$
18. $5^2 \cdot 4$
19. $(2.1)(3)^2$
20. $(3.14)(2)^2$

*Tell the area of each square. Use $A = s^2$.*

21. $s = 8$ cm
22. $s = 12$ km
23. $s = 0.5$ m
24. $s = 1.2$ dm
25. $s = 15$ mm
26. $s = 1.5$ cm

*Tell the perimeter of each triangle. Use $p = a + b + c$.*

27. $a = 5$ cm; $b = 4$ cm; $c = 8$ cm
28. $a = 12$ mm; $b = 7$ mm; $c = 9$ mm
29. $a = 15$ km; $b = 13$ km; $c = 9$ km
30. $a = 1.6$ m; $b = 2.3$ m; $c = 2.1$ m

*Tell the circumference of each circle. Use $c = 2\pi r$. ($\pi \approx 3.14$)*

31. $r = 2$ cm
32. $r = 1$ km
33. $r = 0.5$ m
34. $r = 2.5$ mm

## WRITTEN EXERCISES 1.5

**A**   **Goal:** To use a formula to find a perimeter, circumference, or area
**Sample Problem:** $c = 2\pi r$; $r = 14$ cm   ($\pi \approx 3.14$)   **Answer:** 87.92 cm

*Find each perimeter, circumference, or area. Use the given formula.*
*(Example 1, Example 2)*

**TRIANGLE:** $p = a + b + c$

1. $a = 29$ dm; $b = 43$ dm; $c = 25$ dm        2. $a = 4.7$ mm; $b = 5.6$ mm; $c = 6.9$ mm

**RECTANGLE:** $p = 2l + 2w$    $p = ltw + ltw$

3. $l = 76$ km; $w = 59$ km                4. $l = 129$ m; $w = 97$ m
5. $l = 4.3$ dm; $w = 3.8$ dm              6. $l = 13.6$ mm; $w = 9.2$ mm

**RECTANGLE:** $A = lw$

7. $l = 28$ m; $w = 19$ m                   8. $l = 43$ cm; $w = 38$ cm
9. $l = 8.3$ dm; $w = 6.9$ dm              10. $l = 13.2$ mm; $w = 8.5$ mm

**SQUARE:** $A = s^2$

11. $s = 24$ km          12. $s = 37$ cm          13. $s = 0.8$ mm          14. $s = 2.7$ m

**TRIANGLE:** $A = \frac{1}{2}bh$

15. $b = 12$ km; $h = 9$ km                16. $b = 18$ cm; $h = 17$ cm
17. $b = 6.4$ m; $h = 1.2$ m               18. $b = 8.6$ dm; $h = 6.2$ dm

**CIRCLE:** $c = 2\pi r$   ($\pi \approx 3.14$)

19. $r = 2.3$ cm          20. $r = 4.8$ m          21. $r = 35$ mm          22. $r = 29$ km

**CIRCLE:** $A = \pi r^2$   ($\pi \approx 3.14$)

23. $r = 12$ dm          24. $r = 14$ cm          25. $r = 2.5$ m          26. $r = 1.6$ mm

27. The lengths of the sides of a triangle are 27 mm, 3.3 cm, and 46 mm. Find the perimeter in centimeters.

28. The length of a rectangle is 128 dm and the width is 7.9 m. Find the perimeter in meters.

**B**   *A formula relating the lengths of a diameter and a radius of a circle is $r = \frac{1}{2}d$.*

29. Find the circumference of a circle if the length of a diameter is 12.9 centimeters. ($\pi \approx 3.14$)

30. Find the area of a circle if the length of a diameter is 15.4 meters. ($\pi \approx 3.14$)

# CHAPTER SUMMARY

| | | |
|---|---|---|
| **IMPORTANT TERMS** | Measure *(p. 2)* <br> Unit of measure *(p. 2)* <br> Centimeter *(p. 2)* <br> Millimeter *(p. 3)* <br> Linear metric units *(p. 5)* <br> Meter *(p. 5)* <br> Decimeter *(p. 5)* <br> Decameter *(p. 5)* <br> Hectometer *(p. 5)* <br> Kilometer *(p. 5)* | Perimeter *(p. 8)* <br> Variable *(p. 8)* <br> Phrase *(p. 8)* <br> Open phrase *(p. 8)* <br> Value *(p. 8)* <br> Square metric units *(p. 11)* <br> Square centimeter *(p. 11)* <br> Area *(p. 11)* <br> Equation *(p. 14)* <br> Formula *(p. 14)* |

**IMPORTANT IDEAS**

*1.* To measure an object, compare it with a unit of measure.

*2.* To change to the next smaller metric unit, multiply by 10. To change to the next larger metric unit, divide by 10.

*3.* Mathematicians agree to multiply or divide before adding or subtracting.

*4.* To change from one square metric unit to the next smaller unit, multiply by 100. To change from one square metric unit to the next larger unit, divide by 100.

*5.* A perimeter or circumference is expressed in linear units. An area is expressed in square units.

## CHAPTER REVIEW

### SECTION 1.1

*Write the measure.*

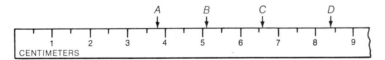

**1.** *A* to the nearest centimeter

**2.** *B* to the nearest centimeter

**3.** *C* to the nearest 0.5 centimeter

**4.** *D* to the nearest 0.5 centimeter

### SECTION 1.2

*Write the missing numeral.*

**5.** 3.4 m = _?_ cm

**6.** 9.2 cm = _?_ mm

**7.** 72 dm = _?_ m

**8.** 13 cm = _?_ dm

**9.** 1.3 dm = _?_ mm

**10.** 12.5 m = _?_ cm

**SECTION 1.3**

*Simplify.*

**11.** $13 + 5 \cdot 2$

**12.** $32 - 4 \cdot 7$

**13.** $24 - 18 \div 3$

**14.** $8 + 24 \div 8$

**15.** $48 \div 6 \cdot 2$

**16.** $96 \div 16 \cdot 2$

**17.** $15 - 4 \cdot 3 + 9$

**18.** $40 - 32 \div 8 + 5$

**19.** $48 + 64 \div 16 \cdot 2$

**20.** $42 - 18 \div 6 \cdot 8$

**21.** $16 \div 2 - 2 \cdot 3$

**22.** $20 \cdot 5 - 6 \div 3$

*Replace the variable by 4. Then simplify.*

**23.** $2x - 3$

**24.** $6x + 5$

**25.** $19 + 3y$

**26.** $17 - 2t$

**27.** $12 + k - 7$

**28.** $13 - x + 9$

**29.** $78 \div 3 \cdot n$

**30.** $36 \cdot r \div 18$

**SECTION 1.4**

*Write each missing numeral.*

**31.** $53 \text{ m}^2 = \underline{\ \ ?\ \ } \text{ dm}^2$

**32.** $4.5 \text{ dm}^2 = \underline{\ \ ?\ \ } \text{ cm}^2$

**33.** $43{,}500 \text{ cm}^2 = \underline{\ \ ?\ \ } \text{ m}^2$

**34.** $4800 \text{ mm}^2 = \underline{\ \ ?\ \ } \text{ dm}^2$

**35.** $2.83 \text{ m}^2 = \underline{\ \ ?\ \ } \text{ mm}^2$

**36.** $0.093 \text{ km}^2 = \underline{\ \ ?\ \ } \text{ m}^2$

**SECTION 1.5**

*Find each perimeter. Use $p = 2l + 2w$.*

**37.** $l = 13.2 \text{ cm}; w = 11.9 \text{ cm}$

**38.** $l = 47.62 \text{ mm}; w = 38.37 \text{ mm}$

*Find each area. Use $A = \pi r^2$.  ($\pi \approx 3.14$)*

**39.** $r = 3.6 \text{ cm}$

**40.** $r = 24 \text{ mm}$

**41.** $r = 0.64 \text{ km}$

**42.** $r = 10.1 \text{ m}$

# 2

# Properties of Numbers

# 2.1　The Special Numbers 0 and 1

**P-1**　What property of the number <u>zero</u> is suggested by the following?

　　**a.** $5 + 0 = 5$　　　**b.** $\frac{1}{2} + 0 = \frac{1}{2}$　　　**c.** $a + 0 = a$

> **Addition Property of Zero**　　　　　　　　$4\frac{1}{3} + 0 = 4\frac{1}{3}$
>
> For any number $a$, $\boldsymbol{a + 0 = a}$.　　　　　　$0 + 2 = 2$

**P-2**　What number will make each of the following equations true?

　　**a.** $x + \frac{2}{3} = \frac{2}{3}$　　　**b.** $3.45 + n = 3.45$　　　**c.** $a + 0 = 225$

**P-3**　What property of zero is suggested by the following?

　　**a.** $(\frac{1}{2})(0) = 0$　　　**b.** $(0)(0.17) = 0$　　　**c.** $(a)(0) = 0$

> **Multiplication Property of Zero**　　　　　　$(7)(0) = 0$
>
> For any number $a$, $\boldsymbol{a \cdot 0 = 0}$.　　　　　$(0.6p)(0) = 0$

**P-4**　What numbers will make each of the following equations true?

　　**a.** $35.7(0) = x$　　　**b.** $(n)(0) = 0$　　　**c.** $(0)(x) = 0$

**P-5**　What property of the number <u>one</u> is suggested by the following?

　　**a.** $(5)(1) = 5$　　　**b.** $(\frac{3}{4})(1) = \frac{3}{4}$　　　**c.** $(a)(1) = a$

> **Multiplication Property of One**　　　　　　$(7)(1) = 7$
>
> For any number $a$, $\boldsymbol{a \cdot 1 = a}$.　　　　　$3y(1) = 3y$

**P-6**　What number will make each of the following equations true?

　　**a.** $(x)(1) = 15$　　　**b.** $(\frac{2}{3})(x) = \frac{2}{3}$　　　**c.** $(16\frac{1}{2})(1) = x$

**P-7**　Which of the following are true?

　　**a.** $(1752)\frac{368}{368} = 1752$　　　**b.** $\frac{7}{7} \cdot 0 = \frac{7}{7}$

　　**c.** $2 \cdot 0 + 6 \cdot 1 = 6$

$\frac{368}{368}$ and $\frac{7}{7}$ are names for one.

## ORAL EXERCISES 2.1

*Say True or False.* (P-1, P-3, P-5, P-7)

**1.** $\frac{3}{5} + 0 = \frac{3}{5}$  **2.** $(15)(1) = 1$  **3.** $\frac{2}{3} + 0 = 0$

**4.** $(16)(\frac{5}{5}) = 16$  **5.** $(12)(0) = 12$  **6.** $(0.8)(0) = 0$

**7.** $(9.25)(1) = 9.25$  **8.** $(25 + 0)(1) = 25$  **9.** $(16.3 + 0)(0) = 16.3$

*Tell what number will make each equation true.* (P-2, P-4, P-6)

**10.** $x + \frac{1}{4} = \frac{1}{4}$  **11.** $x + 0 = \frac{5}{6}$  **12.** $1a = 1$

**13.** $x + 0 = 0$  **14.** $5n = 0$  **15.** $(\frac{2}{2})(75x + 0) = 75$

## WRITTEN EXERCISES 2.1

**A**  **Goal:** To find the number that will make an equation true by using one of these properties: Addition Property of Zero, Multiplication Property of Zero, or Multiplication Property of One

**Sample Problems: a.** $x + 0 = 4$  **b.** $\frac{3}{3} \cdot a = 0$  **c.** $1 \cdot 6 = y$

**Answers:**  **a.** 4  **b.** 0  **c.** 6

*Write True or False.* (P-1, P-3, P-5, P-7)

**1.** $\frac{1}{4} + 0 = 0$  **2.** $0.15 + 0 = 0$  **3.** $(0.8)(1) = 0.8$

**4.** $(0.75)(1) = 1$  **5.** $17(\frac{3}{3}) = 17$  **6.** $5(\frac{7}{7}) = 1$

**7.** $\frac{5}{5} \cdot 0 = \frac{5}{5}$  **8.** $\frac{2}{2} \cdot 0 = 0$  **9.** $3 + 5 \cdot 0 = 15$

**10.** $15 \cdot 0 + 3 = 3$  **11.** $999(\frac{12}{12}) + 18 \cdot 0 = 999$  **12.** $12.8(0) + 456(\frac{2}{2}) = 0$

*Write a number that will make each equation true. Use the properties of zero and one.* (P-2, P-4, P-6)

**13.** $x + 0.45 = 0.45$  **14.** $y + 0.08 = 0.08$  **15.** $x + 0 = 23$

**16.** $a + 0 = 29.5$  **17.** $1(y) = 0$  **18.** $1(x) = 1$

**19.** $x(\frac{3}{3}) = 13$  **20.** $y(\frac{10}{10}) = 15$  **21.** $t + 0 = 0$

**22.** $s(1) = 1$  **23.** $x(3.7 + 0) = 3.7$  **24.** $15y + 0 = 15$

**B**

**25.** $12 + n(\frac{3}{3}) - 42(0) = 18$  **26.** $25 \div 5n + n(0) = 1$

**27.** $(11 - 2 \cdot 5)(3x + x \cdot 0) = 12$  **28.** $(5 \cdot n + 5 \cdot 0)(4 + n \cdot 0) = 20$

# 2.2 Properties of Multiplication

The product $2 \cdot 3$ can be written as the sum $3 + 3$.

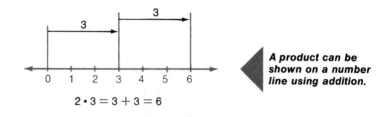

$$2 \cdot 3 = 3 + 3 = 6$$

> A product can be shown on a number line using addition.

**P-1** How can you write $3 \cdot 2$ as the sum of three equal numbers, as shown below?

$$3 \cdot 2 = ? + ? + ?$$

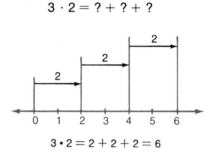

$$3 \cdot 2 = 2 + 2 + 2 = 6$$

The steps for finding $2 \cdot 3$ are not the same as for finding $3 \cdot 2$. However, each product equals 6. Therefore, $2 \cdot 3 = 3 \cdot 2$.

---

**Commutative Property of Multiplication**

Any two numbers can be multiplied in either order.

$$3(x) = x(3)$$

$$4(\tfrac{1}{2}) = \tfrac{1}{2}(4)$$

$a \cdot b = b \cdot a$

---

**P-2** Which of these sentences are examples of the Commutative Property of Multiplication?

**a.** $(\tfrac{1}{2})(29) = (29)(\tfrac{1}{2})$    **b.** $5 \cdot 7 + 8 = 8 \cdot 5 + 7$

**c.** $r(s + t) = (s + t)r$    **d.** $a(b + c) = a(c + b)$

**P-3** What numbers do you multiply first in the phrase $3 \cdot (4 \cdot 5)$?

**P-4** What is the value of $3 \cdot (4 \cdot 5)$?

**P-5** What numbers do you multiply first in the phrase $(3 \cdot 4) \cdot 5$?

**P-6** What is the value of $(3 \cdot 4) \cdot 5$?

The steps are different, but the answers are the same.

---

**Associative Property of Multiplication**

When you find the product of any
three numbers, it does not matter
how you group them.

$16(2 \cdot \frac{1}{3}) = (16 \cdot 2)\frac{1}{3}$

$(2x)x = 2(x \cdot x)$

▲ $(a \cdot b) \cdot c = a \cdot (b \cdot c)$

---

**P-7** Which of these sentences is an example of the Associative Property
of Multiplication?

**a.** $\frac{1}{2}(14 \cdot 8.6) = (\frac{1}{2} \cdot 14)8.6$     **b.** $(12 \cdot 9)23 = 23(12 \cdot 9)$

## example 1   Multiply: $4(3x)$

1 Regroup (Associative Property). ⟶ $4(3x) = (4 \cdot 3)x$

2 Multiply. ⟶ $= 12x$

---

**P-8** What is the simplest name of each product?

**a.** $\frac{1}{2}(10y)$     **b.** $6(8m)$     **c.** $(9t)4$

## example 2   Multiply: $(6x)(7y)$

$(6x)(7y) = (6 \cdot 7)(x \cdot y)$

$= 42xy$

◄ *You can use the Commutative
and Associative Properties
of Multiplication.*

The third **power** of 2 is $2^3$.
This means $2 \cdot 2 \cdot 2$, or 8.

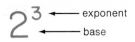

3$a^4$ means $3 \cdot a \cdot a \cdot a \cdot a$ and is read
"three times $a$ to the fourth power."

P-9    **How can you write each phrase without exponents?**

$x^2$ is read
"x squared."
$b^3$ is read
"b cubed."

**a.** $5x^2$     **b.** $x^2y$     **c.** $ab^3$     **d.** $7m^3n^2$

example 3    Multiply: $(4x^2)(5xy)(2yz)$

Notice that $x$ occurs three times in $(4x^2)(5xy)(2yz)$. Notice also that
$y$ occurs twice and that $z$ occurs once.

$$(4x^2)(5xy)(2yz) = (4 \cdot 5 \cdot 2)(x^2 \cdot x \cdot y \cdot y \cdot z)$$
$$= 40x^3y^2z$$

P-10    **Which property or properties are shown in each sentence?**

**a.** $(2b)3 = 3(2b)$     **b.** $3(2b) = (3 \cdot 2)b$     **c.** $(2b)3 = (3 \cdot 2)b$

## ORAL EXERCISES 2.2

*Say Commutative Property of Multiplication, Associative Property of
Multiplication, or Both Properties to describe each sentence.* (P-2, P-7, P-10)

**1.** $5(8 \cdot 3) = 5(3 \cdot 8)$

**2.** $(7 \cdot 10)2 = 7(10 \cdot 2)$

**3.** $10(20 \cdot 30) = (10 \cdot 20)30$

**4.** $(17 \cdot 3)8 = 8(3 \cdot 17)$

**5.** $(\frac{1}{2} \cdot \frac{1}{4})\frac{1}{8} = (\frac{1}{8} \cdot \frac{1}{2})\frac{1}{4}$

**6.** $\frac{1}{3}(\frac{1}{2} \cdot 1) = (1 \cdot \frac{1}{2})\frac{1}{3}$

**7.** $(2 \cdot 16)30 = 2(16 \cdot 30)$

**8.** $20(15 \cdot 5) = 5(15 \cdot 20)$

**9.** $r \cdot s \cdot t \cdot w = (r \cdot s)(t \cdot w)$

**10.** $(0.5x)(1.2y) = (0.5 \cdot 1.2)(x \cdot y)$

*Multiply.* (Example 1, Example 2, and Example 3)

**11.** $10(5y)$     **12.** $\frac{1}{2}(12t)$     **13.** $(4k)7$     **14.** $(9r)9$

**15.** $(14m)\frac{1}{2}$     **16.** $(12t)(0.3)$     **17.** $(6x)(3y)$     **18.** $(8a)(7a)$

**19.** $(2x)(3xy)$     **20.** $(\frac{1}{2}rs)(12s)$     **21.** $(2r)(4s)(t)$     **22.** $(3pq)(qr)(7p)$

## WRITTEN EXERCISES 2.2

**A**  **Goal:** To simplify phrases in which only multiplication occurs
**Sample Problem:** $(3x^2y)2xy$
**Answer:** $6x^3y^2$

*Multiply.* (Example 1, Example 2, Example 3)

1. $5(7x)$  2. $6(4y)$  3. $\frac{2}{3}(6a)$  4. $\frac{1}{5}(10b)$

5. $0.3(5x)$  6. $0.5(9t)$  7. $8(0.7s)$  8. $10(0.5q)$

9. $(1.2n)7$  10. $(2.3k)4$  11. $(16w)\frac{1}{2}$  12. $(21m)\frac{1}{3}$

13. $(0.3r)(0.2)$  14. $(0.5n)(0.3)$  15. $(9a)(7b)$  16. $(8s)(12t)$

17. $(13x)(3x)$  18. $(6y)(14y)$  19. $(12mn)(3n)$  20. $(3k)(17kt)$

21. $(\frac{1}{2}x)(4xy)$  22. $(\frac{1}{3}m)(6m^2n)$  23. $(10p)(0.2np)$

24. $(15st)(0.4t^2)$  25. $(\frac{1}{4}x^2)(8xy)$  26. $(20mn^2)(\frac{1}{5}mn)$

27. $(0.5x^2)(18xy)$  28. $(12m)(0.5mn^2)$  29. $(\frac{1}{2}k)(3gt^2)(8kt)$

30. $(9dp)(3a^2p)(\frac{1}{3}d)$  31. $(r)(rs)(2st)(3t^2)$  32. $(2mn)(m^2p)(3p)(4n)$

**B**  *Simplify. Then compute the value if $x = 2$ and $y = 1$.*

**EXAMPLE:** $(2x)(3y)(3x^2)$  **SOLUTION:** $(2x)(3y)(3x^2) = 18x^3y$
$$= 18(2^3)(1)$$
$$= (18)(8)(1)$$
$$= 144$$

33. $(x^2)(xy)(3y)$  34. $(2xy)(4x)(3y)$  35. $x \cdot x \cdot y \cdot y^2 \cdot x \cdot y$

36. $y \cdot y \cdot x \cdot x \cdot y^3$  37. $(\frac{1}{2}x)(3xy)(4y^2)$  38. $(\frac{1}{3}y)(2x^2y)(9xy^3)$

**C**  Let * mean "square the first number—then multiply by the second number."
Compute each value.

**EXAMPLE:** $3 * 2$  **SOLUTION:** $3 * 2 = 3^2 \cdot 2$
$$= 9 \cdot 2$$
$$= 18$$

39. $2 * 3$  40. $3 * 5$  41. $5 * 3$

42. Compare Exercises 40 and 41. Is * a commutative operation? Explain.

# 2.3　Distributive Property

*X* represents the number of stars in Figure 1.
*Y* represents the number of stars in the left group of Figure 2.
*Z* represents the number of stars in the right group of Figure 2.

$$4 \left\{ \begin{array}{c} \star\star\star\star\star\star\star\star\star\star\star\star \\ \star\star\star\star\star\star\star\star\star\star\star\star \\ \star\star\star\star\star\star\star\star\star\star\star\star \\ \star\star\star\star\star\star\star\star\star\star\star\star \end{array} \right.$$

12

**Figure 1**

12　　　　　　　　7　　　5

**Figure 2**

**P-1**　**What is the value of *X*?　of *Y* + *Z*?**

Therefore, $X = Y + Z$.

**P-2**　**What product can you write for *X*?　for *Y*?　for *Z*?**

Replace *X*, *Y*, and *Z* with these products. $\longrightarrow$ $\begin{cases} X = Y + Z \\ 4 \cdot 12 = 4 \cdot 7 + 4 \cdot 5 \end{cases}$

Replace 12 by 7 + 5. $\longrightarrow$ $4(7 + 5) = 4 \cdot 7 + 4 \cdot 5$

The multiplication by 4 has been <u>distributed</u> over the addition of 7 and 5.

---

**Distributive Property**

For any numbers *a*, *b*, and *c*,

1. **$a(b + c) = ab + ac$**, and

2. **$(b + c)a = ba + ca$**.

$3(2 + 7) = 3 \cdot 2 + 3 \cdot 7$

$(4 + 1)x = 4x + 1x$

---

With the Distributive Property you can change a product to a sum.

Product:　　$2(5 + 8)$　　　　$3(x + 3)$　　　　$(3 + 7) \cdot 6$　　　$(x + y) \cdot 5$

Sum:　　　$2 \cdot 5 + 2 \cdot 8$　　$3 \cdot x + 3 \cdot 3$　　$3 \cdot 6 + 7 \cdot 6$　　$x \cdot 5 + y \cdot 5$

## example 1

Write $2x(3y + 5)$ as a sum in simplest form.

$$2x(3y + 5) = 2x \cdot 3y + 2x \cdot 5$$
$$= 6xy + 10x$$

## ORAL EXERCISES 2.3

*Say Product or Sum.*

**1.** $2(10 + 3)$

**2.** $2 \cdot 10 + 2 \cdot 3$

**3.** $3(x + y)$

**4.** $(5 + 3)10$

**5.** $5a + 5b$

**6.** $(x + 2)(x + 3)$

*Say each product as a sum in simplest form.* (Example 1)

**EXAMPLE:** $5(2 + 7)$     **ANSWER:** $5 \cdot 2 + 5 \cdot 7 = 10 + 35$   (Five times two plus five times seven equals ten plus thirty-five.)

**7.** $2(10 + 3)$

**8.** $3(5 + 2)$

**9.** $3(5 + \frac{1}{3})$

**10.** $4(12 + \frac{1}{2})$

**11.** $(10 + 5)\frac{1}{2}$

**12.** $3(x + y)$

**13.** $5(m + n)$

**14.** $(r + s)7$

**15.** $x(x + 3)$

**16.** $r(2r + 3)$

**17.** $3a(b + 2)$

**18.** $(m + 5)2n$

## WRITTEN EXERCISES 2.3

**A**

**Goal:** To write a product as a sum in simplest form using the Distributive Property

**Sample Problem:** $(8 + y)4$

**Answer:** $32 + 4y$

*Write each product as a sum in simplest form.* (Example 1)

**1.** $4(r + t)$

**2.** $7(c + d)$

**3.** $(m + n)15$

**4.** $(p + q)25$

**5.** $(r + 2)x$

**6.** $(k + 7)y$

**7.** $a(12 + t)$

**8.** $n(a + 13)$

**9.** $2(x + 12)$

**10.** $3(r + 9)$

**11.** $(0.5n + 8)4$

**12.** $(7s + 0.5)8$

**13.** $s(s + 13)$

**14.** $p(p + 20)$

**15.** $(2a + 5)a$

**16.** $(3m + 7)m$

**17.** $3r(4r + 5)$

**18.** $7w(2w + 6)$

**19.** $(x + y)2x$

**20.** $(3b + c)c$

**21.** $12(4a + 3b)$

**22.** $9(6m + 12n)$

**23.** $2t(6t + 7s)$

**24.** $4k(7k + 5g)$

**25.** $(8p + 12q)\frac{1}{2}pq$

**26.** $(12r + 15s)\frac{1}{3}rs$

**27.** $4(\frac{1}{2}a + \frac{3}{4})$

**28.** $8(\frac{1}{4}y + \frac{3}{4})$

**29.** $3ax(12a + 9bx)$

**30.** $(16r + 12st)9rt$

**B**     **EXAMPLE:** $3x(x^2 + 5x + 9)$     **ANSWER:** $3x^3 + 15x^2 + 27x$

**31.** $4(3a^2 + 9a + 7)$

**32.** $9(6t^2 + 2t + 12)$

**33.** $5x(2x^3 + 10x + 7)$

**34.** $8k(7k^2 + 9k + 11)$

**35.** $(3m^2 + 12mn + 9)4mn$

**36.** $(a^2b + 4ab + 5ab^2)3b$

# 2.4 Writing Sums or Differences as Products

**P-1** **What is the simplest name for the product shown below?**

$$3(12 - 8)$$

The value of this phrase can be found in two ways.

| **Method 1** | **Method 2** |
|---|---|
| $3(12 - 8) = 3(4)$ | $3(12 - 8) = 3 \cdot 12 - 3 \cdot 8$ |
| $= 12$ | $= 36 - 24$ |
| | $= 12$ |

Method 2 illustrates a distributive property of <u>multiplication over subtraction</u>.

> For any numbers $a$, $b$, and $c$,
>
> 1. $a(b - c) = ab - ac$, and
>
> 2. $(b - c)a = ba - ca$.
>
> $8(9 - 3) = 8 \cdot 9 - 8 \cdot 3$
>
> $(x - 1)4 = x \cdot 4 - 1 \cdot 4$

**P-2** **How can you write each of the following as a difference?**

**a.** $2(x - y)$    **b.** $3(a - 4)$    **c.** $4(6t - 7)$    **d.** $2r(3r - 5)$

Each Distributive Property can be used to change sums or differences to products.

| **Sum** | **Product** | **Difference** | **Product** |
|---|---|---|---|
| $ab + ac$ | $= a(b + c)$ | $ab - ac$ | $= a(b - c)$ |
| $2x + 2y$ | $= 2(x + y)$ | $3r - 3 \cdot 1$ | $= 3(r - 1)$ |
| $ba + ca$ | $= (b + c)a$ | $ba - ca$ | $= (b - c)a$ |
| $4t + st$ | $= (4 + s)t$ | $kx - 1x$ | $= (k - 1)x$ |

**P-3** **How can you write each of the following as a product?**

**a.** $5a + 5b$    **b.** $10r - 10s$    **c.** $6a - 6$

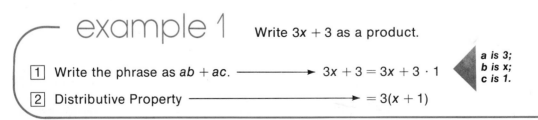

example 1    Write $3x + 3$ as a product.

1. Write the phrase as $ab + ac$. ⟶ $3x + 3 = 3x + 3 \cdot 1$

*a is 3;*
*b is x;*
*c is 1.*

2. Distributive Property ⟶ $= 3(x + 1)$

**P-4** How can you write each of the following as a product?

    **a.** $4t - 4$    **b.** $12m + 12$    **c.** $8q + 8$    **d.** $17j - j$

## example 2   Write $x^2 - 5x$ as a product.

$$x^2 - 5x = x \cdot x - 5 \cdot x$$
$$= (x - 5)x$$
$$= x(x - 5)$$

**P-5** How would you write each of the following as a product?

    **a.** $m^2 + 7m$    **b.** $t^2 - 12t$    **c.** $r^2 - 4r$

## example 3   Write $5a + 10$ as a product.

$$5a + 10 = 5a + 5 \cdot 2$$
$$= 5(a + 2)$$

Sometimes the phrase in parentheses can be simplified further.

$$3x + 9x = (3 + 9)x \qquad\qquad 15y - y = 15y - 1y$$
$$= 12x \qquad\qquad\qquad\qquad = (15 - 1)y$$
$$\qquad\qquad\qquad\qquad\qquad = 14y$$

## ORAL EXERCISES 2.4

*Say each sum or difference as a product.* (Example 1, Example 2, Example 3)

**EXAMPLE:** $10x + 10 \cdot 2$    **ANSWER:** $10(x + 2)$  (Say, "Ten times the quantity $x$ plus two.")

**1.** $3p + 3q$       **2.** $5r + 5s$       **3.** $12m - 12n$       **4.** $x(6) + 5(6)$

**5.** $r(4) - s(4)$       **6.** $na + 2a$       **7.** $4a + 4 \cdot 3$       **8.** $9y - 9 \cdot 1$

*Say each sum or difference as a product.* (Example 1, Example 2, Example 3)

9. $\frac{1}{2}c + \frac{1}{2}d$

10. $5k - 5 \cdot 3$

11. $rx + ry$

12. $cn - dn$

13. $2r + 2$

14. $10m - 10$

15. $19t + 19$

16. $\frac{1}{4}q - \frac{1}{4}$

17. $n^2 + 2n$

18. $a^2 + 5a$

19. $t^2 - 10t$

20. $y^2 - 100y$

21. $5w + w^2$

22. $12c - c^2$

23. $3x + 6$

24. $2y - 6$

25. $2m + 10$

26. $5k - 10$

27. $6b - 12$

28. $3r + 12$

29. $ry^2 + 12y$

30. $3g^2 - 12g$

31. $h^2r + k^2r$

32. $rg - 4g$

## WRITTEN EXERCISES 2.4

**A**  **Goal:** To write a sum or difference as a product using the Distributive Property

**Sample Problem:** $32 + 4y$

**Answer:** $(8 + y)4$ or $4(8 + y)$

*Write each sum or difference as a product.* (Example 1, Example 2, Example 3)

1. $7k + 7n$

2. $13t + 13r$

3. $19p - 19q$

4. $15k - 15a$

5. $h(5) + 7(5)$

6. $m(8) + 4(8)$

7. $x(\frac{1}{2}) - n(\frac{1}{2})$

8. $r(\frac{1}{4}) - w(\frac{1}{4})$

9. $pd + 5d$

10. $wb + 12b$

11. $15x + 15 \cdot 1$

12. $23k + 23 \cdot 1$

13. $10r - 10 \cdot 1$

14. $6t - 6 \cdot 1$

15. $\frac{1}{2}q + \frac{1}{2}a$

16. $\frac{2}{3}t + \frac{2}{3}n$

17. $12y - 12 \cdot 5$

18. $7m - 7 \cdot 11$

19. $qa + qb$

20. $tn + tq$

21. $na - ta$

22. $wd - xd$

23. $7n + 7$

24. $14y + 14$

25. $19q - 19$

26. $9b - 9$

27. $y^2 + 5y$

28. $p^2 + 9p$

29. $k^2 - \frac{1}{4}k$

30. $h^2 - \frac{1}{2}h$

31. $13t + t^2$

32. $15b - b^2$

33. $2n + 4$

34. $2r + 6$

35. $7y - 14$

36. $2t - 14$

37. $3y + 15$

38. $5m + 15$

39. $3g^2 + 21g$

40. $7p^2 - 21p$

**B**  **EXAMPLE:** $5a^2 + 5a + 10$    **ANSWER:** $5(a^2 + a + 2)$

41. $3m^2 - 3m + 6$

42. $12x^2 + 12x - 12$

43. $an + bn + cn$

44. $ar^2 + ar + 5a$

45. $x^3 + x^2 - x$

46. $a^3 - 2a^2 + 5a$

47. $9 - 45x + 27y$

48. $15x^2y + 25xy^2 + 5$

49. $42a - 21b - 35c$

## 2.5 Like Terms

The *numerical factor* of $5x^2$ is 5. In $x^2y$ the numerical factor is 1.

**P-1** **What is the numerical factor of each phrase?**

**a.** $\frac{1}{2}x^2$ **b.** $0.8x^2$ **c.** $mn^2$ **d.** $12x^2y^3z$

$\frac{1}{2}x^2$ and $0.8x^2$ are called <u>like terms</u> or similar terms.

> Two or more *like terms* have
> 1. the same variables, and
> 2. the same powers of these variables.
>
> Like: $5x^2y$, $3x^2y$
>
> Unlike: $5x^2y$, $3xy^2$

**P-2** **Which pairs are like terms?**

**a.** $5xy$, $2xy$ **b.** $3rs$, $3ps$ **c.** $2x^2y$, $6xy$ **d.** $8xy^2$, $4xy^2$

You can use one of the Distributive Properties to add or subtract like terms.

## example 1  Add: $10x + 3x$

1 Distributive Property ⟶ $ba + ca = (b + c)a$

2 Substitute. ⟶ $10x + 3x = (10 + 3)x$

3 Simplify. ⟶ $= 13x$

◀ *a is x; b is 10; c is 3.*

There is a shorter method for adding or subtracting like terms.

> To add or subtract like terms
> 1. add or subtract the numerical factors,
> 2. use the same variable(s) and exponent(s).
>
> $10x + 3x = 13x$
>
> $6x^2 - 2x^2 = 4x^2$

## example 2  Add: $5x^2y + 3x^2y$  Subtract: $5x^2y - 3x^2y$

$5x^2y + 3x^2y = 8x^2y$  $5x^2y - 3x^2y = 2x^2y$

## ORAL EXERCISES 2.5

*In Exercises 1–5, say Yes or No to show whether the two terms are like.* (P-2)

**1.** $6a$, $4a$     **2.** $5a$, $5b$     **3.** $2.5a^2$, $3.1a^2$     **4.** $2a^3$, $3a^2$     **5.** $9a^2b$, $13ab^2$

*Name pairs of like terms in each list.* (P-2)

**6.** $3mn$; $5x^2$; $7m^2n$; $6x$; $mn$; $\frac{1}{2}m^2n$; $3x^2y$; $1.8x$     **7.** $5rs$; $3a^2b$; $ab^2$; $12r$; $rst$; $6.2a^2b$; $9r$; $rs$

*Add or subtract like terms.* (Example 1, Example 2)

**8.** $8x + 3x$     **9.** $9t - 4t$     **10.** $6ab + ab$

**11.** $xy + xy$     **12.** $1.2a^2b + 2.5a^2b$     **13.** $5.9rt^2 - 1.3rt^2$

**14.** $4.5mn - mn$     **15.** $26ab^2c + 5ab^2c$     **16.** $35r^2st^3 - 15r^2st^3$

## WRITTEN EXERCISES 2.5

**A**

**Goal:** To add or subtract like terms
**Sample Problems: a.** $1.2ab^3 + 2.6ab^3$     **b.** $16rs - 4.5rs$
**Answers: a.** $3.8ab^3$     **b.** $11.5rs$

*In Exercises 1–10, write the letter or letters of like terms at the right.* (P-2)

**EXAMPLE:** $m^2n^2p$     **ANSWER: E, Q**

| | | | | | |
|---|---|---|---|---|---|
| **1.** $5x$ | **6.** $3rst$ | **A.** $\frac{3}{4}rst$ | **F.** $4y^3$ | **K.** $12a^2b$ | **P.** $3r^2st$ |
| **2.** $3ab^2$ | **7.** $4r^2t$ | **B.** $\frac{1}{4}r^2t$ | **G.** $x$ | **L.** $27ab^2$ | **Q.** $3m^2n^2p$ |
| **3.** $2y^3$ | **8.** $0.7mn^3$ | **C.** $m^3n$ | **H.** $b^2a$ | **M.** $3y^2$ | **R.** $0.1yx^2$ |
| **4.** $x^2y$ | **9.** $\frac{1}{2}rs^2t$ | **D.** $13rs^2t$ | **I.** $3tr^2$ | **N.** $12x^2$ | **S.** $14.2ba^2$ |
| **5.** $7y^2$ | **10.** $1.8a^2b$ | **E.** $\frac{1}{2}m^2n^2p$ | **J.** $mn^3$ | **O.** $12x^2y$ | **T.** $0.5xy^2$ |

*Add or subtract like terms.* (Example 1, Example 2)

**11.** $7a + 9a$     **12.** $6m + 8m$     **13.** $12s - 5s$     **14.** $13t - 7t$

**15.** $12ab + ab$     **16.** $rs + 9rs$     **17.** $6a^2 - a^2$     **18.** $9x^3 - x^3$

**19.** $3\frac{1}{2}y + \frac{1}{2}y$     **20.** $4\frac{3}{4}n + \frac{1}{4}n$     **21.** $2.4x + 1.5x$     **22.** $3.2y + 2.5y$

**23.** $7.8rt - rt$     **24.** $4.9b^2 - b^2$     **25.** $\frac{3}{4}mn + \frac{1}{4}mn$     **26.** $\frac{1}{2}ab^2 + \frac{1}{2}ab^2$

**27.** $\frac{5}{2}x^2 + \frac{1}{2}x^2$     **28.** $\frac{7}{4}xy + \frac{1}{4}xy$     **29.** $\frac{9}{4}ab - \frac{3}{4}ab$     **30.** $\frac{7}{2}rs - \frac{3}{2}rs$

**31.** $24ab^2c - 9ab^2c$     **32.** $19r^2st^3 - 8r^2st^3$     **33.** $5.3r^2t - 2.9r^2t$

**34.** $11.2abc - 5.8abc$     **35.** $3.83m^5n^2 + 12.19m^5n^2$     **36.** $14.08p^4q^3 + 23.59p^4q^3$

# 2.6  Properties of Addition

## example 1

Use a number line to add 3 + 2.

1  Start at 0 and move 3 units to the right.

2  Move 2 more units to the right.

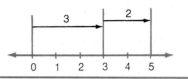

**P-1**  **What is the first step for adding 2 + 3 on a number line?**

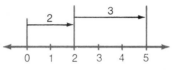

The steps for adding 2 + 3 are not the same as for adding 3 + 2.
However, each sum equals 5. Therefore, 2 + 3 = 3 + 2.

> **Commutative Property of Addition**
>
> Any two numbers can be added in either order.
>
> ▲ $a + b = b + a$
>
> $x + 6 = 6 + x$
>
> $9 + \frac{1}{2} = \frac{1}{2} + 9$

**P-2**  **Which two numbers do you add first in 3 + (8 + 5)?**

> ◀ Do operations inside parentheses first.

**P-3**  **What is the value of 3 + (8 + 5)?**

**P-4**  **Which two numbers do you add first in (3 + 8) + 5?**

**P-5**  **What is the value of (3 + 8) + 5?**

These steps are different, but the answers are the same.
Therefore, 3 + (8 + 5) = (3 + 8) + 5.

> **Associative Property of Addition**
>
> When you find the sum of any
> three numbers, it does not matter
> how you group them.
>
> ▲ $(a + b) + c = a + (b + c)$
>
> $(7 + \frac{3}{4}) + \frac{1}{4} = 7 + (\frac{3}{4} + \frac{1}{4})$
>
> $(2 + x) + x = 2 + (x + x)$

**P-6**   In $3x^2 + 5x + 4x^2$, which terms are like terms?

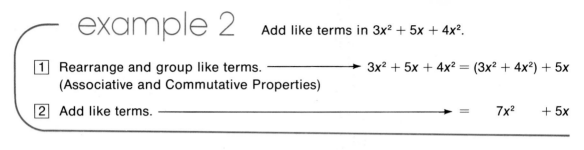

example 2   Add like terms in $3x^2 + 5x + 4x^2$.

[1] Rearrange and group like terms. ⟶ $3x^2 + 5x + 4x^2 = (3x^2 + 4x^2) + 5x$
(Associative and Commutative Properties)

[2] Add like terms. ⟶ $= 7x^2 \quad + 5x$

example 3   Add like terms in $3x + 7x + x + 10x + 2x$.

$$3x + 7x + x + 10x + 2x = 10x + x + 10x + 2x$$

$$= 11x + 10x + 2x$$

$$= 21x + 2x$$

$$= 23x$$

**P-7**   What is the simplest name of $12ab + 3ab + ab + 5ab$?

example 4   Add like terms in $4x^2y + xy + 7x^2y + 5 + 3xy + 7$.

First rearrange and group the like terms. Then add the like terms.

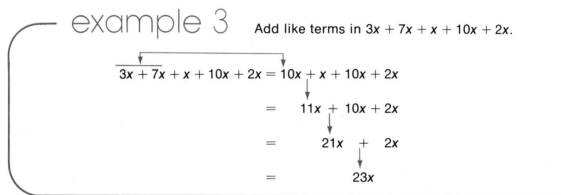

$$4x^2y + xy + 7x^2y + 5 + 3xy + 7 = (4x^2y + 7x^2y) + (xy + 3xy) + (5 + 7)$$

$$= 11x^2y + 4xy + 12$$

**P-8**   Which property or properties are shown in each sentence?

**a.** $2y + (3y^2 + 5y) = 2y + (5y + 3y^2)$

**b.** $2y + (5y + 3y^2) = (2y + 5y) + 3y^2$

**c.** $2y + (3y^2 + 5y) = (2y + 5y) + 3y^2$

## ORAL EXERCISES 2.6

*Say Commutative Property of Addition, Associative Property of Addition, or Both Properties to describe each sentence.* (P-8)

1. $10 + (15 + 20) = (10 + 15) + 20$

2. $(3 + 4) + 5 = 5 + (3 + 4)$

3. $7 + (9 + 11) = (9 + 7) + 11$

4. $(50 + 100) + 25 = 50 + (100 + 25)$

5. $(\frac{1}{2} + \frac{1}{3}) + \frac{1}{4} = (\frac{1}{4} + \frac{1}{3}) + \frac{1}{2}$

6. $(12x + 13) + 7x = (12x + 7x) + 13$

*Add like terms.* (Example 2, Example 3, Example 4)

7. $3n + 5n + 7n$

8. $4xy + xy + 12xy$

9. $a + 6a + 4a + a$

10. $12r^2 + r^2 + 3r^2 + r^2 + 5r^2$

11. $5x + 7 + x + 8$

12. $3x^2 + 2x + x^2 + 9x$

13. $s^2 + 5s + 3 + 2s^2 + 9s$

14. $3ab + 5a^2b + ab + a^2b$

15. $8t + t^2 + 7t + 3t^2 + 5$

## WRITTEN EXERCISES 2.6

**A**  **Goal:** To add like terms in a phrase

**Sample Problem:** $6a^2 + 6a + 12a^2 + 4 + 10a$

**Answer:** $18a^2 + 16a + 4$

*Add like terms.* (Example 2, Example 3, Example 4)

1. $12m + 8m + 13m$

2. $14t + t + 19t$

3. $7x + x + 5x + 12x$

4. $6y + 2y + y + 9y$

5. $1.8k + 2.5k + 7.3k$

6. $9.2b + 1.3b + 3.9b$

7. $0.9r^2 + r^2 + 0.8r^2$

8. $0.6s^3 + 0.9s^3 + s^3$

9. $5x^2 + 3x + x^2 + 12x + 7$

10. $9t + t^2 + 7t + 3 + 9t^2$

11. $2n^2 + n^3 + n^2 + 6 + 3n$

12. $m^3 + 17 + 3m^2 + 4m^3 + 5 + 3m$

13. $0.3p + 1.8r + 0.9pr + p + r$

14. $3.9x + y + 0.7xy + 0.1y + 9.4x$

15. $0.83r^2 + 0.03r + 5.23 + r + 9.17r^2$

16. $3.14mn + 0.09m + 3.27n + mn + 1.76$

*Write Commutative Property of Addition, Associative Property of Addition, or Both Properties to show which property is illustrated in each sentence.* (P-8)

17. $35 + (16 + 23) = (23 + 35) + 16$

18. $(50 + 20) + 70 = 20 + (50 + 70)$

19. $\frac{2}{3} + (\frac{3}{4} + \frac{4}{5}) = (\frac{2}{3} + \frac{3}{4}) + \frac{4}{5}$

20. $(\frac{1}{5} + \frac{1}{3}) + \frac{1}{4} = \frac{1}{5} + (\frac{1}{3} + \frac{1}{4})$

21. $r + (s + t) = (s + r) + t$

22. $(2a + bc) + ac = ac + (bc + 2a)$

# Police Officer

Many opportunities exist for persons who seek careers in law enforcement. The number of jobs available with law enforcement groups is expected to increase through the mid-1980's.

Most city police officers are assigned to patrol or traffic duty. However, there are also many specialized assignments including criminal investigation, chemical and microscopic analysis, firearms identification, and handwriting and fingerprint identification. State police officers provide services to motorists on the highways including help at accident scenes. Their main function is to enforce highway laws.

Both city and state police officers are trained to promote safe driving for motorists. From their training and experience they learn the effects of speed and driving conditions on the ability of a motorist to stop quickly. They must learn to use mathematical formulas such as $d = rt$ that relate driving speed and the distance needed to come to a complete stop in a certain length of time.

The drawing below shows the distance in feet required to stop a car traveling at 40 miles per hour under normal driving conditions. *Reaction distance* is the distance a vehicle travels during the time the driver is getting his or her foot on the brake. *Braking distance* is the distance traveled after the brakes are applied and until the vehicle stops.

40 miles per hour

| Reaction distance | Braking distance |
|---|---|
| 44 feet | 60 feet |

A stopping distance of about 104 feet is required.

City and state police officers are trained to promote safe driving for motorists. Safe driving involves three equally important factors: knowledge, experience, and attitude.

# CHAPTER SUMMARY

| | |
|---|---|
| **IMPORTANT TERMS** | Power *(p. 24)*  Numerical factor *(p. 31)* |
| | Exponent *(p. 24)*  Like terms *(p. 31)* |
| | Base *(p. 24)* |

**IMPORTANT IDEAS**

*1.* Addition Property of Zero
$$a + 0 = a$$

*2.* Multiplication Property of Zero
$$a \cdot 0 = 0$$

*3.* Multiplication Property of One
$$a \cdot 1 = a$$

*4.* To add or subtract like terms
**a.** add or subtract the numerical factors, and
**b.** use the same variable(s) and exponent(s).

*5.* Commutative Properties
Addition: $a + b = b + a$
Multiplication: $a \cdot b = b \cdot a$

*6.* Associative Properties
Addition: $(a + b) + c = a + (b + c)$
Multiplication: $(a \cdot b) \cdot c = a \cdot (b \cdot c)$

*7.* Distributive Properties

$a(b + c) = ab + ac$          $(b + c)a = ba + ca$
$a(b - c) = ab - ac$          $(b - c)a = ba - ca$

# CHAPTER REVIEW

### SECTION 2.1

*Write a number that will make each sentence true.*

**1.** $n + 6.5 = 6.5$

**2.** $r + 0 = 16.3$

**3.** $t(73) = 73$

**4.** $a(8.6) = 0$

**5.** $23.7 = 23.7 + 2x$

**6.** $(35 + k)\frac{2}{2} = 35$

**7.** $\frac{1}{2}n + 0 = \frac{1}{2}$

**8.** $1(r + 0) = 27$

**9.** $18.9 + 5n = 18.9$

**10.** $\frac{3}{3}(12 + 8s) = 12$

### SECTION 2.2

*Multiply.*

**11.** $10(5x)$

**12.** $8(12r)$

**13.** $(4a)(9b)$

**14.** $(6m)(15m)$

**15.** $(7rs)(12r)$

**16.** $(13k)(9kr)$

**17.** $(16p^2q)(0.2pq)$

**18.** $(0.4xy)(22y^2)$

**19.** $(2a)(3ab)(2b)(a^2)$

**20.** $(5n)(3mn)(n)(m)$

### SECTION 2.3

*Write each product as a sum in simplest form.*

**21.** $9(a + 7)$

**22.** $12(k + 4)$

**23.** $(p + q)19$

**24.** $(c + d)25$

**25.** $7(2x + 5)$

**26.** $6(3p + 9)$

**27.** $3y(8y + 4t)$

**28.** $(9g + 3h)6g$

**29.** $(\frac{1}{3}f + \frac{3}{4})12$

**30.** $\frac{1}{2}p(6p + 8q)$

### SECTION 2.4

*Write each sum or difference as a product.*

**31.** $16c + 16d$

**32.** $24m - 24n$

**33.** $k(9.3) - 7(9.3)$

**34.** $r(\frac{1}{3}) + 5(\frac{1}{3})$

**35.** $xk + 19k$

**36.** $23q - pq$

**37.** $20t - 20$

**38.** $39 - 39k$

**39.** $4.2r + r^2$

**40.** $2rb + ra$

### SECTION 2.5

*Add or subtract like terms.*

**41.** $13r + 24r$

**42.** $4.2t + 3.7t$

**43.** $12.1n - 7.9n$

**44.** $29t - t$

*Add or subtract like terms.*

**45.** $19ab^2 + 23ab^2$

**46.** $42x^3y + 17x^3y$

**47.** $5.7m^2n^2 - m^2n^2$

**48.** $13.3ab^2c - 9.7ab^2c$

**49.** $\frac{1}{6}xy^2 + \frac{5}{6}xy^2$

**50.** $8\frac{1}{3}r^3t - \frac{1}{3}r^3t$

**SECTION 2.6**

*Add like terms.*

**51.** $17q + 29q + 34q$

**52.** $19ab + 13ab + 47ab$

**53.** $5t^2 + 3t + t^2 + 9t + 3$

**54.** $12n^2 + 9 + 4n + 3n^2 + n$

**55.** $\frac{1}{4}p + 5r + \frac{3}{4}pr + p + \frac{1}{2}r$

**56.** $7xy + 3y + 21x + 8y + 7x$

**57.** $1.7rs^2 + 2.8rs + rs^2 + 5.3r^2s + rs$

**58.** $12.9ab + 3.8a^2b^2 + 5.3ab + a^2b + a^2b^2$

**59.** $(x^2 + 5x + 9) + (4x^2 + 2x + 23)$

**60.** $(2x^3 + 7x + 12) + (7x^3 + 9x^2 + 26)$

**61.** $(4x + 13) + (3x^2 + 5) + (5x^2 + 9x)$

**62.** $(7a^2 + 5) + (8a + 2) + (6a^2 + 1)$

# 3

# Basic Number Concepts

# 3.1 Factors, Multiples, and Divisibility

The **set of counting numbers** is {1, 2, 3, 4, 5, · · ·}.

> The three dots mean that there are infinitely many elements in the set.

**P-1**   **What are the next four counting numbers after 5?**

If 9 is divided by 7, the remainder is 2.

**P-2**   **What is the remainder in each of these divisions?**

a.
$$6\overline{)13} \quad \begin{array}{c}2\\ \phantom{6)}13\\ \underline{12}\\ 1\end{array}$$

> 13 is not divisible by 6.

b.
$$8\overline{)24} \quad \begin{array}{c}3\\ \phantom{8)}24\\ \underline{24}\\ 0\end{array}$$

> 24 is divisible by 8.

> Any counting number is **divisible** by another counting number if the remainder is 0.

**P-3**   **24 is divisible by what counting numbers?**

1, 2, 3, 4, 6, 8, 12, and 24 are the **counting-number factors** of 24. The number 24 is a **counting-number multiple** of each of these factors.

> $4 \cdot 6 = 24$
> $8 \cdot 3 = 24$
> $12 \cdot 2 = 24$
> $1 \cdot 24 = 24$

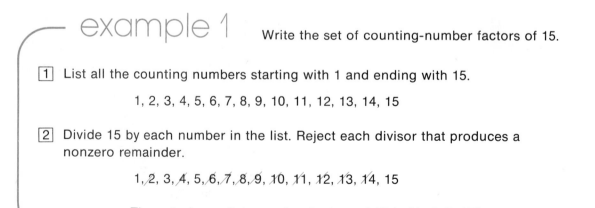

## example 1

Write the set of counting-number factors of 15.

1 List all the counting numbers starting with 1 and ending with 15.

   1, 2, 3, 4, 5, 6, 7, 8, 9, 10, 11, 12, 13, 14, 15

2 Divide 15 by each number in the list. Reject each divisor that produces a nonzero remainder.

   1, 2, 3, 4, 5, 6, 7, 8, 9, 10, 11, 12, 13, 14, 15

The set of counting-number factors of 15 is {1, 3, 5, 15}.

**P-4**  What is the set of counting-number factors of 36?

**P-5**  How can you write 15 as the product of two counting numbers without using 1 or 15?

Each of the following sentences is true.

3 is a factor of 24.             8 is a factor of 24.
24 is divisible by 8.            24 is divisible by 3.
24 is a multiple of 8.           24 is a multiple of 3.

◀ *Sometimes "counting-number" is omitted when referring to factors or multiples.*

**P-6**  Which of the following sentences are true?

**a.** 36 is a multiple of 9.        **b.** 19 is divisible by 8.

**c.** 1 is a factor of 34.          **d.** 12 is a multiple of 12.


## ORAL EXERCISES 3.1

*Say a true statement about each pair. Use the words is divisible by.* (P-3, P-6)

**1.** 35 and 7        **2.** 9 and 45        **3.** 10 and 10        **4.** 26 and 13

**5.** 5 and 30       **6.** 20 and 100      **7.** 18 and 1         **8.** 3 and 21

*Say a true statement about each pair. Use the words is a factor of.* (P-6)

**9.** 2 and 10       **10.** 15 and 3       **11.** 35 and 7        **12.** 5 and 75

**13.** 19 and 1      **14.** 23 and 23      **15.** 17 and 34       **16.** 39 and 13

*Say a true statement about each pair. Use the words is a multiple of.* (P-6)

**17.** 4 and 28      **18.** 18 and 6       **19.** 36 and 9        **20.** 7 and 21

**21.** 27 and 27     **22.** 1 and 19       **23.** 45 and 5        **24.** 6 and 30

*Tell whether each statement is True or False.* (P-6)

**25.** 18 is a factor of 6.            **26.** 18 is divisible by 6.

**27.** 17 is divisible by 17.          **28.** 10 is a multiple of 60.

**29.** 23 is a multiple of 7.          **30.** 1 is a factor of 93.

**31.** 13 is a factor of 26.           **32.** 9 is divisible by 27.

**33.** 33 is a multiple of 13.         **34.** 48 is a factor of 16.

**35.** 19 is divisible by 19.          **36.** 14 is a multiple of 7.

## WRITTEN EXERCISES 3.1

**A**

**Goal:** To identify counting-number factors of a counting number

**Sample Problem:** Write the set of counting-number factors of 6. Then write 6 as the product of two counting numbers. Do not use 1 or 6.

**Answer:** {1, 2, 3, 6}; 2 · 3

*Write the set of counting-number factors of each number.* (Example 1)

| | | | | | |
|---|---|---|---|---|---|
| **1.** 4 | **2.** 6 | **3.** 5 | **4.** 7 | **5.** 8 | **6.** 9 |
| **7.** 10 | **8.** 14 | **9.** 12 | **10.** 16 | **11.** 11 | **12.** 13 |
| **13.** 15 | **14.** 21 | **15.** 18 | **16.** 20 | **17.** 23 | **18.** 19 |
| **19.** 25 | **20.** 27 | **21.** 28 | **22.** 32 | **23.** 48 | **24.** 64 |

*Write each number as the product of two counting numbers. Do not use 1 or the given number.* (P-5)

| | | | | | |
|---|---|---|---|---|---|
| **25.** 6 | **26.** 8 | **27.** 15 | **28.** 14 | **29.** 9 | **30.** 25 |
| **31.** 21 | **32.** 35 | **33.** 12 | **34.** 16 | **35.** 18 | **36.** 24 |
| **37.** 27 | **38.** 28 | **39.** 30 | **40.** 36 | **41.** 33 | **42.** 34 |

*Write True or False for each sentence.* (P-6)

**43.** 21 is divisible by 7.  
**44.** 34 is divisible by 17.  
**45.** 6 is a factor of 43.  
**46.** 9 is a factor of 54.  
**47.** 55 is a multiple of 5.  
**48.** 57 is a multiple of 7.  
**49.** 258 is divisible by 13.  
**50.** 168 is divisible by 14.  
**51.** 126 is a multiple of 126.  
**52.** 7 is a factor of 158.  
**53.** 13 is a factor of 237.  
**54.** 228 is a multiple of 228.

**B**

*Write each division problem in the form (dividend) = (quotient) · (divisor) + (remainder).*

**EXAMPLE:** $120 \div 9$    **SOLUTION:**

$$\begin{array}{r} 13 \\ 9\overline{)120} \\ \underline{9\phantom{0}} \\ 30 \\ \underline{27} \\ 3 \end{array}$$

$120 = 13 \cdot 9 + 3$

| | | | |
|---|---|---|---|
| **55.** $58 \div 7$ | **56.** $72 \div 5$ | **57.** $208 \div 12$ | **58.** $230 \div 14$ |
| **59.** $304 \div 19$ | **60.** $253 \div 23$ | **61.** $581 \div 18$ | **62.** $1031 \div 22$ |

# 3.2    Tests for Divisibility

**P-1**    **How does the set of whole numbers shown below differ from the set of counting numbers?**

**Whole Numbers:** {0, 1, 2, 3, 4, 5, · · ·}

Any whole number is divisible by 2 if its numeral ends in 0, 2, 4, 6, or 8.

◄ *A whole number that is divisible by 2 is called an even number. A whole number that is not divisible by 2 is called an odd number.*

**P-2**    **Which of the numbers below are divisible by 2?**

**a.** 327        **b.** 1084        **c.** 160        **d.** 139

The numerals 0, 1, 2, 3, 4, 5, 6, 7, 8, and 9 are called **digits.**

◄ *"Digit sum," as it is used below, means "sum of the numbers named by the digits."*

**P-3**    **What are the missing answers in the table below?**

| Number | Digit Sum | Is the digit sum divisible by 3? | Is the number divisible by 3? |
|---|---|---|---|
| 84 | 8 + 4 = 12 | Yes | Yes |
| 53 | ? | ? | ? |
| 567 | ? | ? | ? |

If the digit sum is divisible by 3, then the number is divisible by 3.

**P-4**    **Which of the numbers below are divisible by 3?**

**a.** 2346        **b.** 5179        **c.** 12,316        **d.** 58,014

A number is divisible by
2    if its numeral ends in 0, 2, 4, 6, or 8.
3    if its digit sum is divisible by 3.
4    if its last two digits name a multiple of 4.
5    if its numeral ends in 0 or 5.
9    if its digit sum is divisible by 9.
10    if the numeral ends in 0.
Any number that does not meet one of these tests is not divisible by the number shown.

## example 1

Determine whether each number is divisible by 4.

**a.** 26,907     **b.** 80,348

**a.** 26,9<u>07</u> is not divisible by 4 because 7 is not divisible by 4.
**b.** 80,3<u>48</u> is divisible by 4 because 48 is divisible by 4.

**P-5** **Which of the numbers below are divisible by 5? by 10?**

**a.** 730     **b.** 492     **c.** 2385     **d.** 47,800     **e.** 19,726

## example 2

Determine whether each number below is divisible by 9.
**a.** 3825     **b.** 46,876     **c.** 78,363

| | Number | Digit Sum | Is the digit sum divisible by 9? | Is the number divisible by 9? |
|---|---|---|---|---|
| **a.** | 3825 | $3 + 8 + 2 + 5 = 18$ | Yes | Yes |
| **b.** | 46,876 | $4 + 6 + 8 + 7 + 6 = 31$ | No | No |
| **c.** | 78,363 | $7 + 8 + 3 + 6 + 3 = 27$ | Yes | Yes |

## ORAL EXERCISES 3.2

*Say True or False for each sentence. Then tell a reason based on the rules
on page 45.* (P-2, P-3, P-4, P-5, Example 1, Example 2)

**1.** 958 is divisible by 2.
**2.** 10,381 is divisible by 2.
**3.** 2 is a factor of 706.
**4.** 2 is a factor of 197.
**5.** 1023 is a multiple of 2.
**6.** 5640 is a multiple of 2.
**7.** 85 is divisible by 3.
**8.** 96 is divisible by 3.
**9.** 127 is a multiple of 3.
**10.** 138 is a multiple of 3.
**11.** 3 is a factor of 276.
**12.** 3 is a factor of 382.
**13.** 8217 is divisible by 3.
**14.** 4136 is divisible by 3.
**15.** 916 is divisible by 4.
**16.** 504 is divisible by 4.
**17.** 274 is a multiple of 4.
**18.** 4 is a factor of 1738.

**19.** 4 is a factor of 5212.

**20.** 3814 is divisible by 4.

**21.** 835 is divisible by 5.

**22.** 1840 is a multiple of 10.

**23.** 5 is a factor of 538.

**24.** 1095 is divisible by 5 and 10.

## WRITTEN EXERCISES 3.2

**A**     **Goal:** To test a counting number for divisibility by 2, 3, 4, 5, 9, or 10
**Sample Problem:** Write <u>True</u> or <u>False</u>: 47,205 is divisible by 9. Write a reason.
**Answer:** True. $4 + 7 + 2 + 0 + 5 = 18$; 18 is divisible by 9. So, 47,205 is also divisible by 9.

*Write <u>True</u> or <u>False</u> for each sentence. Then write a reason based on the rules on page 45.* (P-2, P-3, P-4, P-5, Example 1, Example 2)

**1.** 546 is divisible by 2.

**2.** 513 is divisible by 2.

**3.** 2 is a factor of 811.

**4.** 2 is a factor of 838.

**5.** 1048 is a multiple of 2.

**6.** 2040 is a multiple of 2.

**7.** 15,207 is divisible by 2.

**8.** 10,876 is divisible by 2.

**9.** 813 is divisible by 3.

**10.** 747 is divisible by 3.

**11.** 3 is a factor of 82.

**12.** 3 is a factor of 91.

**13.** 3037 is a multiple of 3.

**14.** 5193 is a multiple of 3.

**15.** 10,521,175 is divisible by 3.

**16.** 15,281,923 is divisible by 3.

**17.** 324 is divisible by 4.

**18.** 814 is divisible by 4.

**19.** 4 is a factor of 938.

**20.** 4 is a factor of 416.

**21.** 1028 is a multiple of 4.

**22.** 2540 is a multiple of 4.

**23.** 5332 is divisible by 4.

**24.** 11,106 is divisible by 4.

**25.** 56 is divisible by 5.

**26.** 45 is divisible by 5.

**27.** 5 is a factor of 85.

**28.** 5 is a factor of 92.

**29.** 120 is a multiple of 5.

**30.** 160 is a multiple of 5.

**31.** 180 is divisible by 10.

**32.** 230 is divisible by 10.

**33.** 5 and 10 are factors of 105.

**34.** 5 and 10 are factors of 2300.

**35.** 18,000 is a multiple of 5 and 10.

**36.** 255 is a multiple of 5 and 10.

**37.** 1035 is divisible by 9.

**38.** 23,567 is divisible by 9.

**39.** 65,736 is a multiple of 9.

**40.** 402,795 is a multiple of 9.

**41.** 9 is a factor of 713,685.

**42.** 9 is a factor of 1,208,403.

**43.** 64,272 is divisible by 3 and 9.

**44.** 714,681 is divisible by 3 and 9.

# 3.3  Prime Numbers

**P-1**  **What seems to be special about the sets of counting-number factors of the numbers shown in the table below?**

| Number | Set of Counting-number Factors |
|--------|-------------------------------|
| 13 | {1, 13} |
| 19 | {1, 19} |
| 37 | {1, 37} |
| 397 | {1, 397} |

> A **prime number** is a counting number greater than 1 that has exactly two counting-number factors, 1 and the number itself.
>
> $7 = 7 \cdot 1$
>
> $41 = 41 \cdot 1$

The set of prime numbers that are less than 25 is shown below.

$$\{2, 3, 5, 7, 11, 13, 17, 19, 23\}$$

◄ *You should memorize these nine prime numbers.*

Numbers such as 4, 6, 8, 15, 50, etc., are called composite numbers.

> A **composite number** is a counting number greater than 1 that is not a prime number.
>
> $22 = 2 \cdot 11$
>
> $45 = 3 \cdot 3 \cdot 5$

**P-2**  **What counting-number factors does each of these numbers have other than 1 and the given number?**

**a.** 4     **b.** 6     **c.** 8     **d.** 15     **e.** 50

## example 1

Write the prime numbers less than 50.

◄ *The method used is called a prime-number sieve.*

1  Arrange the numerals from 2 to 50.

```
 2  3  4  5  6  7  8  9 10
11 12 13 14 15 16 17 18 19 20
21 22 23 24 25 26 27 28 29 30
31 32 33 34 35 36 37 38 39 40
41 42 43 44 45 46 47 48 49 50
```

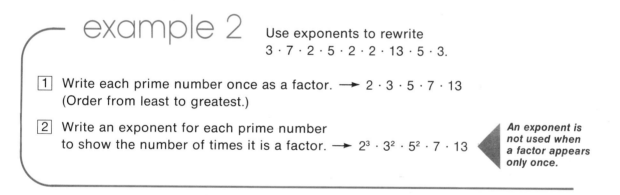

2 | Cross out numerals after **2** for numbers divisible by 2. (4, 6, 8, 10, · · ·)

3 | Cross out numerals after **3**, the next prime, for numbers divisible by 3. (6, 9, 12, 15, · · ·)

4 | Cross out numerals after **5** for numbers divisible by 5. (10, 15, 20, 25, · · ·)

5 | Cross out numerals after **7** for numbers divisible by 7. (14, 21, 28, 35, · · ·)

6 | Look for numerals after **11** for numbers divisible by 11. Since there are none, you are finished. The numerals not crossed out represent the prime numbers less than 50:

$$2, 3, 5, 7, 11, 13, 17, 19, 23, 29, 31, 37, 41, 43, 47$$

**P-3**   **How can you write 51 as the product of two prime numbers?**

## example 2

Use exponents to rewrite
$3 \cdot 7 \cdot 2 \cdot 5 \cdot 2 \cdot 2 \cdot 13 \cdot 5 \cdot 3$.

1 | Write each prime number once as a factor. → $2 \cdot 3 \cdot 5 \cdot 7 \cdot 13$
(Order from least to greatest.)

2 | Write an exponent for each prime number to show the number of times it is a factor. → $2^3 \cdot 3^2 \cdot 5^2 \cdot 7 \cdot 13$

◀ *An exponent is not used when a factor appears only once.*

## ORAL EXERCISES 3.3

1. What is the least prime number?

2. Why is 2 the only even prime number? ·

3. Explain why 49 is not a prime number.

4. Name all prime numbers between 10 and 50.

*Say each number as a product of two prime factors.* (P-3)

5. 10          6. 14          7. 21          8. 33          9. 35          10. 121

*Use exponents to say each product.* (Example 2)

**EXAMPLE:** $2 \cdot 3 \cdot 2 \cdot 3 \cdot 2$    **ANSWER:** $2^3 \cdot 3^2$   (Say, "Two cubed times three squared.")

**11.** $2 \cdot 5 \cdot 2 \cdot 3$                  **12.** $2 \cdot 7 \cdot 5 \cdot 5 \cdot 2$

**13.** $2 \cdot 11 \cdot 3 \cdot 5 \cdot 3 \cdot 2 \cdot 2$       **14.** $7 \cdot 5 \cdot 7 \cdot 5 \cdot 5 \cdot 5$

**15.** $17 \cdot 5 \cdot 5 \cdot 17 \cdot 11 \cdot 17$      **16.** $23 \cdot 3 \cdot 2 \cdot 23 \cdot 11 \cdot 3 \cdot 3$

**17.** $2 \cdot 2 \cdot 2 \cdot 3 \cdot 3 \cdot 3 \cdot 3 \cdot 7 \cdot 7 \cdot 7 \cdot 7 \cdot 7$

**18.** $11 \cdot 17 \cdot 5 \cdot 7 \cdot 5 \cdot 17 \cdot 11 \cdot 7 \cdot 5 \cdot 11$

## WRITTEN EXERCISES 3.3

**A**     **Goal:** To write a counting number as a product of prime factors
       **Sample Problem:** 115
       **Answer:** $5 \cdot 23$

**1.** Make a prime-number sieve for the numbers from 2 to 75. (Example 1)

**2.** Make a prime-number sieve for the numbers from 2 to 100. (Example 1)

*Write each number as a product of two prime factors.* (P-3)

| | | | | | |
|---|---|---|---|---|---|
| **3.** 26 | **4.** 34 | **5.** 38 | **6.** 46 | **7.** 55 | **8.** 57 |
| **9.** 69 | **10.** 87 | **11.** 65 | **12.** 95 | **13.** 77 | **14.** 91 |
| **15.** 119 | **16.** 253 | **17.** 451 | **18.** 481 | **19.** 201 | **20.** 413 |

*Use exponents to rewrite each product.* (Example 2)

**21.** $2 \cdot 3 \cdot 3 \cdot 5$             **22.** $2 \cdot 2 \cdot 3 \cdot 5 \cdot 5$

**23.** $2 \cdot 3 \cdot 5 \cdot 5 \cdot 7 \cdot 7$        **24.** $2 \cdot 3 \cdot 3 \cdot 5 \cdot 7 \cdot 7$

**25.** $7 \cdot 2 \cdot 3 \cdot 5 \cdot 7 \cdot 3 \cdot 3$      **26.** $5 \cdot 3 \cdot 3 \cdot 7 \cdot 2 \cdot 5 \cdot 2 \cdot 2$

**27.** $3 \cdot 7 \cdot 13 \cdot 7 \cdot 7 \cdot 5 \cdot 2 \cdot 3$    **28.** $11 \cdot 2 \cdot 3 \cdot 7 \cdot 2 \cdot 2 \cdot 5 \cdot 13$

**29.** $17 \cdot 11 \cdot 3 \cdot 5 \cdot 11 \cdot 7 \cdot 3 \cdot 2 \cdot 2 \cdot 17 \cdot 5$    **30.** $23 \cdot 19 \cdot 2 \cdot 3 \cdot 2 \cdot 2 \cdot 5 \cdot 5 \cdot 7 \cdot 23 \cdot 5$

**B**     Mathematicians believe that every even number greater than 2 can be written as the sum of two prime numbers. For example, $6 = 3 + 3$; $18 = 13 + 5$.
       Write each number as the sum of two prime numbers.

| | | | | | |
|---|---|---|---|---|---|
| **31.** 8 | **32.** 10 | **33.** 12 | **34.** 14 | **35.** 20 | **36.** 22 |
| **37.** 28 | **38.** 34 | **39.** 48 | **40.** 50 | **41.** 70 | **42.** 72 |

# 3.4 Prime Factorization

## example 1
Write 105 as a product of prime factors.

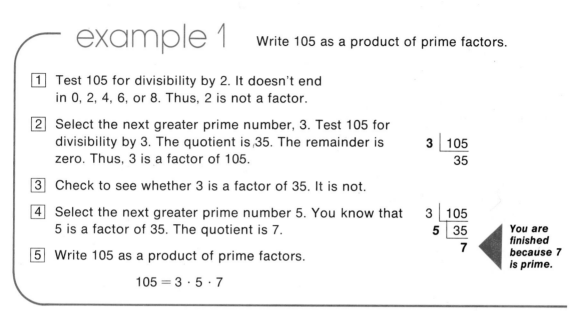

1. Test 105 for divisibility by 2. It doesn't end in 0, 2, 4, 6, or 8. Thus, 2 is not a factor.

2. Select the next greater prime number, 3. Test 105 for divisibility by 3. The quotient is 35. The remainder is zero. Thus, 3 is a factor of 105.

$$3 \underline{| 105}$$
$$35$$

3. Check to see whether 3 is a factor of 35. It is not.

4. Select the next greater prime number 5. You know that 5 is a factor of 35. The quotient is 7.

$$3 \underline{| 105}$$
$$5 \underline{| 35}$$
$$7$$

You are finished because 7 is prime.

5. Write 105 as a product of prime factors.

$$105 = 3 \cdot 5 \cdot 7$$

The phrase 3 · 5 · 7 is called the **prime factorization** of 105.

**P-1**    **What is the least prime factor of 126?**

## example 2
Write the prime factorization of 126.

1. Divide 126 by 2. Write the quotient 63.

$$2 \underline{| 126}$$
$$63$$

2. Check to see whether 2 is a factor of 63. It is not.

3. Select the next greater prime number 3. You know that 3 is a factor of 63. Divide and write the quotient 21.

$$2 \underline{| 126}$$
$$3 \underline{| 63}$$
$$21$$

4. Check again to see whether 3 is a factor of 21. It is. The quotient is 7. Since 7 is a prime number, the problem is finished.

$$2 \underline{| 126}$$
$$3 \underline{| 63}$$
$$3 \underline{| 21}$$
$$7$$

5. Write the prime factorization of 126.

$$126 = 2 \cdot 3 \cdot 3 \cdot 7 \quad \text{or} \quad 2 \cdot 3^2 \cdot 7$$

In a prime factorization, the prime factors may be written in any order. However, they are usually written in order from least to greatest. The prime factors are the same no matter what order is used.

*2 · 3 · 3 · 7 or 2 · 3² · 7 can be written 3 · 7 · 2 · 3 or 7 · 3 · 3 · 2 or in any other order.*

There is only one possible selection of prime numbers in the prime factorization of a composite number.

## ORAL EXERCISES 3.4

**1.** What prime number do you test first in writing the prime factorization of a number?

**2.** What do you call a counting number greater than 1 that is not prime?

**3.** What are the prime numbers less than 25?

**4.** How many different sets of prime factors can a number have?

*Tell the prime factorization of each number.* (Example 1, Example 2)

**5.** 455

5 | 455
7 | 91
13

**6.** 261

3 | 261
3 | 87
29

**7.** 150

2 | 150
3 | 75
5 | 25
5

**8.** 204

2 | 204
2 | 102
3 | 51
17

**9.** 492

2 | 492
2 | 246
3 | 123
41

**10.** 315

3 | 315
3 | 105
5 | 35
7

**11.** 198

198
99
33
11

**12.** 220

220
110
55
11

**13.** 261

261
87
29

**14.** 396

396
198
99
33
11

**15.** 450

450
225
75
25
5

**16.** 312

312
156
78
39
13

**17.** 6

**18.** 8

**19.** 9

**20.** 12

**21.** 16

**22.** 20

**23.** 14

**24.** 15

**25.** 22

**26.** 25

**27.** 26

**28.** 49

**29.** 220

**30.** 34

## WRITTEN EXERCISES 3.4

**A**      **Goal:** To write the prime factorization of a composite number
**Sample Problem:** 980
**Answer:** $2^2 \cdot 5 \cdot 7^2$

*Write the prime factorization of each number. (Example 1, Example 2)*

| | | | | | |
|---|---|---|---|---|---|
| **1.** 18 | **2.** 24 | **3.** 27 | **4.** 32 | **5.** 40 | **6.** 42 |
| **7.** 44 | **8.** 48 | **9.** 50 | **10.** 52 | **11.** 54 | **12.** 56 |
| **13.** 60 | **14.** 81 | **15.** 64 | **16.** 70 | **17.** 78 | **18.** 84 |
| **19.** 88 | **20.** 96 | **21.** 115 | **22.** 125 | **23.** 248 | **24.** 378 |
| **25.** 324 | **26.** 288 | **27.** 225 | **28.** 364 | **29.** 420 | **30.** 475 |
| **31.** 494 | **32.** 483 | **33.** 399 | **34.** 504 | **35.** 512 | **36.** 729 |
| **37.** 2431 | **38.** 1547 | **39.** 36,225 | **40.** 56,840 | **41.** 16,335 | **42.** 12,675 |

**C**      The **greatest common factor** of two counting numbers is the greatest number that is a factor of both given numbers. To find the greatest common factor, write the prime factorization of each given number. Then write the factors appearing in both prime factorizations and multiply them.

*Write the greatest common factor of the numbers in each exercise.*

**EXAMPLE:** 60 and 72      **SOLUTION:** $60 = 2 \cdot 2 \cdot 3 \cdot 5$
$72 = 2 \cdot 2 \cdot 2 \cdot 3 \cdot 3$ $\Big\}$ $2 \cdot 2 \cdot 3 = 12$
The greatest common factor of 60 and 72 is 12.

| | | | | |
|---|---|---|---|---|
| **43.** 18 and 27 | **44.** 24 and 36 | **45.** 15 and 25 | **46.** 40 and 70 | **47.** 16 and 40 |
| **48.** 27 and 45 | **49.** 75 and 50 | **50.** 42 and 30 | **51.** 54 and 72 | **52.** 48 and 56 |

*A counting number is divisible by a smaller counting number if their greatest common factor is the smaller number. In each of the following pairs, write Yes or No to show whether the first number is divisible by the second.*

**EXAMPLE:** 414 by 18      **SOLUTION:** Yes, because 18 is the greatest common factor of 414 and 18.

| | | | | |
|---|---|---|---|---|
| **53.** 450 by 15 | **54.** 364 by 14 | **55.** 288 by 36 | **56.** 342 by 18 | **57.** 468 by 24 |
| **58.** 572 by 26 | **59.** 396 by 32 | **60.** 220 by 44 | **61.** 372 by 93 | **62.** 456 by 38 |

# 3.5    Least Common Multiple

P-1    **What numbers do these sets have in common?**

**Multiples of 2**                                    **Multiples of 5**

$\{2, 4, 6, 8, 10, 12, 14, 16, 18, 20, \cdots\}$        $\{5, 10, 15, 20, 25, 30, \cdots\}$

The ***set of common multiples*** of 2 and 5 is $\{10, 20, 30, \cdots\}$.

P-2    **What is the least number in this set?**

The number 10 is called the <u>least common multiple</u> of 2 and 5.

> The ***least common multiple*** (*LCM*) of two or more counting numbers is the smallest counting number that is divisible by the given numbers.
>
> 24 is the *LCM* of 6 and 8.

P-3    **What is the least common multiple of 3 and 4?   of 4 and 6?**

## example 1    Find the least common multiple of 8, 30, and 45.

1  Write the prime factorization of each number. ⟶ $8 = 2^3$
$30 = 2 \cdot 3 \cdot 5$
$45 = 3^2 \cdot 5$

2  Write a product using each prime factor only once. ⟶ $2 \cdot 3 \cdot 5$

3  For each factor, write the highest exponent
used in any of the prime factorizations. ⟶ $2^3 \cdot 3^2 \cdot 5$

4  Multiply. ⟶ 360

> To find the least common multiple of two or more numbers, write each prime factor the greatest number of times it is a factor of any one of the given numbers. Then multiply these factors.

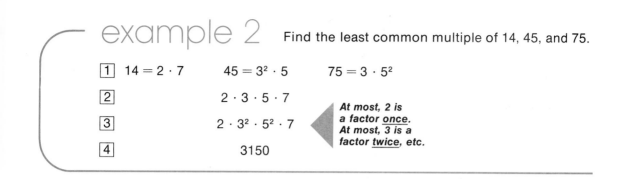

example 2     Find the least common multiple of 14, 45, and 75.

|1|   $14 = 2 \cdot 7$     $45 = 3^2 \cdot 5$     $75 = 3 \cdot 5^2$

|2|         $2 \cdot 3 \cdot 5 \cdot 7$

|3|         $2 \cdot 3^2 \cdot 5^2 \cdot 7$     *At most, 2 is a factor <u>once</u>. At most, 3 is a factor <u>twice</u>, etc.*

|4|         3150

**P-4**     **What is the *LCM* of 8 and 9?**

> The least common multiple of two numbers which have no common factor is the product of the two numbers.

Thus, 8 and 9 have the least common multiple 72.

**P-5**     **What is the least common multiple of each pair of numbers?**

      **a.** 12 and 5     **b.** 4 and 9     **c.** 10 and 21

## ORAL EXERCISES 3.5

*Tell the least common multiple of each pair of numbers.* (P-3, P-4, P-5, Example 1, Example 2)

| | | | |
|---|---|---|---|
| **1.** 2 and 3 | **2.** 3 and 5 | **3.** 2 and 7 | **4.** 2 and 5 |
| **5.** 3 and 7 | **6.** 5 and 7 | **7.** 3 and 11 | **8.** 5 and 11 |
| **9.** 4 and 5 | **10.** 8 and 7 | **11.** 6 and 7 | **12.** 4 and 11 |
| **13.** 4 and 6 | **14.** 2 and 8 | **15.** 3 and 15 | **16.** 4 and 12 |
| **17.** 8 and 12 | **18.** 4 and 10 | **19.** 6 and 9 | **20.** 6 and 15 |

*The prime factorizations of two or three numbers are given in each exercise. Tell the prime factorization of their least common multiple.* (Examples 1 and 2)

    **EXAMPLE:** $2^2 \cdot 3$,   $2 \cdot 3 \cdot 5$,   $2 \cdot 3^3 \cdot 5^2$     **ANSWER:** $2^2 \cdot 3^3 \cdot 5^2$

**21.** $2 \cdot 3$,   $2^2 \cdot 5$           **22.** $3^2 \cdot 5 \cdot 7$,   $5^2 \cdot 2$       **23.** 17,   $11 \cdot 13$

**24.** $2 \cdot 3 \cdot 2 \cdot 5$,   $3 \cdot 3 \cdot 5 \cdot 2$     **25.** $2 \cdot 3^2 \cdot 5$,   $2^3 \cdot 3 \cdot 5^3$     **26.** $2 \cdot 3$,   $3 \cdot 5$,   $5^2 \cdot 3^2$

## WRITTEN EXERCISES 3.5

**A**  **Goal:** To find the least common multiple of two or more numbers
**Sample Problem:** 9, 12, and 15     **Answer:** 180

*The prime factorizations of two or three numbers are given in each exercise.*
*Write the prime factorization of their least common multiple. (Examples 1 and 2)*

**EXAMPLE:** $2 \cdot 3 \cdot 5^2$,   $3 \cdot 5 \cdot 7$,   $2^2 \cdot 3 \cdot 5$    **ANSWER:** $2^2 \cdot 3 \cdot 5^2 \cdot 7$

**1.** $2 \cdot 3$,   $2^2 \cdot 7$
**2.** $3 \cdot 5$,   $2 \cdot 5^2$
**3.** $2^3 \cdot 3 \cdot 5$,   $2 \cdot 3 \cdot 5$

**4.** $3 \cdot 5^2$,   $2 \cdot 3^2 \cdot 5$
**5.** $7 \cdot 3^2 \cdot 13$,   $2 \cdot 3 \cdot 7^2$
**6.** $5 \cdot 11^2 \cdot 3$,   $2 \cdot 5^2 \cdot 3$

**7.** $13$,   $2^3 \cdot 11$
**8.** $5^2 \cdot 17$,   $19$
**9.** $2 \cdot 5$,   $2^2 \cdot 3$,   $3 \cdot 5$

**10.** $2 \cdot 3^2$,   $3 \cdot 5$,   $2^2 \cdot 7$
**11.** $7$,   $11$,   $29$
**12.** $23$,   $5$,   $13$

**13.** $5^3 \cdot 23$,   $3^5 \cdot 5 \cdot 17$,   $3 \cdot 5 \cdot 17^2$

**14.** $2^4 \cdot 7 \cdot 11$,   $3^5 \cdot 11^2 \cdot 13$,   $2 \cdot 3 \cdot 5 \cdot 17$

**15.** $2 \cdot 3 \cdot 5 \cdot 7 \cdot 11 \cdot 13 \cdot 17$,   $5 \cdot 7 \cdot 11 \cdot 13 \cdot 17 \cdot 19$,   $11^2 \cdot 13 \cdot 23^2$

**16.** $11^2 \cdot 13 \cdot 23^3$,   $5^3 \cdot 7 \cdot 19^2$,   $2^4 \cdot 5^3 \cdot 17$

**17.** $2 \cdot 3 \cdot 5^2 \cdot 13$,   $2^3 \cdot 3 \cdot 5 \cdot 11$,   $3^2 \cdot 5 \cdot 11$

**18.** $2 \cdot 7^2 \cdot 19$,   $3 \cdot 5 \cdot 11$,   $2 \cdot 3 \cdot 5^2 \cdot 19$

*Write the least common multiple of the given numbers. (Example 1, Example 2)*

**19.** 6 and 12
**20.** 8 and 24
**21.** 10 and 28

**22.** 12 and 20
**23.** 45 and 54
**24.** 36 and 80

**25.** 8, 12, and 15
**26,** 9, 15, and 16
**27.** 24, 30, and 42

**28.** 27, 35, and 63
**29.** 20, 16, and 12
**30.** 30, 18, and 12

**31.** 18, 28, and 21
**32.** 15, 25, and 35
**33.** 14, 21, and 24

**34.** 36, 24, and 40
**35.** 27, 45, and 75
**36.** 40, 30, and 25

**C**  *Assume that each variable is to be replaced by a prime number. Write a*
*phrase for the least common multiple of the two numbers.*

**EXAMPLE:** $r^2st^3$ and $rs^3$    **ANSWER:** $r^2s^3t^3$

**37.** $ab^2c^4$ and $ac^3$
**38.** $p^2q^3r$ and $pq^5r$
**39.** $k^3ng^4$ and $k^2ng^3$

# CHAPTER SUMMARY

**IMPORTANT TERMS**

Set of counting numbers *(p. 42)*
Divisible by *(p. 42)*
Counting-number factors *(p. 42)*
Counting-number multiple *(p. 42)*
Set of whole numbers *(p. 45)*
Even number *(p. 45)*
Odd number *(p. 45)*

Digits *(p. 45)*
Prime number *(p. 48)*
Composite number *(p. 48)*
Prime-number sieve *(p. 48)*
Prime factorization *(p. 51)*
Set of common multiples *(p. 54)*
Least common multiple *(p. 54)*

**IMPORTANT IDEAS**

*1.* Any counting number is divisible by another counting number if the remainder is zero.

*2.* A number is divisible by
   2  if its numeral ends in 0, 2, 4, 6, or 8.
   3  if its digit sum is divisible by 3.
   4  if its last two digits name a multiple of 4.
   5  if its numeral ends in 0 or 5.
   9  if its digit sum is divisible by 9.
  10  if the numeral ends in 0.
   Any number that does not meet one of these tests is not divisible by the number shown.

*3.* There is only one possible selection of prime numbers in the prime factorization of a composite number.

*4.* To find the least common multiple of two or more numbers, write each prime factor the greatest number of times ———— one of the given numbers. Then multiply these factor

*5.* The least common multiple of two numbers ———— mon factor is the product of the two numbers.

# CHAPTER REVIEW

**SECTION 3.1**

*Write the set of counting-number factors of each number.*

**1.** 17               **2.** 43               **3.** 50               **4.** 56

*Write True or False for each sentence.*

**5.** 36 is divisible by 9.          **6.** 7 is a factor of 49.          **7.** 34 is a multiple of 4.

**8.** 30 is divisible by 8.          **9.** 16 is a factor of 144.          **10.** 92 is a multiple of 12.

**SECTION 3.2**

*Write True or False for each sentence. Then write a reason based on the rules on page 45.*

11. 4725 is divisible by 3.

12. 90,286 is divisible by 3.

13. 4 is a factor of 1802.

14. 4 is a factor of 12,328.

15. 43,902 is a multiple of 9.

16. 715,824 is a multiple of 9.

17. 73,195 is divisible by 5 and 10.

18. 9760 is a multiple of 5 and 10.

19. 2 is a factor of 26,703.

20. 2 is a factor of 8,906.

21. 78,920 is divisible by 2, 3, 4, 5, 9, and 10.

22. 182,760 is divisible by 2, 3, 4, 5, 9, and 10.

**SECTION 3.3**

*Use exponents to rewrite each product.*

23. $19 \cdot 5 \cdot 5 \cdot 7 \cdot 3 \cdot 2 \cdot 2 \cdot 7 \cdot 2$

24. $37 \cdot 17 \cdot 2 \cdot 5 \cdot 2 \cdot 3 \cdot 5 \cdot 2 \cdot 3 \cdot 5$

25. $5 \cdot 3 \cdot 5 \cdot 3 \cdot 3 \cdot 2 \cdot 2 \cdot 5 \cdot 5 \cdot 2 \cdot 3$

26. $29 \cdot 23 \cdot 7 \cdot 7 \cdot 2 \cdot 5 \cdot 3 \cdot 5 \cdot 3 \cdot 3 \cdot 3$

**SECTION 3.4**

*Write the prime factorization of each number.*

27. 12

28. 16

29. 28

30. 44

31. 68

32. 74

33. 92

34. 98

**SECTION 3.5**

*The prime factorizations of two or three numbers are given in each exercise. Write the prime factorization of their least common multiple.*

35. $2 \cdot 3^3 \cdot 5^2 \cdot 13, \quad 2 \cdot 3 \cdot 11 \cdot 13^2$

36. $2^5 \cdot 3 \cdot 7^2 \cdot 11, \quad 2^3 \cdot 5^2 \cdot 11^3$

37. $2 \cdot 3 \cdot 5^2, \quad 3^4 \cdot 5 \cdot 7, \quad 2^3 \cdot 5 \cdot 11$

38. $2^3 \cdot 3 \cdot 17, \quad 2 \cdot 3^4 \cdot 11, \quad 2^2 \cdot 5^2 \cdot 7^3$

*Write the least common multiple of the given numbers.*

39. 8 and 20

40. 14 and 10

41. 12 and 18

42. 24 and 30

43. 7, 5, and 11

44. 3, 11, and 13

45. 8, 12, and 20

46. 9, 21, and 49

47. 25, 35, and 21

48. 18, 24, and 32

49. 8, 18, and 20

50. 15, 18, and 45

# 4

# Fractions

# 4.1    Simplifying Fractions

Numerals such as $\frac{3}{5}$, $\frac{12}{4}$, and $\frac{2}{6}$ are called **fractions**.

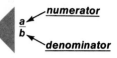

**P-1**    **In the fraction $\frac{a}{b}$, what number can never replace $b$?**

> The denominator of a fraction can never equal 0.

**P-2**    **What whole number does each fraction name?**

a. $\dfrac{10}{1}$      b. $\dfrac{0}{1}$      c. $\dfrac{5}{5}$      d. $\dfrac{100}{100}$

> Any fraction with a denominator of 1 names the same number as its numerator.
>
> ▲ $\dfrac{a}{1} = a$
>
> $\dfrac{35}{1} = 35$
>
> $\dfrac{2x}{1} = 2x$

> Any fraction with the same nonzero numerator and denominator equals 1.
>
> ▲ $\dfrac{a}{a} = 1$  *(a is not zero.)*
>
> $\dfrac{35}{35} = 1$
>
> $\dfrac{2 \cdot 2 \cdot 3}{2 \cdot 2 \cdot 3} = 1$

**P-3**    **What are the missing numerals?**

a. $\dfrac{12}{2} \cdot \dfrac{10}{5} = ? \cdot ?$      b. $\dfrac{12 \cdot 10}{2 \cdot 5} = \dfrac{\rightarrow ?}{\rightarrow ?}$

In both cases the final answer is 12.

> **Product Rule for Fractions**
>
> 1. Multiply the numerators.
> 2. Multiply the denominators.
>
> ▲ $\dfrac{a}{b} \cdot \dfrac{c}{d} = \dfrac{a \cdot c}{b \cdot d}$  *(b and d are not zero.)*
>
> $\dfrac{2}{3} \cdot \dfrac{5}{7} = \dfrac{2 \cdot 5}{3 \cdot 7}$
>
> $= \dfrac{10}{21}$

**P-4** **What are the missing numerals?**

a. $\dfrac{5}{6} \cdot \dfrac{7}{8} = ?$ 　　b. $\dfrac{2}{5} \cdot \dfrac{1}{3} = ?$ 　　c. $\dfrac{14}{15} = \dfrac{2}{3} \cdot \dfrac{?}{5}$

**P-5** **In each of these fractions, what factors do the numerator and denominator have in common?**

a. $\dfrac{3}{6}$ 　　b. $\dfrac{2}{4}$ 　　c. $\dfrac{1}{2}$ 　　d. $\dfrac{5}{10}$

> A fraction is simplified when the numerator and denominator have no common factor except 1. 　　$\dfrac{6}{35} = \dfrac{1 \cdot 2 \cdot 3}{1 \cdot 5 \cdot 7}$

example 1　　Simplify $\dfrac{15}{18}$. ◀ *You may also say, "Write the reduced form of $\dfrac{15}{18}$."*

1 Factor the numerator and denominator. ⟶ $\dfrac{15}{18} = \dfrac{3 \cdot 5}{2 \cdot 3 \cdot 3}$

2 Identify a name for 1. ⟶ $= \dfrac{3}{3} \cdot \dfrac{5}{2 \cdot 3}$ ◀ *Product Rule for Fractions*

3 Simplify each fraction. ⟶ $= 1 \cdot \dfrac{5}{6}$ ◀ $\dfrac{3}{3} = 1$

4 Multiplication Property of One ⟶ $= \dfrac{5}{6}$

example 2　　Simplify $\dfrac{12}{60}$.

**Method 1**

1 $\dfrac{12}{60} = \dfrac{2 \cdot 2 \cdot 3}{2 \cdot 2 \cdot 3 \cdot 5}$

2 $= \dfrac{2 \cdot 2 \cdot 3}{2 \cdot 2 \cdot 3} \cdot \dfrac{1}{5}$

3 $= 1 \cdot \dfrac{1}{5}$

4 $= \dfrac{1}{5}$

**Method 2**

$\dfrac{12}{60} = \dfrac{2 \cdot 2 \cdot 3}{2 \cdot 2 \cdot 3 \cdot 5}$

$= \dfrac{\overset{1}{\cancel{2}} \cdot \overset{1}{\cancel{2}} \cdot \overset{1}{\cancel{3}}}{\underset{1}{\cancel{2}} \cdot \underset{1}{\cancel{2}} \cdot \underset{1}{\cancel{3}} \cdot 5}$

$= \dfrac{1}{5}$

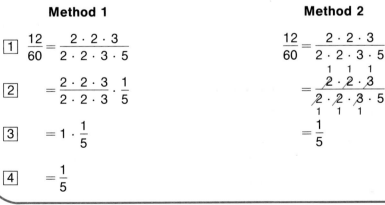

**P-6** Which of these fractions are other names for $\frac{1}{2}$?

a. $\frac{2}{4}$    b. $\frac{12}{6}$    c. $\frac{3}{5}$    d. $\frac{3}{6}$

---

*Equivalent fractions* name the same number.    $\frac{1}{2}, \frac{2}{4}$, and $\frac{3}{6}$

---

**P-7** Which of these are equivalent fractions?

a. $\frac{10}{14}$    b. $\frac{3}{4}$    c. $\frac{21}{15}$    d. $\frac{5}{7}$    e. $\frac{12}{16}$

## ORAL EXERCISES 4.1

*Simplify each fraction. (Example 1, Example 2)*

1. $\frac{2 \cdot 3}{2 \cdot 5}$

2. $\frac{3 \cdot 7}{3 \cdot 11}$

3. $\frac{2 \cdot 2}{5 \cdot 2}$

4. $\frac{3}{2 \cdot 3}$

5. $\frac{2 \cdot 3 \cdot 5}{2 \cdot 3 \cdot 7}$

6. $\frac{2 \cdot 3 \cdot 2}{2 \cdot 7 \cdot 2}$

7. $\frac{2 \cdot 2 \cdot 5}{2 \cdot 2 \cdot 2 \cdot 3}$

8. $\frac{2 \cdot 3 \cdot 3 \cdot 5}{3 \cdot 5 \cdot 7}$

9. $\frac{2 \cdot 2 \cdot 3}{2 \cdot 2 \cdot 2 \cdot 2 \cdot 3 \cdot 3}$

10. $\frac{2 \cdot 3 \cdot 5 \cdot 7 \cdot 7}{2 \cdot 3 \cdot 7 \cdot 11}$

11. $\frac{2 \cdot 3 \cdot 3 \cdot 3}{2 \cdot 2 \cdot 2 \cdot 3 \cdot 3}$

12. $\frac{2 \cdot 7 \cdot 11 \cdot 19}{3 \cdot 7 \cdot 11 \cdot 11}$

13. $\frac{5 \cdot 2 \cdot 7 \cdot 3 \cdot 2 \cdot 5 \cdot 3}{3 \cdot 2 \cdot 2 \cdot 5 \cdot 7 \cdot 5 \cdot 11}$

14. $\frac{2 \cdot 2 \cdot 2 \cdot 2 \cdot 2 \cdot 2 \cdot 3}{2 \cdot 3 \cdot 3 \cdot 3 \cdot 3 \cdot 3}$

15. $\frac{2}{12}$

16. $\frac{2}{16}$

17. $\frac{3}{12}$

18. $\frac{3}{15}$

19. $\frac{4}{10}$

20. $\frac{4}{14}$

21. $\frac{6}{15}$

22. $\frac{6}{14}$

23. $\frac{6}{18}$

24. $\frac{5}{15}$

25. $\frac{6}{4}$

26. $\frac{12}{9}$

27. $\frac{6}{24}$

28. $\frac{5}{10}$

29. $\frac{7}{21}$

30. $\frac{10}{40}$

31. $\frac{2}{18}$

32. $\frac{4}{28}$

33. $\frac{8}{42}$

34. $\frac{10}{25}$

35. $\frac{14}{35}$

## WRITTEN EXERCISES 4.1

**A**    **Goal:** To simplify a fraction

**Sample Problems: a.** $\dfrac{2 \cdot 2 \cdot 3}{2 \cdot 3 \cdot 5}$    **b.** $\dfrac{18}{12}$    **Answers: a.** $\dfrac{2}{5}$    **b.** $\dfrac{3}{2}$

*Simplify each fraction.* (Example 1, Example 2)

1. $\dfrac{3 \cdot 13}{3 \cdot 17}$    
2. $\dfrac{5 \cdot 23}{5 \cdot 19}$    
3. $\dfrac{2 \cdot 5 \cdot 7}{2 \cdot 7 \cdot 11}$

4. $\dfrac{3 \cdot 11 \cdot 19}{5 \cdot 11 \cdot 19}$    
5. $\dfrac{2 \cdot 2 \cdot 5}{2 \cdot 3 \cdot 7}$    
6. $\dfrac{2 \cdot 2 \cdot 7}{2 \cdot 3 \cdot 5}$

7. $\dfrac{2 \cdot 5 \cdot 3 \cdot 2 \cdot 2}{7 \cdot 2 \cdot 3 \cdot 11}$    
8. $\dfrac{13 \cdot 3 \cdot 2 \cdot 2 \cdot 5}{19 \cdot 5 \cdot 2 \cdot 3 \cdot 3}$    
9. $\dfrac{2 \cdot 3 \cdot 3 \cdot 3}{2 \cdot 2 \cdot 2 \cdot 3 \cdot 3}$

10. $\dfrac{2 \cdot 3 \cdot 3 \cdot 5 \cdot 7}{2 \cdot 2 \cdot 3 \cdot 3 \cdot 3 \cdot 5 \cdot 5}$    
11. $\dfrac{5^2 \cdot 3^2 \cdot 2^3}{2^6 \cdot 3 \cdot 5}$    
12. $\dfrac{2^6 \cdot 3^2 \cdot 7}{2^2 \cdot 3^5 \cdot 11}$

13. $\dfrac{14}{28}$    14. $\dfrac{15}{30}$    15. $\dfrac{8}{24}$    16. $\dfrac{14}{21}$    17. $\dfrac{12}{16}$    18. $\dfrac{9}{24}$

19. $\dfrac{10}{16}$    20. $\dfrac{14}{16}$    21. $\dfrac{12}{18}$    22. $\dfrac{35}{42}$    23. $\dfrac{12}{20}$    24. $\dfrac{24}{30}$

25. $\dfrac{21}{24}$    26. $\dfrac{20}{32}$    27. $\dfrac{12}{64}$    28. $\dfrac{15}{48}$    29. $\dfrac{14}{32}$    30. $\dfrac{45}{80}$

31. $\dfrac{66}{96}$    32. $\dfrac{65}{80}$    33. $\dfrac{15}{21}$    34. $\dfrac{12}{21}$    35. $\dfrac{15}{27}$    36. $\dfrac{24}{28}$

37. $\dfrac{27}{36}$    38. $\dfrac{60}{72}$    39. $\dfrac{28}{42}$    40. $\dfrac{24}{64}$    41. $\dfrac{32}{12}$    42. $\dfrac{45}{36}$

43. $\dfrac{48}{36}$    44. $\dfrac{48}{9}$    45. $\dfrac{64}{28}$    46. $\dfrac{48}{39}$    47. $\dfrac{35}{15}$    48. $\dfrac{36}{20}$

**C**    *Write the missing numeral to make the fractions equivalent.*

49. $\dfrac{3}{8} = \dfrac{?}{24}$    
50. $\dfrac{5}{12} = \dfrac{?}{48}$    
51. $\dfrac{5}{16} = \dfrac{?}{64}$    
52. $\dfrac{7}{15} = \dfrac{?}{45}$

53. $\dfrac{2 \cdot 3}{2 \cdot 2 \cdot 5} = \dfrac{?}{2 \cdot 2 \cdot 5 \cdot 3 \cdot 2}$    
54. $\dfrac{2 \cdot 5}{3 \cdot 7} = \dfrac{?}{2 \cdot 3 \cdot 3 \cdot 7 \cdot 5}$

# 4.2  Algebraic Fractions

Fractions such as $\dfrac{3}{x}$, $\dfrac{a+4}{5}$, and $\dfrac{2x}{y}$ are called <u>algebraic fractions</u>.

> In an *algebraic fraction* a variable or open phrase represents the numerator or denominator.
>
> $\dfrac{2}{x-3}$

**P-1**  **What number does each fraction below represent if x equals 2?**

   **a.** $\dfrac{x}{5}$   **b.** $\dfrac{6}{x}$   **c.** $\dfrac{x}{3x}$   **d.** $\dfrac{x+3}{12}$

In algebraic fractions you must not replace a variable by a number that will make a denominator equal 0.

**P-2**  **What value for *a* should not be used in order to avoid making the denominator equal 0?**

   **a.** $\dfrac{5}{a}$   **b.** $\dfrac{3}{7a}$   **c.** $\dfrac{a+2}{a-5}$

Algebraic fractions can be expressed in simplified form by the same methods as for ordinary fractions.

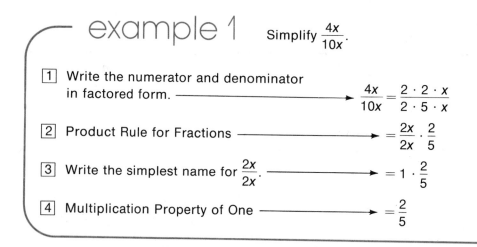

example 1   Simplify $\dfrac{4x}{10x}$.

[1]  Write the numerator and denominator in factored form. $\longrightarrow$   $\dfrac{4x}{10x} = \dfrac{2 \cdot 2 \cdot x}{2 \cdot 5 \cdot x}$

[2]  Product Rule for Fractions $\longrightarrow$   $= \dfrac{2x}{2x} \cdot \dfrac{2}{5}$

[3]  Write the simplest name for $\dfrac{2x}{2x}$. $\longrightarrow$   $= 1 \cdot \dfrac{2}{5}$

[4]  Multiplication Property of One $\longrightarrow$   $= \dfrac{2}{5}$

**P-3** In the algebraic fraction $\dfrac{x^2y^3}{x^3y}$, what number can x not represent? What number can y not represent?

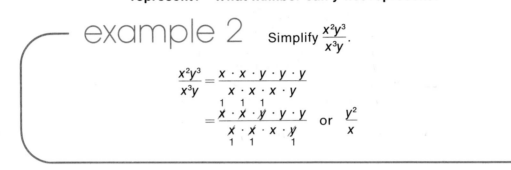

example 2 Simplify $\dfrac{x^2y^3}{x^3y}$.

$$\frac{x^2y^3}{x^3y} = \frac{x \cdot x \cdot y \cdot y \cdot y}{x \cdot x \cdot x \cdot y}$$

$$= \frac{\overset{1}{x} \cdot \overset{1}{x} \cdot \overset{1}{y} \cdot y \cdot y}{\underset{1}{x} \cdot \underset{1}{x} \cdot x \cdot \underset{1}{y}} \quad \text{or} \quad \frac{y^2}{x}$$

**P-4** What name for 1 is identified in the steps of Example 2?

example 3 Simplify $\dfrac{6ab^2c}{9abc^3}$.

Two methods are shown. The first step is the same in each method.

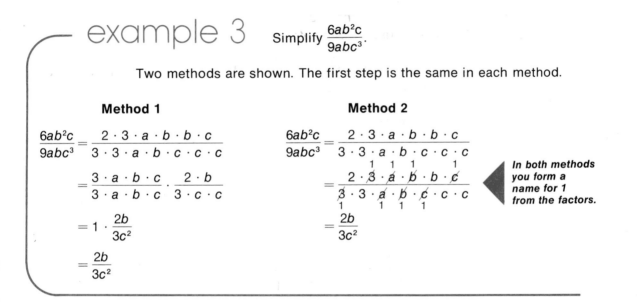

**Method 1**

$$\frac{6ab^2c}{9abc^3} = \frac{2 \cdot 3 \cdot a \cdot b \cdot b \cdot c}{3 \cdot 3 \cdot a \cdot b \cdot c \cdot c \cdot c}$$

$$= \frac{3 \cdot a \cdot b \cdot c}{3 \cdot a \cdot b \cdot c} \cdot \frac{2 \cdot b}{3 \cdot c \cdot c}$$

$$= 1 \cdot \frac{2b}{3c^2}$$

$$= \frac{2b}{3c^2}$$

**Method 2**

$$\frac{6ab^2c}{9abc^3} = \frac{2 \cdot 3 \cdot a \cdot b \cdot b \cdot c}{3 \cdot 3 \cdot a \cdot b \cdot c \cdot c \cdot c}$$

$$= \frac{2 \cdot \overset{1}{3} \cdot \overset{1}{a} \cdot \overset{1}{b} \cdot b \cdot \overset{1}{c}}{\underset{1}{3} \cdot 3 \cdot \underset{1}{a} \cdot \underset{1}{b} \cdot \underset{1}{c} \cdot c \cdot c}$$

$$= \frac{2b}{3c^2}$$

In both methods you form a name for 1 from the factors.

## ORAL EXERCISES 4.2

*Tell the values of variables that should not be used in order to avoid making the denominator equal 0. (P-2)*

**EXAMPLE:** $\dfrac{7}{x-1}$ **ANSWER:** 1

1. $\dfrac{3}{y}$
2. $\dfrac{9}{2r}$
3. $\dfrac{6}{n^2}$
4. $\dfrac{3a}{5b}$
5. $\dfrac{1}{p-5}$
6. $\dfrac{n^2}{2n-2}$

*Simplify.* (Example 1, Example 2, Example 3)

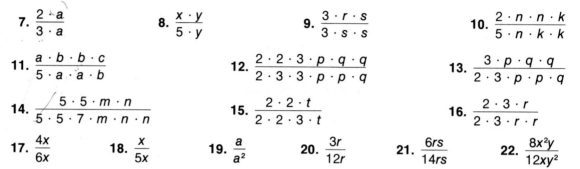

7. $\dfrac{2 \cdot a}{3 \cdot a}$

8. $\dfrac{x \cdot y}{5 \cdot y}$

9. $\dfrac{3 \cdot r \cdot s}{3 \cdot s \cdot s}$

10. $\dfrac{2 \cdot n \cdot n \cdot k}{5 \cdot n \cdot k \cdot k}$

11. $\dfrac{a \cdot b \cdot b \cdot c}{5 \cdot a \cdot a \cdot b}$

12. $\dfrac{2 \cdot 2 \cdot 3 \cdot p \cdot q \cdot q}{2 \cdot 3 \cdot 3 \cdot p \cdot p \cdot q}$

13. $\dfrac{3 \cdot p \cdot q \cdot q}{2 \cdot 3 \cdot p \cdot p \cdot q}$

14. $\dfrac{5 \cdot 5 \cdot m \cdot n}{5 \cdot 5 \cdot 7 \cdot m \cdot n \cdot n}$

15. $\dfrac{2 \cdot 2 \cdot t}{2 \cdot 2 \cdot 3 \cdot t}$

16. $\dfrac{2 \cdot 3 \cdot r}{2 \cdot 3 \cdot r \cdot r}$

17. $\dfrac{4x}{6x}$

18. $\dfrac{x}{5x}$

19. $\dfrac{a}{a^2}$

20. $\dfrac{3r}{12r}$

21. $\dfrac{6rs}{14rs}$

22. $\dfrac{8x^2y}{12xy^2}$

## WRITTEN EXERCISES 4.2

**A**

**Goal:** To simplify an algebraic fraction

**Sample Problem:** $\dfrac{5x^2y}{15xy^4}$

**Answer:** $\dfrac{x}{3y^3}$

*Simplify.* (Example 1, Example 2, Example 3)

1. $\dfrac{5 \cdot r}{11 \cdot r}$

2. $\dfrac{2 \cdot m}{7 \cdot m}$

3. $\dfrac{3 \cdot y}{x \cdot y}$

4. $\dfrac{s \cdot t}{11 \cdot t}$

5. $\dfrac{2 \cdot k \cdot t}{2 \cdot k \cdot t}$

6. $\dfrac{3 \cdot p \cdot n}{5 \cdot p \cdot p}$

7. $\dfrac{3 \cdot 5 \cdot q}{2 \cdot 5 \cdot p \cdot q}$

8. $\dfrac{2 \cdot 5 \cdot b}{2 \cdot 2 \cdot a \cdot b}$

9. $\dfrac{2 \cdot 3 \cdot x \cdot y}{2 \cdot 3 \cdot 3 \cdot 5 \cdot x \cdot x \cdot y}$

10. $\dfrac{3 \cdot 7 \cdot m \cdot n}{3 \cdot 3 \cdot 7 \cdot m \cdot m \cdot n}$

11. $\dfrac{2 \cdot 3^2 \cdot 5 \cdot y \cdot z^2}{2^2 \cdot 3 \cdot 5^3 \cdot x \cdot y^2 \cdot z}$

12. $\dfrac{2 \cdot 3^2 \cdot 7 \cdot r \cdot s \cdot t}{2^3 \cdot 3 \cdot 7^2 \cdot r^2 \cdot s^3}$

13. $\dfrac{6r}{8r}$

14. $\dfrac{8t}{12t}$

15. $\dfrac{2x}{10x}$

16. $\dfrac{5y}{20y}$

17. $\dfrac{n}{n^2}$

18. $\dfrac{k}{2k^2}$

19. $\dfrac{2y^2}{3y^3}$

20. $\dfrac{4w}{15w^3}$

21. $\dfrac{12m^2n}{18mnp}$

22. $\dfrac{6rs}{16r^2t}$

23. $\dfrac{15ra}{24ab}$

24. $\dfrac{12s^2t}{15rt}$

25. $\dfrac{10x^2y^3}{12r^2s^2t}$

26. $\dfrac{16rst}{12r^2s^2t}$

27. $\dfrac{6efg^2}{4ef^2g}$

28. $\dfrac{9acd^2}{6bc^2d}$

29. $\dfrac{24xz}{16x^3yz^2}$

30. $\dfrac{24rst}{21r^2s^2t}$

**C**

*Write the missing numeral to make the fractions equivalent.*

**EXAMPLE:** $\dfrac{2}{x} = \dfrac{?}{x^2}$    **ANSWER:** $\dfrac{2}{x} = \dfrac{2x}{x^2}$

31. $\dfrac{5}{a} = \dfrac{?}{ab}$

32. $\dfrac{r}{s} = \dfrac{?}{s^2}$

33. $\dfrac{2y}{z} = \dfrac{?}{3z}$

34. $\dfrac{7}{3t} = \dfrac{?}{3t^2}$

35. $\dfrac{5a}{3b} = \dfrac{?}{6b^2}$

# 4.3 Multiplication

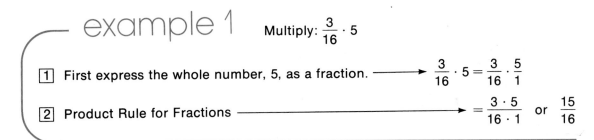

example 1    Multiply: $\frac{3}{16} \cdot 5$

1   First express the whole number, 5, as a fraction. ⟶  $\frac{3}{16} \cdot 5 = \frac{3}{16} \cdot \frac{5}{1}$

2   Product Rule for Fractions ⟶  $= \frac{3 \cdot 5}{16 \cdot 1}$  or  $\frac{15}{16}$

When multiplying with fractions, it is easier sometimes to factor numerators and denominators of the original fractions first.

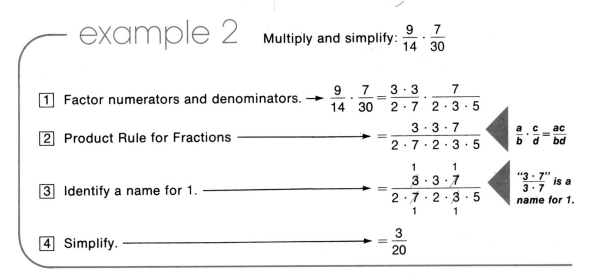

example 2    Multiply and simplify: $\frac{9}{14} \cdot \frac{7}{30}$

1   Factor numerators and denominators. ⟶  $\frac{9}{14} \cdot \frac{7}{30} = \frac{3 \cdot 3}{2 \cdot 7} \cdot \frac{7}{2 \cdot 3 \cdot 5}$

2   Product Rule for Fractions ⟶  $= \frac{3 \cdot 3 \cdot 7}{2 \cdot 7 \cdot 2 \cdot 3 \cdot 5}$    ◀  $\frac{a}{b} \cdot \frac{c}{d} = \frac{ac}{bd}$

3   Identify a name for 1. ⟶  $= \frac{\overset{1}{\cancel{3}} \cdot 3 \cdot \overset{1}{\cancel{7}}}{2 \cdot \underset{1}{\cancel{7}} \cdot 2 \cdot \underset{1}{\cancel{3}} \cdot 5}$    ◀  *"$\frac{3 \cdot 7}{3 \cdot 7}$" is a name for 1.*

4   Simplify. ⟶  $= \frac{3}{20}$

Often, you can factor numerators and denominators and apply the Product Rule in the same step.

example 3    Multiply and simplify: $\frac{2x^2}{9y^2} \cdot \frac{3y}{10x}$

$$\frac{2x^2}{9y^2} \cdot \frac{3y}{10x} = \frac{(2 \cdot x \cdot x) \cdot (3 \cdot y)}{(3 \cdot 3 \cdot y \cdot y) \cdot (2 \cdot 5 \cdot x)}$$

$$= \frac{2 \cdot \overset{1}{\cancel{x}} \cdot x \cdot \overset{1}{\cancel{3}} \cdot \overset{1}{\cancel{y}}}{\underset{1}{\cancel{3}} \cdot 3 \cdot \underset{1}{\cancel{y}} \cdot y \cdot \underset{1}{\cancel{2}} \cdot 5 \cdot \underset{1}{\cancel{x}}} \quad \text{or} \quad \frac{x}{15y}$$

◀  *Unless told otherwise, always write the answer in simplified form.*

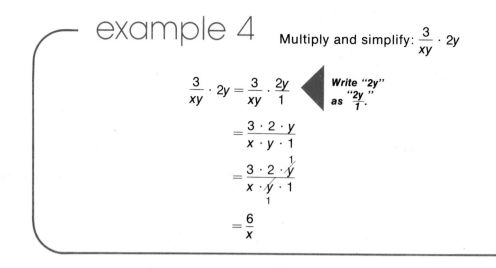

example 4    Multiply and simplify: $\dfrac{3}{xy} \cdot 2y$

$$\dfrac{3}{xy} \cdot 2y = \dfrac{3}{xy} \cdot \dfrac{2y}{1}$$

Write "2y" as "$\dfrac{2y}{1}$".

$$= \dfrac{3 \cdot 2 \cdot y}{x \cdot y \cdot 1}$$

$$= \dfrac{3 \cdot 2 \cdot \overset{1}{\cancel{y}}}{x \cdot \underset{1}{\cancel{y}} \cdot 1}$$

$$= \dfrac{6}{x}$$

**Steps for multiplying with fractions:**

1. Factor numerators and denominators.
2. Write the product as a single fraction.
3. Identify a name for 1 by using all factors common to the numerator and denominator.
4. Write the result in simplified form.

## ORAL EXERCISES 4.3

*Multiply.* (Example 1)

1. $\dfrac{1}{2} \cdot \dfrac{1}{7}$    2. $\dfrac{1}{4} \cdot \dfrac{1}{5}$    3. $\dfrac{1}{10} \cdot \dfrac{1}{3}$    4. $\dfrac{1}{4} \cdot \dfrac{1}{12}$    5. $\dfrac{2}{3} \cdot 4$    6. $8 \cdot \dfrac{3}{7}$

7. $\dfrac{2}{x} \cdot \dfrac{3}{y}$    8. $\dfrac{a}{3} \cdot \dfrac{2}{b}$    9. $\dfrac{2r}{s} \cdot \dfrac{3}{t}$    10. $\dfrac{2x}{3y} \cdot \dfrac{2x}{5}$    11. $\dfrac{2}{3} \cdot x$    12. $\dfrac{3}{5} \cdot 2a$

*Multiply. Simplify where necessary.* (Example 2, Example 3, Example 4)

13. $\dfrac{1}{5} \cdot 5$    14. $\dfrac{1}{9} \cdot 9$    15. $\dfrac{2}{3} \cdot 3$    16. $\dfrac{3}{4} \cdot 4$    17. $\dfrac{1}{3} \cdot 6x$    18. $\dfrac{3}{4} \cdot 4y$

19. $\dfrac{2}{5} \cdot \dfrac{3}{2}$    20. $\dfrac{5}{12} \cdot \dfrac{3}{5}$    21. $\dfrac{1}{x} \cdot \dfrac{x}{5}$    22. $\dfrac{y}{7} \cdot \dfrac{y}{3}$    23. $\dfrac{a^2}{5} \cdot \dfrac{3}{a}$    24. $\dfrac{3}{2x} \cdot \dfrac{x^2}{3y}$

## WRITTEN EXERCISES 4.3

**A**  **Goal:** To multiply with fractions

**Sample Problem:** $\dfrac{12x^2}{15y^3} \cdot \dfrac{5xy}{2}$

**Answer:** $\dfrac{2x^3}{y^2}$

*Multiply.* (Example 1)

1. $\dfrac{1}{12} \cdot \dfrac{1}{3}$    2. $\dfrac{1}{5} \cdot \dfrac{1}{11}$    3. $\dfrac{4a}{7} \cdot \dfrac{1}{b}$    4. $\dfrac{2m}{7} \cdot \dfrac{5}{3n}$    5. $\dfrac{1}{2} \cdot 7$    6. $\dfrac{1}{4} \cdot 11$

7. $\dfrac{2}{3} \cdot 5$    8. $\dfrac{3}{4} \cdot 9$    9. $\dfrac{3}{4} \cdot x$    10. $\dfrac{5}{6} \cdot y$    11. $\dfrac{1}{3} \cdot 2r$    12. $\dfrac{1}{8} \cdot 5t$

*Multiply. Simplify where necessary.* (Example 2, Example 3, Example 4)

13. $\dfrac{2}{3} \cdot \dfrac{5}{2}$    14. $\dfrac{3}{7} \cdot \dfrac{2}{3}$    15. $\dfrac{7}{8} \cdot \dfrac{8}{9}$    16. $\dfrac{4}{5} \cdot \dfrac{5}{11}$    17. $\dfrac{4}{5} \cdot \dfrac{5}{8}$

18. $\dfrac{6}{7} \cdot \dfrac{7}{12}$    19. $\dfrac{3}{x} \cdot \dfrac{x}{7}$    20. $\dfrac{a}{5} \cdot \dfrac{3}{a}$    21. $\dfrac{3s}{5} \cdot \dfrac{5}{2t}$    22. $\dfrac{11}{13x} \cdot \dfrac{7y}{11}$

23. $\dfrac{12}{15} \cdot \dfrac{5}{8}$    24. $\dfrac{10}{27} \cdot \dfrac{9}{4}$    25. $\dfrac{5}{2} \cdot \dfrac{6}{35}$    26. $\dfrac{7}{3} \cdot \dfrac{6}{35}$

27. $\dfrac{7}{8} \cdot \dfrac{12}{35}$    28. $\dfrac{5}{27} \cdot \dfrac{18}{55}$    29. $\dfrac{4t}{9} \cdot \dfrac{3}{10t^2}$    30. $\dfrac{6}{5n} \cdot \dfrac{10n^2}{9}$

31. $\dfrac{5}{ab^2} \cdot \dfrac{bc}{10}$    32. $\dfrac{4xy}{3z} \cdot \dfrac{15z}{16y^2}$    33. $\dfrac{18a^2}{25b^2} \cdot \dfrac{25b}{18a}$    34. $\dfrac{39r}{85st} \cdot \dfrac{85t}{39rs}$

35. $\dfrac{7}{ab} \cdot 3a$    36. $\dfrac{8}{x^2} \cdot xy$    37. $\dfrac{t}{5} \cdot 10s$    38. $\dfrac{pq}{7} \cdot 84r$

**B**  **EXAMPLE:** $\dfrac{6a}{35} \cdot \dfrac{14bc}{9a^2b} \cdot \dfrac{3a^2}{10bc^2} = \dfrac{2 \cdot 3 \cdot a \cdot 2 \cdot 7 \cdot b \cdot c \cdot 3 \cdot a \cdot a}{5 \cdot 7 \cdot 3 \cdot 3 \cdot a \cdot a \cdot b \cdot 2 \cdot 5 \cdot b \cdot c \cdot c}$

$$= \dfrac{\overset{1}{\cancel{2}} \cdot 2 \cdot \overset{1}{\cancel{3}} \cdot \overset{1}{\cancel{3}} \cdot \overset{1}{\cancel{7}} \cdot \overset{1}{\cancel{a}} \cdot \overset{1}{\cancel{a}} \cdot a \cdot \overset{1}{\cancel{b}} \cdot \overset{1}{\cancel{c}}}{\underset{1}{\cancel{2}} \cdot \underset{1}{\cancel{3}} \cdot \underset{1}{\cancel{3}} \cdot 5 \cdot 5 \cdot \underset{1}{\cancel{7}} \cdot \underset{1}{\cancel{a}} \cdot \underset{1}{\cancel{a}} \cdot b \cdot b \cdot \underset{1}{\cancel{c}} \cdot c} \quad \text{or} \quad \dfrac{2a}{25bc}$$

39. $\dfrac{1}{2} \cdot \dfrac{2}{5} \cdot \dfrac{5}{7} \cdot \dfrac{7}{8}$    40. $\dfrac{2}{3} \cdot \dfrac{3}{7} \cdot \dfrac{7}{11} \cdot \dfrac{11}{12}$    41. $\dfrac{2x}{3z} \cdot \dfrac{6y^2}{7} \cdot \dfrac{14}{15xy}$

42. $\dfrac{5t^2}{6r} \cdot \dfrac{8}{27st} \cdot \dfrac{9r^2}{10t}$    43. $\dfrac{2ab}{25} \cdot \dfrac{9}{7b^2c} \cdot \dfrac{35b^3}{12a}$    44. $\dfrac{9xz}{10} \cdot \dfrac{6z}{5x^2y} \cdot \dfrac{35y^2}{21z^3}$

# 4.4 Division

**P-1**  **What is the simplest name for each product?**

**a.** $\dfrac{3}{5} \cdot \dfrac{5}{3}$  **b.** $\dfrac{1}{x} \cdot \dfrac{x}{1}$  **c.** $\dfrac{3}{y} \cdot \dfrac{y}{3}$

> Two numbers having 1 as their product are called **reciprocals.**
>
> $\dfrac{2}{3}$ and $\dfrac{3}{2}$
>
> $4x$ and $\dfrac{1}{4x}$

**P-2**  **What is the reciprocal of each number?**

**a.** $\dfrac{5}{16}$  **b.** 12  **c.** $\dfrac{x}{y}$  **d.** $7n$

**P-3**  **Which of these problems have the same answer?**

**a.** $14 \div 2$  **b.** $14 \cdot \dfrac{1}{2}$  **c.** $27 \div 3$  **d.** $27 \cdot \dfrac{1}{3}$

> **Quotient Rule for Fractions**
>
> Dividing by a number is the same as multiplying by its reciprocal.
>
> ▲ $\dfrac{a}{b} \div \dfrac{c}{d} = \dfrac{a}{b} \cdot \dfrac{d}{c}$  *(b, c, d are not zero.)*
>
> $14 \div 2 = 14 \cdot \dfrac{1}{2}$
>
> $\dfrac{x}{2} \div \dfrac{x}{4} = \dfrac{x}{2} \cdot \dfrac{4}{x}$

## example 1

Divide: $\dfrac{2}{3} \div \dfrac{x}{7}$

Dividing by $\dfrac{x}{7}$ is the same as multiplying by $\dfrac{7}{x}$.

$$\dfrac{2}{3} \div \dfrac{x}{7} = \dfrac{2}{3} \cdot \dfrac{7}{x}$$

$$= \dfrac{14}{3x}$$

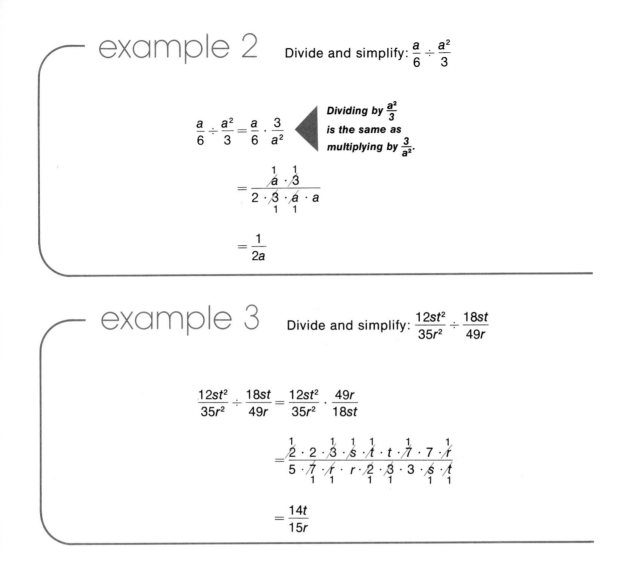

## example 2

Divide and simplify: $\dfrac{a}{6} \div \dfrac{a^2}{3}$

$$\frac{a}{6} \div \frac{a^2}{3} = \frac{a}{6} \cdot \frac{3}{a^2}$$

◀ Dividing by $\dfrac{a^2}{3}$ is the same as multiplying by $\dfrac{3}{a^2}$.

$$= \frac{\overset{1}{\cancel{a}} \cdot \overset{1}{\cancel{3}}}{2 \cdot \underset{1}{\cancel{3}} \cdot \underset{1}{\cancel{a}} \cdot a}$$

$$= \frac{1}{2a}$$

## example 3

Divide and simplify: $\dfrac{12st^2}{35r^2} \div \dfrac{18st}{49r}$

$$\frac{12st^2}{35r^2} \div \frac{18st}{49r} = \frac{12st^2}{35r^2} \cdot \frac{49r}{18st}$$

$$= \frac{\overset{1}{\cancel{2}} \cdot 2 \cdot \overset{1}{\cancel{3}} \cdot \overset{1}{\cancel{s}} \cdot \overset{1}{\cancel{t}} \cdot t \cdot \overset{1}{\cancel{7}} \cdot 7 \cdot \overset{1}{\cancel{r}}}{5 \cdot \underset{1}{\cancel{7}} \cdot \underset{1}{\cancel{r}} \cdot r \cdot \underset{1}{\cancel{2}} \cdot \underset{1}{\cancel{3}} \cdot 3 \cdot \underset{1}{\cancel{s}} \cdot \underset{1}{\cancel{t}}}$$

$$= \frac{14t}{15r}$$

## ORAL EXERCISES 4.4

*Change to product form.* (P-3)

**1.** $\dfrac{3}{4} \div \dfrac{5}{3}$   **2.** $\dfrac{1}{5} \div \dfrac{2}{3}$   **3.** $\dfrac{7}{8} \div \dfrac{4}{3}$   **4.** $\dfrac{5}{6} \div \dfrac{8}{7}$   **5.** $\dfrac{5}{12} \div \dfrac{2}{7}$   **6.** $\dfrac{2}{9} \div \dfrac{7}{4}$

**7.** $\dfrac{4}{3} \div \dfrac{3}{2}$   **8.** $\dfrac{3}{8} \div \dfrac{7}{16}$   **9.** $\dfrac{3}{8} \div 4$   **10.** $\dfrac{3}{x} \div 10$   **11.** $\dfrac{y}{3} \div \dfrac{1}{8}$   **12.** $\dfrac{2a}{5} \div \dfrac{4}{b}$

**13.** $\dfrac{3}{8} \div y$   **14.** $\dfrac{7}{4} \div 3n$   **15.** $\dfrac{r}{s} \div \dfrac{1}{t}$   **16.** $\dfrac{k}{a} \div \dfrac{w}{q}$

*Divide. Simplify where necessary.* (Example 1, Example 2)

**17.** $\dfrac{2}{5} \div \dfrac{3}{5}$  **18.** $\dfrac{1}{4} \div \dfrac{3}{4}$  **19.** $\dfrac{1}{2} \div \dfrac{3}{2}$  **20.** $\dfrac{2}{3} \div \dfrac{5}{2}$  **21.** $\dfrac{1}{5} \div \dfrac{3}{2}$  **22.** $\dfrac{3}{4} \div 2$

**23.** $\dfrac{3}{4} \div \dfrac{1}{2}$  **24.** $\dfrac{1}{4} \div \dfrac{3}{2}$  **25.** $\dfrac{a}{2} \div \dfrac{b}{3}$  **26.** $\dfrac{1}{x} \div \dfrac{3}{x}$  **27.** $\dfrac{4}{3} \div \dfrac{4}{x}$  **28.** $\dfrac{2n}{3} \div \dfrac{m}{3}$

**29.** $\dfrac{r}{4} \div \dfrac{r}{5}$  **30.** $\dfrac{t}{11} \div \dfrac{t^2}{7}$  **31.** $\dfrac{x}{w} \div \dfrac{y}{w}$  **32.** $\dfrac{n}{2k} \div \dfrac{n}{k}$  **33.** $\dfrac{s}{11} \div s$  **34.** $y \div \dfrac{3}{x}$

## WRITTEN EXERCISES 4.4

**A**    **Goal:** To divide with fractions

**Sample Problem:** $\dfrac{6x^2}{10y} \div \dfrac{2x}{3}$    **Answer:** $\dfrac{9x}{10y}$

*Divide. Simplify where necessary.* (Example 1, Example 2, Example 3)

**1.** $\dfrac{1}{2} \div \dfrac{5}{3}$  **2.** $\dfrac{3}{4} \div \dfrac{7}{5}$  **3.** $\dfrac{2}{3} \div \dfrac{5}{3}$  **4.** $\dfrac{2}{7} \div \dfrac{9}{7}$  **5.** $\dfrac{1}{4} \div \dfrac{3}{2}$  **6.** $\dfrac{5}{6} \div \dfrac{4}{3}$

**7.** $\dfrac{2}{3} \div \dfrac{8}{3}$  **8.** $\dfrac{5}{12} \div \dfrac{5}{3}$  **9.** $\dfrac{3}{4} \div \dfrac{9}{6}$  **10.** $\dfrac{3}{8} \div \dfrac{9}{2}$  **11.** $\dfrac{a}{5} \div \dfrac{3}{10}$  **12.** $\dfrac{7}{12} \div \dfrac{g}{18}$

**13.** $\dfrac{r}{21} \div \dfrac{q}{14}$  **14.** $\dfrac{12}{m} \div \dfrac{30}{a}$  **15.** $\dfrac{x}{3} \div \dfrac{x}{5}$  **16.** $\dfrac{4}{n} \div \dfrac{3}{n}$  **17.** $\dfrac{5}{2a} \div \dfrac{7}{2a}$  **18.** $\dfrac{4k}{9} \div \dfrac{3k}{7}$

**19.** $\dfrac{2t}{3} \div t$  **20.** $\dfrac{3r}{4} \div 2r$  **21.** $4b \div \dfrac{2c}{b}$  **22.** $10m \div \dfrac{5m}{p}$

**23.** $\dfrac{r}{s} \div \dfrac{rt}{s^2}$  **24.** $\dfrac{b^2}{a^2c} \div \dfrac{b}{a}$  **25.** $\dfrac{4p}{3r} \div \dfrac{2q^2}{9r}$  **26.** $\dfrac{6a}{c} \div \dfrac{9b}{c^2}$

**27.** $\dfrac{rs^2}{t^3} \div \dfrac{rs}{t}$  **28.** $\dfrac{a^2b^2}{cd^2} \div \dfrac{a^3b}{c^3d}$  **29.** $\dfrac{21kd}{20p} \div \dfrac{14d^2t}{18p^2}$  **30.** $\dfrac{9nc}{14dh^2} \div \dfrac{30n^2d}{77h}$

**B**    **EXAMPLE:** $\dfrac{3}{5} \div \dfrac{9}{4} \div \dfrac{8}{5}$    **SOLUTION:** $\dfrac{3}{5} \div \dfrac{9}{4} \div \dfrac{8}{5} = \dfrac{3}{5} \cdot \dfrac{4}{9} \cdot \dfrac{5}{8}$

$$= \dfrac{\overset{1}{3} \cdot \overset{1}{2} \cdot \overset{1}{2} \cdot \overset{1}{5}}{\underset{1}{5} \cdot \underset{1}{3} \cdot 3 \cdot \underset{1}{2} \cdot \underset{1}{2} \cdot 2} \quad \text{or} \quad \dfrac{1}{6}$$

**31.** $\dfrac{3}{4} \div \dfrac{7}{2} \div \dfrac{3}{7}$    **32.** $\dfrac{7}{2} \div \dfrac{9}{4} \div \dfrac{7}{3}$    **33.** $\dfrac{a}{5b} \div \dfrac{2a}{c} \div \dfrac{c^2}{6b}$

**34.** $\dfrac{4rt}{3s} \div \dfrac{t^2}{6} \div \dfrac{10r}{s^2}$    **35.** $\dfrac{w^2y}{z} \cdot \dfrac{xz^2}{wy^2} \div \dfrac{yz}{x^2}$    **36.** $\dfrac{qm}{pn^2} \cdot \dfrac{p^2n}{q^2m} \div \dfrac{m^2}{p}$

# 4.5 Addition and Subtraction

**Like fractions** have a <u>common denominator</u>.

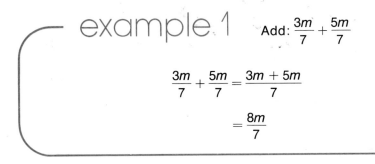

$\frac{2}{7}$ and $\frac{3}{7}$ are like fractions.

**Sum Rule for Like Fractions**

1. Add the numerators.
2. Write the sum over the common denominator.

$\frac{a}{c} + \frac{b}{c} = \frac{a+b}{c}$   *(c is not zero.)*

$$\frac{2}{7} + \frac{3}{7} = \frac{2+3}{7}$$
$$= \frac{5}{7}$$

**P-1** What is the simplest name for each sum?

**a.** $\frac{4}{13} + \frac{6}{13}$    **b.** $\frac{5}{x} + \frac{8}{x}$    **c.** $\frac{r}{t} + \frac{s}{t}$

**P-2** What is the simplest name for $3m + 5m$?

example 1   Add: $\frac{3m}{7} + \frac{5m}{7}$

$$\frac{3m}{7} + \frac{5m}{7} = \frac{3m + 5m}{7}$$
$$= \frac{8m}{7}$$

**Difference Rule for Like Fractions**

1. Subtract the numerators.
2. Write the difference over the common denominator.

$\frac{a}{c} - \frac{b}{c} = \frac{a-b}{c}$   *(c is not zero.)*

$$\frac{8}{y} - \frac{2}{y} = \frac{8-2}{y}$$
$$= \frac{6}{y}$$

**P-3** What is the simplest name for each fraction?

**a.** $\frac{12}{15} - \frac{4}{15}$    **b.** $\frac{7}{5x} - \frac{3}{5x}$    **c.** $\frac{p}{x} - \frac{q}{x}$

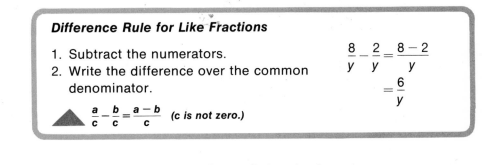

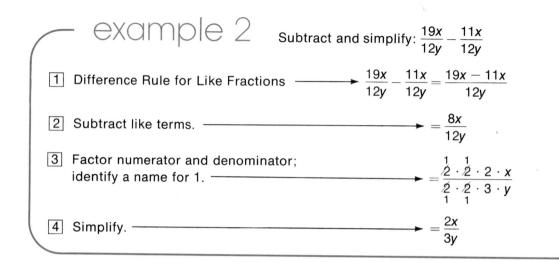

example 2    Subtract and simplify: $\dfrac{19x}{12y} - \dfrac{11x}{12y}$

1.   Difference Rule for Like Fractions  ⟶  $\dfrac{19x}{12y} - \dfrac{11x}{12y} = \dfrac{19x - 11x}{12y}$

2.   Subtract like terms.  ⟶  $= \dfrac{8x}{12y}$

3.   Factor numerator and denominator; identify a name for 1.  ⟶  $= \dfrac{\cancel{2} \cdot \cancel{2} \cdot 2 \cdot x}{\cancel{2} \cdot \cancel{2} \cdot 3 \cdot y}$

4.   Simplify.  ⟶  $= \dfrac{2x}{3y}$

example 3    Add, subtract, and simplify: $\dfrac{4a}{15b} + \dfrac{8a}{15b} - \dfrac{2a}{15b}$

$$\frac{4a}{15b} + \frac{8a}{15b} - \frac{2a}{15b} = \frac{4a + 8a - 2a}{15b}$$

$$= \frac{10a}{15b}$$

$$= \frac{2 \cdot \cancel{5}^{1} \cdot a}{3 \cdot \cancel{5}_{1} \cdot b} \quad \text{or} \quad \frac{2a}{3b}$$

## ORAL EXERCISES 4.5

*Add or subtract.* (Example 1)

1. $\dfrac{1}{3} + \dfrac{1}{3}$     2. $\dfrac{1}{4} + \dfrac{2}{4}$     3. $\dfrac{2}{x} + \dfrac{3}{x}$     4. $\dfrac{x}{5} + \dfrac{x}{5}$     5. $\dfrac{6}{8} - \dfrac{1}{8}$     6. $\dfrac{8}{n} - \dfrac{5}{n}$

7. $\dfrac{7t}{13} - \dfrac{3t}{13}$     8. $\dfrac{8s}{17} + \dfrac{s}{17}$     9. $\dfrac{5}{3c} - \dfrac{3}{3c}$     10. $\dfrac{a}{4} - \dfrac{3}{4}$     11. $\dfrac{a}{b} + \dfrac{a}{b}$     12. $\dfrac{7m}{n} - \dfrac{2m}{n}$

*Add or subtract. Simplify where necessary.* (Example 2, Example 3)

**13.** $\dfrac{1}{2x} + \dfrac{1}{2x}$  **14.** $\dfrac{r}{4} + \dfrac{r}{4}$  **15.** $\dfrac{4y}{8} - \dfrac{y}{8}$  **16.** $\dfrac{13t}{10} - \dfrac{7t}{10}$

**17.** $\dfrac{r}{6w} + \dfrac{r}{6w}$  **18.** $\dfrac{7x}{8n} - \dfrac{3x}{8n}$  **19.** $\dfrac{1}{8} + \dfrac{3}{8} + \dfrac{2}{8}$  **20.** $\dfrac{2}{a} + \dfrac{7}{a} + \dfrac{12}{a}$

**21.** $\dfrac{3p}{10} + \dfrac{5p}{10} + \dfrac{9p}{10}$  **22.** $\dfrac{4r}{s} + \dfrac{3r}{s} + \dfrac{r}{s}$  **23.** $\dfrac{k}{11} + \dfrac{9k}{11} - \dfrac{4k}{11}$  **24.** $\dfrac{19}{3t} + \dfrac{5}{3t} - \dfrac{7}{3t}$

## WRITTEN EXERCISES 4.5

**A**  **Goal:** To add or subtract with fractions that have common denominators

**Sample Problem:** $\dfrac{2x}{5y^2} + \dfrac{3x}{5y^2}$

**Answer:** $\dfrac{x}{y^2}$

*Add or subtract.* (Example 1)

**1.** $\dfrac{3}{11} + \dfrac{5}{11}$  **2.** $\dfrac{4}{17} + \dfrac{11}{17}$  **3.** $\dfrac{7}{y} + \dfrac{12}{y}$  **4.** $\dfrac{6}{r} + \dfrac{11}{r}$  **5.** $\dfrac{r}{9} + \dfrac{r}{9}$

**6.** $\dfrac{k}{5} + \dfrac{k}{5}$  **7.** $\dfrac{14}{16} - \dfrac{1}{16}$  **8.** $\dfrac{18}{10} - \dfrac{9}{10}$  **9.** $\dfrac{25}{3x} - \dfrac{20}{3x}$  **10.** $\dfrac{19}{4b} - \dfrac{18}{4b}$

**11.** $\dfrac{9h}{11} - \dfrac{h}{11}$  **12.** $\dfrac{17t}{5} - \dfrac{t}{5}$  **13.** $\dfrac{2w}{13} + \dfrac{6w}{13}$  **14.** $\dfrac{7q}{9} + \dfrac{13q}{9}$

**15.** $\dfrac{k}{9} + \dfrac{7}{9}$  **16.** $\dfrac{5}{7} + \dfrac{y}{7}$  **17.** $\dfrac{3a}{n} - \dfrac{2a}{n}$  **18.** $\dfrac{7m}{x} - \dfrac{6m}{x}$

*Add or subtract. Simplify where necessary.* (Example 2, Example 3)

**19.** $\dfrac{9}{16} + \dfrac{5}{16}$  **20.** $\dfrac{3}{12} + \dfrac{7}{12}$  **21.** $\dfrac{3x}{10} + \dfrac{5x}{10}$  **22.** $\dfrac{8a}{15} + \dfrac{2a}{15}$  **23.** $\dfrac{7}{12x} - \dfrac{5}{12x}$

**24.** $\dfrac{17}{18k} - \dfrac{15}{18k}$  **25.** $\dfrac{7r}{16s} + \dfrac{5r}{16s}$  **26.** $\dfrac{3a}{10b} + \dfrac{3a}{10b}$  **27.** $\dfrac{13k}{12m} - \dfrac{5k}{12m}$  **28.** $\dfrac{22x}{24y} - \dfrac{x}{24y}$

**29.** $\dfrac{15a}{4p} - \dfrac{3a}{4p}$  **30.** $\dfrac{19r}{3g} - \dfrac{4r}{3g}$  **31.** $\dfrac{5}{19} + \dfrac{3}{19} + \dfrac{6}{19}$  **32.** $\dfrac{9}{23} + \dfrac{9}{23} + \dfrac{6}{23}$

**33.** $\dfrac{27}{y} - \dfrac{3}{y} + \dfrac{1}{y}$  **34.** $\dfrac{4}{t} + \dfrac{17}{t} - \dfrac{6}{t}$  **35.** $\dfrac{12x}{7} + \dfrac{x}{7} + \dfrac{9x}{7}$  **36.** $\dfrac{3a}{19} + \dfrac{a}{19} + \dfrac{12a}{19}$

**37.** $\dfrac{7}{8s} + \dfrac{11}{8s} - \dfrac{6}{8s}$  **38.** $\dfrac{9}{16n} - \dfrac{4}{16n} + \dfrac{13}{16n}$  **39.** $\dfrac{11a}{18b} - \dfrac{4a}{18b} + \dfrac{9a}{18b}$  **40.** $\dfrac{13x}{36y} + \dfrac{19x}{36y} - \dfrac{4x}{36y}$

# 4.6 Unequal Denominators

Often, fractions in addition or subtraction problems do not have the same denominator.

example 1    Add: $\dfrac{1}{4} + \dfrac{7}{16}$    ◀ **You must rename a fraction.**

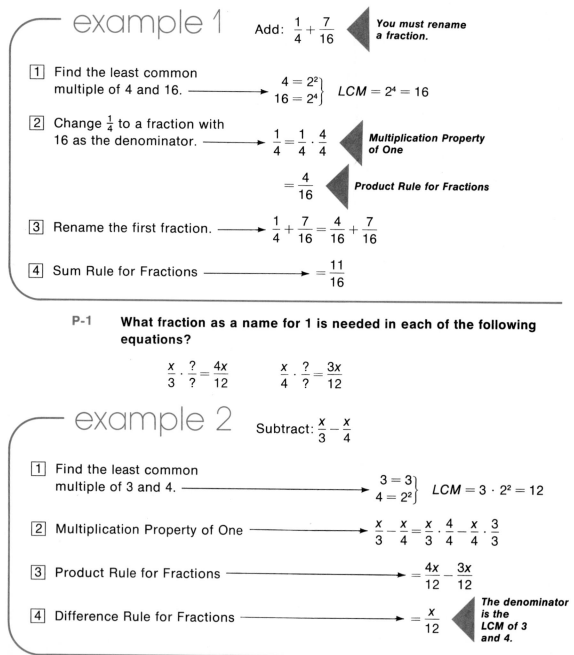

1. Find the least common multiple of 4 and 16. ⟶ $\left.\begin{array}{l} 4 = 2^2 \\ 16 = 2^4 \end{array}\right\}$  $LCM = 2^4 = 16$

2. Change $\dfrac{1}{4}$ to a fraction with 16 as the denominator. ⟶ $\dfrac{1}{4} = \dfrac{1}{4} \cdot \dfrac{4}{4}$ ◀ **Multiplication Property of One**

$= \dfrac{4}{16}$ ◀ **Product Rule for Fractions**

3. Rename the first fraction. ⟶ $\dfrac{1}{4} + \dfrac{7}{16} = \dfrac{4}{16} + \dfrac{7}{16}$

4. Sum Rule for Fractions ⟶ $= \dfrac{11}{16}$

**P-1** What fraction as a name for 1 is needed in each of the following equations?

$$\dfrac{x}{3} \cdot \dfrac{?}{?} = \dfrac{4x}{12} \qquad \dfrac{x}{4} \cdot \dfrac{?}{?} = \dfrac{3x}{12}$$

example 2    Subtract: $\dfrac{x}{3} - \dfrac{x}{4}$

1. Find the least common multiple of 3 and 4. ⟶ $\left.\begin{array}{l} 3 = 3 \\ 4 = 2^2 \end{array}\right\}$  $LCM = 3 \cdot 2^2 = 12$

2. Multiplication Property of One ⟶ $\dfrac{x}{3} - \dfrac{x}{4} = \dfrac{x}{3} \cdot \dfrac{4}{4} - \dfrac{x}{4} \cdot \dfrac{3}{3}$

3. Product Rule for Fractions ⟶ $= \dfrac{4x}{12} - \dfrac{3x}{12}$

4. Difference Rule for Fractions ⟶ $= \dfrac{x}{12}$ ◀ **The denominator is the LCM of 3 and 4.**

**What is the least common multiple of 21x and 14x?**

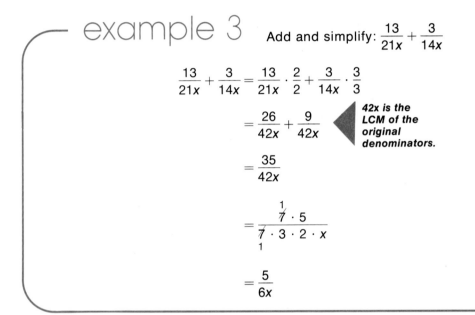

example 3   Add and simplify: $\dfrac{13}{21x} + \dfrac{3}{14x}$

$$\frac{13}{21x} + \frac{3}{14x} = \frac{13}{21x} \cdot \frac{2}{2} + \frac{3}{14x} \cdot \frac{3}{3}$$

$$= \frac{26}{42x} + \frac{9}{42x}$$

◀ **42x is the LCM of the original denominators.**

$$= \frac{35}{42x}$$

$$= \frac{\overset{1}{\cancel{7}} \cdot 5}{\underset{1}{\cancel{7}} \cdot 3 \cdot 2 \cdot x}$$

$$= \frac{5}{6x}$$

**P-3**   **How do you know that $\dfrac{5}{6x}$ is in simplified form?**

> **Steps for adding or subtracting with fractions:**
>
> 1. Find the least common multiple of the denominators.
> 2. Rename each fraction as an equivalent fraction with the least common multiple as the denominator.
> 3. Apply the Sum Rule or the Difference Rule for Fractions as appropriate.
> 4. Add like terms or simplify the resulting fraction where necessary.

## ORAL EXERCISES 4.6

*Tell the least common multiple of each pair of denominators.* (P-1, P-2)

1. $\dfrac{1}{4} + \dfrac{3}{8}$

2. $\dfrac{5}{12} + \dfrac{7}{24}$

3. $\dfrac{17}{30} - \dfrac{7}{15}$

4. $\dfrac{1}{5} + \dfrac{3}{25}$

5. $\dfrac{1}{3} - \dfrac{1}{5}$

6. $\dfrac{2}{7} + \dfrac{5}{11}$

7. $\dfrac{1}{2} + \dfrac{2}{13}$

8. $\dfrac{3}{10} - \dfrac{1}{6}$

Tell the least common multiple of the denominators in each problem.
(P-1, P-2)

**9.** $\dfrac{5}{6} - \dfrac{3}{4}$

**10.** $\dfrac{3}{8} + \dfrac{7}{12}$

**11.** $\dfrac{5}{9} + \dfrac{9}{10}$

**12.** $\dfrac{7}{8} - \dfrac{5}{6}$

**13.** $\dfrac{1}{2} + \dfrac{1}{4} + \dfrac{7}{12}$

**14.** $\dfrac{1}{3} + \dfrac{1}{6} + \dfrac{1}{18}$

Tell the fraction name for 1 that is needed in each sentence. (P-1)

**15.** $\dfrac{2}{3} \cdot \dfrac{?}{?} = \dfrac{4}{6}$

**16.** $\dfrac{5}{6} \cdot \dfrac{?}{?} = \dfrac{15}{18}$

**17.** $\dfrac{7}{8} \cdot \dfrac{?}{?} = \dfrac{28}{32}$

**18.** $\dfrac{3}{5} \cdot \dfrac{?}{?} = \dfrac{18}{30}$

**19.** $\dfrac{7}{12} \cdot \dfrac{?}{?} = \dfrac{35}{60}$

**20.** $\dfrac{7}{4} \cdot \dfrac{?}{?} = \dfrac{49}{28}$

**21.** $\dfrac{x}{6} \cdot \dfrac{?}{?} = \dfrac{4x}{24}$

**22.** $\dfrac{3x}{7} \cdot \dfrac{?}{?} = \dfrac{9x}{21}$

**23.** $\dfrac{5a}{9} \cdot \dfrac{?}{?} = \dfrac{15a}{27}$

**24.** $\dfrac{3x}{4y} \cdot \dfrac{?}{?} = \dfrac{9x}{12y}$

Simplify each sum or difference. (Example 1, Example 2)

**25.** $\dfrac{1}{2} + \dfrac{1}{3}$

**26.** $\dfrac{a}{3} + \dfrac{a}{6}$

**27.** $\dfrac{3x}{8} - \dfrac{x}{4}$

**28.** $\dfrac{3a}{2} - \dfrac{a}{4}$

**29.** $\dfrac{1}{3x} + \dfrac{2}{x}$

## WRITTEN EXERCISES 4.6

**A**

**Goal:** To add or subtract with fractions that have different denominators

**Sample Problem:** $\dfrac{7y}{10x} + \dfrac{2y}{15x}$

**Answer:** $\dfrac{5y}{6x}$

Copy each problem. Replace the question marks with numerals to make each sentence true. (Example 1, Example 2, Example 3)

**1.** $\dfrac{2}{3} + \dfrac{4}{5} = \dfrac{2}{3} \cdot \dfrac{?}{?} + \dfrac{4}{5} \cdot \dfrac{?}{?}$

$= \dfrac{?}{15} + \dfrac{?}{15}$

$= \dfrac{?}{?}$

**2.** $\dfrac{4}{7} + \dfrac{1}{3} = \dfrac{4}{7} \cdot \dfrac{?}{?} + \dfrac{1}{3} \cdot \dfrac{?}{?}$

$= \dfrac{?}{21} + \dfrac{?}{21}$

$= \dfrac{?}{?}$

**3.** $\dfrac{1}{6} + \dfrac{1}{4} = \dfrac{1}{6} \cdot \dfrac{2}{2} + \dfrac{1}{4} \cdot \dfrac{?}{?}$

$= \dfrac{?}{?} + \dfrac{?}{?}$

$= \dfrac{?}{?}$

**4.** $\dfrac{1}{9}+\dfrac{1}{15}=\dfrac{1}{9}\cdot\dfrac{5}{5}+\dfrac{1}{15}\cdot\dfrac{?}{?}$

$\qquad=\dfrac{?}{?}+\dfrac{?}{?}$

$\qquad=\dfrac{?}{?}$

**5.** $\dfrac{a}{4}+\dfrac{3a}{10}=\dfrac{a}{4}\cdot\dfrac{?}{?}+\dfrac{3a}{10}\cdot\dfrac{?}{?}$

$\qquad=\dfrac{?}{20}+\dfrac{?}{20}$

$\qquad=\dfrac{?}{?}$

**6.** $\dfrac{x}{6}+\dfrac{3x}{10}=\dfrac{x}{6}\cdot\dfrac{?}{?}+\dfrac{3x}{10}\cdot\dfrac{?}{?}$

$\qquad=\dfrac{?}{30}+\dfrac{?}{30}$

$\qquad=\dfrac{?}{?}$

*Add or subtract. Simplify where necessary.* (Example 1, Example 2, Example 3)

**7.** $\dfrac{3}{8}+\dfrac{1}{4}$

**8.** $\dfrac{5}{12}+\dfrac{1}{6}$

**9.** $\dfrac{9}{10}-\dfrac{3}{5}$

**10.** $\dfrac{13}{16}-\dfrac{3}{8}$

**11.** $\dfrac{3}{2n}+\dfrac{1}{n}$

**12.** $\dfrac{2}{3t}+\dfrac{3}{t}$

**13.** $\dfrac{2}{x}-\dfrac{3}{5x}$

**14.** $\dfrac{3}{r}-\dfrac{2}{3r}$

**15.** $\dfrac{5}{2s}+\dfrac{1}{6s}$

**16.** $\dfrac{7}{12y}+\dfrac{1}{6y}$

**17.** $\dfrac{2}{3x}-\dfrac{1}{9x}$

**18.** $\dfrac{4}{5q}-\dfrac{1}{10q}$

**19.** $\dfrac{x}{3}+\dfrac{x}{5}$

**20.** $\dfrac{r}{7}+\dfrac{r}{2}$

**21.** $\dfrac{3d}{2}-\dfrac{d}{5}$

**22.** $\dfrac{5x}{4}-\dfrac{x}{3}$

**23.** $\dfrac{w}{6}+\dfrac{w}{8}$

**24.** $\dfrac{t}{6}+\dfrac{t}{4}$

**25.** $\dfrac{3k}{4}-\dfrac{2k}{5}$

**26.** $\dfrac{5n}{6}-\dfrac{n}{9}$

**27.** $\dfrac{3}{2r}+\dfrac{1}{3r}$

**28.** $\dfrac{5}{6y}+\dfrac{1}{4y}$

**29.** $\dfrac{2}{3q}-\dfrac{1}{5q}$

**30.** $\dfrac{3}{2x}-\dfrac{1}{7x}$

**B**   **EXAMPLE:** $\dfrac{x}{2}+\dfrac{3x}{4}+\dfrac{x}{6}$

**SOLUTION:** $\dfrac{x}{2}\cdot\dfrac{6}{6}+\dfrac{3x}{4}\cdot\dfrac{3}{3}+\dfrac{x}{6}\cdot\dfrac{2}{2}=\dfrac{6x}{12}+\dfrac{9x}{12}+\dfrac{2x}{12}=\dfrac{17x}{12}$

**31.** $\dfrac{r}{2}+\dfrac{3r}{4}+\dfrac{5r}{8}$

**32.** $\dfrac{m}{3}+\dfrac{5m}{12}+\dfrac{m}{6}$

**33.** $\dfrac{n}{3}+\dfrac{5n}{6}+\dfrac{n}{4}$

**34.** $\dfrac{2s}{3}+\dfrac{s}{5}+\dfrac{s}{2}$

**35.** $\dfrac{1}{2x}+\dfrac{2}{3x}-\dfrac{1}{6x}$

**36.** $\dfrac{2}{3a}+\dfrac{3}{5a}-\dfrac{2}{15a}$

# Home Economist

Most home economists work as teachers in junior high schools, senior high schools, and in colleges and universities. Others work for private industry where they may be involved in promoting products or in helping design and test new products. Food companies employ home economists to work in test kitchens. Utility companies often have home economists available to demonstrate home equipment and to advise consumers on energy costs and costs of maintenance. Fabric companies, department stores, and furniture and drapery stores may employ home economists as purchasers or as interior decorators.

A person hoping to enter this field should plan to major in home economics at a college or university.

Home economists who are working in food related industries or who are teaching courses in foods and food preparation must know the fundamentals of food purchasing. One very important skill is being able to determine a "good buy." The most important factor in determining a good buy is the unit price. _Unit price_ means the price of an item per unit such as a pound, ounce, kilogram, gram, liter, etc.

**EXAMPLE:** A brand of pickles is sold in three different sizes and prices as shown. Find which size is the best buy.

| Size | Price | Unit Price |
|------|-------|------------|
| 14 oz (397 g) | $0.42 | $0.03 per ounce |
| 20 oz (567 g) | 0.61 | 0.0305 per ounce |
| 32 oz (907 g) | 0.84 | 0.026 per ounce |

**SOLUTION:** The unit price is least on the 32-ounce jar. Therefore, it is the "best buy" for that brand.

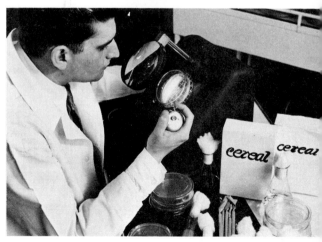

Many home economists work in private industry where they test new products or are responsible for product quality control.

# CHAPTER SUMMARY

| IMPORTANT TERMS | Fraction *(p. 60)* | Algebraic fraction *(p. 64)* |
|---|---|---|
| | Numerator *(p. 60)* | Reciprocals *(p. 70)* |
| | Denominator *(p. 60)* | Like fractions *(p. 73)* |
| | Equivalent fractions *(p. 62)* | Common denominator *(p. 73)* |

**IMPORTANT IDEAS**

For any number replacing a variable, each of the following sentences is true. No denominator is zero.

**1.** $\dfrac{a}{1} = a$ **2.** $\dfrac{a}{a} = 1$ **3.** $\dfrac{a}{b} \cdot \dfrac{c}{d} = \dfrac{ac}{bd}$

**4.** $\dfrac{a}{b} \div \dfrac{c}{d} = \dfrac{a}{b} \cdot \dfrac{d}{c}$ **5.** $\dfrac{a}{c} + \dfrac{b}{c} = \dfrac{a+b}{c}$ **6.** $\dfrac{a}{c} - \dfrac{b}{c} = \dfrac{a-b}{c}$

**7.** Steps for multiplying with fractions:
   **a.** Factor numerators and denominators.
   **b.** Write the product as a single fraction.
   **c.** Identify a name for 1 by using all factors common to the numerator and denominator.
   **d.** Write the result in simplified form.

**8.** Steps for adding or subtracting with fractions:
   **a.** Find the least common multiple of the denominators.
   **b.** Rename each fraction as an equivalent fraction with the least common multiple as the denominator.
   **c.** Apply the Sum Rule or the Difference Rule for Fractions as appropriate.
   **d.** Add like terms or simplify the resulting fraction where necessary.

# CHAPTER REVIEW

## SECTION 4.1

*Simplify each fraction.*

$$\textbf{EXAMPLE:} \;\; \frac{2 \cdot 2}{2 \cdot 3} \qquad \textbf{ANSWER:} \;\; \frac{\overset{1}{2} \cdot 2}{\underset{1}{2} \cdot 3} = \frac{2}{3}$$

**1.** $\dfrac{2 \cdot 3 \cdot 3 \cdot 5}{3 \cdot 5 \cdot 5}$ **2.** $\dfrac{2 \cdot 5 \cdot 5 \cdot 7}{2 \cdot 3 \cdot 5 \cdot 7}$ **3.** $\dfrac{8}{14}$ **4.** $\dfrac{8}{12}$ **5.** $\dfrac{14}{18}$ **6.** $\dfrac{20}{24}$

## SECTION 4.2

*Simplify.*

**7.** $\dfrac{10r}{8rs}$  **8.** $\dfrac{3pq}{15pr}$  **9.** $\dfrac{x}{5x^2}$  **10.** $\dfrac{2t}{3t^2}$  **11.** $\dfrac{14a^2b}{24ab^2}$  **12.** $\dfrac{27mn^2}{15m^3n}$

## SECTION 4.3

*Multiply. Simplify where necessary.*

**EXAMPLE:** $\dfrac{5}{3y} \cdot \dfrac{6y^2}{35}$  **SOLUTION:** $\dfrac{5 \cdot 2 \cdot 3 \cdot y \cdot y}{3 \cdot y \cdot 5 \cdot 7} = \dfrac{2 \cdot \overset{1}{\cancel{3}} \cdot \overset{1}{\cancel{5}} \cdot \overset{1}{\cancel{y}} \cdot y}{\underset{1}{\cancel{3}} \cdot \underset{1}{\cancel{5}} \cdot 7 \cdot \underset{1}{\cancel{y}}}$

$$= \dfrac{2y}{7}$$

**13.** $\dfrac{4n}{5} \cdot \dfrac{7}{12n}$  **14.** $\dfrac{14}{5a^2} \cdot \dfrac{3a}{10}$  **15.** $\dfrac{3}{4} \cdot 12r$  **16.** $\dfrac{2}{3} \cdot 39x$

**17.** $\dfrac{4a}{3m} \cdot \dfrac{15m^2}{18a^2}$  **18.** $\dfrac{6rs}{5t} \cdot \dfrac{15rt}{18st}$  **19.** $\dfrac{5a}{2b} \cdot \dfrac{2b}{3a} \cdot \dfrac{3}{b}$  **20.** $\dfrac{m}{3n} \cdot \dfrac{9n}{4m} \cdot \dfrac{2m}{15n}$

## SECTION 4.4

*Divide. Simplify where necessary.*

**EXAMPLE:** $\dfrac{25n}{4k} \div \dfrac{5n^2}{18k}$  **SOLUTION:** $\dfrac{25n}{4k} \cdot \dfrac{18k}{5n^2} = \dfrac{5 \cdot 5 \cdot n \cdot 2 \cdot 3 \cdot 3 \cdot k}{2 \cdot 2 \cdot k \cdot 5 \cdot n \cdot n}$

$$= \dfrac{2 \cdot 3 \cdot 3 \cdot \overset{1}{\cancel{5}} \cdot 5 \cdot \overset{1}{\cancel{k}} \cdot \overset{1}{\cancel{n}}}{\underset{1}{\cancel{2}} \cdot 2 \cdot \underset{1}{\cancel{5}} \cdot \underset{1}{\cancel{k}} \cdot \underset{1}{\cancel{n}} \cdot n} \quad \text{or} \quad \dfrac{45}{2n}$$

**21.** $\dfrac{3}{10} \div \dfrac{6}{5}$  **22.** $\dfrac{15}{12} \div \dfrac{35}{8}$  **23.** $\dfrac{3}{8b^2} \div \dfrac{5}{2b}$  **24.** $\dfrac{6a}{7} \div \dfrac{9a^2}{5}$

**25.** $\dfrac{6ab}{25c} \div \dfrac{9b}{5ac^2}$  **26.** $\dfrac{12q^2}{7pq} \div \dfrac{30q}{21p}$

**27.** $\dfrac{r^2}{2s} \div \dfrac{r}{3st} \div \dfrac{3r}{2}$  **28.** $\dfrac{3n}{5m} \div \dfrac{3p}{5} \div \dfrac{2n}{mp}$

## SECTION 4.5

*Add or subtract. Simplify where necessary.*

**29.** $\dfrac{2}{17} + \dfrac{13}{17}$

**30.** $\dfrac{3}{a} + \dfrac{5}{a}$

**31.** $\dfrac{3x}{11} + \dfrac{6x}{11}$

**32.** $\dfrac{4a}{9} + \dfrac{a}{9}$

**33.** $\dfrac{10r}{16} - \dfrac{r}{16}$

**34.** $\dfrac{13x}{4} - \dfrac{3x}{4}$

**35.** $\dfrac{13}{12y} - \dfrac{4}{12y}$

**36.** $\dfrac{17t}{8} - \dfrac{5t}{8}$

## SECTION 4.6

**EXAMPLE:** $\dfrac{5s}{8} + \dfrac{3s}{4}$

**SOLUTION:** 
$$\dfrac{5s}{8} + \dfrac{3s}{4} = \dfrac{5s}{8} + \dfrac{3s}{4} \cdot \dfrac{2}{2}$$
$$= \dfrac{5s}{8} + \dfrac{6s}{8}$$
$$= \dfrac{11s}{8}$$

**37.** $\dfrac{x}{5} + \dfrac{3x}{10}$

**38.** $\dfrac{n}{12} + \dfrac{3n}{4}$

**39.** $\dfrac{5y}{4} - \dfrac{y}{3}$

**40.** $\dfrac{9k}{6} - \dfrac{k}{4}$

**41.** $\dfrac{5}{3t} + \dfrac{2}{t}$

**42.** $\dfrac{3}{r} + \dfrac{6}{5r}$

**43.** $\dfrac{2}{3n} - \dfrac{3}{5n}$

**44.** $\dfrac{7}{6y} - \dfrac{3}{8y}$

# 5

# Open Sentences and Graphs

# 5.1  Number Sets and Graphs

There are different ways to show a set of numbers.

| Roster Form | Word Description |
|---|---|
| {1, 2, 3} | {counting numbers less than 4} |

Read, "the set of counting numbers less than 4."

**P-1** **How would you show the following sets in roster form?**

**a.** {whole numbers less than 5}   **b.** {counting-number multiples of 4}

**P-2** **What is a word description for each of the sets below?**

**a.** {0, 1, 2}    **b.** {2, 4, 6, 8, · · ·}

**P-3** **How many elements are in {whole numbers between 6 and 7}?**

The **empty set** has no elements. It is shown as { } or as $\phi$.

You can also show {1, 2, 3} as a number-line graph.

The number paired with each point is called the **coordinate** of the point. The set of points on a number line that corresponds to a set of numbers is called the **graph** of the set of numbers.

## example 1    Draw a graph of {1, 3, 5, 7}.

**Solution:**

Compare the number lines below.

**One-half Units**

**One-third Units**

Every number of arithmetic that can be named by a fraction can be paired with a point on a number line. The coordinates above are examples of rational numbers of arithmetic.

A **rational number of arithmetic** is any number that can be expressed as the quotient of two whole numbers. (Remember that 0 cannot be a divisor.)

$$3.1 = \frac{31}{10}$$

$$8 = \frac{8}{1}$$

**P-4** What is one way to write each number below as a quotient of two whole numbers?

a. 5    b. $3\frac{1}{8}$    c. 0.27    d. 2.56

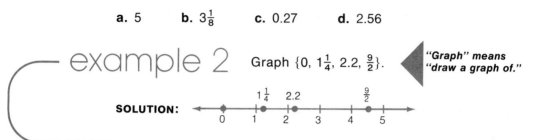

example 2   Graph $\{0, 1\frac{1}{4}, 2.2, \frac{9}{2}\}$.    *"Graph"* means *"draw a graph of."*

SOLUTION:

## ORAL EXERCISES 5.1

*Tell a word description of each set.* (P-2)

1. {1, 2, 3}
2. {0, 1, 2, 3, 4}
3. {2, 4, 6, 8, 10}
4. {9}
5. {  }
6. {$5\frac{1}{2}$}
7. {12, 15, 18, · · ·}
8. {12, 3, 9, 6, 15}

*Tell the elements of each set or say* <u>*Empty Set*</u>. (P-1, P-3)

9. {whole numbers between $5\frac{1}{2}$ and $7\frac{1}{3}$}
10. {odd numbers between 0 and 10}
11. {counting numbers between $5\frac{1}{4}$ and $5\frac{1}{2}$}
12. {even numbers between $4\frac{1}{3}$ and $7\frac{2}{3}$}
13. {prime numbers between 10 and 30}
14. {prime factors of 6}

*Tell the elements of the set shown by each graph.* (Example 1, Example 2)

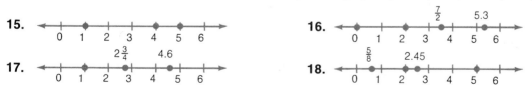

15.

16.

17.

18.

*Say each rational number of arithmetic as a quotient of two whole numbers.* (P-4)

**EXAMPLE:** $1\frac{1}{4}$    **ANSWER:** $\frac{5}{4}, \frac{10}{8}$, etc.

19. 0
20. 1
21. 1000
22. $5\frac{1}{2}$
23. $3\frac{7}{8}$
24. 0.6
25. 5.2
26. 1.35
27. $12\frac{1}{3}$
28. 16
29. 0.13
30. 0.49

## WRITTEN EXERCISES 5.1

**A**     **Goal:** To identify and graph number sets
           **Sample Problem: a.** Name the set graphed.    **Answers: a.** {2}
                   **b.** Graph {1, 2.4}.             **b.**

*Write a word description of each set. (P-2)*

**1.** {1, 3, 5, 7, 9, · · ·}         **2.** {0, 2, 4, 6, 8, · · ·}       **3.** {0, 1, 2, 3, 4, 5, · · ·}

**4.** {1, 2, 3, 4, · · ·}            **5.** {$7\frac{1}{2}$}                   **6.** {9}

**7.** {16, 20, 24, 28}          **8.** {95, 100, 105, 110}       **9.** {2, 3, 5, 7, 11}

**10.** {4, 6, 8, 9}                **11.** {10, 100, 1000}         **12.** {200, 400, 600}

*Name each set using the roster form. Use { } for the empty set. (P-1)*

**13.** {whole numbers between 12 and 20}     **14.** {whole numbers between 25 and 27}

**15.** {even numbers between $12\frac{1}{2}$ and $13\frac{3}{4}$}     **16.** {odd whole numbers less than 11}

**17.** {prime factors of 30}                 **18.** {prime numbers between 13 and 17}

**19.** {counting-number factors of 12}        **20.** {counting-number factors of 18}

**21.** {counting-number multiples of 11}      **22.** {whole-number multiples of 5}

*Name each set that is graphed using the roster form. (Example 1, Example 2)*

**23.**

**24.**

**25.**

**26.**

**27.**

**28.**

*Graph each set. (Example 1, Example 2)*

**29.** {0, 1, 2, 3}            **30.** {0, 2, 4, 5}            **31.** {0.5, 1.5, 2.5}

**32.** {1, 0.5, 2.75}         **33.** {$\frac{1}{3}, \frac{4}{3}, \frac{7}{3}$}           **34.** {$\frac{8}{3}, \frac{9}{4}, \frac{29}{8}$}

*Write each number as a quotient of two whole numbers. (P-4)*

**35.** 15       **36.** 1       **37.** 100       **38.** 55       **39.** $3\frac{1}{5}$       **40.** $7\frac{1}{3}$

**41.** 2.3      **42.** 5.7     **43.** $2\frac{3}{100}$     **44.** $5\frac{7}{1000}$     **45.** 3.81      **46.** 2.48

**B**     *Describe each set below by the roster*      $A = \{0, \frac{3}{4}, 2, 2.6, \frac{24}{8}, 3\frac{1}{7}, 4, \frac{35}{7}\}$
         *method. Refer to set A at the right.*

**47.** {all elements of A that     **48.** {all elements of A that     **49.** {all elements of A that
      are whole numbers}           are counting numbers}        are prime numbers}

# 5.2   Inequalities

*Statements* are sentences that are either true or false.

> In a true statement, numerals on each side of the symbol "=" name the same number.
> In a true statement, numerals on each side of the inequality symbol "≠" name different numbers. ("≠" is read "is not equal to.")
>
> $6 + 3 = 18 \div 2$
>
> $5 - 2 \neq 7 + 1$

**P-1**  **Which symbol, = or ≠, can be used in place of ○ to make each of the following statements true?**

     **a.** $9 - 3 \cdot 2 \bigcirc 12$      **b.** $3(6 + 2) \bigcirc 3 \cdot 6 + 3 \cdot 2$

**P-2**  **How can you place parentheses in the left side of each statement to make it true?**

     **a.** $3 \cdot 2 + 3 \cdot 5 = 45$      **b.** $\frac{1}{2} \cdot \frac{1}{5} + \frac{3}{10} \neq \frac{2}{5}$

> The inequality symbol ">" means "is greater than."    $12 > 4$
> The inequality symbol "<" means "is less than."
> Each symbol points toward the lesser number.     $6 < 13$

**P-3**  **Which of these inequalities is true?  false?**

     **a.** $2 + 8 > 5 + 4$      **b.** $2 \cdot 3 + 6 < (25 - 3) \div 2$

The same inequality relation can be written in two different ways.

$$7.0 + 3.4 < 12 \qquad 12 > 7.0 + 3.4$$

## example 1

Place parentheses to make a false statement. Then use inequality symbols to write a true statement in three ways.

$$2 \cdot 5 + 3 = 13$$

**Solution:**   $2(5 + 3) = 13$   (False Statement)      $13 < 2(5 + 3)$   (True Statement)
           $2(5 + 3) > 13$   (True Statement)      $2(5 + 3) \neq 13$   (True Statement)

## ORAL EXERCISES 5.2

*Say* True *or* False *for each statement.* (P-1, P-3)

**1.** $15 < 21$

**2.** $21 > 15$

**3.** $2 + 5 \neq 5 + 2$

**4.** $4 + 7 \cdot 2 = 22$

**5.** $5(6 + 1) = 35$

**6.** $\frac{1}{4} + \frac{2}{4} > \frac{3}{8}$

**7.** $\frac{1}{4} = \frac{2}{8}$

**8.** $7 \div 5 \neq 5 \div 7$

**9.** $\frac{1}{4} > \frac{1}{8}$

**10.** $\frac{15}{8} < \frac{15}{9}$

**11.** $\frac{3}{8} \cdot \frac{7}{8} > \frac{21}{8}$

**12.** $\frac{3}{4} \div \frac{9}{2} \neq \frac{4}{3} \cdot \frac{9}{2}$

*Say each of these true statements in two other ways.* (Example 1)

**EXAMPLE:** $14 < 19$   **ANSWER:** $19 > 14$; $14 \neq 19$

**13.** $7.3 > 5.9$

**14.** $12\frac{1}{2} < 15\frac{1}{4}$

**15.** $\frac{24}{37} > \frac{24}{53}$

**16.** $\frac{3}{19} < \frac{7}{19}$

**17.** $17.3 \neq 18.6$

**18.** $\frac{1}{4} \neq \frac{2}{5}$

**19.** $\frac{1}{3} + \frac{1}{2} \neq \frac{2}{5}$

**20.** $\frac{17}{73} \neq \frac{1}{3}$

## WRITTEN EXERCISES 5.2

**A**

**Goal:** To write true statements using "=", "≠", ">", "<"

**Sample Problem:** Replace ○ with >, <, or = to make a true statement:
$$3 + 2 \bigcirc \tfrac{1}{5}$$
**Answer:** $3 + 2 > \frac{1}{5}$

*Copy each statement. Then place one or more pairs of parentheses in the left side in order to make the statement true.* (P-2)

**EXAMPLE:** $6 + 3 \cdot 2 - 1 < 10$   **ANSWER:** $6 + 3 \cdot (2 - 1) < 10$

**1.** $2 \cdot 3 + 5 > 15$

**2.** $18 - 5 \cdot 3 > 10$

**3.** $15 + 8 \div 2 \neq 11\frac{1}{2}$

**4.** $24 \div 8 - 2 \neq 1$

**5.** $8 - 3 \cdot 2 + 5 > 30$

**6.** $2 \cdot 3 + 2 \cdot 7 = 34$

**7.** $\frac{1}{2} \cdot \frac{1}{3} + \frac{2}{3} < \frac{5}{6}$

**8.** $\frac{2}{3} \cdot \frac{3}{2} + 1 < 2$

**9.** $5 + 3 \cdot 5 + 4 = 72$

**10.** $8 - 18 \div 13 - 4 = 6$

**11.** $8.2 - 1.2 \div 2 < 5$

**12.** $5.6 \div 4 - 1.2 > 1.9$

*Replace ○ with >, <, or = to make a true statement.* (P-1, P-3)

**13.** $12 \cdot 13 \bigcirc 13 \cdot 12$

**14.** $3(21) \bigcirc 21(3)$

**15.** $14 + 15 \bigcirc 15 + 16$

**16.** $7(5 \cdot 8) \bigcirc (7 \cdot 5)8$

**17.** $\frac{3}{53} \bigcirc \frac{2}{53}$

**18.** $\frac{82}{87} \bigcirc \frac{83}{87}$

**19.** $\frac{15}{16} \bigcirc \frac{16}{17}$

**20.** $\frac{12}{13} \bigcirc \frac{11}{12}$

**21.** $\frac{2}{3} \bigcirc 0.66$

**22.** $1.33 \bigcirc \frac{4}{3}$

**23.** $\frac{3}{8} \bigcirc 0.375$

**24.** $\frac{4}{5} \bigcirc 0.80$

**25.** $(12 \cdot 3) + 2 \bigcirc (12 + 2) \cdot (3 + 2)$

**26.** $6 - (4 \div 2) \bigcirc (6 - 4) \div (6 - 2)$

**27.** $5(8 + 3) \bigcirc 5 \cdot 8 + 5 \cdot 3$

**28.** $(17 + 4) \cdot 3 \bigcirc 17 \cdot 3 + 4 \cdot 3$

**29.** $\frac{1}{2} \cdot \frac{3}{2} \cdot \frac{4}{3} \bigcirc \frac{2}{1} \cdot \frac{2}{3} \cdot \frac{3}{4}$

**30.** $\frac{4}{5} \cdot \frac{7}{2} \cdot \frac{2}{3} \bigcirc \frac{2}{7} \cdot \frac{5}{4} \cdot \frac{3}{2}$

# 5.3 Truth Sets of Open Sentences

**P-1**  **What number for x makes the equation $x + 3 = 5$ true?**

> An **open sentence** contains a variable and becomes true or false when the variable is replaced by a number.
>
> $x + 2 = 8$
>
> $6 + 2 = 8$  (true)
>
> $4 + 2 = 8$  (false)

Examples of open sentences are shown below.

$$x + 3 = 5 \qquad x + 4 > 9 \qquad x - 7 \neq 12$$

**P-2**  **What are three numbers which make $x + 1 < 10$ true?**

**P-3**  **What are three numbers which make $x + 2 \neq 9$ true?**

A set of numbers from which replacements of a variable may be chosen is called the **domain** of the variable.

**P-4**  **What are the values of $2x + 5$ if the domain is $\{0, 1, 2, 3\}$?**

A **truth number** is a number of the domain which makes an open sentence true when it replaces the variable.

## example 1

Write the truth numbers of $x + 1 < 10$ for the following domains.

{whole numbers}  {counting numbers}
{even numbers}

| Open Sentence | Domain | Truth Numbers |
|---|---|---|
| $x + 1 < 10$ | {whole numbers} | 0, 1, 2, 3, 4, 5, 6, 7, 8 |
| $x + 1 < 10$ | {counting numbers} | 1, 2, 3, 4, 5, 6, 7, 8 |
| $x + 1 < 10$ | {even numbers} | 0, 2, 4, 6, 8 |

The **truth set** of an open sentence is the set of all truth numbers of the sentence.

## example 2

Write the truth set of $2x + 3 < 8$.
Use {whole numbers} as the domain.

| x | 2x + 3 | Value less than 8? |
|---|--------|--------------------|
| 0 | $2 \cdot 0 + 3 = 3$ | Yes |
| 1 | $2 \cdot 1 + 3 = 5$ | Yes |
| 2 | $2 \cdot 2 + 3 = 7$ | Yes |
| 3 | $2 \cdot 3 + 3 = 9$ | No |

*Replace x by whole numbers in order starting with 0. See whether each one is a truth number.*

The truth set is {0, 1, 2}.

*Any value for x greater than 2 will make 2x + 3 greater than 8.*

## example 3

Write the truth set of $3x + 1 = x + 9$.
Use {2, 3, 4, 5} as the domain.

| x | 3x + 1 | x + 9 | Do 3x + 1 and x + 9 name the same number? |
|---|--------|-------|--------------------------------------------|
| 2 | $3 \cdot 2 + 1 = 7$ | $2 + 9 = 11$ | No |
| 3 | $3 \cdot 3 + 1 = 10$ | $3 + 9 = 12$ | No |
| 4 | $3 \cdot 4 + 1 = 13$ | $4 + 9 = 13$ | Yes |
| 5 | $3 \cdot 5 + 1 = 16$ | $5 + 9 = 14$ | No |

The truth set is {4}.

## ORAL EXERCISES 5.3

*Tell the values of each open phrase. Use {0, 1, 2} as the domain.* (P-4)

**1.** $5x + 1$     **2.** $8 - 3n$     **3.** $x + x$

**4.** $4y \div 2$     **5.** $7 - y + 2$     **6.** $3a + a$

**7.** $4 + 2y$     **8.** $8 - t \div 2$     **9.** $6 + r \div 2$

*Tell a truth number for each equation. Use {whole numbers} as the domain.*
(P-1, Example 2, Example 3)

**10.** $x + 1 = 4$

**11.** $x - 1 = 7$

**12.** $8 - x = 3$

**13.** $5 + a = 9$

**14.** $2x = 16$

**15.** $3x = 21$

**16.** $4 = 8 \div x$

**17.** $x - 5 = 10$

**18.** $t + t = 10$

*Tell the truth set of each open sentence. Use {0, 1, 2, 3, 4, 5} as the domain.*
(Example 2, Example 3)

**19.** $x + 2 = 7$

**20.** $x > 3$

**21.** $x + 1 < 3$

**22.** $2x < 1$

**23.** $x + 2 > 8$

**24.** $2x + 1 = 11$

**25.** $2x < 12$

**26.** $2x + 1 > 0$

**27.** $x + \frac{1}{2} = 4$

**28.** $x - 2 = 1$

**29.** $x \div 2 = 3$

**30.** $4 \div x = 2$

## WRITTEN EXERCISES 5.3

**A**

**Goal:** To write the truth set of an open sentence for a given domain
**Sample Problem:** Write the truth set of $x + 3 > 5$.
Use {0, 1, 2, 3, 4, 5} as the domain.
**Answer:** {3, 4, 5}

*Write the truth set of each equation. Use {whole numbers} as the domain.*
(P-1, Example 2, Example 3)

**1.** $2 + x = 10$

**2.** $a + 3 = 9$

**3.** $y - 3 = 15$

**4.** $r - 2 = 19$

**5.** $t \div 2 = 4$

**6.** $w \div 5 = 6$

**7.** $2 + v = 15$

**8.** $5 + x = 16$

**9.** $10 - x = 3$

**10.** $13 - y = 1$

**11.** $x + \frac{1}{2} = 3$

**12.** $y + \frac{1}{3} = 1$

**13.** $x + x = 12$

**14.** $y + y = 16$

**15.** $2x = 6$

**16.** $3x = 36$

**17.** $2a = 7$

**18.** $3b = 10$

*Write the truth set of each open sentence. Use {0, 1, 2, 3, 4, 5} as the
domain.* (Example 2, Example 3)

**19.** $x + 7 = 11$

**20.** $x + 9 = 14$

**21.** $a + 1 > 4$

**22.** $a + 3 > 5$

**23.** $2r + 1 = 7$

**24.** $2r + 3 = 11$

**25.** $2x < 2$

**26.** $3x < 4$

**27.** $2x + 1 > 12$

**28.** $2 + 2x < 1$

**29.** $x \div 2 = 2.5$

**30.** $x \div 3 = 1\frac{1}{3}$

**31.** $3c + 1 < 20$

**32.** $2m + 1 < 15$

**33.** $y + 3 \neq 7$

**34.** $t + \frac{1}{2} \neq 2\frac{1}{2}$

**35.** $3x + 1 < 12 + x$

**36.** $12 + 3x > 5x + 3$

**37.** $2x + 1 > 6 + x$

**38.** $3x + 2 > 13 + x$

**39.** $n(n + 1) < 10$

**40.** $(2y + 1)y > 25$

# 5.4 Graphs of Truth Sets of Inequalities

**P-1**    **What is an approximation for $\pi$ using two decimal places?**

The number $\pi$ expressed to ten decimal places is 3.1415926536. This value is also an approximation.

**P-2**    **What set does the graph below represent?**

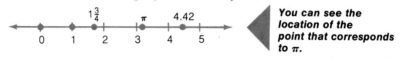

You can see the location of the point that corresponds to $\pi$.

> The set consisting of 0 and the coordinates of points to the right of 0 is the set of **numbers of arithmetic.**
>
> ▲    *The graph of {numbers of arithmetic}:*    0 1 2 3 4 5 6

The graphs below show truth sets of $x < 5$ using different domains.

**Domain: {whole numbers}**      **Domain: {numbers of arithmetic}**

0 1 2 3 4 5 6      0 1 2 3 4 5 6

In the graph on the right, the truth set is infinite. The coordinates of all points in the darkened portion of the line form the truth set. The circle at 5 means that 5 is not in the truth set.

**P-3**    **What is the least whole number in the truth set of $x > 2\frac{1}{2}$?**

## example 1

Graph the truth set of $x > 2\frac{1}{2}$ for each domain.

**a.** {whole numbers}    **b.** {numbers of arithmetic}

**a.** Domain: {whole numbers}

0 1 2 3 4 5 6    etc.

Note that "etc." is used to show that the graph extends infinitely to the right.

**b.** Domain: {numbers of arithmetic}

$2\frac{1}{2}$

0 1 2 3 4 5 6

The heavy arrow is used to show that the graph extends infinitely to the right.

**P-4**  **What number is not in the truth set of x ≠ 4?**

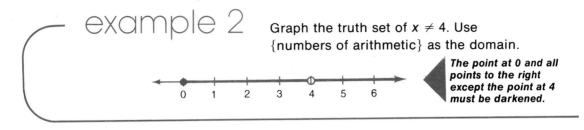

example 2    Graph the truth set of x ≠ 4. Use {numbers of arithmetic} as the domain.

**The point at 0 and all points to the right except the point at 4 must be darkened.**

**P-5**  **What is an inequality for each graph below?**

**a.**

The graph of the empty set has no point darkened.

**b.**

## ORAL EXERCISES 5.4

*Say Yes or No to tell whether the graph shows the truth set of the sentence. The domain is given at the right of each sentence.*

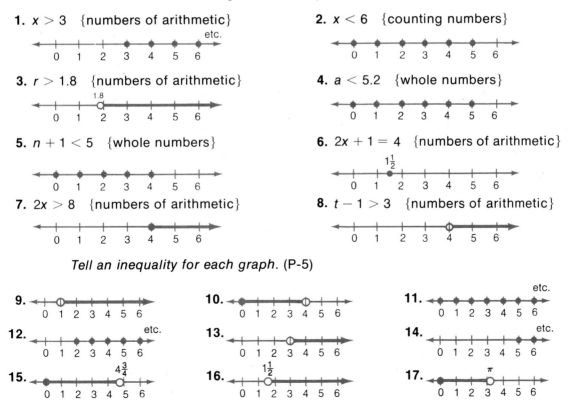

**1.** x > 3   {numbers of arithmetic}

**2.** x < 6   {counting numbers}

**3.** r > 1.8   {numbers of arithmetic}

**4.** a < 5.2   {whole numbers}

**5.** n + 1 < 5   {whole numbers}

**6.** 2x + 1 = 4   {numbers of arithmetic}

**7.** 2x > 8   {numbers of arithmetic}

**8.** t − 1 > 3   {numbers of arithmetic}

*Tell an inequality for each graph.* (P-5)

**9.**    **10.**    **11.**

**12.**    **13.**    **14.**

**15.**    **16.**    **17.**

## WRITTEN EXERCISES 5.4

**A**

**Goal:** To graph the truth set of an inequality

**Sample Problem:** Graph the truth set of $x + 1 < 6$ if the domain is {numbers of arithmetic}.

**Answer:**

0 1 2 3 4 5 6

*Graph the truth set of each inequality. Use {numbers of arithmetic} as the domain.* (Example 1, Example 2)

**1.** $x > 2$  **2.** $m > 5$  **3.** $y < 6$  **4.** $a < 2$

**5.** $y > 4.6$  **6.** $x > 3.5$  **7.** $w \neq 5$  **8.** $g \neq 0$

*Graph the truth set of each inequality. Use {whole numbers} as the domain.* (Example 1)

**9.** $x < 7$  **10.** $x > 5$  **11.** $y < 2$  **12.** $y < 5$

**13.** $a \neq 5$  **14.** $n \neq 1$  **15.** $y > 3\frac{1}{2}$  **16.** $x < 2.5$

*Write an inequality for each graph.* (P-5)

**17.**
0 1 2 3 4 5 6

**18.**
0 1 2 3 4 5 6

**19.**
0 1 2 3 4 5 6

**20.**
0 1 2 3 4 5 6
etc.

**21.**
0 1 2 3 4 5 6

**22.**
0 1 2 3 4 5 6
etc.

**23.**
0 1 2 3 4 5 6
etc.

**24.**
0 1 2 3 4 5 6
etc.

**25.**
0 1 2 3 4 5 6

**26.**
0 1 2 3 4 5 6
etc.

**27.**
0 1 2 3 4 5 6

**28.**
0 1 2 3 4 5 6

**B**

*Graph the truth set of each inequality. Use {numbers of arithmetic} as the domain.*

**29.** $x + 2 < 5$  **30.** $2x > 5$  **31.** $x + 1 > x$  **32.** $5x \neq 10$

**C**

The symbol $\nless$ means "is not less than"; $\ngtr$ means "is not greater than." Graph the truth set of each sentence. The domain is {numbers of arithmetic}.

**EXAMPLE:** $r \nless 2$  **SOLUTION:**

0 1 2 3 4 5 6

**33.** $x \ngtr 5$  **34.** $x \nless 3$  **35.** $a \nless 6$  **36.** $y \ngtr 4$

# 5.5 *Or* Sentences

Suppose that Jane makes the following statement concerning her plans for Friday: "I am going to the game or I am going to the dance."

If she goes to the game on Friday and does not go to the dance, then her statement is true.

If she does not go to the game on Friday but goes to the dance, then her statement is true.

If she goes to the game on Friday and also goes to the dance, then her statement is true.

If she goes neither to the game on Friday nor to the dance, then her statement is false.

A statement such as Jane's that has two clauses is called a <u>compound statement</u> or <u>compound sentence</u>. It is also an example of an *or* sentence.

A **compound *or* sentence** is made up of two clauses connected by "or."

$$7 \cdot 3 > 5 \cdot 4 \ or \ 6 \div 5 < 6 + 5$$

P-1    **In which one of these *or* sentences are both clauses false?**

**a.** $3 + 4 = 7 \ or \ 5 < 9$    **b.** $15 - 8 = 6 \ or \ 8 + 3 = 11$

**c.** $9 + 3 > 11 \ or \ 2 \cdot 5 = 12$    **d.** $3\frac{1}{2} = 3.2 \ or \ 5 + 4 > 19$

Compound sentences **a, b,** and **c** are true. **d** is false.

> A compound *or* sentence is true when either or both clauses are true.
>
> "$\frac{2}{3} = \frac{3}{2} \ or \ 4 < 9$" is true.
>
> "$\frac{3}{3} = \frac{3}{2} \ or \ 4 > 9$" is false.

**P-2**  **Which of the following compound sentences are true? Explain.**

**a.** $15 - 8 = 7$ *or* $12 > 19 - 5$      **b.** $10 - 3 \neq 7$ *or* $13 - 4 < 17 - 8$

**c.** $1.7 + 4.3 = 5.0$ *or* $24 < 33 - 8$   **d.** $20 - 8 = 12$ *or* $8 + 3 \cdot 4 = 20$

## example 1

Write the truth set of "$x + 1 = 5$ *or* $x < 3$."
Use {whole numbers} as the domain.

1. Write the truth set of $x + 1 = 5$. ————————→ $\{4\}$

2. Write the truth set of $x < 3$. ————————→ $\{0, 1, 2\}$

3. Write the set that contains all
   the numbers in the first two sets. ————————→ $\{0, 1, 2, 4\}$

Therefore, $\{0, 1, 2, 4\}$ is the truth set of "$x + 1 = 5$ *or* $x < 3$."

The ***union*** of two sets is the set of elements in <u>either</u> one of the two sets or in <u>both</u> of them.

$$\{0, 1, 2\} \cup \{4\} = \{0, 1, 2, 4\}$$

◄ **"$A \cup B$" means "the union of A and B."**

The truth set of an *or* sentence is the union of the truth sets of the clauses.

## example 2

Graph the truth set of "$x < 2$ *or* $x < 5$."
Use {whole numbers} as the domain.

1. Graph the first truth set. ——→ $x < 2$:

2. Graph the second truth set. ——→ $x < 5$:

3. Graph the union of the
   truth sets. ——→ $x < 2$ *or* $x < 5$:

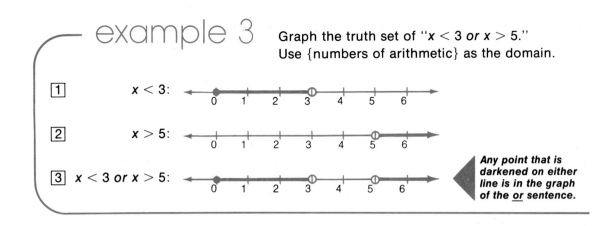

example 3    Graph the truth set of "x < 3 or x > 5."
Use {numbers of arithmetic} as the domain.

1   x < 3:

2   x > 5:

3   x < 3 or x > 5:

Any point that is darkened on either line is in the graph of the *or* sentence.

## ORAL EXERCISES 5.5

Say *True* or *False*. (P-2)

1. $2 + 8 = 10$ or $5 + 2 = 6$

2. $12 - 5 = 8$ or $18 \div 9 = 2$

3. $17 + 3 = 21$ or $25 - 7 = 19$

4. $13 + 12 = 25$ or $21 + 8 = 29$

5. $5 + 2 \cdot 3 < 11$ or $12 - 4 \cdot 2 \neq 16$

6. $3 \cdot 4 - 2 = 6$ or $8 - 3 + 2 = 3$

Tell the truth set of each clause of the compound sentence. Then tell the truth set of the compound sentence. Use {whole numbers} as the domain. (Example 1)

7. $x = 2$ or $x + 1 = 5$

8. $x < 3$ or $x = 0$

9. $x < 5$ or $x < 3$

10. $x + 2 = 10$ or $x < 4$

11. $x = 5$ or $x < 5$

12. $x > 5$ or $x > 4$

Say *Yes* or *No* to tell whether the graph shows the truth set of the sentence. Use {numbers of arithmetic} as the domain. (Example 3)

13. $x < 3$ or $x = 3$

14. $x > 2$ or $x < 4$

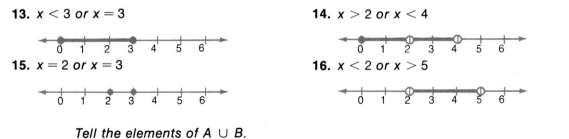

15. $x = 2$ or $x = 3$

16. $x < 2$ or $x > 5$

Tell the elements of $A \cup B$.

17. A:

    B:

18. A:

    etc.

    B:

19. A:

    B:

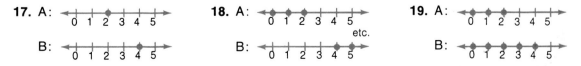

## WRITTEN EXERCISES 5.5

**A**   **Goal:** To write and graph the truth set of a compound *or* sentence

**Sample Problem:** $x < 3$ *or* $x > 5$   Use {whole numbers} as the domain.

**Answer:** Truth set: $\{0, 1, 2, 6, 7, 8, 9, \cdots\}$

Graph:

etc.

*Write True or False.* (P-2)

**1.** $1 + 2 = 3$ *or* $8 - 5 = 4$

**2.** $3 + 7 = 11$ *or* $13 + 12 = 25$

**3.** $\frac{1}{8} + \frac{7}{8} = 1$ *or* $\frac{2}{11} > \frac{2}{13}$

**4.** $3 + 2 \cdot 4 = 20$ *or* $2 \cdot 5 \neq 12 - 2$

**5.** $\frac{2}{5} \neq 0.4$ *or* $10 < 10$

**6.** $\frac{3}{7} < \frac{5}{7}$ *or* $\frac{1}{4} + \frac{3}{4} = 1$

**7.** $15 + 17 = 32$ *or* $\frac{19}{37} > \frac{20}{36}$

**8.** $\frac{153}{167} < \frac{154}{168}$ *or* $28 + 13 = 41$

*Write the truth set of each clause. Then write the truth set of the compound sentence. Use {whole numbers} as the domain.* (Example 1)

**9.** $x = 2$ *or* $x < 5$

**10.** $x < 7$ *or* $x + 1 = 4$

**11.** $a < 4$ *or* $a < 3$

**12.** $r < 7$ *or* $r < 1$

**13.** $y < 2$ *or* $y + 1 = 10$

**14.** $t - 2 = 6$ *or* $t < 5$

**15.** $w > 8$ *or* $w - 1 = 11$

**16.** $x + 5 = 15$ *or* $x > 5$

**17.** $m \neq 5$ *or* $m > 3$

**18.** $n < 6$ *or* $n \neq 1$

**19.** $x \neq 4$ *or* $x < 5$

**20.** $x > 4$ *or* $x < 5$

*Draw a graph of the truth set of each clause. Then draw a graph of the truth set of the compound sentence. Use {whole numbers} as the domain.* (Example 2)

**21.** $x < 5$ *or* $x = 6$

**22.** $x = 1$ *or* $x > 4$

**23.** $x < 5$ *or* $x < 3$

**24.** $x > 1$ *or* $x > 5$

**25.** $x \neq 2$ *or* $x < 4$

**26.** $x > 2$ *or* $x \neq 5$

*Follow the same directions for Exercises 27–38 as for Exercises 21–26 but use {numbers of arithmetic} as the domain.* (Example 3)

**27.** $x = 5$ *or* $x < 3$

**28.** $x > 4$ *or* $x = 0$

**29.** $x = 1$ *or* $x = 5$

**30.** $x = 3$ *or* $x = 0$

**31.** $x > 3$ *or* $x > 6$

**32.** $x > 5$ *or* $x > 3$

**33.** $x < 2\frac{1}{2}$ *or* $x > 5\frac{1}{2}$

**34.** $x < 3.7$ *or* $x > 5.3$

**35.** $x \neq 3$ *or* $x < 5$

**36.** $x > 3$ *or* $x \neq 6$

**37.** $x < 2.3$ *or* $x > 2.3$

**38.** $x < \pi$ *or* $x > \pi$

# 5.6 *And* Sentences

A **compound *and* sentence** is made up of two clauses connected by "and."

$$5 + 2 = 7 \text{ and } 8 + 1 = 10$$

**P-1**  **Is the first clause true or false?   the second?**

The compound sentence is false because one of its clauses is false.

A compound *and* sentence is true only when both clauses are true.

"$2 < 3$ and $\frac{10}{2} = 5$" is true.

"$2 = 3$ and $\frac{10}{2} = 5$" is false.

**P-2**  **Which one of the following compound sentences is true?**

a. $2 + 19 > 21$ *and* $5 < 0$       b. $2\frac{3}{4} = 2.75$ *and* $5 < 6$

c. $13.8 < 13\frac{4}{5}$ *and* $17 \neq 19$       d. $27 \neq 36 - 9$ *and* $1\frac{3}{4} > 1\frac{3}{8}$

## example 1

Write the truth set of "$x > 2$ *and* $x < 5$." Use $\{0, 1, 2, 3, 4, 5\}$ as the domain.

1 Write the truth set of $x > 2$. ⟶ $\{3, 4, 5\}$

2 Write the truth set of $x < 5$. ⟶ $\{0, 1, 2, 3, 4\}$

3 Write the set of numbers that are common to the first two sets. ⟶ $\{3, 4\}$

Therefore, $\{3, 4\}$ is the truth set of "$x > 2$ *and* $x < 5$."

The set of elements common to two sets is called their ***intersection.***

$$\{3, 4, 5\} \cap \{0, 1, 2, 3, 4\} = \{3, 4\}$$

"$A \cap B$" means "the intersection of A and B."

The truth set of an *and* sentence is the intersection of the truth sets of both clauses.

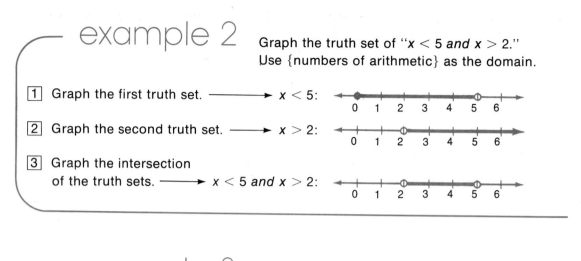

## example 2

Graph the truth set of "$x < 5$ and $x > 2$."
Use {numbers of arithmetic} as the domain.

1. Graph the first truth set. ⟶ $x < 5$:

2. Graph the second truth set. ⟶ $x > 2$:

3. Graph the intersection
   of the truth sets. ⟶ $x < 5$ and $x > 2$:

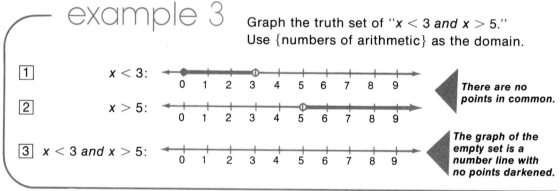

## example 3

Graph the truth set of "$x < 3$ and $x > 5$."
Use {numbers of arithmetic} as the domain.

1. $x < 3$:

2. $x > 5$:

There are no points in common.

3. $x < 3$ and $x > 5$:

The graph of the empty set is a number line with no points darkened.

## ORAL EXERCISES 5.6

*Say True or False.* (P-2)

1. $10 - 6 = 3$ *and* $2 + 3 = 6$

2. $8 + 7 = 15$ *and* $20 - 2 = 17$

3. $13 + 28 = 41$ *and* $18 + 5 > 22$

4. $15 + 19 \neq 34$ *and* $16 < 23 - 5$

5. $\frac{1}{2} < \frac{1}{3}$ *and* $0.03 > 0.005$

6. $\frac{1}{4} + \frac{2}{4} = \frac{3}{4}$ *and* $\frac{1}{2} + \frac{1}{3} = \frac{1}{5}$

*Tell the truth set of each clause of the compound sentence. Then tell the truth set of the compound sentence. Use {whole numbers} as the domain.* (Example 1)

7. $x + 1 = 3$ *and* $x < 5$

8. $x < 4$ *and* $x > 1$

9. $x < 4$ *and* $x < 2$

10. $x = 2$ *and* $x > 3$

11. $x < 5$ *and* $x > 5$

12. $x \neq 3$ *and* $x < 2$

*Say Yes or No to tell whether the graph shows the truth set of the sentence.*
*Use {numbers of arithmetic} as the domain. (Example 2, Example 3)*

**13.** $x = 2$ *and* $x > 2$:

**14.** $x < 4$ *and* $x > 1$:

**15.** $x < 1$ *and* $x > 3$:

**16.** $x + 1 = 3$ *and* $x > 4$:

*Tell the elements of A ∩ B. (Step 3 of Examples 2 and 3)*

**17.** A:

B:

**18.** A:

B:

**19.** A:

B:

## WRITTEN EXERCISES 5.6

**A** **Goal:** To write and graph the truth set of a compound *and* sentence
**Sample Problem:** $x > 4$ *and* $x < 8$   Use {whole numbers} as the domain.
**Answer:** Truth set: {5, 6, 7}    Graph:

*Write True or False. (P-2)*

**1.** $2 + 8 = 10$ *and* $13 - 9 = 4$

**2.** $2(25) = 50$ *and* $24 \div 8 = 3$

**3.** $50 + 30 = 70$ *and* $80 + 20 = 100$

**4.** $35 + 15 = 50$ *and* $37 + 23 = 50$

**5.** $13 > 12 + 2$ *and* $15 < 8 + 9$

**6.** $5\frac{1}{4} + 2\frac{3}{4} > 8$ *and* $8 + 13 < 22$

**7.** $13 + 2 < 16$ *and* $2 + 9 \neq 12$

**8.** $23 - 5 > 18$ *and* $53 + 17 \neq 60$

*Write the truth set of each clause. Then write the truth set of the compound*
*sentence. Use {whole numbers} as the domain. (Example 1)*

**9.** $x < 5$ *and* $x > 0$

**10.** $x < 7$ *and* $x > 3$

**11.** $x < 6$ *and* $x < 4$

**12.** $x > 5$ *and* $x > 7$

**13.** $x + 1 = 6$ *and* $x < 10$

**14.** $x > 3$ *and* $x - 1 = 5$

*Draw a graph of the truth set of each clause. Then draw a graph of the*
*truth set of the compound sentence. Use {whole numbers} as the domain.*
*(Example 2, Example 3)*

**15.** $x < 6$ *and* $x < 3$

**16.** $y > 2$ *and* $y > 5$

**17.** $a < 5$ *and* $a < 3$

**18.** $b > 2$ *and* $b < 7$

**19.** $t \neq 3$ *and* $t < 6$

**20.** $w > 4$ *and* $w \neq 2$

*Draw a graph of the truth set of each clause. Then draw a graph of the
truth set of the compound sentence. Use {numbers of arithmetic} as the
domain.* (Example 2, Example 3)

21. $x > 2$ and $x < 7$

22. $x < 5$ and $x > 0$

23. $a < 5$ and $a \neq 3$

24. $r > 4$ and $r \neq 5$

25. $x = 5$ and $x < 6$

26. $y > 2$ and $y = 4$

27. $x < 5\frac{1}{2}$ and $x > 2\frac{1}{2}$

28. $t > 3.7$ and $t < 5.3$

29. $n > 2$ and $n > 5$

30. $s < 4$ and $s < 6$

31. $x \neq 3$ and $x < 8$

32. $x < 4$ and $x \neq 10$

**C**   *Write a compound and sentence for each graph. Use {numbers of arithmetic}
as the domain.*

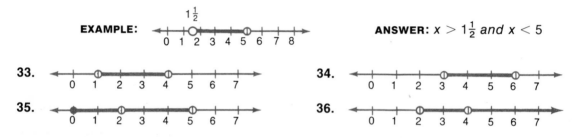

**EXAMPLE:**   **ANSWER:** $x > 1\frac{1}{2}$ and $x < 5$

33.   34.

35.   36.

*Write a compound or sentence for each graph. Use {numbers of arithmetic}
as the domain.*

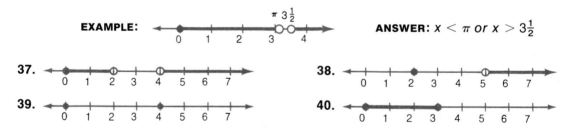

**EXAMPLE:**   **ANSWER:** $x < \pi$ or $x > 3\frac{1}{2}$

37.   38.

39.   40.

*Write either a compound and sentence or a compound or sentence for each
graph. Use {numbers of arithmetic} as the domain.*

41.   42.

43.   44.

# 5.7 Sentences Using ≤ and ≥

**P-1** **How do you read this compound sentence?**

$$x < 5 \text{ or } x = 5$$

There is a short way to read and write this *or* sentence.

"*x* is less than *or* equal to 5"    $x \le 5$

"≤" is a combination of "<" and "=".

**P-2** **What whole numbers are in the truth set of "x > 4 or x = 4"? of "x ≥ 4"?**

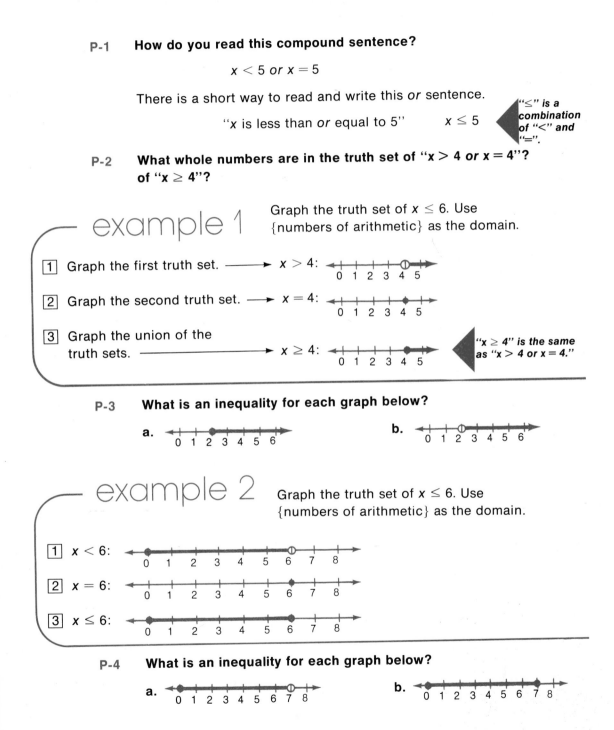

example 1    Graph the truth set of $x \le 6$. Use {numbers of arithmetic} as the domain.

1 Graph the first truth set. ⟶ $x > 4$:   0 1 2 3 4 5

2 Graph the second truth set. ⟶ $x = 4$:   0 1 2 3 4 5

3 Graph the union of the truth sets. ⟶ $x \ge 4$:   0 1 2 3 4 5

"x ≥ 4" is the same as "x > 4 or x = 4."

**P-3** **What is an inequality for each graph below?**

a.   0 1 2 3 4 5 6

b.   0 1 2 3 4 5 6

example 2    Graph the truth set of $x \le 6$. Use {numbers of arithmetic} as the domain.

1 $x < 6$:   0 1 2 3 4 5 6 7 8

2 $x = 6$:   0 1 2 3 4 5 6 7 8

3 $x \le 6$:   0 1 2 3 4 5 6 7 8

**P-4** **What is an inequality for each graph below?**

a.   0 1 2 3 4 5 6 7 8

b.   0 1 2 3 4 5 6 7 8

## ORAL EXERCISES 5.7

*Say True or False.*

**1.** $3 \leq 5$      **2.** $7 \geq 10$      **3.** $5 \geq 1$      **4.** $\frac{1}{2} \geq 1$      **5.** $8 \leq 8$      **6.** $2 \geq 2$

*Tell the truth set. Use {0, 1, 2, 3, 4, 5} as the domain.* (P-2)

**7.** $x \leq 3$      **8.** $x \leq 1$      **9.** $x \geq 2$      **10.** $x \geq 5$

**11.** $x \leq 0$      **12.** $x \geq 6$      **13.** $x \leq 100$      **14.** $x \geq 100$

**15.** $2x \leq 3$      **16.** $2x \geq 6$      **17.** $x + 1 \leq 5$      **18.** $x + 1 \geq 3$

*Tell an inequality for each graph.* (P-3, P-4)

**19.**    **20.**    **21.**

**22.**    **23.**    **24.**

## WRITTEN EXERCISES 5.7

**A**    **Goal:** To find the truth set of an inequality containing $\leq$ or $\geq$

**Sample Problem:** Graph the truth set of $x \leq 5$.
            Use {numbers of arithmetic} as the domain.

**Answer:**

*Write the truth set. Use {0, 2, 4, 6, 8, 10} as the domain.* (P-2)

**1.** $x \leq 6$      **2.** $x \leq 3$      **3.** $x \geq 12$      **4.** $x \geq 50$

**5.** $x \leq 35$      **6.** $x \leq 75$      **7.** $2x \geq 3$      **8.** $2x \leq 12$

**9.** $x + 1 \leq 7$      **10.** $x + 1 \geq 3$      **11.** $2x + 1 \geq 12$      **12.** $2x + 1 \leq 11$

*Graph the truth set. Use {numbers of arithmetic} as the domain.* (Example 1, Example 2)

**13.** $x \leq 3$      **14.** $x \leq 5$      **15.** $x \geq 4$

**16.** $x \geq 2$      **17.** $x \geq 4\frac{1}{2}$      **18.** $x \leq 3\frac{1}{2}$

**C**    **EXAMPLE:** $x \leq 1$ *or* $x > 3$    **ANSWER:**

**19.** $x \leq 3$ *or* $x > 5$      **20.** $x < 2$ *or* $x \geq 4$      **21.** $x \leq 2$ *and* $x \geq 5$

**22.** $x \geq 6$ *and* $x \leq 3$      **23.** $a < 2.6$ *and* $a \geq 4.5$      **24.** $r \leq \pi$ *and* $r > 5$

# CHAPTER SUMMARY

| | |
|---|---|
| **IMPORTANT TERMS** | Empty set *(p. 86)*      Domain *(p. 91)* <br> Number line *(p. 86)*      Truth number *(p. 91)* <br> Coordinate *(p. 86)*      Truth set *(p. 91)* <br> Graph *(p. 86)*      Numbers of arithmetic *(p. 94)* <br> Rational numbers      Compound *or* sentence *(p. 97)* <br>   of arithmetic *(p. 87)*      Union *(p. 98)* <br> Statement *(p. 89)*      Compound *and* sentence *(p. 101)* <br> Inequality *(p. 89)*      Intersection *(p. 101)* <br> Open sentence *(p. 91)* |

**IMPORTANT IDEAS**

1. "$=$" means the numerals on each side name the same number.
   "$\neq$" means the numerals on each side name different numbers.
   "$>$" means "is greater than."
   "$<$" means "is less than."

2. A compound *or* sentence is true when either or both clauses are true.

3. The truth set of an *or* sentence is the union of the truth sets of the clauses.

4. A compound *and* sentence is true only when both clauses are true.

5. The truth set of an *and* sentence is the intersection of the truth sets of both clauses.

# CHAPTER REVIEW

## SECTION 5.1

*Name each set using the roster form.*

1. {whole numbers between 23 and 28}

2. {counting numbers less than 6}

3. {prime numbers less than 12}

4. {whole numbers greater than 15}

*Write each number as a quotient of two whole numbers.*

5. 12      6. 5      7. $2\frac{1}{2}$      8. $3\frac{1}{4}$      9. 2.3      10. 1.28

## SECTION 5.2

*Copy each sentence. Then place one or more pairs of parentheses in the left side in order to make a true statement.*

11. $18 - 5 + 7 < 10$      12. $24 \div 8 \cdot 3 = 1$      13. $8 + 2 \cdot 5 > 45$

14. $42 - 18 \div 6 < 25$      15. $3 + 2 \cdot 4 - 1 = 15$      16. $24 - 6 + 2 \cdot 3 = 12$

## SECTION 5.3

Write the truth set. Use {whole numbers} as the domain.

**17.** $r + 12 = 19$    **18.** $n - 9 = 17$    **19.** $x \div 7 = 9$    **20.** $5y = 90$

Write the truth set. Use {0, 1, 2, 3, 4, 5} as the domain.

**21.** $n + 12 \neq 16$    **22.** $r + 2\frac{1}{4} \neq 5\frac{1}{4}$    **23.** $3t < t + 5$    **24.** $3n \cdot n < 20$

## SECTION 5.4

Graph the truth set. Use {whole numbers} as the domain.

**25.** $x < 5\frac{1}{4}$    **26.** $y < 3.9$    **27.** $t > 5$    **28.** $n > 1\frac{1}{2}$

Graph the truth set. Use {numbers of arithmetic} as the domain.

**29.** $r < 7.4$    **30.** $a < \pi$    **31.** $x \neq 3$    **32.** $y \neq 1.6$

## SECTION 5.5

Write the truth set of each clause. Then write the truth set of the compound sentence. Use {whole numbers} as the domain.

**33.** $x + 1 = 5$ or $x < 6.8$    **34.** $y < 5.1$ or $y < \pi$

Graph the truth set of each clause. Then graph the truth set of the compound sentence. Use {numbers of arithmetic} as the domain.

**35.** $x < 7.3$ or $x < 5.2$    **36.** $x > 2.5$ or $x > 4.8$

**37.** $x < 3\frac{1}{2}$ or $x > 5\frac{1}{2}$    **38.** $x > 6$ or $x < 3\frac{1}{4}$

## SECTION 5.6

Write the truth set of each clause. Then write the truth set of the compound sentence. Use {whole numbers} as the domain.

**39.** $x \neq 5$ and $x < 5\frac{1}{4}$    **40.** $x > 15$ and $x < 21$

Graph the truth set of each clause. Then graph the truth set of the compound sentence. Use {numbers of arithmetic} as the domain.

**41.** $n > 3\frac{1}{2}$ and $n < 5\frac{1}{4}$    **42.** $t < 8$ and $t > 1.6$

**43.** $w < 6\frac{1}{2}$ and $w < 3$    **44.** $y > 6.5$ and $y > 4$

## SECTION 5.7

Write the truth set. Use {10, 11, 12, 13, $\cdots$} as the domain.

**45.** $x \leq 15$    **46.** $x + 1 \geq 20$    **47.** $2x \geq 26$    **48.** $2x + 1 \leq 29$

Graph the truth set. Use {numbers of arithmetic} as the domain.

**49.** $x \geq 5$    **50.** $x \leq 8$    **51.** $x \leq 6\frac{1}{2}$    **52.** $x \geq 7\frac{1}{2}$

# Solving Equations

**6**

# 6.1  Subtraction Property of Equality

**P-1**  **What is the simplest name for each phrase?**

    **a.** $10 + 3 - 3$      **b.** $5\frac{1}{2} + \frac{3}{4} - \frac{3}{4}$      **c.** $n + 5 - 5$

The following steps show the operations performed in P-1.

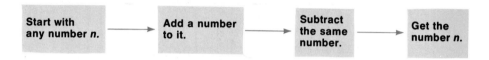

The subtraction step reverses the addition step.

You always get back the original number. This illustrates that subtraction is the **_inverse operation_** of addition.

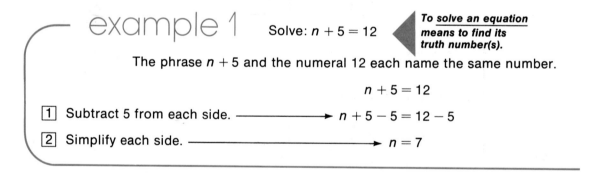

example 1      Solve: $n + 5 = 12$      ◄ *To solve an equation means to find its truth number(s).*

The phrase $n + 5$ and the numeral 12 each name the same number.

$$n + 5 = 12$$

1️⃣ Subtract 5 from each side. ⟶ $n + 5 - 5 = 12 - 5$

2️⃣ Simplify each side. ⟶ $n = 7$

**P-2**  **If _n_ is replaced by 7, which of these equations are true?**

    **a.** $n + 5 = 12$      **b.** $n + 5 - 5 = 12 - 5$      **c.** $n = 7$

These equations are **_equivalent._** They have the same truth number.

> **_Subtraction Property of Equality_**
>
> Subtracting the same number from each side of an equation forms an equivalent equation.
>
> $$n + 5 = 12$$
> $$n + 5 - 5 = 12 - 5$$
> $$n = 7$$

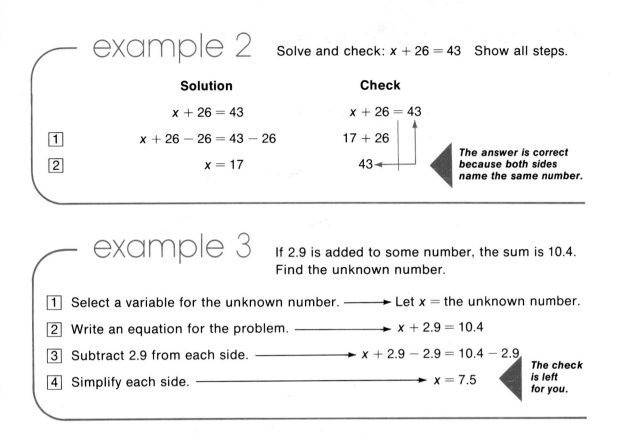

example 2    Solve and check: $x + 26 = 43$    Show all steps.

**Solution**

$x + 26 = 43$

[1]    $x + 26 - 26 = 43 - 26$

[2]    $x = 17$

**Check**

$x + 26 = 43$

$17 + 26$

$43$

The answer is correct because both sides name the same number.

example 3    If 2.9 is added to some number, the sum is 10.4. Find the unknown number.

[1] Select a variable for the unknown number. ⟶ Let $x =$ the unknown number.

[2] Write an equation for the problem. ⟶ $x + 2.9 = 10.4$

[3] Subtract 2.9 from each side. ⟶ $x + 2.9 - 2.9 = 10.4 - 2.9$

[4] Simplify each side. ⟶ $x = 7.5$

The check is left for you.

## ORAL EXERCISES 6.1

*Tell the simplest name.* (P-1)

**1.** $x + 7 - 7$

**2.** $r + 30 - 30$

**3.** $b + 0.5 - 0.5$

**4.** $t + \frac{1}{2} - \frac{1}{2}$

**5.** $n + 19 - 19$

**6.** $a + \frac{3}{4} - \frac{3}{4}$

**7.** $k + 12.5 - 12.5$

**8.** $p + 2\frac{1}{2} - 2\frac{1}{2}$

**9.** $12 + n - n$

**10.** $3.6 + x - x$

**11.** $112 + r - r$

**12.** $x + n - n$

*Tell the equivalent equation you form as the first step in solving the equation.* (Step 1 of Example 1, Example 2)

**EXAMPLE:** $s + 23 = 31$    **ANSWER:** $s + 23 - 23 = 31 - 23$

**13.** $x + 5 = 19$

**14.** $a + 12 = 14$

**15.** $n + 92 = 105$

**16.** $r + 36 = 87$

**17.** $t + 1.8 = 2.3$

**18.** $w + 2.9 = 8.1$

**19.** $b + \frac{1}{2} = 19$

**20.** $y + 2\frac{3}{4} = 6\frac{7}{8}$

**21.** $x + 12.5 = 21.3$

## WRITTEN EXERCISES 6.1

**A**

**Goal:** To solve an equation using the Subtraction Property of Equality
**Sample Problem:** $x + 2.7 = 5.3$
**Answer:** 2.6

*Solve and check. Show all steps.* (Example 1, Example 2)

1. $n + 14 = 21$

2. $x + 18 = 35$

3. $y + 29 = 46$

4. $r + 23 = 42$

5. $t + 19 = 43$

6. $s + 34 = 51$

7. $a + 39 = 56$

8. $b + 45 = 71$

9. $q + 37 = 64$

10. $k + 52 = 70$

11. $x + 3.4 = 7.6$

12. $y + 2.3 = 5.8$

13. $n + 4.5 = 6.9$

14. $t + 6.8 = 9.9$

15. $b + 12.8 = 15.1$

16. $r + 23.7 = 35.2$

17. $s + 0.19 = 0.43$

18. $y + 0.47 = 0.85$

19. $q + 0.87 = 5.03$

20. $g + 0.59 = 4.15$

21. $x + 3\frac{1}{2} = 5\frac{3}{4}$

22. $n + 5\frac{1}{4} = 9\frac{1}{2}$

23. $t + 3\frac{3}{4} = 7\frac{1}{4}$

24. $a + 10\frac{1}{2} = 15\frac{1}{4}$

*Write an equation for each problem. Then solve and check it.* (Example 3)

25. If 29 is added to an unknown number, the sum is 105. Find the unknown number.

26. If 73 is added to an unknown number, the sum is 121. Find the unknown number.

27. The sum of an unknown number and 18.7 is 34.3. Find the unknown number.

28. The sum of an unknown number and 34.9 is 52.3. Find the unknown number.

**C**

*Simplify.*

29. $t - 16 + 16$

30. $w - 92 + 92$

31. $x - 5.6 + 5.6$

32. $s - 19.2 + 19.2$

33. $12 - n + n$

34. $45 - y + y$

*Solve.*

35. $n - 5 + 5 = 12 + 5$

36. $r - 9 + 9 = 3 + 9$

37. $x - \frac{1}{4} + \frac{1}{4} = 3\frac{1}{4} + \frac{1}{4}$

38. $w - 2\frac{1}{2} + 2\frac{1}{2} = 3\frac{1}{4} + 2\frac{1}{2}$

39. $a - 0.6 + 0.6 = 0.8 + 0.6$

40. $k - 2.9 + 2.9 = 1.4 + 2.9$

## 6.2 Addition Property of Equality

**P-1**   **What is the simplest name for each phrase?**

   **a.** $13 - 8 + 8$      **b.** $9.7 - 3.2 + 3.2$      **c.** $3\frac{1}{2} - \frac{3}{4} + \frac{3}{4}$

   **d.** $n - 19 + 19$      **e.** $5 - 18 + 18$

The following steps show the operations performed in P-1.

| Start with any number $n$. | $\longrightarrow$ | Subtract a number. | $\longrightarrow$ | Add the same number. | $\longrightarrow$ | Get the number $n$. |

You can get the answer to **e** even though $5 - 18$ is not a number of arithmetic. You know that the answer is 5 because addition and subtraction are inverse operations.

**P-2**   **What is the simplest name for each phrase?**

   **a.** $12 - 19 + 19$      **b.** $3\frac{1}{2} - 5\frac{1}{4} + 5\frac{1}{4}$      **c.** $7.3 - a + a$

Solve: $x - 12 = 9$   Show all steps.

The phrase $x - 12$ and the numeral 9 each name the same number.

$$x - 12 = 9$$

1 Add 12 to each side. $\longrightarrow$ $x - 12 + 12 = 9 + 12$

2 Simplify each side. $\longrightarrow$ $x = 21$

**P-3**   **If x is replaced by 21, which of these equations are true?**

   **a.** $x - 12 = 9$      **b.** $x - 12 + 12 = 9 + 12$      **c.** $x = 21$

---

**Addition Property of Equality**

Adding the same number to each side of an equation forms an equivalent equation.

$$x - 12 = 9$$
$$x - 12 + 12 = 9 + 12$$
$$x = 21$$

---

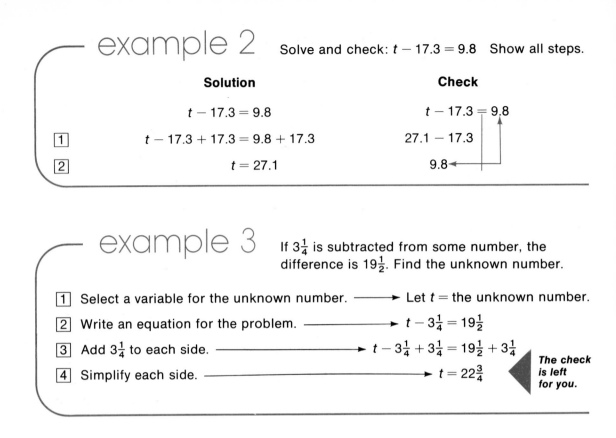

example 2    Solve and check: $t - 17.3 = 9.8$   Show all steps.

| **Solution** | **Check** |
|---|---|
| $t - 17.3 = 9.8$ | $t - 17.3 = 9.8$ |
| ①   $t - 17.3 + 17.3 = 9.8 + 17.3$ | $27.1 - 17.3$ |
| ②       $t = 27.1$ | $9.8$ |

example 3    If $3\frac{1}{4}$ is subtracted from some number, the difference is $19\frac{1}{2}$. Find the unknown number.

① Select a variable for the unknown number. ⟶ Let $t =$ the unknown number.

② Write an equation for the problem. ⟶ $t - 3\frac{1}{4} = 19\frac{1}{2}$

③ Add $3\frac{1}{4}$ to each side. ⟶ $t - 3\frac{1}{4} + 3\frac{1}{4} = 19\frac{1}{2} + 3\frac{1}{4}$

④ Simplify each side. ⟶ $t = 22\frac{3}{4}$

◀ *The check is left for you.*

## ORAL EXERCISES 6.2

*Tell the simplest name.* (P-1, P-2)

**1.** $r - 12 + 12$          **2.** $s - 37 + 37$          **3.** $x - 2.8 + 2.8$

**4.** $a - \frac{1}{4} + \frac{1}{4}$          **5.** $n - 0.8 + 0.8$          **6.** $p - 6\frac{1}{2} + 6\frac{1}{2}$

**7.** $b - 19.2 + 19.2$          **8.** $72 - s + s$          **9.** $3\frac{1}{4} - x + x$

*Tell the equivalent equation you form as the first step in solving the equation.* (Step 1 of Example 1, Example 2)

**10.** $x - 7 = 19$          **11.** $a - 12 = 5$          **12.** $s - 27 = 23$

**13.** $t - 83 = 47$          **14.** $q - 2.7 = 3.9$          **15.** $b - 5.6 = 12.9$

**16.** $w - \frac{3}{4} = 2\frac{1}{2}$          **17.** $n - 1\frac{7}{8} = 4\frac{1}{4}$          **18.** $y - 13.2 = 17.9$

*Tell the equivalent equation you form as the first step in solving the equation.*
*(Example 1 of Section 6.1, Example 1 of Section 6.2)*

**EXAMPLE:** $x + 29 = 43$    **ANSWER:** $x + 29 - 29 = 43 - 29$

**19.** $y + 87 = 193$      **20.** $r - 56 = 23$      **21.** $t + 15.9 = 28.3$

**22.** $a + 12\frac{1}{2} = 15\frac{1}{4}$      **23.** $q - \frac{3}{4} = 6\frac{1}{2}$      **24.** $k + 128 = 312$

## WRITTEN EXERCISES 6.2

**A**

**Goal:** To solve an equation using the Addition Property of Equality

**Sample Problem:** $n - 3.2 = 6.7$

**Answer:** $n = 9.9$

*Solve and check. Show all steps.* (Example 1, Example 2)

**1.** $x - 32 = 26$      **2.** $r - 23 = 36$      **3.** $t - 48 = 53$

**4.** $p - 59 = 47$      **5.** $n - 128 = 75$      **6.** $b - 136 = 87$

**7.** $a - 207 = 185$      **8.** $p - 235 = 95$      **9.** $m - 169 = 169$

**10.** $k - 378 = 378$      **11.** $s - 4.2 = 5.9$      **12.** $q - 7.9 = 6.7$

**13.** $w - 0.27 = 0.86$      **14.** $n - 0.89 = 0.54$      **15.** $g - 28.3 = 19.7$

**16.** $h - 42.7 = 28.5$      **17.** $r - 9.08 = 15.29$      **18.** $x - 12.37 = 9.09$

**19.** $b - 2\frac{1}{2} = 5\frac{1}{2}$      **20.** $a - 3\frac{1}{4} = 2\frac{1}{2}$      **21.** $n - 10\frac{3}{4} = 3\frac{3}{4}$

**22.** $q - 12\frac{3}{8} = 5\frac{1}{8}$      **23.** $x - 432 = 316$      **24.** $y - 378 = 295$

*Write an equation for each problem. Then solve and check it.* (Example 3)

**25.** If 78 is subtracted from an unknown number, the difference is 97. Find the unknown number.

**26.** If 59 is subtracted from an unknown number, the difference is 136. Find the unknown number.

**27.** The difference of an unknown number less 29.7 is 35.8. Find the unknown number.

**28.** The difference of an unknown number less 53.6 is 47.9. Find the unknown number.

**29.** If $2\frac{3}{4}$ is added to an unknown number, the sum is $12\frac{1}{4}$. Find the unknown number.

**30.** The sum of an unknown number and $12\frac{1}{8}$ is $21\frac{3}{8}$. Find the unknown number.

**C**      *Simplify.*

**31.** $\dfrac{12 \cdot 8}{12}$      **32.** $\dfrac{3 \cdot 15}{3}$      **33.** $\dfrac{19 \cdot 17}{19}$      **34.** $\dfrac{27 \cdot 27}{27}$

**35.** $\dfrac{5x}{5}$      **36.** $\dfrac{12y}{12}$      **37.** $\dfrac{100a}{100}$      **38.** $\dfrac{56n}{56}$

## 6.3　Division Property of Equality

P-1　**What is the simplest name for each phrase?**

**a.** $2 \cdot 5 \div 5$　**b.** $\dfrac{3 \cdot 12}{12}$　**c.** $\dfrac{14x}{14}$　**d.** $\dfrac{96y}{96}$

The following steps show the operations performed in P-1.

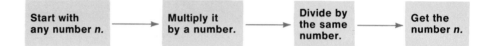

| Start with any number *n*. | → | Multiply it by a number. | → | Divide by the same number. | → | Get the number *n*. |

You always get back the original number. This illustrates that division is the inverse operation of multiplication.

## example 1　Solve: $3n = 48$　Show all steps.

1　Divide each side by 3. ——————————————→ $\dfrac{3n}{3} = \dfrac{48}{3}$

2　Simplify each side. ————————————————→ $n = 16$

P-2　**If *n* is replaced by 16, which of these equations are true?**

**a.** $3n = 48$　**b.** $\dfrac{3n}{3} = \dfrac{48}{3}$　**c.** $n = 16$

---

**Division Property of Equality**　　　　　$3n = 48$

Dividing each side of an equation by　　　$\dfrac{3n}{3} = \dfrac{48}{3}$
the same nonzero number forms an
equivalent equation.　　　　　　　　　　$n = 16$

---

## example 2　Solve and check: $2.1t = 147$　Show all steps.

**Solution**　　　　　　　　　　　　**Check**

$2.1t = 147$　　　　　　　　　　　$2.1t = 147$

1　$\dfrac{2.1t}{2.1} = \dfrac{147}{2.1}$　　　　　　$2.1 \cdot 70$

2　$t = 70$　　　　　　　　　　　$147$

## example 3

Solve and check: $1\frac{3}{4}w = 63$   Show all steps.

**Solution**

$$1\frac{3}{4}w = 63$$

1  $$\frac{1\frac{3}{4}w}{1\frac{3}{4}} = \frac{63}{1\frac{3}{4}}$$

2  $$w = \frac{\overset{9}{\cancel{63}}}{1} \cdot \frac{4}{\underset{1}{\cancel{7}}}$$

$$w = 36$$

**Check**

$$1\frac{3}{4}w = 63$$

$$1\frac{3}{4} \cdot 36$$

$$\frac{7}{4} \cdot 36$$

$$\frac{7}{\cancel{4}} \cdot \frac{\overset{9}{\cancel{36}}}{1}$$

$$63$$

## example 4

If some number is multiplied by 24, the product is 126. Find the unknown number.

1  Select a variable for the unknown number. ⟶ Let $x$ = the unknown number.

2  Write an equation for the problem. ⟶ $24x = 126$

3  Divide each side by 24. ⟶ $\dfrac{24x}{24} = \dfrac{126}{24}$

4  Simplify each side. ⟶ $x = 5\frac{6}{24}$ or $5\frac{1}{4}$

**The check is left for you.**

## ORAL EXERCISES 6.3

*Tell the simplest name.* (P-1)

1. $\dfrac{13x}{13}$

2. $\dfrac{27r}{27}$

3. $\dfrac{0.9t}{0.9}$

4. $\frac{1}{4} \cdot q \div \frac{1}{4}$

5. $\dfrac{128k}{128}$

6. $3\frac{1}{2}(y) \div 3\frac{1}{2}$

7. $\dfrac{35n}{n}$, $n \neq 0$

8. $\dfrac{42s}{s}$, $s \neq 0$

9. $\dfrac{x \cdot a}{a}$, $a \neq 0$

*Tell the equivalent equation you form as the first step in solving the equation.* (Step 1 of Example 1, Example 2, Example 3)

**EXAMPLE:** $12t = 36$  **ANSWER:** $\dfrac{12t}{12} = \dfrac{36}{12}$

**10.** $4n = 32$      **11.** $9x = 72$      **12.** $11y = 44$      **13.** $53t = 87$

**14.** $2.6a = 28$      **15.** $0.7w = 21$      **16.** $19.2x = 25.6$      **17.** $108b = 226$

*Decide whether the number shown is the truth number for the equation. Say <u>Yes</u> or <u>No</u>.* (Check of Example 2, Example 3)

**18.** $4x = 8$
$x = \frac{1}{2}$

**19.** $36x = 12$
$x = \frac{1}{3}$

**20.** $8x = 30$
$x = 3\frac{3}{4}$

**21.** $0.2x = 12.4$
$x = 6.2$

**22.** $3\frac{1}{2}x = 42$
$x = 12$

**23.** $\frac{3}{4}x = 8$
$x = 6$

## WRITTEN EXERCISES 6.3

**A**

**Goal:** To solve an equation using the Division Property of Equality
**Sample Problem:** $7x = 84$
**Answer:** 12

*Solve and check. Show all steps.* (Example 1, Example 2, Example 3)

**1.** $6x = 54$     **2.** $9x = 63$     **3.** $12n = 60$     **4.** $14w = 90$

**5.** $8y = 256$     **6.** $7a = 161$     **7.** $16q = 88$     **8.** $18t = 78$

**9.** $0.6r = 8.4$     **10.** $0.9n = 22.5$     **11.** $5.2k = 213.2$     **12.** $2.8m = 64.4$

**13.** $1.9x = 38$     **14.** $2.7y = 162$     **15.** $0.08t = 9.6$     **16.** $0.03p = 7.2$

**17.** $3\frac{1}{2}x = 84$     **18.** $5\frac{1}{4}y = 126$     **19.** $\frac{5}{8}x = 85$     **20.** $\frac{3}{4}r = 111$

**21.** $212y = 3074$     **22.** $164a = 2542$     **23.** $23.2p = 41.76$     **24.** $35.6m = 92.56$

*Write an equation for each problem. Then solve and check it.* (Example 4)

**25.** If a number is multiplied by 23, the product is 207. Find the unknown number.

**26.** If a number is multiplied by 39, the product is 429. Find the unknown number.

**27.** The product of an unknown number and 56 is 604.8. Find the unknown number.

**28.** The product of an unknown number and 72 is 691.2. Find the unknown number.

# 6.4    Multiplication Property of Equality

**P-1**   **What is the simplest name for each phrase?**

   **a.** $36 \div 12 \cdot 12$    **b.** $\dfrac{25}{13} \cdot 13$    **c.** $\dfrac{n}{22} \cdot 22$

The following steps show the operations performed in P-1.

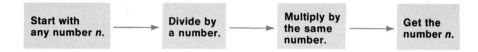

| Start with any number $n$. | → | Divide by a number. | → | Multiply by the same number. | → | Get the number $n$. |

This illustrates that multiplication is the inverse operation of division.

## example 1    Solve: $\dfrac{x}{15} = 9$  Show all steps.

1  Multiply each side by 15. ⟶ $\dfrac{x}{15} \cdot 15 = 9 \cdot 15$

2  Simplify each side. ⟶ $x = 135$

**P-2**   **If x is replaced by 135, which of these equations are true?**

   **a.** $\dfrac{x}{15} = 9$    **b.** $\dfrac{x}{15} \cdot 15 = 9 \cdot 15$    **c.** $x = 135$

> **Multiplication Property of Equality**
>
> Multiplying each side of an equation by the same nonzero number forms an equivalent equation.
>
> $\dfrac{x}{15} = 9$
>
> $\dfrac{x}{15} \cdot 15 = 9 \cdot 15$
>
> $x = 135$

## example 2    Solve and check: $\dfrac{y}{2.6} = 10$  Show all steps.

**Solution:** $\dfrac{y}{2.6} = 10$      **Check:** $\dfrac{y}{2.6} = 10$

1      $\dfrac{y}{2.6}(2.6) = 10(2.6)$      $\dfrac{26}{2.6}$

2      $y = 26$      $10$

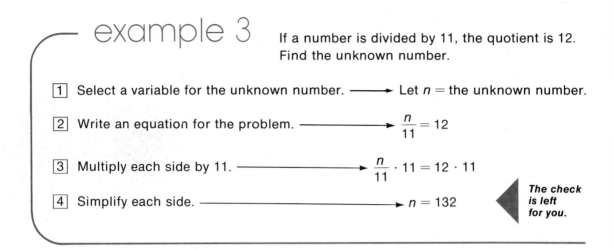

example 3    If a number is divided by 11, the quotient is 12.
Find the unknown number.

1  Select a variable for the unknown number. ──────➤ Let $n$ = the unknown number.

2  Write an equation for the problem. ──────➤ $\dfrac{n}{11} = 12$

3  Multiply each side by 11. ──────➤ $\dfrac{n}{11} \cdot 11 = 12 \cdot 11$

4  Simplify each side. ──────➤ $n = 132$

The check is left for you.

**P-3**    **What equivalent equation would you write next in solving each equation?**

**a.** $t + 26 = 42$      **b.** $s - 19 = 47$      **c.** $39k = 136$      **d.** $\dfrac{a}{116} = 23$

## ORAL EXERCISES 6.4

*Tell the simplest name.* (P-1)

**1.** $a \div 19 \cdot 19$          **2.** $q \div 43 \cdot 43$          **3.** $\dfrac{s}{89} \cdot 89$          **4.** $22 \cdot \dfrac{x}{22}$

**5.** $112 \cdot \dfrac{b}{112}$          **6.** $\dfrac{r}{9.3}(9.3)$          **7.** $\dfrac{16p}{11} \cdot 11$          **8.** $\dfrac{12h}{12}$

*Tell the equivalent equation you form as the first step in solving each equation.* (Step 1 of Example 1, Example 2)

**9.** $\dfrac{x}{15} = 13$          **10.** $\dfrac{s}{23} = 7$          **11.** $\dfrac{y}{1.8} = 12$          **12.** $\dfrac{w}{14} = 19$

**13.** $\dfrac{t}{3\frac{1}{2}} = 8$          **14.** $\dfrac{a}{\frac{1}{4}} = 36$          **15.** $\dfrac{5r}{19} = 12$          **16.** $\dfrac{4x}{135} = 43$

*Tell the equivalent equation you form as the first step in solving each equation.* (Example 1 of Section 6.1, Section 6.2, Section 6.3, Section 6.4)

**17.** $x + 102 = 193$          **18.** $y - 31 = 29$          **19.** $83t = 317$          **20.** $a - 15.9 = 20.8$

**21.** $w + 5\frac{3}{4} = 13\frac{1}{4}$          **22.** $0.9q = 14.3$          **23.** $\dfrac{s}{61} = 28$          **24.** $n - 253 = 86$

## WRITTEN EXERCISES 6.4

**A** **Goal:** To solve an equation using the Multiplication Property of Equality

**Sample Problem:** $\dfrac{w}{15} = 42$    **Answer:** 630

*Solve and check. Show all steps. (Example 1, Example 2)*

**1.** $\dfrac{t}{8} = 17$

**2.** $\dfrac{r}{12} = 9$

**3.** $\dfrac{x}{23} = 12$

**4.** $\dfrac{y}{34} = 15$

**5.** $\dfrac{a}{1.8} = 70$

**6.** $\dfrac{n}{2.3} = 90$

**7.** $\dfrac{x}{10\frac{1}{2}} = 27$

**8.** $\dfrac{k}{6\frac{1}{4}} = 18$

*Write an equation for each problem. Then solve and check it. (Example 3)*

**9.** If a number is divided by 28, the quotient is 17. Find the unknown number.

**10.** If a number is divided by 19, the quotient is 36. Find the unknown number.

**11.** The quotient of a number divided by 6 is 16. Find the unknown number.

**12.** The quotient of a number divided by 3.2 is 15. Find the unknown number.

*Write the equivalent equation you form as the first step in solving each equation. (Example 1 of Section 6.1, Section 6.2, Section 6.3, Section 6.4)*

**13.** $x - 140 = 68$

**14.** $y - 49 = 83$

**15.** $16s = 112$

**16.** $2.1t = 16.8$

**17.** $y + 74 = 78$

**18.** $w + 10.3 = 19.7$

**19.** $\dfrac{n}{34} = 18$

**20.** $\dfrac{g}{3.9} = 8$

**B** *Solve and check. Show all steps.*

**EXAMPLE:** $\dfrac{3x}{5} = 12$    **SOLUTION:** $\dfrac{3x}{5} = 12$

$$5 \cdot \dfrac{3x}{5} = 5 \cdot 12$$

$$3x = 60$$

$$\dfrac{3x}{3} = \dfrac{60}{3}$$

$$x = 20$$

**21.** $\dfrac{3x}{5} = 24$

**22.** $\dfrac{2x}{7} = 30$

**23.** $\dfrac{8x}{13} = 7$

**24.** $\dfrac{12x}{9} = 14$

**25.** $\dfrac{24b}{25} = 12$

**26.** $\dfrac{18t}{23} = 9$

**27.** $\dfrac{2.5r}{12} = 35$

**28.** $\dfrac{3.2s}{13} = 48$

# 6.5 Equations with More Than One Operation

P-1 **What is the missing instruction in the steps below?**

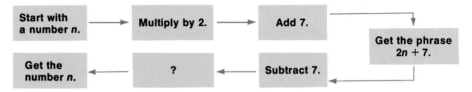

The inverse of "Multiply by 2" is "Divide by 2"—the missing instruction. Also, note that "Subtract 7" is the inverse of "Add 7."

P-2 **What is the missing instruction in step A below?   in step B?**

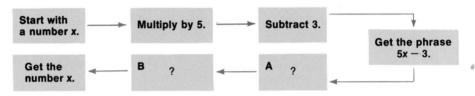

P-3 **What is the missing instruction in the steps below?**

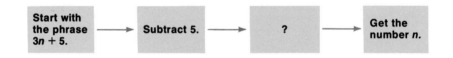

## example 1

Solve and check: $3n + 5 = 26$   Show all steps.

Note: In solving an equation, addition and subtraction are done before multiplication and division.

$$3n + 5 = 26$$

**Check:** $3n + 5 = 26$

1. Subtract 5 from each side. ⟶ $3n + 5 - 5 = 26 - 5$      $3(7) + 5$

2. Simplify each side. ⟶ $3n = 21$      $21 + 5$

3. Divide each side by 3. ⟶ $\dfrac{3n}{3} = \dfrac{21}{3}$      $26$

4. Simplify each side. ⟶ $n = 7$

**P-4** **What is the missing instruction in step A below? in step B?**

Start with the phrase $4x - 10$. → **A** ? → **B** ? → Get the number $x$.

**P-5** **To solve $4x - 10 = 14$, what operation do you perform first?**

example 2  Solve and check: $4x - 10 = 14$  Show all steps.

| Solution | Check |
|---|---|
| $4x - 10 = 14$ | $4x - 10 = 14$ |
| ① $4x - 10 + 10 = 14 + 10$ | $4(6) - 10$ |
| ② $4x = 24$ | $24 - 10$ |
| ③ $\dfrac{4x}{4} = \dfrac{24}{4}$ | $14$ |
| ④ $x = 6$ | |

**P-6** **To solve $\dfrac{x}{5} + 7 = 18$, what operation do you perform first?**

example 3  Solve and check: $\dfrac{x}{5} + 7 = 18$  Show all steps.

**Solution**

$\dfrac{x}{5} + 7 = 18$

① Subtract 7 from each side. ⟶ $\dfrac{x}{5} + 7 - 7 = 18 - 7$

② Simplify each side. ⟶ $\dfrac{x}{5} = 11$

③ Multiply each side by 5. ⟶ $5 \cdot \dfrac{x}{5} = 5 \cdot 11$

④ Simplify each side. ⟶ $x = 55$

**Check**

$\dfrac{x}{5} + 7 = 18$

$\dfrac{55}{5} + 7$

$11 + 7$

$18$

## example 4

A number is multiplied by 3. Then 4 is subtracted from the product. The result is 17. Find the unknown number.

Let $n$ = the unknown number.

| Solution | Check |
|---|---|
| $3n - 4 = 17$ | $3n - 21 = 17$ |
| $3n - 4 + 4 = 17 + 4$ | $3 \cdot 7 - 4$ |
| $3n = 21$ | $21 - 4$ |
| $n = 7$ | $17$ |

## ORAL EXERCISES 6.5

Tell an equivalent equation that you form as the first step in solving the equation. (Example 2 of Section 6.1, Section 6.2, Section 6.3, Section 6.4)

**1.** $x + 56 = 91$     **2.** $x - 28 = 32$     **3.** $x - 12.7 = 8.9$

**4.** $x + 3\frac{1}{4} = 5\frac{1}{2}$     **5.** $12x = 256$     **6.** $1.08x = 12.32$

**7.** $\dfrac{x}{19} = 56$     **8.** $\dfrac{x}{0.9} = 1.3$     **9.** $21 + x = 92$

Tell an equivalent equation that you form as the first step in solving the equation. (Step 1 of Example 1, Example 2, Example 3)

**10.** $4n - 1 = 5$     **11.** $9y + 3 = 16$     **12.** $12s - 5 = 13$

**13.** $11w + 8 = 25$     **14.** $8a + 5.6 = 21.8$     **15.** $13x - 6.9 = 47.1$

**16.** $3b - 2\frac{1}{2} = 19$     **17.** $5p + 6\frac{1}{4} = 12\frac{3}{4}$     **18.** $0.7x + 0.9 = 3.1$

**19.** $22.3y - 19.5 = 3.6$     **20.** $\dfrac{x}{5} - 2 = 13$     **21.** $\dfrac{q}{12} + 7 = 19$

Decide whether the number shown is the truth number for the equation. Say <u>Yes</u> or <u>No</u>. (Check of Example 1, Example 2, Example 3)

**22.** $3x + 4 = 22$     **23.** $5x - 2 = 12$     **24.** $\dfrac{x}{3} - 5 = 8$     **25.** $\dfrac{x}{2} + 14 = 26$

        $x = 6$             $x = 2$            $x = 3$           $x = 24$

## WRITTEN EXERCISES 6.5

**A** **Goal:** To solve an equation with more than one operation
**Sample Problem:** $3x - 6 = 18$
**Answer:** 8

*Solve and check. Show all steps.* (Example 2 of Section 6.1, Section 6.2, Section 6.3, Section 6.4)

**1.** $x + 39 = 53$

**2.** $x + 26 = 85$

**3.** $x - 17 = 39$

**4.** $x - 28 = 47$

**5.** $9x = 252$

**6.** $12x = 192$

**7.** $\dfrac{x}{15} = 11$

**8.** $\dfrac{x}{14} = 23$

*Solve and check. Show all steps.* (Example 1, Example 2, Example 3)

**9.** $4x + 7 = 39$

**10.** $2x + 13 = 37$

**11.** $5x - 19 = 51$

**12.** $6x - 9 = 87$

**13.** $12x + 37 = 139$

**14.** $8x + 27 = 143$

**15.** $\dfrac{x}{5} - 8 = 13$

**16.** $\dfrac{x}{4} - 11 = 12$

**17.** $\dfrac{x}{12} + 5 = 23$

**18.** $\dfrac{x}{9} + 13 = 32$

**19.** $\dfrac{x}{8} + 12.7 = 24.9$

**20.** $\dfrac{x}{6} + 16.9 = 30.3$

**21.** $2.3x - 18.2 = 9.4$

**22.** $4.8x - 19.7 = 61.9$

**23.** $12 + 15x = 147$

**24.** $33 + 12x = 201$

**25.** $20x - 4.5 = 73.5$

**26.** $60x - 38.5 = 339.5$

*Write an equation for each problem. Then solve and check it.* (Example 4)

**27.** A number is multiplied by 2. Then 17 is subtracted from the product. The result is 67. Find the unknown number.

**28.** A number is multiplied by 12. Then 30 is added to the product. The result is 258. Find the unknown number.

**29.** A number is divided by 8. Then $13\frac{1}{2}$ is added to the quotient. The result is 19. Find the unknown number.

**30.** A number is divided by 6. Then $19\frac{1}{2}$ is subtracted from the quotient. The result is 4. Find the unknown number.

**B** *Solve and check the equation.*

**31.** $\dfrac{3x}{4} + 14 = 26$

**32.** $\dfrac{4x}{3} + 26 = 34$

**33.** $\dfrac{12x}{5} - 13 = 35$

**34.** $\dfrac{5x}{18} - 11 = 19$

**35.** $32 + \dfrac{3x}{24} = 34$

**36.** $39 + \dfrac{10x}{25} = 53$

# 6.6 More Equations

P-1 **What is the simplest name of each phrase?**

**a.** $3x + 2x + 5$    **b.** $5a + 4 + a$    **c.** $2x + 4x - 5$

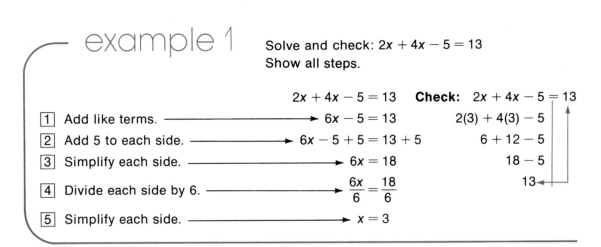

## example 1

Solve and check: $2x + 4x - 5 = 13$
Show all steps.

$$2x + 4x - 5 = 13 \qquad \textbf{Check:} \quad 2x + 4x - 5 = 13$$

1. Add like terms. ⟶ $6x - 5 = 13$     $2(3) + 4(3) - 5$
2. Add 5 to each side. ⟶ $6x - 5 + 5 = 13 + 5$     $6 + 12 - 5$
3. Simplify each side. ⟶ $6x = 18$     $18 - 5$
4. Divide each side by 6. ⟶ $\dfrac{6x}{6} = \dfrac{18}{6}$     $13$
5. Simplify each side. ⟶ $x = 3$

P-2 **How can you write each phrase as a sum or difference using a Distributive Property?**

**a.** $2(x + 5)$    **b.** $3(a - 7)$    **c.** $4(3t + 7)$    **d.** $5(2k - 9)$

In some equations you have to apply the Distributive Property first. You then add or subtract.

## example 2

Solve and check: $3(4x - 2) = 54$   Show all steps.

$$3(4x - 2) = 54 \qquad \textbf{Check:} \quad 3(4x - 2) = 54$$

1. Use a Distributive Property. ⟶ $12x - 6 = 54$     $3(4 \cdot 5 - 2)$
2. Add 6 to each side. ⟶ $12x - 6 + 6 = 54 + 6$     $3(20 - 2)$
3. Simplify. ⟶ $12x = 60$     $3(18)$
4. Divide each side by 12. ⟶ $\dfrac{12x}{12} = \dfrac{60}{12}$     $54$
5. Simplify. ⟶ $x = 5$

**P-3**   **How can you write 2(3a + 7) as a sum?**

example 3   Solve: 2(3a + 7) + a = 70   Show all steps.

$$2(3a + 7) + a = 70$$

1. Distributive Property ⟶ $6a + 14 + a = 70$
2. Add like terms. ⟶ $7a + 14 = 70$
3. Subtraction Property of Equality ⟶ $7a + 14 - 14 = 70 - 14$
4. Simplify each side. ⟶ $7a = 56$
5. Division Property of Equality ⟶ $\dfrac{7a}{7} = \dfrac{56}{7}$
6. Simplify each side. ⟶ $a = 8$

example 4   In the rectangle at the right the perimeter is 26 centimeters. Find the length and width.

x cm

(x + 3) cm

Write an equation based on the formula for the perimeter of a rectangle.

$$2l + 2w = p$$
$$2(x + 3) + 2x = 26$$
$$2x + 6 + 2x = 26$$
$$4x + 6 = 26$$
$$4x + 6 - 6 = 26 - 6$$
$$4x = 20$$
$$\frac{4x}{4} = \frac{20}{4}$$
$$x = 5$$
$$x + 3 = 8$$

◀ **The width is 5 centimeters. The length is 8 centimeters.**

## ORAL EXERCISES 6.6

*Tell the simplest name.* (P-1)

1. $12r + 8r + 3$

2. $7t + 9t - 5$

3. $10b - 7b + 6$

4. $6w + 8 + w$

5. $5s + 12 - s$

6. $3x + x + 5x$

7. $n + n + n + n$

8. $2.5p + 3.5 + 1.5p$

9. $4k - 10 + 3k$

10. $3q + 1 + 5q + 2q + 3$

*Tell the simplest name as a sum or difference.* (P-2)

11. $7(m + 2)$
    *7m + 14.*

12. $12(y - 3)$

13. $4(2t + 3)$

14. $5(4n - 9)$
    *2on - 45*

15. $(12w + 5)3$

16. $0.5(8a + 6)$

17. $\frac{1}{4}(3s - 8)$

18. $12(\frac{3}{4}r - \frac{1}{2})$

*Tell the equivalent equation you form as the first step in solving each equation.* (Example 1, Example 2, Example 3)

19. $5(x + 7) = 14$
    *5x + 35*

20. $4x + 13x + 7 = 92$

21. $2(x - 3) + x = 9$

22. $3(2x + 7) + 3x = 12$

23. $4(5x - 1) - 3x = 19$

24. $3a + 9 + 4a + 2 = 27$

25. $7x + 3(x - 5) = 42$

26. $5 + 4(4x + 2) = 87$

27. $2(x + 1) + 3(x + 5) = 17$

28. $3x + 2(3x - 5) + 4x = 126$

*5 + 16x + 8 = 87*
*16x = 87 - 13*
*16x = 74 ÷ 16*
*16 x = 4.6*

## WRITTEN EXERCISES 6.6

Ⓐ **Goal:** To solve an equation that has parentheses and like terms
**Sample Problem:** $3(x + 7) + 5x = 37$
**Answer:** 2

*Solve and check. Show all steps.* (Example 1, Example 2, Example 3)

1. $3x + 2x + 4 = 39$

2. $4x + 3x + 5 = 47$

3. $x + 5x - 8 = 46$

4. $3x + x - 12 = 56$

5. $5x - 3x + 13 = 67$

6. $8x - 5x + 20 = 59$

**7.** $10x + 8 - 7x = 23$

**8.** $6x + 12 - 3x = 51$

**9.** $3(x - 8) = 15$

**10.** $4(x - 12) = 8$

**11.** $2(3x + 4) = 35$

**12.** $3(4x + 5) = 54$

**13.** $6(x - 3) + 2x = 38$

**14.** $8(x - 2) + 3x = 61$

**15.** $\frac{1}{2}(4x + 6) - x = 57$

**16.** $\frac{1}{2}(6x + 2) - 2x = 82$

**17.** $3x + 2(x - 5) = 35$

**18.** $5x + 3(x - 4) = 60$

**19.** $4x + 3(4x + 3) = 61$

**20.** $4x + 2(8x - 3) = 95$

**21.** $2(x + 1) + 3(x + 4) = 49$

**22.** $4(x + 2) + 3(x + 3) = 73$

**23.** $3x + 3(4x + 3) + x = 152$

**24.** $x + 4(2x + 3) + 3x = 99$

*Write an equation based on the perimeter formula that is given. Then solve the equation. Write the length of each side.* (Example 4)

**25.** $p = 4s$
Perimeter: 51.6 cm

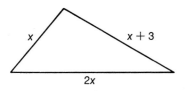

**26.** $p = s + s + s$
Perimeter: 94.2 cm

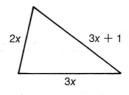

**27.** $p = a + b + c$
Perimeter: 23.8 cm

**28.** $p = a + b + c$
Perimeter: 35.4 m

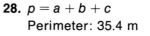

**29.** $p = 2l + 2w$
Perimeter: 90 mm

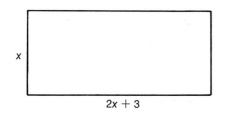

**30.** $p = 2l + 2w$
Perimeter: 106 cm

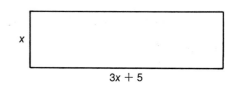

# Optician

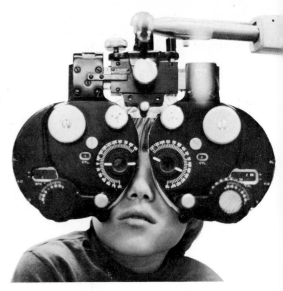

Dispensing opticians assist customers in selecting eyeglass frames and in adjusting the fit of their eyeglasses. Optical mechanics grind and polish lenses according to prescriptions.

Many community colleges now provide a two-year curriculum for opticians leading to an associate degree. Several vocational schools offer one-year courses for optical mechanics. Many persons learn the trade through a formal apprenticeship program that lasts three to four years depending on the ability of the trainee.

Anyone who wants to become an optician should plan to earn a high school diploma with courses in algebra, geometry, physics, and mechanical drawing. Dispensing opticians must meet the public, so a neat appearance and a pleasant personality are important.

All measurements in the optical industry are made in metric units. One important unit of measure that opticians must know is the _diopter._ A lens having one diopter of power will bring parallel rays of light to a focus at a distance of one meter. The formula below relates the power of a lens in diopters ($D$) and its focal length ($f$) in meters.

$$D = \frac{1}{f}$$

**EXAMPLE:** Find the focal length of a 4.00 $D$ lens.

**SOLUTION:**

$$D = \frac{1}{f}$$

$$4.00 = \frac{1}{f}$$

$$4.00f = 1$$

$$f = \frac{1}{4.00}$$

$$f = 0.25 \text{ meter or 25 centimeters}$$

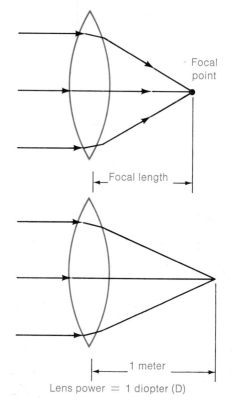

Lens power = 1 diopter (D)

*Opticians must have a knowledge of the geometric properties of lenses. The focal distance of a lens is the distance between the focal point and the center of the lens.*

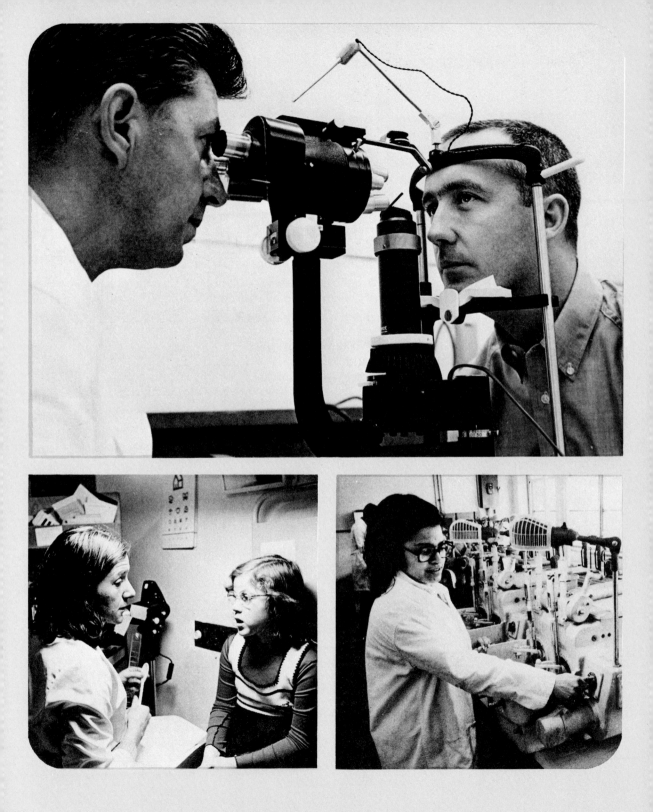

# CHAPTER SUMMARY

# CHAPTER REVIEW

### SECTION 6.1

*Solve and check. Show all steps.*

**1.** $r + 28 = 73$

**2.** $a + 35 = 102$

**3.** $y + 19.3 = 32.1$

**4.** $t + 43.9 = 60.2$

**5.** $x + 13\frac{1}{2} = 24\frac{1}{4}$

**6.** $n + 27\frac{3}{4} = 42\frac{1}{2}$

*Write an equation for each problem. Then solve and check it.*

**7.** The sum of an unknown number and 96 is 123. Find the unknown number.

**8.** If 46.0 is added to an unknown number, the sum is 92.4. Find the unknown number.

**SECTION 6.2**

*Solve and check. Show all steps.*

9. $a - 59 = 23$

10. $w - 109 = 58$

11. $k - 37.8 = 58.6$

12. $b - 23.4 = 47.8$

13. $m - 25\frac{1}{4} = 36\frac{1}{8}$

14. $t - 16\frac{3}{4} = 23\frac{7}{8}$

*Write an equation for each problem. Then solve and check it.*

15. If 14.9 is subtracted from an unknown number, the difference is 29.7. Find the unknown number.

16. The difference of an unknown number less 68 is 119. Find the unknown number.

**SECTION 6.3**

*Solve and check. Show all steps.*

17. $14x = 126$

18. $22y = 132$

19. $0.8a = 344$

20. $2.9n = 136$

21. $1\frac{3}{4}t = 98$

22. $5\frac{1}{2}w = 374$

*Write an equation for each problem. Then solve and check it.*

23. The product of an unknown number and 29 is 406. Find the unknown number.

24. If a number is multiplied by 23.8, the product is 2856. Find the unknown number.

**SECTION 6.4**

*Solve and check. Show all steps.*

25. $\frac{x}{7} = 19$

26. $\frac{a}{24} = 13$

27. $\frac{r}{11.3} = 27$

28. $\frac{n}{9.7} = 35$

29. $\frac{t}{18} = 12\frac{1}{2}$

30. $\frac{b}{24} = 15\frac{1}{4}$

*Write an equation for each problem. Then solve and check it.*

31. If a number is divided by 37, the quotient is 52. Find the unknown number.

32. The quotient of a number divided by 16.3 is 42. Find the unknown number.

## SECTION 6.5

*Solve and check. Show all the steps.*

**33.** $3x + 8 = 65$

**34.** $7r + 24 = 185$

**35.** $5.3w - 23 = 189$

**36.** $3.6t - 19.8 = 27$

**37.** $\dfrac{a}{14} - 28 = 9$

**38.** $\dfrac{n}{9} + 43 = 62$

*Write an equation for each problem. Then solve and check it.*

**39.** A number is divided by 29, and 15 is subtracted from the quotient. The result is 13. Find the unknown number.

**40.** A number is multiplied by 14 and 18.2 is added to the product. The result is 312.2. Find the unknown number.

## SECTION 6.6

*Solve and check. Show all steps.*

**41.** $4x + x + 3 = 38$

**42.** $8a + 12 - 5a = 51$

**43.** $4(2r + 1) - 4r = 25$

**44.** $t + 3(2t - 5) = 97$

**45.** $2(b + 3) + 4(2b + 5) = 182$

**46.** $5n + 4(3n + 2) - n = 120$

*Write an equation based on the perimeter formula that is given. Then solve the equation. Write the length of each side.*

**47.** $p = a + b + c$
Perimeter: 81 cm

**48.** $p = 2l + 2w$
Perimeter: 112 m

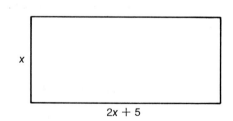

**134** / *Chapter 6*

## REVIEW EXERCISES FOR CHAPTERS 1–6

*Write the length of each block to the nearest millimeter. (Section 1.1)*

1.

2.

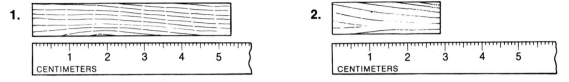

*Write each missing numeral. (Section 1.2)*

**3.** 4.8 m = __?__ mm  **4.** 0.28 km = __?__ m  **5.** 28.3 dm = __?__ m  **6.** 6.72 mm = __?__ cm

*Replace the variable by 4. Then simplify. (Section 1.3)*

**7.** $5t - 16$     **8.** $28 - 3y$     **9.** $12 + 7n - 18$     **10.** $49 + 48 \div r \cdot 3$

*Write each missing numeral. (Section 1.4)*

**11.** 28.3 dm² = __?__ cm²     **12.** 0.509 cm² = __?__ mm²

*Use the formula $A = \frac{1}{2}bh$ to find the area of each triangle. (Section 1.5)*

**13.** $b = 15$ mm; $h = 12$ mm     **14.** $b = 23$ m; $h = 14$ m

*Write a number that will make each equation true. (Section 2.1)*

**15.** $x + 5\frac{1}{2} = 5\frac{1}{2}$     **16.** $n + 0 = 2.7$     **17.** $t(\frac{6}{6}) = 18$     **18.** $\frac{4.5}{4.5}(y) = 19.6$

*Multiply. (Section 2.2)*

**19.** $12(4t)$     **20.** $0.8(7w)$     **21.** $(11r)(12s)$     **22.** $(12k)(15n)$

*Write each product as a sum in simplest form. (Section 2.3)*

**23.** $9(3r + 4)$     **24.** $(5w + 3)12$     **25.** $(6p + 5)(2p)$     **26.** $3t(11t + 4)$

*Write each sum or difference as a product. (Section 2.4)*

**27.** $12r + 12s$     **28.** $42m + 42n$     **29.** $3t^2 - 6t$     **30.** $4h^2 - 8h$

*Add or subtract like terms. (Section 2.5)*

**31.** $15t + 12t$     **32.** $24y - 9y$     **33.** $12.3n - 5.9n$     **34.** $22.5p - 14.8p$

*Add like terms. (Section 2.6)*

**35.** $33r + 17r + 51r$     **36.** $26q + 35q + 13q$

*Write the set of counting-number factors of each number.* (Section 3.1)

**37.** 22          **38.** 28          **39.** 45          **40.** 56          **41.** 47          **42.** 43

*Write True or False for each sentence.* (Section 3.1)

**43.** 91 is a multiple of 3.                    **44.** 54 is divisible by 9.

*Write True or False for each sentence. Then write a reason based on the rules on page 45.* (Section 3.2)

**45.** 5 is a factor of 527.                    **46.** 12,034 is divisible by 4.

*Write each number as a product of two prime factors.* (Section 3.3)

**47.** 86          **48.** 123          **49.** 85          **50.** 62

*Use exponents to rewrite each product.* (Section 3.3)

**51.** $2 \cdot 7 \cdot 5 \cdot 2 \cdot 3 \cdot 2 \cdot 3$                    **52.** $5 \cdot 3 \cdot 11 \cdot 2 \cdot 3 \cdot 11 \cdot 5$

*Write the prime factorization of each number.* (Section 3.4)

**53.** 34          **54.** 57          **55.** 90          **56.** 112

*The prime factorizations of two numbers are given in each exercise. Write the prime factorization of their least common multiple.* (Section 3.5)

**57.** $2 \cdot 3^2 \cdot 5 \quad 2^3 \cdot 3 \cdot 7$                    **58.** $2^2 \cdot 3 \cdot 5^3 \quad 2 \cdot 3^3 \cdot 5 \cdot 11$

*Write the least common multiple of the given numbers.* (Section 3.5)

**59.** 10 and 60          **60.** 9 and 45          **61.** 6 and 20          **62.** 28 and 21

*Simplify each fraction.* (Section 4.1)

**63.** $\dfrac{4}{18}$          **64.** $\dfrac{6}{21}$          **65.** $\dfrac{9}{33}$          **66.** $\dfrac{8}{44}$

*Simplify each fraction.* (Section 4.2)

**67.** $\dfrac{10t}{26t}$          **68.** $\dfrac{9r}{33r}$          **69.** $\dfrac{14a^2b}{35ab^3}$          **70.** $\dfrac{12rs}{66rs^2}$

*Multiply. Simplify where necessary.* (Section 4.3)

**71.** $\dfrac{3t}{4} \cdot \dfrac{8}{9t}$          **72.** $\dfrac{25r}{6} \cdot \dfrac{3}{5r}$          **73.** $\dfrac{7ab}{12} \cdot \dfrac{9}{14a^2}$          **74.** $\dfrac{6r^2s}{7} \cdot \dfrac{28}{9rs^2}$

*Divide. Simplify where necessary. (Section 4.4)*

**75.** $\dfrac{5}{4} \div \dfrac{25}{8}$

**76.** $\dfrac{7}{3} \div \dfrac{14}{9}$

**77.** $\dfrac{m}{2p} \div \dfrac{n}{6p}$

**78.** $\dfrac{6a^2}{b^3} \div \dfrac{21a}{b}$

*Add or subtract. (Section 4.5)*

**79.** $\dfrac{t}{11} + \dfrac{3t}{11}$

**80.** $\dfrac{5n}{17} + \dfrac{n}{17}$

**81.** $\dfrac{13r}{3w} - \dfrac{11r}{3w}$

**82.** $\dfrac{16k}{17y} - \dfrac{k}{17y}$

*Simplify each sum or difference. (Section 4.6)*

**83.** $\dfrac{5}{6} + \dfrac{1}{12}$

**84.** $\dfrac{5}{8} + \dfrac{5}{12}$

**85.** $\dfrac{3}{2x} - \dfrac{1}{6x}$

**86.** $\dfrac{5}{12y} - \dfrac{7}{18y}$

*Name each set using the roster form. (Section 5.1)*

**87.** {prime factors of 42}

**88.** {counting-number factors of 15}

*Graph each set. (Section 5.1)*

**89.** {2, 4, 6}

**90.** $\{0, 2\frac{1}{2}, 3.8, 4\frac{1}{4}\}$

**91.** $\{\frac{3}{4}, \frac{7}{4}, \frac{9}{4}, \frac{14}{4}\}$

**92.** $\{0, \frac{3}{2}, \frac{5}{4}, \frac{19}{8}\}$

*Replace ○ with >, <, or = to make a true statement. (Section 5.2)*

**93.** $4 \cdot 3 + 11 \cdot 3 \bigcirc (4 + 11)3$

**94.** $\frac{5}{3} \bigcirc 1.666$

*Write the truth set of each open sentence. Use {0, 1, 2, 3, 4, 5} as the domain. (Section 5.3)*

**95.** $r(r + 2) < 16$

**96.** $3x + 1 > 2x + 3$

*Graph the truth set of each inequality. The domain is {numbers of arithmetic}. (Section 5.4)*

**97.** $t > 4\frac{1}{2}$

**98.** $n \neq 3.6$

**99.** $r < 5$

**100.** $y > 2.3$

*Draw a graph of the truth set of each compound sentence. The domain is {numbers of arithmetic}. (Section 5.5)*

**101.** $x < 2.3$ *or* $x > 4.8$

**102.** $x > 6.5$ *or* $x < 3.5$

*Draw a graph of the truth set of each compound sentence. The domain is {numbers of arithmetic}. (Section 5.6)*

**103.** $x > 5$ *and* $x > 1$

**104.** $x > 4.2$ *and* $x < 6.5$

*Write the truth set. Use {21, 23, 25, 27, · · ·} as the domain. (Section 5.7)*

**105.** $x \le 45$ **106.** $x + 4 \ge 33$ **107.** $3x \ge 66$ **108.** $3x + 5 \le 107$

*Solve and check. Show all steps. (Section 6.1)*

**109.** $x + 0.26 = 2.09$ **110.** $x + 27.8 = 40.1$

*Solve and check. Show all steps. (Section 6.2)*

**111.** $x - 3.08 = 7.24$ **112.** $x - 0.27 = 0.09$

*Solve and check. Show all steps. (Section 6.3)*

**113.** $3.4x = 612$ **114.** $5.8x = 1798$

*Solve and check. Show all steps. (Section 6.4)*

**115.** $\dfrac{x}{17} = 23$ **116.** $\dfrac{x}{21} = 20$

*Solve and check. Show all steps. (Section 6.5)*

**117.** $5x + 18 = 83$ **118.** $12x - 15 = 243$

*Write an equation for each problem. Then solve and check it. (Section 6.5)*

**119.** A number is multiplied by 3 and 13.8 is added to the product. The result is 27.9. Find the unknown number.

**120.** A number is divided by 1.8 and 24.6 is subtracted from the quotient. The result is 18.3. Find the unknown number.

*Solve and check. Show all steps. (Section 6.6)*

**121.** $4(x - 3) = 58$ **122.** $3(2x + 5) = 111$

*Write an equation based on the perimeter formula that is given. Then solve the equation. Write the length of each side. (Section 6.6)*

**123.** $p = a + b + c$
Perimeter: 28 cm

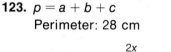
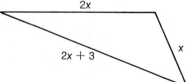

**124.** $p = 2l + 2w$
Perimeter: 22 mm

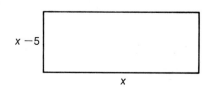

# 7

# Ratio, Proportion, and Per Cent

# 7.1 Ratio

For the rectangle in Figure 1, the <u>ratio</u> of the width to the length is 2 to 7.

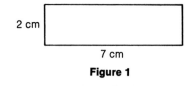

2 cm

7 cm

**Figure 1**

> A **ratio** is a quotient that compares two numbers.

**P-1** **For the rectangle in Figure 1, what is the ratio of the length to the width?**

The ratio 2 to 7 can be written 2 : 7.

**P-2** **How can you write the ratio 7 to 2?**

Notice that the ratios 2 : 7 and 7 : 2 are not the same.

**P-3** **What is the ratio of the number of uneaten pieces of pizza to the number of missing pieces in Figure 2?**

**P-4** **What ratio compares the number of uneaten pieces to the original number of pieces in the whole pizza?**

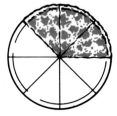

**Figure 2**

Another way to write 3 : 5 is $\frac{3}{5}$. Similarly, 3 : 8 can be written $\frac{3}{8}$.

In $a : b$ or $\frac{a}{b}$, $a$ is the **first term** and $b$ is the **second term.**

## example 1

Write the simplest name of the ratio 8 to 12.

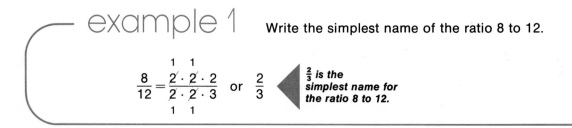

$$\frac{8}{12} = \frac{\overset{1}{\cancel{2}} \cdot \overset{1}{\cancel{2}} \cdot 2}{\underset{1}{\cancel{2}} \cdot \underset{1}{\cancel{2}} \cdot 3} \quad \text{or} \quad \frac{2}{3}$$

$\frac{2}{3}$ is the **simplest name for the ratio 8 to 12.**

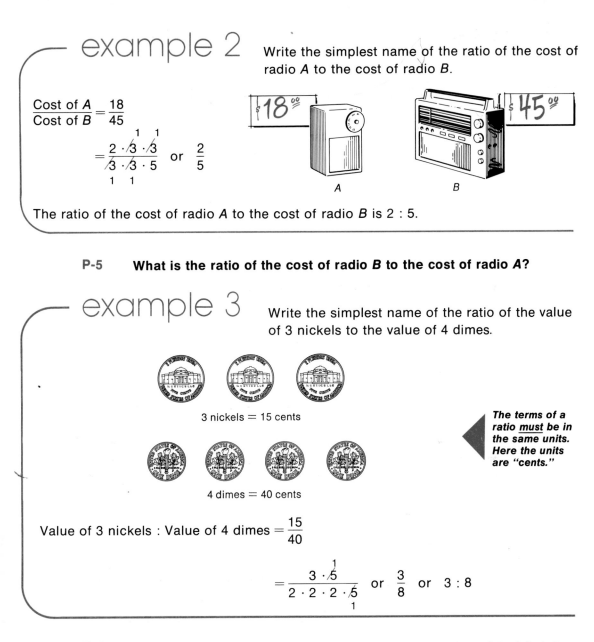

## example 2

Write the simplest name of the ratio of the cost of radio *A* to the cost of radio *B*.

$$\frac{\text{Cost of } A}{\text{Cost of } B} = \frac{18}{45}$$

$$= \frac{2 \cdot \cancel{3} \cdot \cancel{3}}{\cancel{3} \cdot \cancel{3} \cdot 5} \quad \text{or} \quad \frac{2}{5}$$

The ratio of the cost of radio *A* to the cost of radio *B* is 2 : 5.

**P-5**  **What is the ratio of the cost of radio *B* to the cost of radio *A*?**

## example 3

Write the simplest name of the ratio of the value of 3 nickels to the value of 4 dimes.

3 nickels = 15 cents

4 dimes = 40 cents

*The terms of a ratio **must** be in the same units. Here the units are "cents."*

$$\text{Value of 3 nickels : Value of 4 dimes} = \frac{15}{40}$$

$$= \frac{3 \cdot \cancel{5}}{2 \cdot 2 \cdot 2 \cdot \cancel{5}} \quad \text{or} \quad \frac{3}{8} \quad \text{or} \quad 3 : 8$$

**P-6**  **What is the ratio of the value of 7 dimes to the value of 5 nickels?**

**P-7**  **In the ratio $\dfrac{7}{x}$, what number cannot replace *x*?**

The second term of a ratio cannot be zero.

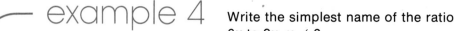

example 4    Write the simplest name of the ratio
6x to 9x, x ≠ 0.

$$\frac{6x}{9x} = \frac{2 \cdot \overset{1}{\cancel{3}} \cdot \overset{1}{\cancel{x}}}{3 \cdot \underset{1}{\cancel{3}} \cdot \underset{1}{\cancel{x}}} \quad \text{or} \quad \frac{2}{3}$$

## ORAL EXERCISES 7.1

*Say each ratio.*

**1.** $\frac{3}{5}$      **2.** $\frac{25}{3}$      **3.** $2 : 9$      **4.** $10 : 3$      **5.** $\frac{x}{y}$      **6.** $\frac{5a}{4b}$

*Tell the simplest name for each ratio.* (Example 1)

**7.** $\frac{9}{12}$      **8.** $\frac{27}{9}$      **9.** $10 : 100$      **10.** $300 : 100$

*The table shows the result of a survey taken in class.*

|  | Black Hair | Brown Hair | Red Hair | Blond Hair | Total |
|---|---|---|---|---|---|
| **Boys:** | 4 | 6 | 2 | 5 | 17 |
| **Girls:** | 11 | 8 | 1 | 3 | 23 |

*Tell the simplest name of each ratio.* (P-3, P-4)

**11.** Number of boys with black hair to number of girls with blond hair

**12.** Number of girls with red hair to number of boys with red hair

**13.** Number of boys to number of girls

**14.** Number of girls with blond hair to number of students with blond hair

**15.** Number of girls with black hair to number of boys with brown hair

**16.** Number of girls to total number of students

*Tell the simplest name for each ratio.* (Example 2, Example 3, Example 4)

**17.** 3x centimeters to 5x centimeters

**18.** 4x meters to 10y meters

**19.** Value of 6 pennies to the value of 3 nickels

**20.** Twenty centimeters to five millimeters

## WRITTEN EXERCISES 7.1

**A**

**Goal:** To write the ratio of two numbers in a given order

**Sample Problem:** Value of 50 cents to 3 quarters    **Answer:** 50 : 75 or $\frac{2}{3}$

*Write the simplest name for each ratio.* (Examples 1, 2, 3, and 4)

**1.** 5 to 9

**2.** 12 to 27

**3.** 7 to 12

**4.** 15 to 29

**5.** 30 to 4

**6.** 18 to 9

**7.** 10 to 1000

**8.** 1000 to 100

**9.** 12 cm to 15 cm

**10.** 9 mm to 24 mm

**11.** 8 days to 2 weeks

**12.** 3 weeks to 9 days

**13.** 1 m to 20 cm

**14.** 40 cm to 2 m

**15.** $x$ to 5

**16.** 17 to $n$, $n \neq 0$

**17.** $b$ to $a$, $a \neq 0$

**18.** $y$ to $x$, $x \neq 0$

**19.** $10a$ to $12a$, $a \neq 0$

**20.** $14y$ to $21y$, $y \neq 0$

**21.** $2m$ to $5n$, $n \neq 0$

**22.** $15r$ to $6s$, $s \neq 0$

**23.** $8x : 20y$, $y \neq 0$

**24.** $18a : 15b$, $b \neq 0$

*The table shows the number of different instruments in an orchestra.*

| String | Woodwind | Brass | Percussion |
|---|---|---|---|
| 5 First violins | 3 Oboes | 3 Trumpets | 1 Bass drum |
| $y$ Second violins | 3 Clarinets | 2 Trombones | 2 Kettle drums |
| 4 Basses | $x$ Flutes | 2 French horns | 1 Snare drum |
| 3 Cellos | 2 Bassoons | 1 Tuba | 2 Cymbals |
| **Total:**  24 | 11 | 8 | 6 |

*Write the simplest name for each ratio.* (P-3, P-4, Example 1)

**25.** Number of woodwind instruments to the number of string instruments

**26.** Number of percussion instruments to the number of brass instruments

**27.** Number of cellos to the number of string instruments

**28.** Number of brass instruments to the number of trombones

**29.** Number of string instruments to the total number of instruments

**30.** Number of brass instruments to the total number of instruments

*Write the simplest name for each ratio.* (Example 3)

**31.** Value of 4 dimes to the value of 2 quarters

**32.** Ten meters to ten centimeters

# 7.2 Proportion

**P-1**  **Which of these equations is true?**

**a.** $\dfrac{2}{3} = \dfrac{4}{5}$    **b.** $\dfrac{2}{5} = \dfrac{4}{10}$

Equation **a** is false. The work below shows that Equation **b** is true.

$$\frac{4}{10} = \frac{\overset{1}{\cancel{2}} \cdot 2}{\underset{1}{\cancel{2}} \cdot 5} \quad \text{or} \quad \frac{2}{5} \quad \blacktriangleleft \quad \text{$\frac{2}{5}$ and $\frac{4}{10}$ are equivalent fractions.}$$

An equation such as $\dfrac{2}{5} = \dfrac{4}{10}$ is called a <u>proportion</u>.

> A **proportion** is an equation that states that two ratios are equal.

Note how the four **terms** are numbered in the following proportion.

First term ⟶ 5 = 10 ⟵ Third term
Second term ⟶ 8    16 ⟵ Fourth term

5 × 16: "outside" cross product
8 × 10: "inside" cross product

The product of the first and fourth terms is a **cross product.** The product of the second and third terms is also a cross product.

**P-2**  **What are the cross products in each of the following?**

**a.** $\dfrac{2}{3} \times \dfrac{4}{6}$    **b.** $\dfrac{3}{4} \times \dfrac{5}{6}$

Note that $2 \cdot 6 = 3 \cdot 4$ is true and $\dfrac{2}{3} = \dfrac{4}{6}$ is a true proportion.

Note that $3 \cdot 6 = 4 \cdot 5$ is false and $\dfrac{3}{4} = \dfrac{5}{6}$ is a false proportion.

> **Cross Products Property**
>
> 1. If the cross products of a proportion are equal, it is a true proportion.
> 2. If the cross products of a proportion are not equal, it is a false proportion.

## example 1

Determine whether $\frac{7}{13} = \frac{9}{17}$ is a true proportion.

$$\frac{7}{13} \overset{?}{=} \frac{9}{17} \qquad \longrightarrow \qquad 7 \cdot 17 \overset{?}{=} 13 \cdot 9$$

$$119 \mid 117$$

Since the cross products are not equal, $\frac{7}{13} = \frac{9}{17}$ is a false proportion.

You can use the Cross Products Property to solve proportions.

## example 2

Solve the proportion $\frac{x}{4} = \frac{9}{12}$.

$$\frac{x}{4} = \frac{9}{12}$$

**Check**

| 1 | Cross Products Property | $x \cdot 12 = 4 \cdot 9$ |

or    $12x = 36$

$\frac{3}{4} = \frac{9}{12}$

$3 \cdot 12 \mid 4 \cdot 9$

| 2 | Division Property of Equality | $\frac{12x}{12} = \frac{36}{12}$ |

$36 \mid 36$

| 3 | Simplify each side. | $x = 3$ |

---

A proportion is equivalent to the equation formed by its cross products.

$\frac{2}{3} = \frac{x}{9}$ and

$2 \cdot 9 = 3 \cdot x$

are equivalent.

---

## example 3

Solve: $\frac{12}{x} = \frac{3}{2}$

| 1 | Cross Products Property | $12 \cdot 2 = x \cdot 3$ |

or    $3x = 24$

**Check**

$\frac{12}{8} = \frac{3}{2}$

| 2 | Division Property of Equality | $\frac{3x}{3} = \frac{24}{3}$ |

$12 \cdot 2 \mid 8 \cdot 3$

| 3 | Simplify each side. | $x = 8$ |

$24 \mid 24$

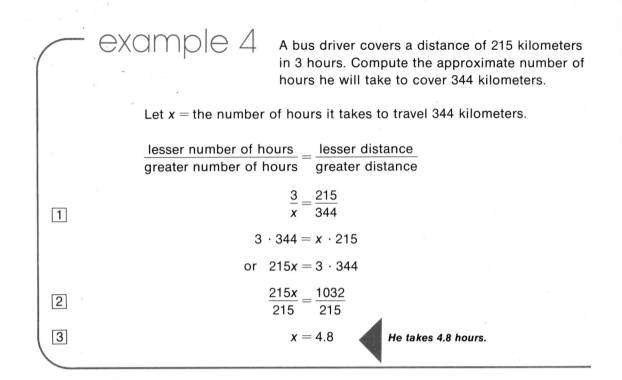

example 4 A bus driver covers a distance of 215 kilometers in 3 hours. Compute the approximate number of hours he will take to cover 344 kilometers.

Let $x$ = the number of hours it takes to travel 344 kilometers.

$$\frac{\text{lesser number of hours}}{\text{greater number of hours}} = \frac{\text{lesser distance}}{\text{greater distance}}$$

1  $$\frac{3}{x} = \frac{215}{344}$$

$$3 \cdot 344 = x \cdot 215$$

$$\text{or} \quad 215x = 3 \cdot 344$$

2  $$\frac{215x}{215} = \frac{1032}{215}$$

3  $$x = 4.8$$  ◀ **He takes 4.8 hours.**

## ORAL EXERCISES 7.2

*Say True or False for each proportion.* (Example 1)

**1.** $\frac{3}{5} = \frac{9}{15}$    **2.** $\frac{1}{2} = \frac{4}{10}$    **3.** $\frac{1}{3} = \frac{12}{36}$    **4.** $\frac{5}{4} = \frac{20}{15}$    **5.** $\frac{5}{6} = \frac{10}{12}$    **6.** $\frac{3}{2} = \frac{9}{6}$

**7.** $\frac{4}{3} = \frac{2}{5}$    **8.** $\frac{3}{100} = \frac{2}{75}$    **9.** $\frac{8}{12} = \frac{3}{4}$    **10.** $\frac{4}{5} = \frac{20}{25}$    **11.** $\frac{11}{12} = \frac{7}{8}$    **12.** $\frac{3}{18} = \frac{2}{12}$

*Solve each proportion.* (Example 2, Example 3)

**13.** $\frac{1}{2} = \frac{x}{6}$    **14.** $\frac{2}{x} = \frac{1}{3}$    **15.** $\frac{a}{5} = \frac{1}{5}$    **16.** $\frac{2}{7} = \frac{b}{7}$    **17.** $\frac{t}{8} = \frac{3}{24}$    **18.** $\frac{w}{3} = \frac{4}{6}$

**19.** $\frac{1}{10} = \frac{2}{r}$    **20.** $\frac{2}{3} = \frac{p}{9}$    **21.** $\frac{15}{x} = \frac{6}{2}$    **22.** $\frac{3}{4} = \frac{x}{12}$    **23.** $\frac{x}{100} = \frac{2}{25}$    **24.** $\frac{12}{4} = \frac{9}{x}$

*Tell a proportion.* (Example 4)

**25.** 100 kilometers in 3 hours;
500 kilometers in $x$ hours

**26.** $y$ kilometers in 8 hours;
300 kilometers in 6 hours

**27.** $150 earned in 1 week;
$3600 earned in $w$ weeks

**28.** 2 chapters contain 60 pages;
$x$ pages in 24 chapters

## WRITTEN EXERCISES 7.2

**A** 　**Goal:** To use the Cross Products Property to solve proportions
**Sample Problem:** If 90 pages of a book can be read in $1\frac{1}{2}$ hours, how long
will it take for 350 pages to be read?
**Answer:** $5\frac{5}{6}$ hours

*Write True or False for each proportion.* (Example 1)

1. $\frac{2}{3} = \frac{16}{24}$　　2. $\frac{3}{4} = \frac{18}{24}$　　3. $\frac{5}{6} = \frac{21}{25}$　　4. $\frac{4}{7} = \frac{23}{41}$　　5. $\frac{3}{18} = \frac{4}{24}$　　6. $\frac{7}{8} = \frac{20}{24}$

7. $\frac{6}{32} = \frac{8}{48}$　　8. $\frac{9}{12} = \frac{12}{16}$　　9. $\frac{22}{32} = \frac{32}{48}$　　10. $\frac{14}{32} = \frac{21}{48}$　　11. $\frac{23}{57} = \frac{19}{48}$　　12. $\frac{17}{29} = \frac{33}{42}$

*Solve each proportion.* (Example 2, Example 3)

13. $\frac{1}{3} = \frac{x}{15}$　　14. $\frac{1}{4} = \frac{n}{28}$　　15. $\frac{x}{30} = \frac{3}{5}$　　16. $\frac{y}{24} = \frac{5}{6}$　　17. $\frac{5}{2} = \frac{45}{t}$　　18. $\frac{4}{3} = \frac{32}{r}$

19. $\frac{7}{8} = \frac{x}{4}$　　20. $\frac{9}{16} = \frac{x}{8}$　　21. $\frac{s}{24} = \frac{13}{16}$　　22. $\frac{3}{n} = \frac{27}{15}$　　23. $\frac{y}{8} = \frac{180}{72}$　　24. $\frac{t}{12} = \frac{54}{36}$

*Write a proportion. Then solve it.* (Example 4)

25. 3 yards mowed in 1 day;
    $x$ yards mowed in 5 days

26. 8 cars washed in 10 hours;
    40 cars washed in $x$ hours

27. 12 hits in 10 games;
    $x$ hits in 25 games

28. 24 free throws in 3 games;
    $x$ free throws in 10 games

29. 16 dollars earned in 8 hours;
    $x$ hours to earn 40 dollars

30. 3 cans of soup for 84 cents;
    $x$ cents for 10 cans of soup

31. The ratio of the number of boys to
    the number of girls in a school is
    3 : 2. If 1200 students are boys, how
    many are girls?

32. The ratio of the number of teachers
    to the number of students in a
    school is 2 : 59. There are 649
    students enrolled. How many
    teachers are in the school?

# 7.3 Meaning of Per Cent

P-1 **What is the ratio of the number of shaded squares to the total number of squares?**

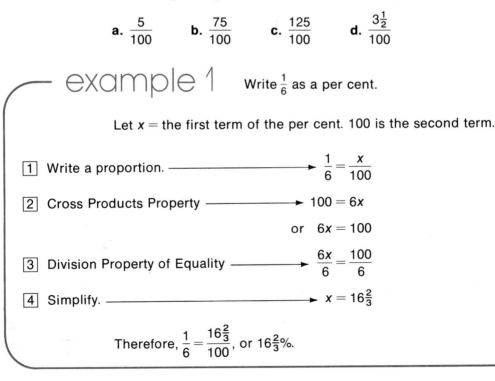

The ratio $\frac{17}{100}$ can be read 17 <u>per cent</u>. It can also be shown as 17%.

17% of the rectangle is shaded.

> A **per cent** is a ratio in which the second term is 100.
>
> $9\% = \frac{9}{100}$
>
> $a\% = \frac{a}{100}$

P-2 **How can you say each of these ratios as a per cent?**

a. $\dfrac{5}{100}$    b. $\dfrac{75}{100}$    c. $\dfrac{125}{100}$    d. $\dfrac{3\frac{1}{2}}{100}$

## example 1   Write $\frac{1}{6}$ as a per cent.

Let $x$ = the first term of the per cent. 100 is the second term.

1. Write a proportion. ⟶ $\dfrac{1}{6} = \dfrac{x}{100}$

2. Cross Products Property ⟶ $100 = 6x$

     or   $6x = 100$

3. Division Property of Equality ⟶ $\dfrac{6x}{6} = \dfrac{100}{6}$

4. Simplify. ⟶ $x = 16\frac{2}{3}$

Therefore, $\dfrac{1}{6} = \dfrac{16\frac{2}{3}}{100}$, or $16\frac{2}{3}\%$.

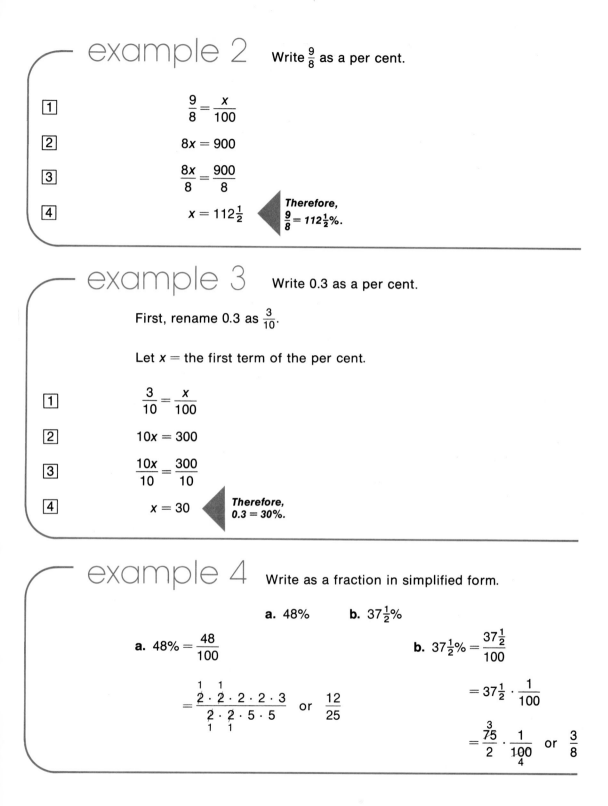

example 2    Write $\frac{9}{8}$ as a per cent.

[1]         $$\frac{9}{8} = \frac{x}{100}$$

[2]         $$8x = 900$$

[3]         $$\frac{8x}{8} = \frac{900}{8}$$

[4]         $$x = 112\frac{1}{2}$$    **Therefore,**
            $\frac{9}{8} = 112\frac{1}{2}\%.$

example 3    Write 0.3 as a per cent.

First, rename 0.3 as $\frac{3}{10}$.

Let $x =$ the first term of the per cent.

[1]         $$\frac{3}{10} = \frac{x}{100}$$

[2]         $$10x = 300$$

[3]         $$\frac{10x}{10} = \frac{300}{10}$$

[4]         $$x = 30$$    **Therefore,**
            **0.3 = 30%.**

example 4    Write as a fraction in simplified form.

            **a.** 48%        **b.** $37\frac{1}{2}\%$

**a.** $48\% = \dfrac{48}{100}$

$$= \frac{\overset{1}{2} \cdot \overset{1}{2} \cdot 2 \cdot 2 \cdot 3}{\underset{1}{2} \cdot \underset{1}{2} \cdot 5 \cdot 5} \quad \text{or} \quad \frac{12}{25}$$

**b.** $37\frac{1}{2}\% = \dfrac{37\frac{1}{2}}{100}$

$$= 37\frac{1}{2} \cdot \frac{1}{100}$$

$$= \frac{\overset{3}{75}}{2} \cdot \frac{1}{\underset{4}{100}} \quad \text{or} \quad \frac{3}{8}$$

The table below shows numbers and their corresponding per cents.

| Decimal | Per Cent | Decimal | Per Cent |
|---------|----------|---------|----------|
| 0.8 | 80% | 2.4 | 240% |
| 0.25 | 25% | 8.005 | 800.5% |
| 0.002 | 0.2% | 0.09 | 9% |

**P-3**  **How many places must the decimal point be moved to change a decimal to a per cent?   in which direction?**

**P-4**  **How many places must the decimal point be moved to change a per cent to a decimal?   in which direction?**

1. To change a number from a decimal to a per cent, multiply by 100 (move the decimal point two places to the right). Then write the per cent symbol.

$$7.20 = 720\%$$
$$0.01 = 1\%$$

2. To change a number from a per cent to a decimal, divide by 100 (move the decimal point two places to the left). Then write the decimal without the per cent symbol.

$$1.42\% = 0.0142$$
$$50.00\% = 50$$

## ORAL EXERCISES 7.3

Say each number as a per cent. (P-2, Example 1, Example 3, P-3)

1. $\frac{8}{100}$  2. $\frac{17}{100}$  3. $\frac{56}{100}$  4. $\frac{78}{100}$  5. $\frac{137}{100}$  6. $\frac{251}{100}$

7. $\frac{x}{100}$  8. $\frac{r}{100}$  9. $\frac{37\frac{1}{2}}{100}$  10. $\frac{66\frac{2}{3}}{100}$  11. $\frac{1.8}{100}$  12. $\frac{0.37}{100}$

13. 0.43  14. 0.87  15. 0.05  16. 0.01  17. 2.7  18. 0.113

19. $\frac{3}{4}$  20. $\frac{1}{2}$  21. $\frac{4}{5}$  22. $\frac{3}{20}$  23. $\frac{5}{5}$  24. $\frac{325}{325}$

Say each per cent as a fraction in simplified form. (Example 4)

25. 10%  26. 20%  27. 35%  28. 71%  29. $33\frac{1}{3}\%$  30. $12\frac{1}{2}\%$

Say each per cent as a decimal. (P-4)

31. 39%  32. 5.2%  33. 27.6%  34. 212%  35. 0.18%  36. 0.5%

*Tell the numerals missing from each row of the table.* (Example 4, P-3, P-4)

| Per Cent | Decimal | Fraction | | Per Cent | Decimal | Fraction |
|---|---|---|---|---|---|---|
| 37. 40% | ? | ? | 38. | ? | 0.18 | ? |
| 39. ? | ? | $\frac{7}{10}$ | 40. | 150% | ? | ? |

## WRITTEN EXERCISES 7.3

**A**  **Goal:** To write numerals in per cent form

**Sample Problem:** Write $\frac{1}{50}$ as a per cent.    **Answer:** 2%

*Write each number as a per cent.* (P-2, P-3)

1. $\frac{19}{100}$    2. $\frac{23}{100}$    3. $\frac{256}{100}$    4. $\frac{348}{100}$    5. $\frac{62\frac{1}{2}}{100}$    6. $\frac{87\frac{1}{2}}{100}$

7. $\frac{8.3}{100}$    8. $\frac{13.6}{100}$    9. $\frac{306.1}{100}$    10. $\frac{524.3}{100}$    11. $\frac{120\frac{1}{2}}{100}$    12. $\frac{133\frac{1}{3}}{100}$

13. 0.25    14. 0.43    15. 0.98    16. 0.67    17. 0.08    18. 0.05

19. 2.5    20. 7.4    21. 0.6    22. 0.3    23. 0.283    24. 0.109

*Write each number as a per cent. Use a proportion.* (Example 1, Example 2, Example 3)

25. $\frac{1}{4}$    26. $\frac{1}{5}$    27. $\frac{3}{10}$    28. $\frac{7}{10}$    29. $\frac{12}{10}$    30. $\frac{14}{10}$

31. $\frac{25}{20}$    32. $\frac{30}{20}$    33. $\frac{13}{25}$    34. $\frac{16}{25}$    35. $\frac{5}{6}$    36. $\frac{7}{6}$

37. 0.4    38. 0.7    39. 3.6    40. 9.4    41. 0.37    42. 0.83

*Write the numerals missing from each row of the table.* (Example 1, Example 2, Example 3, Example 4)

| Per Cent | Decimal | Fraction | | Per Cent | Decimal | Fraction |
|---|---|---|---|---|---|---|
| 43. ? | 0.17 | ? | 44. | ? | 0.041 | ? |
| 45. 22% | ? | ? | 46. | 76% | ? | ? |
| 47. ? | ? | $\frac{19}{20}$ | 48. | ? | ? | $\frac{17}{25}$ |

*Write each per cent as a fraction in simplified form.* (Example 4)

49. 15%    50. 18%    51. 45%    52. 64%    53. $66\frac{2}{3}\%$    54. $87\frac{1}{2}\%$

# 7.4 Proportion and Per Cent

Three basic kinds of per cent problems are illustrated below.
Each problem is described by a proportion.

**1**

Shade 25% of the area
of the rectangle.

$$\frac{25}{100} = \frac{x}{8}$$

**2**

What per cent of the
total area is shaded?

$$\frac{x}{100} = \frac{4}{8}$$

**3**

What is the total area
if 10% of the area is
shaded?

$$\frac{10}{100} = \frac{2}{x}$$

**P-1** **How many squares should be shaded in Problem 1?**

**P-2** **What is the value of x in Problem 2?**

**P-3** **What is the total area in Problem 3?**

## example 1

In a recent election at Crescent High School,
65% of the students voted. There are 1240 students in the school. How many students voted?

Let $x =$ the number of students who voted.

The number of students voting is less than the number of students
enrolled. Therefore the ratio used to represent 65% must be $\frac{x}{1240}$,
which is less than 100%.

$$\frac{65}{100} = \frac{x}{1240}$$

$$100x = (65)(1240)$$

$$\frac{100x}{100} = \frac{80600}{100}$$

$$x = 806 \qquad \blacktriangleleft \quad \textbf{\textit{806 students voted.}}$$

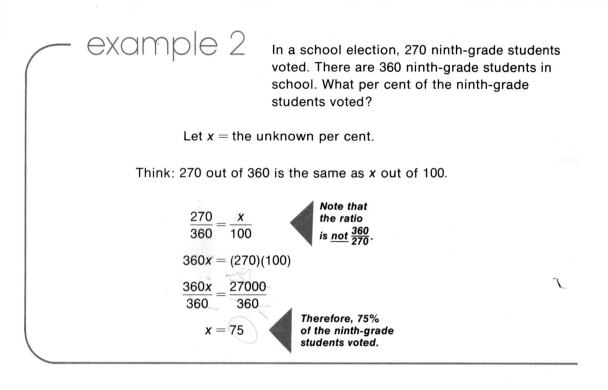

example 2    In a school election, 270 ninth-grade students voted. There are 360 ninth-grade students in school. What per cent of the ninth-grade students voted?

Let $x$ = the unknown per cent.

Think: 270 out of 360 is the same as $x$ out of 100.

$$\frac{270}{360} = \frac{x}{100}$$

Note that the ratio is **not** $\frac{360}{270}$.

$$360x = (270)(100)$$

$$\frac{360x}{360} = \frac{27000}{360}$$

$$x = 75$$

Therefore, 75% of the ninth-grade students voted.

example 3    In the same school election, 154 seniors voted. This number is 55% of the number of seniors in the school. How many senior students are in the school?

Let $x$ = the number of seniors.

Note that $\frac{154}{x}$ is less than 100% because 154, the number of seniors who voted, is less than $x$, the total number of seniors.

$$\frac{55}{100} = \frac{154}{x}$$

$$55x = 15400$$

$$\frac{55x}{55} = \frac{15400}{55}$$

$$x = 280$$

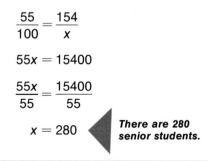

There are 280 senior students.

> **Steps in solving per cent problems:**
>
> 1. Represent the unknown number by a variable.
> 2. Write a proportion. One ratio equals the per cent and has 100 as its second term. The terms of the other ratio are the two numbers being compared in the problem.
> 3. Solve the proportion.

## ORAL EXERCISES 7.4

*State a proportion that describes each sentence.* (Examples 1, 2, 3)

**1.** $x$ is 25% of 36.

**2.** $r$ is 12% of 512.

**3.** 17 is $y$% of 82.

**4.** 23 is $t$% of 156.

**5.** 10 is 15% of $a$.

**6.** 19 is 80% of $b$.

**7.** $t$% of 15 is 92.

**8.** 8% of 90 $= x$.

**9.** 25% of $t = 144$.

**10.** 26 $=$ 15% of $a$.

*The following table shows the record of a basketball free-throw contest. Tell what numerals are missing from the table.* (P-1, P-2, P-3)

| | Player | Free Throws Attempted | Free Throws Made | Per Cent Made |
|---|---|---|---|---|
| **11.** | Julio | 20 | 15 | ? |
| **12.** | Dot | 12 | ? | 25% |
| **13.** | Livia | ? | 9 | 60% |
| **14.** | Roy | 18 | ? | $33\frac{1}{3}$% |

## WRITTEN EXERCISES 7.4

**A**
**Goal:** To solve per cent problems using proportions

**Sample Problem:** Find the per cent of correct problems on an examination if 17 problems were correct and there were 20 problems.

**Answer:** 85%

*Write a proportion. Then solve it.* (P-1, P-2, P-3)

**1.** 25% of 28 $= x$.

**2.** 40% of 35 $= y$.

**3.** $r$% of 92 $=$ 69.

**4.** $y$% of 65 $=$ 39.

**5.** 15 is 20% of $a$.

**6.** 21 is 30% of $b$.

**7.** 150 is $x$% of 100.

**8.** 250 is $y$% of 100.

**9.** 12% of 13 is $n$.

**10.** 8% of 72 is $p$.

**11.** 15 is $x$% of 40.

**12.** 30 is $y$% of 48.

**13.** 14 is $12\frac{1}{2}$% of $t$.

**14.** 36 is $37\frac{1}{2}$% of $w$.

**15.** $66\frac{2}{3}$% of 126 $= y$.

**16.** $16\frac{2}{3}$% of 114 $= n$.

**17.** 20 is 0.8% of $m$.

**18.** 7 is 0.5% of $w$.

**19.** 84 is $83\frac{1}{3}$% of $n$.

**20.** 112 is $87\frac{1}{2}$% of $x$.

*The table below shows partial results of a school primary election. Find the unknown number in each row. Show your work.* (P-1, P-2, P-3)

| | Candidates | | Total Number Voting | Votes Received | Per Cent of Votes Received |
|---|---|---|---|---|---|
| **21.** | President | Jill | 128 | 48 | ? |
| **22.** | | John | 128 | 32 | ? |
| **23.** | Vice-Pres. | Pat | 120 | ? | 40% |
| **24.** | | Harry | 120 | ? | 55% |
| **25.** | Secretary | Jean | ? | 44 | 40% |
| **26.** | | Mark | ? | 66 | 60% |

*Solve each problem. Use a proportion.* (Examples 1, 2, 3)

**27.** There are 12 girls on the tennis squad of a school. Twenty-five per cent of the girls are seniors. How many seniors are on the squad?

**28.** A quarterback completes 60% of his passes in a football game. How many passes does he complete if he throws 25 passes?

**29.** A reporter spends 20% of her monthly salary for rent. How much is her monthly salary if she spends $192 for rent?

**30.** A baseball player got a hit in 32% of the times he batted. If he batted 75 times, how many hits did he get?

**31.** A worker who earns $4.00 per hour receives a raise of $0.20 per hour. What is the per cent of increase in the wages?

**32.** Of the 120 students in a school band, 24 play woodwind instruments. What per cent play woodwind instruments?

# 7.5   Per Cent of a Number

**P-1**   **What proportion describes the following sentence?**

$$x = 25\% \text{ of } 60$$

Here is the work for finding the value of $x$.

$$\frac{25}{100} = \frac{x}{60}$$

$$100x = (25)(60)$$

$$\frac{100x}{100} = \frac{(25)(60)}{100}$$

$$x = \frac{1500}{100}$$

$$x = 15$$   ◀   *Therefore, 15 is "25% of 60."*

The third step could also be written as shown below.

$$x = \frac{25}{100}(60)$$

**P-2**   **What is the decimal form of $\frac{25}{100}$ ?**

This form suggests a way to find 25% of 60 without a proportion. Multiply 60 by 0.25.

$$(0.25)(60) = 15$$

Such problems can always be worked by the proportion method. However, this short cut method is useful to know.

> To compute a per cent of a number, multiply the number by the per cent expressed in decimal form.
>
> 5% of 12 is (0.05)(12).
>
> 14% of $x$ is 0.14$x$.

**P-3**   **How can you find the value of "12% of 75" by this rule?**

You have had practice in changing word phrases to open phrases. Here are some examples that involve the "per cent of a number."

| Word Phrase | Open Phrase |
|---|---|
| 5% of some number | 0.05$n$ |
| 18% of the cost | 0.18$x$ |
| 3% of the weight | 0.03$w$ |
| 30% of the number of students | 0.3$s$ |
| 120% of the number of cars | 1.2$y$ |

P-4 **What is the decimal form of 42.7%?**

example 1 Find 42.7% of 150.

Since the decimal form of 42.7% is 0.427, then 42.7% of 150 is (0.427)(150).

Here is the work.

$$(0.427)(150) = 64.05$$

This same method can be used to find an unknown per cent in a problem.

P-5 **What is the decimal form of 4%?**

example 2 The sales tax is 4% on an item. Write an open phrase for the tax.

Let $a$ = the cost of the purchase.

Then 0.04$a$ = the tax, since 4% = 0.04.

The phrase for the tax is 0.04$a$.

P-6 **What is an open phrase if the sales tax in Example 2 is 6%? $7\frac{1}{2}$%?**

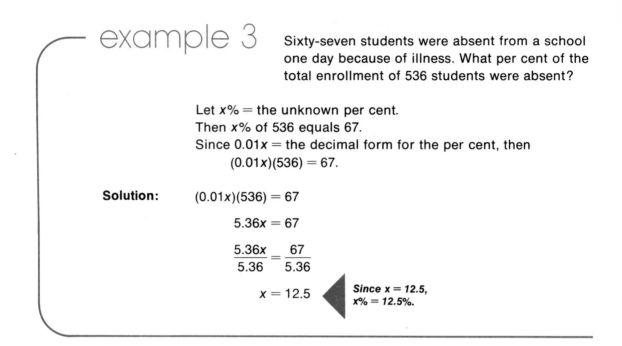

## example 3

Sixty-seven students were absent from a school one day because of illness. What per cent of the total enrollment of 536 students were absent?

Let $x\%$ = the unknown per cent.
Then $x\%$ of 536 equals 67.
Since $0.01x$ = the decimal form for the per cent, then
$(0.01x)(536) = 67$.

**Solution:**

$$(0.01x)(536) = 67$$

$$5.36x = 67$$

$$\frac{5.36x}{5.36} = \frac{67}{5.36}$$

$$x = 12.5$$

◀ *Since x = 12.5,*
*x% = 12.5%.*

## ORAL EXERCISES 7.5

*Tell a product or open phrase.* (Examples 1, 2, and 3)

1. 14% of 25
2. 36% of 50
3. 120% of 83
4. 225% of 41

5. $x\%$ of 10
6. $y\%$ of 125
7. 12% of $r$
8. 27% of $t$

9. 10% of $a$
10. 1% of $b$
11. $r\%$ of 15.8
12. $w\%$ of 0.8

*Tell an open phrase for each word phrase.* (Examples 1, 2, and 3)

13. 15% of $x$ players
14. 75% of $y$ students

15. 28% of the number of cars
16. 50% of the number of dentists

17. 5% of the number of dollars saved
18. 20% of the cost of the records

19. 63% of the number of buses
20. 48% of the number of voters

21. 70% of the number of high school graduates
22. 125% of the number of newspapers

23. $x\%$ of 2600 students
24. $y\%$ of 480 cartons

25. An unknown per cent of 6500 residents
26. An unknown per cent of 132 rabbits

# WRITTEN EXERCISES 7.5

**A**     **Goal:** To write a per cent of a number
         **Sample Problems: a.** Find 16.1% of 200.     **b.** Find 16.1% of *y*.
         **Answers: a.** 32.2     **b.** 0.161*y*

*Write the value of each phrase.* (Example 1)

1. 5% of 25
2. 6% of 30
3. 20% of 35
4. 25% of 80

5. 12% of 225
6. 18% of 336
7. 135% of 85
8. 150% of 72

9. 0.8% of 12
10. 0.5% of 17
11. 14.7% of 90
12. 23.4% of 60

13. $3\frac{1}{4}$% of 124
14. $5\frac{3}{4}$% of 1200
15. $\frac{3}{4}$% of 204
16. $\frac{1}{4}$% of 96

*Write a product for each word phrase.* (Example 2, Example 3)

17. 12% of *x* dollars
18. 15% of *y* grams

19. 53% of *f* free throws
20. 35% of *t* touchdowns

21. *x*% of $2500
22. *y*% of $4200

23. *p*% of 3000 students
24. *r*% of 95 points

25. 10% of the number of planes
26. 15% of the number of schools

27. 225% of the number of votes
28. 153% of the number of people

29. 0.7% of the number of workers
30. 0.9% of the number of accidents

31. An unknown per cent of 225 hours
32. An unknown per cent of 375 pilots

*Solve for x in each sentence.* (Example 3)

33. *x*% of 96 = 11.52
34. *x*% of 75 = 11.25

35. *x*% of 600 = 672
36. *x*% of 850 = 1232.5

37. *x*% of 84 = 0.42
38. *x*% of 45 = 0.36

39. *x*% of 104 = 39
40. *x*% of 144 = 126

*Solve each problem.* (Example 3)

41. Ninety-three sophomores participated in the annual science fair.
What per cent of the 248 sophomores participated?

42. 350 students attended the football
victory dance. What per cent of
the 840 students attended the dance?

# 7.6 Simple Interest

One important application of per cent is in computing <u>interest</u>.

> **Interest** is the amount of money that is charged for the use of borrowed money.
> The amount of money borrowed is called the **principal.**

A woman borrowed $2500 from a bank to buy a car. After a period of time she repaid the $2500 to the bank. She also paid the bank an additional $300.

**P-1** **What is the amount $2500 called?   the additional $300?**

Interest is usually expressed as a per cent of the principal.

Suppose that $600 is borrowed at 5% per year.

**P-2** **How much interest is 5% of $600?**

The per cent that is used in an interest problem is called the **rate.** The following formula shows how to compute **simple interest.** Simple interest depends on the principal, rate, and time (in years).

$$\text{Interest} = (\text{Principal})(\text{Rate})(\text{Time})$$

$$I = PRT$$

## example 1

Compute the interest on $200 for one year at a rate of 8%.

$P = 200; R = 0.08; T = 1$

$I = PRT$

$I = (200)(0.08)(1)$

$I = 16$

◀ *The interest on $200 for one year at a rate of 8% is $16.*

Time expressed in months must be written as a fractional part of a year.

| Months | Fractional Part of a Year |
|--------|---------------------------|
| 5 | $\frac{5}{12}$ |
| 8 | $\frac{8}{12}$ or $\frac{2}{3}$ |
| 30 | $\frac{30}{12}$ or $\frac{5}{2}$ |

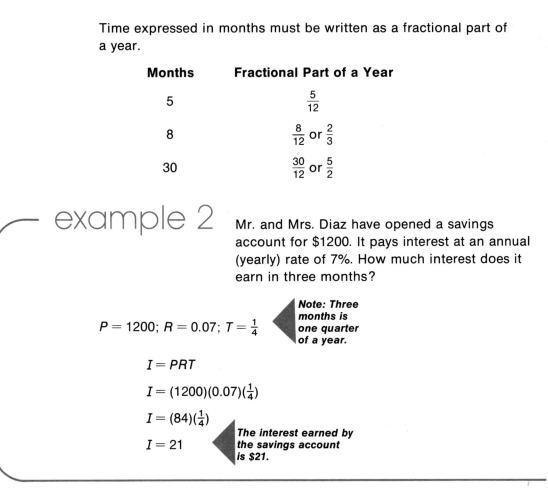

## example 2

Mr. and Mrs. Diaz have opened a savings account for $1200. It pays interest at an annual (yearly) rate of 7%. How much interest does it earn in three months?

$P = 1200$; $R = 0.07$; $T = \frac{1}{4}$

**Note: Three months is one quarter of a year.**

$I = PRT$

$I = (1200)(0.07)(\frac{1}{4})$

$I = (84)(\frac{1}{4})$

$I = 21$

*The interest earned by the savings account is $21.*

## example 3

Chris borrows $44,000 at $9\frac{1}{2}$% simple annual interest to open a cooking school. Compute the interest if she pays back the loan in 5 years.

$P = 44,000$; $R = 0.095$; $T = 5$

$I = PRT$

$I = (44,000)(0.095)(5)$

$I = (4180)(5)$

$I = 20,900$

*She pays $20,900 in interest.*

In algebra, a variable is often used to represent an unknown principal or rate as shown in this table.

| Principal | Rate | Time | Interest |
|---|---|---|---|
| $x$ | 6% | 1 year | $(x)(0.06)(1)$ or $0.06x$ |
| $200 | $y$% | 9 months | $(200)(0.01y)(\frac{3}{4})$ or $1.5y$ |
| $n$ | $5\frac{1}{2}$% | 5 years | $(n)(0.055)(5)$ or $0.275n$ |
| $5000 | $r$% | $2\frac{1}{2}$ years | $(5000)(0.01r)(2\frac{1}{2})$ or $125r$ |

**P-3** **What phrase represents the interest on $d$ dollars at $6\frac{1}{2}$% for 6 months?**

**P-4** **How can you write $r$% as a decimal phrase?**

**P-5** **What phrase represents the interest on $75 at $r$% for 4 years?**

## ORAL EXERCISES 7.6

*Tell the annual interest on each investment.* (Example 1)

**1.** $100 at 5%

**2.** $100 at 6%

**3.** $100 at 7%

**4.** $100 at 8%

**5.** $200 at 6%

**6.** $300 at 7%

**7.** $100 at $5\frac{1}{2}$%

**8.** $100 at $6\frac{1}{2}$%

**9.** $10 at 8%

**10.** $20 at 12%

*Tell the interest on each investment.* (Example 2, Example 3)

**11.** $500 for 2 years at 5%

**12.** $300 for 5 years at 6%

**13.** $100 for 3 months at 12%

**14.** $200 for 6 months at 8%

*Tell a phrase that represents the annual interest on each investment.*

**15.** $t$ dollars at 8%

**16.** $w$ dollars at 12%

**17.** $5 at $x$%

**18.** $300 at $r$%

**19.** $x$ dollars at $5\frac{1}{2}$%

**20.** $y$ dollars at 7.8%

## WRITTEN EXERCISES 7.6

**A**   **Goal:** To compute interest using the formula $I = PRT$
**Sample Problems:** What is the interest on $900 at an annual rate of 8%
          **a.** for 9 months?    **b.** for $n$ years?
**Answers: a.** $54   **b.** 72n

*Compute the annual interest on each investment.* (Examples 1, 2, and 3)

1. $500 at 8%

2. $800 at 12%

3. $225 at 10%

4. $275 at 6%

5. $100 at $8\frac{1}{2}$%

6. $100 at $6\frac{1}{2}$%

7. $200 at 5.6%

8. $300 at 6.2%

9. $400 at $7\frac{1}{4}$%

10. $500 at $6\frac{3}{4}$%

*Compute the interest for each investment.* (Example 2, Example 3)

11. $600 at 5% for 6 months

12. $800 at 6% for 3 months

13. $1200 at 8% for 10 months

14. $1600 at 7% for 15 months

15. $800 at $6\frac{1}{2}$% for 9 months

16. $900 at $5\frac{1}{2}$% for 8 months

*Write an open phrase that represents the interest on each investment.*
(P-3, P-5)

17. $x$ dollars at 5% for 1 year

18. $y$ dollars at 8% for 1 year

19. $r$ dollars at 4% for 2 years

20. $s$ dollars at 6% for 3 years

21. $n$ dollars at 5% for 6 months

22. $m$ dollars at 4% for 3 months

23. $t$ dollars at 3% for 1 month

24. $w$ dollars at 12% for 9 months

25. $100 at $x$% for 1 year

26. $300 at $y$% for 12 months

27. $500 at $r$% for 2 months

28. $600 at $w$% for 8 months

**B**   *Solve each problem.*

29. A man pays $18 interest on $300 that he borrows for one year. What is the rate of interest?

30. A bank pays $65 in interest for each $1000 invested for one year. What is the rate of interest?

31. The interest on an 8% loan for one year is $64. What is the principal?

32. A girl's savings earn $5.50 in one year at a rate of $5\frac{1}{2}$%. What amount did she have in the savings account?

# 7.7    Discount

A *discount* is the amount that an article of merchandise is reduced in price.

**P-1**    **What is the amount of discount on each item that is advertised below?**

Ad 1            Ad 2

Ad 3

The regular price of an article is the *list price.* The price after the discount is deducted is the *net price.*

**P-2**    **What is the list price in Ad 2?   What is the net price?**

Discounts are often expressed as a certain per cent of the list price. The per cent is called the *rate of discount.*

Here are some examples of the relation between list price, rate of discount, and discount.

| List Price | Rate of Discount | Discount |
|---|---|---|
| $50 | 15% | (0.15)(50) = $7.50 |
| $400 | 25% | (0.25)(400) = $100 |
| $500 | 20% | (0.20)(500) = $100 |

The relation between discount, rate of discount, list price, and net price can be shown by the formulas below.

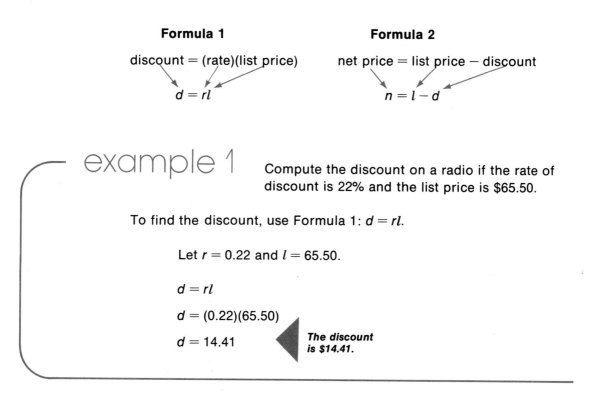

**Formula 1**

discount = (rate)(list price)

$d = rl$

**Formula 2**

net price = list price − discount

$n = l - d$

example 1   Compute the discount on a radio if the rate of discount is 22% and the list price is $65.50.

To find the discount, use Formula 1: $d = rl$.

Let $r = 0.22$ and $l = 65.50$.

$d = rl$

$d = (0.22)(65.50)$

$d = 14.41$   ◀ **The discount is $14.41.**

P-3   **What is the net price for Example 1?**

Problems in discounts sometimes require the use of open phrases. The table below shows some examples.

| List Price | Rate of Discount | Discount | Net Price |
|------------|------------------|----------|-----------|
| $x$ | 15% | $0.15x$ | $x - 0.15x$ |
| $y$ | 30% | $0.30y$ | $y - 0.30y$ |
| $z$ | 50% | $0.50z$ | $z - 0.50z$ |
| $500 | $r$% | $(0.01r)(500)$ | $500 - 5r$ |
| $100 | $2s$% | $(0.02s)(100)$ | $100 - 2s$ |
| $25 | $p$% | ? | ? |

P-4   **What are the missing phrases in the table?**

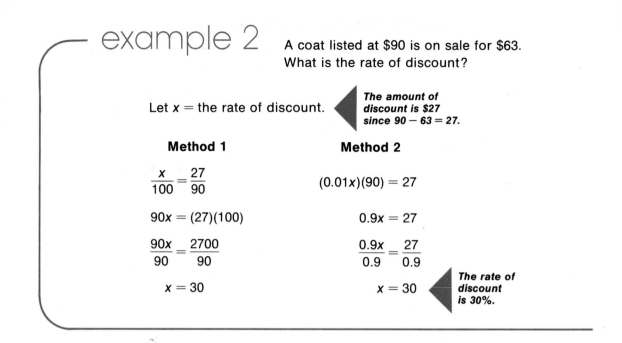

## example 2

A coat listed at $90 is on sale for $63. What is the rate of discount?

Let $x$ = the rate of discount.

> The amount of discount is $27 since $90 - 63 = 27$.

**Method 1**

$$\frac{x}{100} = \frac{27}{90}$$

$$90x = (27)(100)$$

$$\frac{90x}{90} = \frac{2700}{90}$$

$$x = 30$$

**Method 2**

$$(0.01x)(90) = 27$$

$$0.9x = 27$$

$$\frac{0.9x}{0.9} = \frac{27}{0.9}$$

$$x = 30$$

> The rate of discount is 30%.

## ORAL EXERCISES 7.7

*Tell what numerals or phrases are missing from the table.* (P-1, P-2, Formula 2)

|     | List Price | Discount | Net Price |
|-----|------------|----------|-----------|
| 1.  | $30        | $3       | ?         |
| 2.  | $50        | ?        | $48       |
| 3.  | ?          | $10      | $60       |
| 4.  | $100       | $x$      | ?         |
| 5.  | $55        | ?        | $n$       |
| 6.  | ?          | $d$      | $26       |

*Tell the discount on each sale.* (Example 1)

7. A baseball glove listed at $18 with a discount rate of $33\frac{1}{3}\%$

8. A $12 hat reduced by 25%

9. A $40 dress on sale at a 20% discount

10. A refrigerator listed at $500 but reduced by 30%

11. A chair regularly priced at $240 and marked "$\frac{1}{4}$ off"

12. An automobile listed at $3200 but for sale at a $12\frac{1}{2}\%$ discount

*Estimate the net price of each item to the nearest dollar.* (P-3)

**13.** A table marked $49.98 but reduced 10%

**14.** An automobile listed at $1995 with a 25% discount

**15.** A coat marked $19.95 but reduced by 40%

**16.** A radio listed at $99.99 with a 30% discount

*Tell the correct phrase to replace each question mark in this table.* (P-4)

| | List Price | Rate of Discount | Discount | Net Price |
|---|---|---|---|---|
| 17. | $25 | 15% | $3.75 | ? |
| 18. | x | 12% | ? | ? |
| 19. | $150 | r% | ? | ? |
| 20. | $400 | 10% | ? | ? |

*Tell a proportion that describes the quantities in each row below.* (Method 1 of Example 2)

| | List Price | Rate of Discount | Discount |
|---|---|---|---|
| 21. | $300 | 5% | $15 |
| 22. | x | 15% | $35 |
| 23. | $85 | r% | $15 |
| 24. | $125 | 25% | y |

## WRITTEN EXERCISES 7.7

**A**  **Goal:** To solve problems involving discounts
**Sample Problem:** Compute the discount and the net price of a camera if the list price is $30 and the rate of discount is 15%.
**Answer:** The discount is $4.50. The net price is $25.50.

*Write the numeral or phrase missing from each row of the table.* (P-1, P-2, Formula 2)

| | List Price | Discount | Net Price |
|---|---|---|---|
| 1. | $100 | $15 | ? |
| 2. | $125 | $45 | ? |
| 3. | $400 | ? | $370 |

| | List Price | Discount | Net Price |
|---|---|---|---|
| 4. | $750 | ? | $695 |
| 5. | $195 | $x$ | ? |
| 6. | $49 | $d$ | ? |
| 7. | ? | $15 | $n$ |
| 8. | ? | $33 | $p$ |
| 9. | $x$ | $0.15x$ | ? |
| 10. | $y$ | $0.25y$ | ? |
| 11. | $259 | ? | $n$ |
| 12. | $595 | ? | $2x$ |

*Compute the discount and the net price for each item.* (Example 1, P-3)

13. A house listed at $30,000 is reduced 20%.

14. A car listed at $2500 is sold at a discount of 10%.

15. A dress marked for $48 is reduced $33\frac{1}{3}$%.

16. A hat marked $15 is reduced 40%.

17. A stereo priced at $325 is on sale for 15% less.

18. A cycle listed for $576 is reduced by $12\frac{1}{2}$%.

19. A dishwasher listed at $359.50 is on sale at a discount of 10%.

20. A typewriter is reduced 30% from its list price of $295.

*Choose a variable for the unknown and write an equation to describe each problem. Then solve the problem.* (Example 2)

21. The list price of a camera is $50, but it is on sale for $37. What is the rate of discount?

22. A lamp is listed at $27, but Mary buys it for $20 on sale. What is the rate of discount?

23. The discount on a set of golf clubs is $48, and the rate of discount is 15%. What is the list price?

24. The price of a stove is reduced $50 for a sale. If the rate of discount is 20%, what is the list price?

# CHAPTER SUMMARY

| IMPORTANT TERMS | | |
|---|---|---|
| | Ratio *(p. 140)* | Principal *(p. 160)* |
| | Terms of a ratio *(p. 140)* | Rate *(p. 160)* |
| | Proportion *(p. 144)* | Discount *(p. 164)* |
| | Cross product *(p. 144)* | List price *(p. 164)* |
| | Per cent *(p. 148)* | Net price *(p. 164)* |
| | Simple interest *(p. 160)* | Rate of discount *(p. 164)* |

**IMPORTANT IDEAS**

*1.* The second term of a ratio can never be 0.

*2.* The terms of a ratio must be in the same units.

*3.* *Cross Products Property:* If the cross products of a proportion are equal, it is a true proportion. If they are not equal, it is a false proportion.

*4.* A proportion is equivalent to the equation formed by its cross products.

*5.* To change a number from a decimal to a per cent, move the decimal point two places to the right. Then write the per cent symbol.

*6.* To change a number from a per cent to a decimal, move the decimal point two places to the left. Then write the decimal without the per cent symbol.

*7.* To compute a per cent of a number, multiply the number by the per cent expressed in decimal form.

*8.* *Simple Interest Formula:* $I = PRT$. (Interest = Principal × Rate × Time)

*9.* *Discount Formula:* $d = rl$. (Discount = rate × list price)

*10.* *Net Price Formula:* $n = l - d$. (Net price = list price − discount)

# CHAPTER REVIEW

### SECTION 7.1

*Write the simplest name of each ratio.*

**1.** 10 to 80

**2.** 44 to 4

**3.** 10 millimeters to 2 centimeters

**4.** 50 minutes to 1 hour

### SECTION 7.2

*Write True or False for each proportion.*

**5.** $\frac{5}{6} = \frac{11}{12}$

**6.** $\frac{3}{4} = \frac{31}{44}$

**7.** $\frac{12}{17} = \frac{15}{21}$

**8.** $\frac{16}{12} = \frac{12}{9}$

## SECTION 7.2 (Continued)

*Solve each proportion.*

**9.** $\dfrac{x}{5} = \dfrac{28}{35}$  **10.** $\dfrac{3}{5} = \dfrac{12}{x}$  **11.** $\dfrac{1}{x} = \dfrac{13}{16}$  **12.** $\dfrac{5}{12} = \dfrac{x}{12}$

*Write a proportion. Then solve it.*

**13.** 15 pages typed in 2 hours; $x$ pages typed in 8 hours

**14.** 5 gallons of gas for $2.25; 16 gallons of gas for $x$ cents

### SECTION 7.3

*Write each number as a per cent.*

**15.** $\dfrac{83}{100}$  **16.** $\dfrac{253}{100}$  **17.** 0.18  **18.** 3.7  **19.** $\dfrac{3}{5}$

**20.** 0.015  **21.** $\dfrac{29}{10}$  **22.** $\dfrac{37}{25}$  **23.** $\dfrac{3}{8}$  **24.** $\dfrac{5}{16}$

### SECTION 7.4

*Write a proportion for each sentence. Then solve it.*

**25.** 33% of 28 is $x$.  **26.** $12 is $r$% of $36.  **27.** 3 is 15% of $y$.

**28.** $a$ is 12% of 48.  **29.** 23 is $r$% of 276.  **30.** 1.2 is 0.8% of $x$.

### SECTION 7.5

*Write the value of each phrase.*

**31.** 16% of 150  **32.** 7% of 95  **33.** 1.2% of 28  **34.** 12.8% of 42

*Write a product for each word phrase.*

**35.** 12% of $x$  **36.** 9% of $b$  **37.** $r$% of 225  **38.** $t$% of 16

### SECTIONS 7.6 AND 7.7

*Write an open phrase for each word phrase.*

**39.** Interest on $x$ dollars for 6 months at 8%

**40.** Discount on $y$ dollars at a rate of 10%

**41.** Net price of a shirt listed at $15 less $t$%

# 8

Word Problems

# 8.1 Word Phrases to Open Phrases

This table shows some words or expressions that suggest the various operations on numbers.

| Operation | Words or Expressions |
|---|---|
| Addition | sum, total, plus, increased by, more than |
| Subtraction | difference, less, less than, minus, decreased by, diminished by |
| Multiplication | product, multiplied by, times, twice, doubled, tripled |
| Division | quotient, divided by |

**P-1**   **What open phrase represents the following word phrase?**

**Word Phrase:** "five more than an unknown number *n*"

**P-2**   **What are some ways to write each open phrase below in words?**

**a.** $x + 3$        **b.** $t - 5$        **c.** $3y$        **d.** $\dfrac{r}{12}$

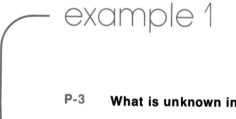

example 1   Write an open phrase for this word phrase.

**Word Phrase:** "6 meters less than the length of a rectangle"

**P-3**   **What is unknown in the phrase?   What operation can you identify?**

Here are the steps in changing a word phrase to an equivalent open phrase.

1️⃣ Select a variable. ⟶ Let $l$ = the length.

2️⃣ Identify an operation. ⟶ subtraction

3️⃣ Write an open phrase. ⟶ $l - 6$

**P-4**   **How does the following word phrase differ from the one above?**

**Word Phrase:** "6 meters less the length of a rectangle"

**P-5**   **What open phrase can you write for this word phrase?**

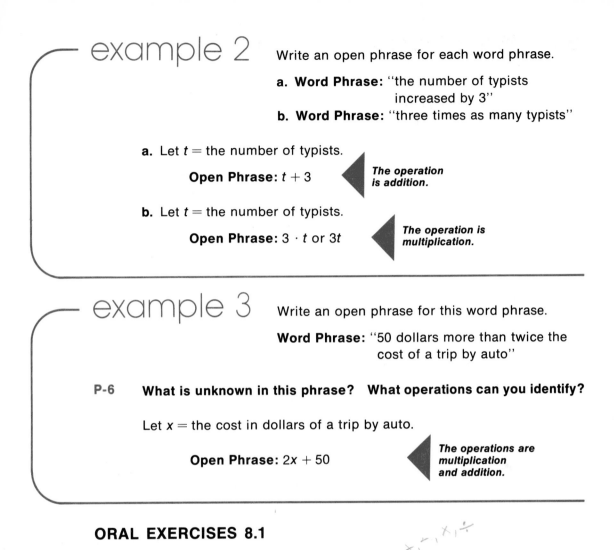

example 2    Write an open phrase for each word phrase.

**a. Word Phrase:** "the number of typists increased by 3"

**b. Word Phrase:** "three times as many typists"

a. Let $t$ = the number of typists.

**Open Phrase:** $t + 3$    ◀ *The operation is addition.*

b. Let $t$ = the number of typists.

**Open Phrase:** $3 \cdot t$ or $3t$    ◀ *The operation is multiplication.*

example 3    Write an open phrase for this word phrase.

**Word Phrase:** "50 dollars more than twice the cost of a trip by auto"

P-6    **What is unknown in this phrase?   What operations can you identify?**

Let $x$ = the cost in dollars of a trip by auto.

**Open Phrase:** $2x + 50$    ◀ *The operations are multiplication and addition.*

## ORAL EXERCISES 8.1

*Tell what operation or operations are suggested.* (P-3, P-6)

1. The number of books decreased by ten

2. The number of dollars tripled

3. The product of twelve and the number of students

4. Twice the number of hours diminished by five

5. A number of meters divided by ten

6. Sixteen less the number of swimmers

7. Twenty-two increased by the number of records

8. Seven and one-half times the number of voters

9. The number of dogs doubled

10. Ten more than the number of programs

*Tell a numerical phrase. Simplify where necessary.*

**EXAMPLE:** The number of meters in 16.2 centimeters
**ANSWER:** $\frac{16.2}{100}$   or   0.162 m

11. The number of months in 3 years

12. The number of months in 5 years

13. The number of days in 10 weeks

14. The number of weeks in 35 days

15. The number of weeks in 56 days

16. The number of millimeters in 25 centimeters

17. The number of square centimeters in 1900 square millimeters

18. The number of square centimeters in 86 square millimeters

*Select a variable for the unknown number. Then tell an open phrase.*
(Example 1, Example 2, Example 3)

19. Six more than the number of fish

20. Five less than the number of swimmers

21. The number of meters divided by 1000

22. The number of points less 20

23. The product of 10 and the number of centimeters

24. The number of kilometers per hour increased by 5

25. Three more than twice the number of centimeters

26. Fifteen less the number of scuba divers

27. Fifteen less than the number of scuba divers

28. The quotient 170 dollars divided by the number of payments

29. The difference formed by subtracting the number of children from 782

30. Twice the number of artists divided by fifteen

## WRITTEN EXERCISES 8.1

Ⓐ     **Goal:** To write an open phrase for a word phrase
**Sample Problems: a.** 5 less than a number $n$     **b.** 5 less a number $n$
**Answers: a.** $n - 5$     **b.** $5 - n$

*Select a variable and write what it represents. Then write an open phrase.*
(Example 1, Example 2, Example 3)

1. The number of hours increased by 12

2. The number of cakes decreased by two

3. Five times the number of dollars

4. The product of 14 and the number of lemons

5. Fifteen less than the number of mice

6. Two more than the number of kilometers

7. The number of months less 120

8. The number of teachers less 31

9. Twenty-five less the number of planes

10. The number of students increased by 119

11. The product of 17.2 and the number of packages

12. The quotient formed by dividing the number of kilometers by 14

13. The difference formed by subtracting 27 from the number of players

14. Sixteen less than the number of cars

15. Seven more than twice the number of doctors

16. Ten fewer than three times the number of accidents

17. Eight less than 16 times the number of square meters

18. Twenty-five more than triple the number of years

19. Fifteen less than the quotient of the number of meters divided by 100

20. Forty-five plus the number of club members less 10

**B** *Write a numerical phrase or open phrase for each word phrase. Simplify where necessary.*

EXAMPLES: **a.** The interest on 850 dollars loaned for one year at 6%  ANSWERS: **a.** (0.06)(850) or $51.00

**b.** The number of centimeters in $x$ meters  **b.** 100$x$

21. The interest on 1200 dollars for 1 year at 5%

22. The interest on 270 dollars for 1 year at 7%

23. The interest on $d$ dollars for 1 year at 8%

24. The interest on $x$ dollars for 1 year at 12%

25. The number of centimeters in 16.9 meters

26. The number of meters in 0.432 kilometers

27. The number of centimeters in $x$ meters

28. The number of meters in $k$ kilometers

29. The number of centimeters in 279 millimeters

30. The number of meters in 86 decimeters

31. The number of centimeters in $m$ millimeters

32. The number of meters in $d$ decimeters

33. The number of years in 48 months

34. The number of weeks in 105 days

35. The number of years in $m$ months

36. The number of weeks in $d$ days

37. The discount on a radio listed at $90 at a rate of 20%

38. The discount on a TV set listed at $450 at a rate of 30%

39. The discount on a radio listed at $d$ dollars at a rate of 15%

40. The discount on a TV set listed at $n$ dollars at a rate of 25%

## 8.2    Word Sentences to Equations

Here are a few word sentences and their equations.

| Word Sentence | Representation of Variable | Equation |
|---|---|---|
| The <u>sum</u> of an unknown number and seven <u>is</u> twenty-six. | Let $t$ = the unknown number. | $t + 7 = 26$ |
| The <u>quotient</u>, an unknown number of students divided by sixteen, <u>equals</u> thirty-three. | Let $n$ = the number of students. | $\dfrac{n}{16} = 33$ |
| <u>Twice</u> an unknown number of cars <u>less</u> four <u>equals</u> twelve hundred. | Let $r$ = the number of cars. | $2r - 4 = 1200$ |

example 1    The total cost of a newspaper for six days is only 25 cents more than the cost of the Sunday paper. The total cost for the week is \$1.05. Find the cost of the Sunday paper.

Let $c$ = the cost of the Sunday paper (in cents).
Then $c + 25$ = the cost for the other six days (in cents).

Think:    The cost for Sunday plus the cost for the other six days is 105 cents.

1. Write the equation ⎯⎯⎯⎯⎯⎯⎯→ $c + c + 25 = 105$

2. Add like terms. ⎯⎯⎯⎯⎯⎯⎯→ $2c + 25 = 105$

3. Subtract 25 from each side. ⎯⎯⎯→ $2c + 25 - 25 = 105 - 25$

4. Simplify. ⎯⎯⎯⎯⎯⎯⎯⎯⎯⎯→ $2c = 80$

5. Divide each side by 2. ⎯⎯⎯⎯→ $\dfrac{2c}{2} = \dfrac{80}{2}$

6. Simplify. ⎯⎯⎯⎯⎯⎯⎯⎯⎯→ $c = 40$

The cost of the Sunday paper is 40 cents.

## example 2

One evening Karen spent twice as much time on her algebra homework as she spent on Spanish. She spent 20 minutes less on science than on algebra. She worked for 130 minutes on the three subjects. How much time did she spend on each one?

Let $n$ = the number of minutes on Spanish.
Then $2n$ = the number of minutes on algebra (twice the number spent on Spanish), and
$2n - 20$ = the number of minutes on science (20 less than the number spent on algebra).

Think:   Time spent on Spanish plus time spent on algebra plus time spent on science equals 130 minutes.

$$n + 2n + 2n - 20 = 130$$
$$5n - 20 = 130$$
$$5n - 20 + 20 = 130 + 20$$
$$5n = 150$$
$$\frac{5n}{5} = \frac{150}{5}$$
$$n = 30 \text{ minutes (Spanish)}$$
$$2n = 60 \text{ minutes (algebra)}$$
$$2n - 20 = 40 \text{ minutes (science)}$$

## ORAL EXERCISES 8.2

*Tell an equation that describes each word sentence.*

1. The sum of $x$ and 7 equals 15.
2. 42 is 3 times as great as $n$.
3. $t$ increased by seven equals eighteen.
4. Thirty-four less $y$ is twenty-two.
5. The sum of $y$ and twice $y$ is thirty.
6. The ratio of $x$ to 5 equals 12.
7. 26 less $q$ is the same as $q$ tripled.
8. 13 diminished by $r$ equals 54.
9. Fifteen is nine less than $t$.
10. Twelve is five per cent of $x$.

*Use the following word problem for Exercises 11–12.*

"Nora and her brother Bill together earned $59 in one week. Bill earned $5 less than Nora. Find how much each earned."

11. Let $n$ equal the amount Nora earned. What open phrase stands for Bill's earnings?
12. What equation describes the problem?

*Use the following word problem for Exercises 13–14.*

> "A doctor drives twice as far on Tuesday as he drives on Monday. He drives 960 kilometers in the two days. Find how far he travels each day."

**13.** Let *d* equal the distance traveled on Monday. What phrase would represent the distance traveled on Tuesday?

**14.** What equation describes the problem?

*Use the following word problem for Exercises 15–16.*

> "Each week during the summer Tom earns three times as much money as he spends for payments on his cycle and lawnmower. He has $45 left each week after his payments. Find how much his weekly payments are."

**15.** Let *p* equal the amount of Tom's weekly payments. What phrase would represent his total earnings each week?

**16.** What equation describes the problem?

*Use the following word problem for Exercises 17–18.*

> "There are twelve more members in the Northeast 4H Club than in the Northwest 4H Club. There are 70 members in the two clubs together. Find how many members are in each club."

**17.** Let *x* equal the number of members in the Northwest Club. What phrase would represent the number in the Northeast Club?

**18.** What equation describes the problem?

## WRITTEN EXERCISES 8.2

🅰 **Goal:** To write an equation for a word problem and then use it to solve the word problem

**Sample Problem:** Steve delivers 10 fewer papers than twice the number his sister delivers. They deliver 116 papers in all. How many papers does each one deliver?

**Answer:** (a) Let $p$ = the number of papers Steve's sister delivers.
(b) Then $2p - 10$ = the number of papers Steve delivers.
(c) Equation: $p + 2p - 10 = 116$
(d) Steve delivers 74 papers, and his sister delivers 42 papers.

*Write an equation that describes each word sentence.*

**1.** Four more than *x* is sixty-three.

**2.** Five less than *y* equals forty-five.

**3.** Fifty-nine is the same as eight less *n*.

**4.** Fifteen less than *r* is thirty-one.

**5.** Twice *q* increased by 5 is 28.

**6.** The sum of twice *x* and 13 is 58.

**7.** 7 less than $t$ is 23.

**8.** $a$ diminished by 15 is 35.

**9.** The sum of 5 times $w$ and 8 is 42.

**10.** 16 increased by 8 times $p$ is 31.

**11.** The quotient, $n$ divided by five, decreased by eight equals fifty.

**12.** The quotient, twice $k$ divided by six, increased by twelve equals sixteen.

*For each problem, (a) select a variable and write what it represents, (b) write the open phrases that are needed, (c) write an equation to describe the problem, and (d) solve the problem.* (Example 1, Example 2)

**13.** Nancy received 30 more votes than Bob in the class election. If there were 150 votes cast, how many did Nancy receive?

**14.** Jill won seven more tennis matches in the season than Elena. Together, they won 31 matches. How many matches did Jill win?

**15.** Mr. Allen drove 54 fewer kilometers on Saturday than he drove on Friday. In the two days he drove a distance of 970 kilometers. How far did he drive each day?

**16.** The airline distance from Chicago to Cleveland is 175 kilometers less than the distance from Cleveland to New York. The total distance from Chicago to New York is 1185 kilometers. Find the distance from Chicago to Cleveland.

**17.** The annual average amount of snow in Detroit is 1.8 centimeters more than the average amount of rain. The total amount of rain and snow is 156.6 centimeters. Find the amounts of rain and snow.

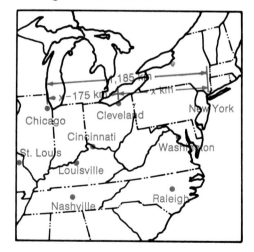

**18.** The average amount of rain in St. Louis is 2.75 centimeters more than twice the average amount of snow. The total amount of rain and snow is 131 centimeters. Find the amounts of rain and snow.

**B**

**19.** The number of children in an audience is 15 less than one fourth the number of adults. If there are 88 children present, how many adults are there?

**20.** The number of students taking science courses in a school is 27 more than one third the number taking English. If there are 241 science students, how many are taking English?

## 8.3  Perimeters

These formulas are the basis for writing equations to solve word problems involving perimeters.

1. Perimeter of a Square:  $p = 4s$
2. Perimeter of a Rectangle:  $p = 2l + 2w$
3. Perimeter of a Triangle:  $p = a + b + c$

**P-1**  **What is the perimeter of each drawing?**

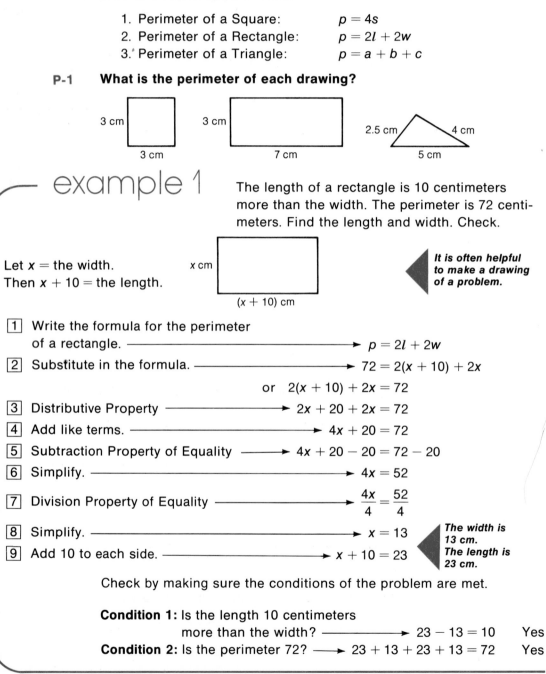

example 1

The length of a rectangle is 10 centimeters more than the width. The perimeter is 72 centimeters. Find the length and width. Check.

Let $x$ = the width.
Then $x + 10$ = the length.

*It is often helpful to make a drawing of a problem.*

1. Write the formula for the perimeter of a rectangle. ⟶ $p = 2l + 2w$
2. Substitute in the formula. ⟶ $72 = 2(x + 10) + 2x$

    or   $2(x + 10) + 2x = 72$
3. Distributive Property ⟶ $2x + 20 + 2x = 72$
4. Add like terms. ⟶ $4x + 20 = 72$
5. Subtraction Property of Equality ⟶ $4x + 20 - 20 = 72 - 20$
6. Simplify. ⟶ $4x = 52$
7. Division Property of Equality ⟶ $\dfrac{4x}{4} = \dfrac{52}{4}$
8. Simplify. ⟶ $x = 13$   *The width is 13 cm.*
9. Add 10 to each side. ⟶ $x + 10 = 23$   *The length is 23 cm.*

Check by making sure the conditions of the problem are met.

**Condition 1:** Is the length 10 centimeters
more than the width? ⟶ $23 - 13 = 10$   Yes
**Condition 2:** Is the perimeter 72? ⟶ $23 + 13 + 23 + 13 = 72$   Yes

## example 2

The length of one side of a triangle is twice the length of the shortest side. The third side is one centimeter longer than the shortest side. The perimeter is 25 centimeters. Find the length of each side.

Let $x$ = the length of the shortest side.
Then $2x$ = the length of the second side, and
$x + 1$ = the length of the third side.

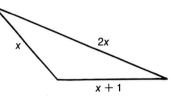

First write an equation based on the formula $p = a + b + c$.

$$a + b + c = p$$
$$x + 2x + x + 1 = 25$$
$$4x + 1 = 25$$
$$4x + 1 - 1 = 25 - 1$$
$$4x = 24$$
$$\frac{4x}{4} = \frac{24}{4}$$
$$x = 6$$
$$2x = 12$$
$$x + 1 = 7$$

The lengths are 6 centimeters, 12 centimeters, and 7 centimeters.

Check to make sure the lengths meet all the conditions of the problem.

---

**Steps in solving word problems:**

1. Make a drawing of the problem if possible.

2. Represent an unknown by a variable.

3. Represent other unknowns by open phrases.

4. Write an equation using all the operations suggested.

5. Solve the equation and find all the unknowns.

## ORAL EXERCISES 8.3

*Tell the number of units in each perimeter. (P-1)*

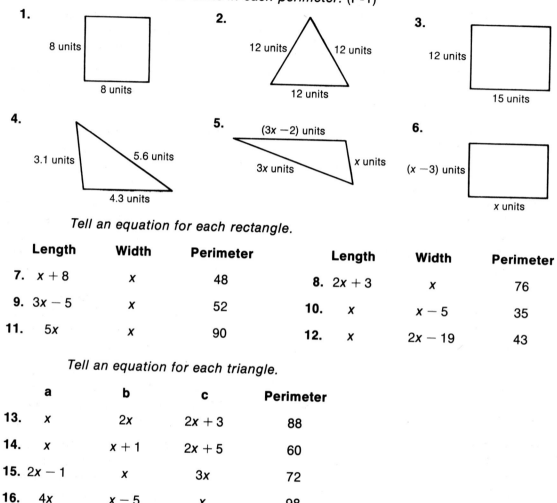

**1.** 8 units, 8 units (square)

**2.** 12 units, 12 units, 12 units (triangle)

**3.** 12 units, 15 units (rectangle)

**4.** 3.1 units, 5.6 units, 4.3 units (triangle)

**5.** $(3x - 2)$ units, $3x$ units, $x$ units (triangle)

**6.** $(x - 3)$ units, $x$ units (rectangle)

*Tell an equation for each rectangle.*

| | Length | Width | Perimeter | | Length | Width | Perimeter |
|---|---|---|---|---|---|---|---|
| **7.** | $x + 8$ | $x$ | 48 | **8.** | $2x + 3$ | $x$ | 76 |
| **9.** | $3x - 5$ | $x$ | 52 | **10.** | $x$ | $x - 5$ | 35 |
| **11.** | $5x$ | $x$ | 90 | **12.** | $x$ | $2x - 19$ | 43 |

*Tell an equation for each triangle.*

| | a | b | c | Perimeter |
|---|---|---|---|---|
| **13.** | $x$ | $2x$ | $2x + 3$ | 88 |
| **14.** | $x$ | $x + 1$ | $2x + 5$ | 60 |
| **15.** | $2x - 1$ | $x$ | $3x$ | 72 |
| **16.** | $4x$ | $x - 5$ | $x$ | 98 |

*Tell an open phrase for the length of a rectangle in each exercise if w represents the width.*

**17.** The length is two more than five times the width.

**18.** The length is double the width.

**19.** The length is three less than four times the width.

**20.** The length is ten times the width less seven.

**21.** The sum of the length and width is 19.

**22.** The sum of the length and width is 43.

## WRITTEN EXERCISES 8.3

**A**

**Goal:** To write an equation for a word problem involving perimeter and then use it to solve the problem

**Sample Problem:** The length of a rectangle is 5 more than twice the width. The perimeter is 40. Find the length and width.

**Answer:** Equation: $40 = 2w + 2(2w + 5)$     Length: 15     Width: 5

*For each problem, (a) select a variable and write what it represents, (b) write open phrases that are needed, (c) write an equation to describe the problem, and (d) solve the problem.* (Example 1, Example 2)

1. The length of a rectangle is six units longer than the width. The perimeter is 44 units. Find the length and width.

2. The length of a rectangle equals the width increased by 15 units. The perimeter is 58 units. Find the length and width.

3. The lengths of two sides of a triangle are equal. The third side is 3 units longer than each of the other sides. The perimeter is 60 units. Find the length of each side.

4. The length of one side of a triangle is two units more than the length of another. The third side is 5 units. The perimeter is 67 units. Find the lengths of the two unknown sides.

5. The width of a rectangle is 12 meters less than the length. The perimeter is 58 meters. Find the length and width.

6. The length of a rectangle less five centimeters equals the width. The perimeter is 66 centimeters. Find the length and width.

7. The length of a rectangle is 2.7 meters less than three times the width. The perimeter is 48.2 meters. Find the length and width.

8. The length of a rectangle is 6.3 meters more than twice the width. The perimeter is 98.4 meters. Find the length and width.

9. The width of a rectangle is 15.9 units less than the length. The perimeter is 65.4 units, and the area is 204.12 square units. Find the length and width.

10. Twice the width of a rectangle decreased by 2.9 millimeters equals the length. The perimeter is 32.6 millimeters. Find the length and width.

**B**

11. The perimeter of a square is 96 units. The length of one side of a triangle with the same perimeter equals the length of each side of the square. The length of the second side of the triangle is three times the length of the third side. Finds the lengths of the sides of the triangle.

12. The lengths of three sides of a triangle are equal, and the perimeter is 18.6 centimeters. The width of a rectangle equals the length of each side of the triangle. The perimeter of the rectangle is 28.6 centimeters. Find the length and width of the rectangle.

# 8.4 Spending and Saving Money

**P-1**    **What is the total cost of 6 cans of soup at 38 cents per can? What is the total cost at *c* cents per can?**

In the following formula, *T* represents the total cost. The number of items is represented by *n* and the cost per item by *c*.

$$T = nc$$

**P-2**    **What is the value of *T* if *n* equals 12 and *c* equals $1.50?**

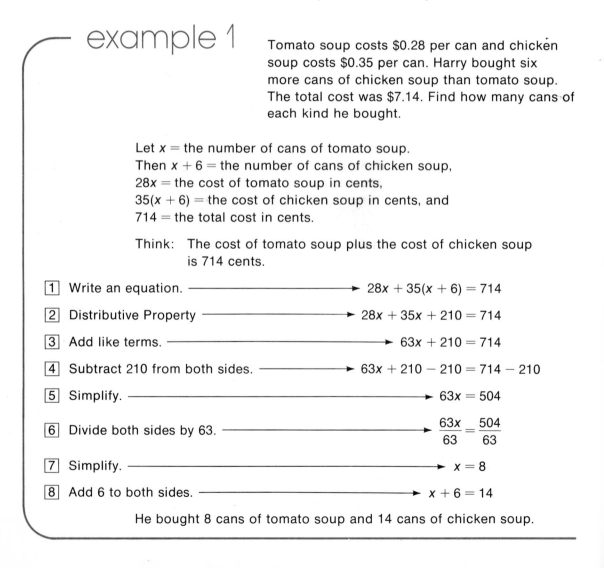

## example 1

Tomato soup costs $0.28 per can and chicken soup costs $0.35 per can. Harry bought six more cans of chicken soup than tomato soup. The total cost was $7.14. Find how many cans of each kind he bought.

Let $x$ = the number of cans of tomato soup.
Then $x + 6$ = the number of cans of chicken soup,
$28x$ = the cost of tomato soup in cents,
$35(x + 6)$ = the cost of chicken soup in cents, and
$714$ = the total cost in cents.

Think:   The cost of tomato soup plus the cost of chicken soup is 714 cents.

1. Write an equation.  ⟶  $28x + 35(x + 6) = 714$

2. Distributive Property  ⟶  $28x + 35x + 210 = 714$

3. Add like terms.  ⟶  $63x + 210 = 714$

4. Subtract 210 from both sides.  ⟶  $63x + 210 - 210 = 714 - 210$

5. Simplify.  ⟶  $63x = 504$

6. Divide both sides by 63.  ⟶  $\dfrac{63x}{63} = \dfrac{504}{63}$

7. Simplify.  ⟶  $x = 8$

8. Add 6 to both sides.  ⟶  $x + 6 = 14$

He bought 8 cans of tomato soup and 14 cans of chicken soup.

# example 2

Connie saves dimes and quarters. Their total value is $6.65. She has seven more quarters than dimes. How many of each kind of coin does she have? Check.

Let $x$ = the number of dimes.
Then $x + 7$ = the number of quarters,
$10x$ = the value of the dimes in cents,
$25(x + 7)$ = the value of the quarters in cents, and
$665$ = the total value of the coins in cents.

A table is often helpful in finding phrases to use in an equation.

| Coins | Number | Value in Cents |
|-------|--------|----------------|
| Dimes | $x$ | $10x$ |
| Quarters | $x + 7$ | $25(x + 7)$ |

Think:   The value of the dimes plus the value of the quarters equals the total value.

$$10x + 25(x + 7) = 665$$
$$10x + 25x + 175 = 665$$
$$35x + 175 = 665$$
$$35x + 175 - 175 = 665 - 175$$
$$35x = 490$$
$$\frac{35x}{35} = \frac{490}{35}$$
$$x = 14$$
$$x + 7 = 21$$

◀ *14 dimes*
*21 quarters*

**Check**

Dimes ⟶ $10(14) = 140$
Quarters ⟶ $25(21) = \underline{525}$
Total ⟶ $665$
or   $6.65$

# example 3

Mrs. Squires invested one amount of money at 6% simple interest for one year. She invested $500 more at 7%. Her investments earned $139 for one year. How much did she invest at each rate? Check.

Let $x$ = the amount invested at 6%.
Then $x + 500$ = the amount invested at 7%.

The phrases needed to form an equation are summarized in a table at the top of the next page.

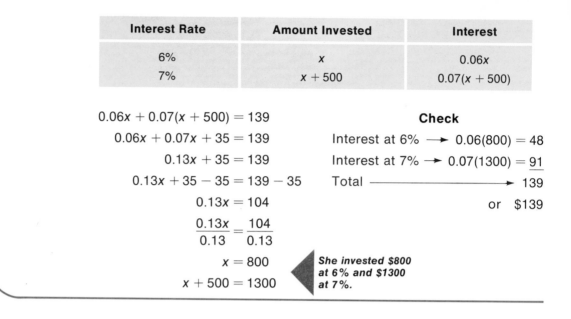

| Interest Rate | Amount Invested | Interest |
|:---:|:---:|:---:|
| 6% | $x$ | $0.06x$ |
| 7% | $x + 500$ | $0.07(x + 500)$ |

$$0.06x + 0.07(x + 500) = 139$$
$$0.06x + 0.07x + 35 = 139$$
$$0.13x + 35 = 139$$
$$0.13x + 35 - 35 = 139 - 35$$
$$0.13x = 104$$
$$\frac{0.13x}{0.13} = \frac{104}{0.13}$$
$$x = 800$$
$$x + 500 = 1300$$

**Check**

Interest at 6% ⟶ $0.06(800) = 48$

Interest at 7% ⟶ $0.07(1300) = \underline{91}$

Total ⟶ 139

or $139

**She invested $800 at 6% and $1300 at 7%.**

## ORAL EXERCISES 8.4

*Tell an open phrase for each word phrase.*

**1.** The cost in cents of $t$ cans of coffee at $1.26 per can

**2.** The cost in cents of $r$ cans of peaches at $0.76 per can

**3.** The value in cents of $x$ nickels

**4.** The value in cents of $y$ dimes

**5.** The value in cents of $q$ quarters

**6.** The value in cents of $h$ half-dollars

**7.** The value in cents of $d$ dollars

**8.** The interest on $x$ dollars at 5% for one year

**9.** The interest on $y$ dollars at 6% for one year

**10.** The interest on $n$ dollars at $6\frac{1}{2}\%$ for one year

*Use the following word problem to answer Exercises 11–15.*

"Jerry has two more quarters than nickels and three times as many dimes as nickels. The collection is worth $4.10."

| Coins | Number | Value in Cents |
|---|:---:|:---:|
| **11.** nickels | $x$ | ? |
| **12.** dimes | ? | $10(3x)$ |
| **13.** quarters | ? | ? |

**14.** What is the total value of the collection in cents?

**15.** What equation describes the problem?

*Use the following word problem to answer Exercises 16–18.*

> "A man invested an amount of money at 6% simple interest for one year. He invested $200 more than twice that amount at $6\frac{1}{2}$%. The investments earned $241 in interest."

| | Interest Rate | Amount Invested | Interest |
|---|---|---|---|
| **16.** | 6% | $x$ | ? |
| **17.** | $6\frac{1}{2}$% | ? | ? |

**18.** What equation describes the problem?

*Use the following word problem to answer Exercises 19–22.*

> "Debbie purchased cola for her club's party. She bought a number of cans for $0.16 per can. She bought twice as many bottles for $0.12 a bottle. The total cost was $8.00."

| | Cola | Number | Cost | | | Cola | Number | Cost |
|---|---|---|---|---|---|---|---|---|
| **19.** | Canned | $x$ | ? | | **20.** | Bottled | ? | ? |

**21.** Tell the total cost in cents.  **22.** What equation describes the problem?

## WRITTEN EXERCISES 8.4

**A** **Goal:** To write an equation for a word problem involving money and then use it to solve the problem

**Sample Problem:** Carol Roosa buys stock in Eaton Business Machines Inc. costing $57 a share and North Shore Lobster costing $17 a share. The number of shares she buys of Eaton Business Machines is twice the number of shares of North Shore Lobster. She invests a total of $2096. How many shares of stock in each company does she buy?

**Answer:** Equation: $17x + 57(2x) = 2096$   Eaton Business Machines: 32 shares
North Shore Lobster: 16 shares

*For each problem, (a) select a variable and write what it represents, (b) write the open phrases that are needed, (c) write an equation to describe the problem, and (d) solve the problem.* (Example 1)

**1.** Scott bought three shirts costing $7.50 each and some socks costing $1.50 a pair. The total cost was $34.50. How many pairs of socks did he buy?

**2.** Alice bought four notebooks costing $1.75 each and some packages of paper costing $0.55 each. The total cost was $12.50. How many packages of paper did she buy?

*For each problem, (a) select a variable and write what it represents, (b) write the open phrases that are needed, (c) write an equation to describe the problem, and (d) solve the problem.* (Example 1, Example 2, Example 3)

**3.** A restaurant manager purchased canned tuna at $14.80 per case and coffee at $23.00 per case. He purchased six more cases of coffee than tuna. Find how many cases of tuna and coffee he bought if the total bill was $516.00.

**4.** Roberto ordered hot dogs and root beer for his club meeting. He ordered eight more hot dogs than bottles of root beer. The hot dogs cost $0.80 each and the bottles of root beer $0.25 each. The total bill was $19.00. How many hot dogs and bottles of root beer did he buy?

**5.** Sally has some nickels and quarters worth $6.40. The number of quarters equals twice the number of nickels less three. Find the number of nickels and quarters.

**6.** Brad has dimes and quarters in his savings bank. The number of dimes is five more than six times the number of quarters. The total value of the coins is $14.10. Find the number of dimes and quarters.

**7.** Mrs. Harper makes a cash deposit of $40.70 in her bank account including dollar bills, quarters, and dimes. There are seven more quarters than dollars. The number of dimes is two less than twice the number of dollars. Find the number of dollars, quarters, and dimes.

**8.** In one week the receipts from a cold drink machine were $21.20. There were 17 more dimes than quarters. The number of nickels was 24 less than twice the number of quarters. Find the number of each type of coin.

**9.** Mr. Johnson invested money at 4% simple interest with a bank. He also invested money at 6% simple interest with a savings and loan company. The amount at 6% was $50 more than twice the amount at 4%. The total interest earned for one year was $59.00. Find the amount invested at each rate.

**10.** Jan Hardy gets two loans of money in order to open her law office. The interest rate on one loan is 12% for one year, and the rate on the other loan is 8%. The amount borrowed at 8% is $800 less than twice the amount at 12%. Her total interest payment is $496.00. Find the amounts of the two loans.

# 8.5 Consecutive Numbers

21, 22, 23, and 24 are **consecutive numbers.**
14, 16, 18, and 20 are **consecutive even numbers.**
33, 35, 37, 39, and 41 are **consecutive odd numbers.**

**P-1** **If _n_ represents a whole number, how can you represent the next greater whole number?**

example 1    Represent consecutive odd and consecutive even whole numbers.

**Consecutive Odd**

Let $n$ = an odd whole number.
$n + 2$ = the next greater odd number.
$n + 4$ = the next greater odd number.

**Consecutive Even**

Let $x$ = an even whole number.
$x + 2$ = the next greater even number.
$x + 4$ = the next greater even number.

**P-2** **In Example 1, how can you represent the next consecutive odd whole number?   the next consecutive even whole number?**

example 2    The sum of two consecutive whole numbers is 47. Find the numbers. Check.

Let $n$ = the lesser number.
Then $n + 1$ = the greater number.

Think:   The sum of the two numbers is 47.

$$n + n + 1 = 47$$
$$2n + 1 = 47$$
$$2n + 1 - 1 = 47 - 1$$
$$2n = 46$$
$$\frac{2n}{2} = \frac{46}{2}$$
$$n = 23$$
$$n + 1 = 24$$

**Check**

1. 23 and 24 are consecutive whole numbers.
2. $23 + 24 = 47$

▸ *23 and 24 are the two numbers.*

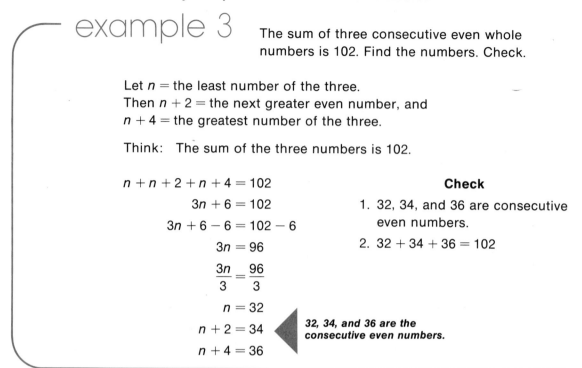

**P-3** If *n* represents the least of three consecutive even whole numbers, how can you represent the other two numbers?

example 3   The sum of three consecutive even whole numbers is 102. Find the numbers. Check.

Let $n$ = the least number of the three.
Then $n + 2$ = the next greater even number, and
$n + 4$ = the greatest number of the three.

Think:   The sum of the three numbers is 102.

$n + n + 2 + n + 4 = 102$

$3n + 6 = 102$

$3n + 6 - 6 = 102 - 6$

$3n = 96$

$\dfrac{3n}{3} = \dfrac{96}{3}$

$n = 32$

$n + 2 = 34$

$n + 4 = 36$

**Check**

1. 32, 34, and 36 are consecutive even numbers.

2. $32 + 34 + 36 = 102$

**32, 34, and 36 are the consecutive even numbers.**

## ORAL EXERCISES 8.5

1. Name four consecutive whole numbers starting with 16.

2. Name five consecutive odd numbers starting with 9.

3. Name four consecutive even numbers starting with 30.

4. Represent five consecutive whole numbers if *t* represents the least of the five. (P-1)

5. Represent three consecutive even whole numbers if *w* represents the least of the three. (P-2, P-3)

6. Represent four consecutive odd whole numbers if *a* represents the least of the four. (P-2)

7. If *2k* represents the lesser of two consecutive whole numbers, what phrase represents the greater number? (P-1)

8. If *2k* represents the lesser of two consecutive even whole numbers, what phrase represents the greater number? (P-2, P-3)

9. If *2k* + 1 represents the lesser of two consecutive odd whole numbers, what phrase represents the greater number? (P-2)

10. If *n* represents the greater of two consecutive whole numbers, what phrase represents the lesser number?

*Say <u>Yes</u> or <u>No</u> to tell whether the truth number of each equation is a whole number.*

**11.** $n = 15\frac{3}{4}$    **12.** $2n = 26$    **13.** $3n = 43$    **14.** $2n + 1 = 18$

**15.** $n + n + 1 = 45$    **16.** $n + n + 2 = 19$    **17.** $n + n + 2 = 28$

**18.** $n + n + 1 + n + 2 = 39$    **19.** $n + n + 1 + n + 2 = 20$    **20.** $n + 1 + n - 1 = 11$

## WRITTEN EXERCISES 8.5

**A**

**Goal:** To write an equation for a word problem involving consecutive numbers and then use it to solve the problem

**Sample Problem:** The sum of three consecutive odd numbers is 87. Find the numbers.

**Answer:** Equation: $x + (x + 2) + (x + 4) = 87$    The numbers are 27, 29, and 31.

*For each problem, (a) select a variable and write what it represents, (b) write open phrases that are needed, (c) write an equation to describe the problem, and (d) solve the problem. (Example 1, Example 2, Example 3)*

**1.** The sum of two consecutive numbers is 35. Find the two numbers.

**2.** The sum of two consecutive numbers is 67. Find the two numbers.

**3.** The sum of two consecutive even numbers is 98. Find the two numbers.

**4.** The sum of two consecutive even numbers is 126. Find the two numbers.

**5.** The sum of two consecutive odd numbers is 72. Find the two numbers.

**6.** The sum of two consecutive odd numbers is 60. Find the two numbers.

**7.** The sum of three consecutive numbers is 129. Find the three numbers.

**8.** The sum of three consecutive numbers is 168. Find the three numbers.

**9.** The length and width of a rectangle are consecutive even whole numbers. The perimeter is 148 centimeters. Find the length and width.

**10.** The lengths of the sides of a triangle are consecutive whole numbers. The perimeter is 87 units. Find the lengths of the three sides.

**11.** Find three consecutive even whole numbers if twice the least number increased by three times the greatest number is 122.

**12.** Find three consecutive odd whole numbers if five times the greatest number decreased by six times the least number equals nine.

**B**

**13.** Show why there cannot be three consecutive whole numbers with a sum of 40. (Hint: Form an equation and show that its truth number is not a whole number.)

**14.** Show why there cannot be three consecutive odd whole numbers with a sum of 110. (See hint for Exercise 13.)

## 8.6 Metric Units of Volume, Capacity, and Mass

A **cubic centimeter** (abbreviated cm³) is a cube with each edge 1 centimeter in length.

**P-1** **How many cubic centimeters are in the rectangular solid of Figure 2?**

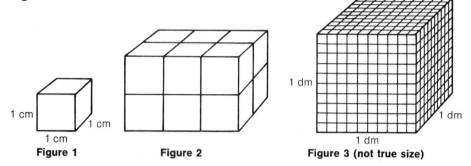

Figure 1          Figure 2          Figure 3 (not true size)

The drawing in Figure 3 represents a **cubic decimeter** (dm³). The length of each edge is 1 decimeter.

**P-2** **What is the length of each edge of a cubic decimeter expressed in centimeters?**

**P-3** **How many cubic centimeters are in a cubic decimeter?**

## example 1

Find the number of cubic millimeters (mm³) in one cubic decimeter.

There are 100 millimeters in the length of each edge of a cubic decimeter. Perform the following multiplication.

(100 mm)(100 mm)(100 mm) = 1,000,000 mm³

Other common metric units of volume are shown below.

1000 mm³ = 1 cm³
1,000,000 mm³ = 1 dm³
1000 cm³ = 1 dm³
1,000,000 cm³ = 1 m³
1000 dm³ = 1 m³

# example 2

Change 2500 cubic centimeters to cubic decimeters.

Let $x$ = the unknown number of cubic decimeters.

1. Write the relationship between cubic centimeters and one cubic decimeter. ──────────▶ $1000 \text{ cm}^3 = 1 \text{ dm}^3$

2. Write the relationship between 2500 cm³ and the unknown number of cubic decimeters. ──────▶ $2500 \text{ cm}^3 = x \text{ dm}^3$

3. Write a proportion. ────────────────▶ $\dfrac{1000}{2500} = \dfrac{1}{x}$

4. Cross Products Property ────────────▶ $1000x = 2500$

5. Divide each side by 1000. ──────────▶ $x = 2.5 \text{ dm}^3$

A basic unit of capacity or liquid measure in the metric system is the **liter** (*l*). A container that has a volume of 1 cubic decimeter also holds 1 liter (Figure 4). Other common units of capacity are the **milliliter** (m*l*) and the **kiloliter** (k*l*), as shown below.

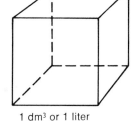

1 dm³ or 1 liter

**Figure 4**

1000 milliliters (m*l*) = 1 liter (*l*)
1000 liters (*l*) = 1 kiloliter (k*l*)

A basic unit of mass in the metric system is the **gram** (g). One milliliter of pure water has a mass of one gram. A paper clip has a mass of about one gram, and a nickel has a mass of five grams.

Other common units of mass are the **milligram** (mg) and the **kilogram** (kg), as shown below.

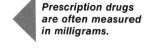 *Prescription drugs are often measured in milligrams.*

1000 milligrams (mg) = 1 gram (g)
1000 grams (g) = 1 kilogram (kg)

The following facts are important.

1 milliliter of water has a mass of 1 gram.
1000 milliliters of water have a mass of 1000 grams or 1 kilogram.
1 liter of water has a mass of 1000 grams or 1 kilogram.

## example 3

Write the missing numeral.

**a.** $2.3\ l = \underline{\phantom{?}}\ ml$    **b.** $3620\ g = \underline{\phantom{?}}\ kg$

Each problem is worked using a proportion.

| **a.** | **b.** |
|---|---|
| $2.3\ l = x\ ml$ | $3620\ g = x\ kg$ |
| $1\ l = 1000\ ml$ (See page 193.) | $1000\ g = 1\ kg$ (See page 193.) |
| $\dfrac{2.3}{1} = \dfrac{x}{1000}$ | $\dfrac{3620}{1000} = \dfrac{x}{1}$ |
| $x = 2300\ ml$ | $1000x = 3620$ |
| | $\dfrac{1000x}{1000} = \dfrac{3620}{1000}$ |
| | $x = 3.62\ kg$ |

## ORAL EXERCISES 8.6

*Tell a proportion that can be used to find the value of x.*
*(Steps 1, 2, and 3 of Example 2)*

**1.** $x$ grams $= 2.3$ kilograms

**2.** 5200 cubic centimeters $= x$ cubic decimeters

**3.** 178 liters $= x$ kiloliters

**4.** $x$ grams $= 3120$ milligrams

**5.** $x$ cubic millimeters $= 19$ cubic centimeters

**6.** $x$ liters $= 14.3$ milliliters

**7.** $x$ milligrams $= 13$ kilograms

**8.** 0.08 cubic meter $= x$ cubic centimeters

*Tell the missing numeral.* (Example 3)

**9.** $2\ dm^3 = \underline{\phantom{?}}\ cm^3$

**10.** $5\ cm^3 = \underline{\phantom{?}}\ mm^3$

**11.** $3000\ cm^3 = \underline{\phantom{?}}\ dm^3$

**12.** $12{,}000\ mm^3 = \underline{\phantom{?}}\ cm^3$

**13.** $8\ l = \underline{\phantom{?}}\ ml$

**14.** $16\ kl = \underline{\phantom{?}}\ l$

**15.** $2400\ ml = \underline{\phantom{?}}\ l$

**16.** $500\ l = \underline{\phantom{?}}\ kl$

**17.** $2.3\ kg = \underline{\phantom{?}}\ g$

**18.** $25\ g = \underline{\phantom{?}}\ mg$

**19.** $8400\ mg = \underline{\phantom{?}}\ g$

**20.** $46{,}000\ g = \underline{\phantom{?}}\ kg$

## WRITTEN EXERCISES 8.6

**A**

**Goal:** To change from one cubic metric measure to another

**Sample Problem:** $x$ cm³ = 0.55 m³

**Answer:** $x$ = 550,000

*Write a proportion. Solve for the unknown measure.*
(Example 2 and Example 3)

**1.** $x$ dm³ = 36 m³

**2.** $y$ mm³ = 42 cm³

**3.** $r$ dm³ = 6000 cm³

**4.** $t$ m³ = 7200 dm³

**5.** 2,500,000 cm³ = $w$ m³

**6.** 650,000 mm³ = $b$ dm³

**7.** $x$ g = 2.6 kg

**8.** 4.8 g = $n$ mg

**9.** 6800 mg = $y$ g

**10.** $r$ kg = 9380 g

**11.** $x$ m$l$ = 20.8 $l$

**12.** $y$ $l$ = 72.6 k$l$

**13.** 84.6 $l$ = $n$ k$l$

**14.** $w$ $l$ = 192 m$l$

**15.** 0.03 k$l$ = $r$ $l$

**16.** 0.0092 $l$ = $x$ m$l$

**17.** 14.8 cm³ = $x$ dm³

**18.** $x$ m³ = 4.06 dm³

**19.** 0.00904 dm³ = $x$ mm³

**20.** $x$ cm³ = 0.000512 m³

**C**     *Write the missing numeral.*

| | To change a measure of | to a measure of | multiply the number of |
|---|---|---|---|
| 21. | cubic centimeters | cubic millimeters | cubic centimeters by __?__ |
| 22. | cubic meters | cubic centimeters | cubic meters by __?__ |
| 23. | cubic decimeters | cubic centimeters | cubic decimeters by __?__ |
| 24. | cubic decimeters | cubic millimeters | cubic decimeters by __?__ |
| 25. | cubic meters | cubic decimeters | cubic meters by __?__ |
| 26. | liters | milliliters | liters by __?__ |
| 27. | kiloliters | liters | kiloliters by __?__ |
| 28. | grams | milligrams | grams by __?__ |
| 29. | kilograms | grams | kilograms by __?__ |
| 30. | kilograms | milligrams | kilograms by __?__ |

*Write the missing numeral.*

| | To change a measure of | to a measure of | divide the number of |
|---|---|---|---|
| 31. | cubic millimeters | cubic decimeters | cubic millimeters by __?__ |
| 32. | cubic centimeters | cubic decimeters | cubic centimeters by __?__ |
| 33. | cubic decimeters | cubic meters | cubic decimeters by __?__ |
| 34. | cubic centimeters | cubic meters | cubic centimeters by __?__ |
| 35. | liters | kiloliters | liters by __?__ |
| 36. | milliliters | liters | milliliters by __?__ |
| 37. | milligrams | grams | milligrams by __?__ |
| 38. | grams | kilograms | grams by __?__ |

# 8.7 Mixture Problems

A recipe for cinnamon toast requires 1 part of cinnamon and 3 parts of sugar.

**P-1** **How much cinnamon would be required for 12 grams of sugar?**

The measures can be expressed in terms of a variable.

> Let $x$ = the number of grams of cinnamon.
> Then $3x$ = the number of grams of sugar.

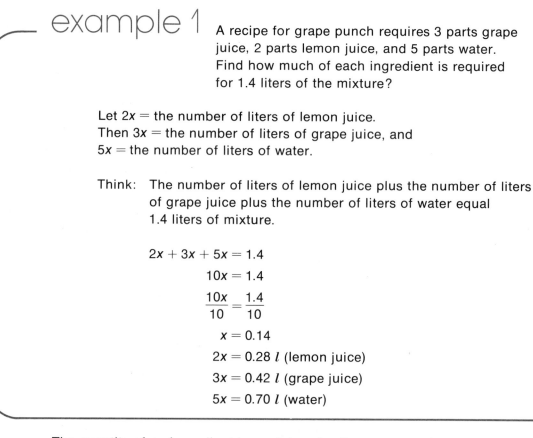

## example 1

A recipe for grape punch requires 3 parts grape juice, 2 parts lemon juice, and 5 parts water. Find how much of each ingredient is required for 1.4 liters of the mixture?

Let $2x$ = the number of liters of lemon juice.
Then $3x$ = the number of liters of grape juice, and
$5x$ = the number of liters of water.

Think: The number of liters of lemon juice plus the number of liters of grape juice plus the number of liters of water equal 1.4 liters of mixture.

$$2x + 3x + 5x = 1.4$$
$$10x = 1.4$$
$$\frac{10x}{10} = \frac{1.4}{10}$$
$$x = 0.14$$
$$2x = 0.28 \; l \text{ (lemon juice)}$$
$$3x = 0.42 \; l \text{ (grape juice)}$$
$$5x = 0.70 \; l \text{ (water)}$$

The quantity of an ingredient in a mixture is often expressed as a per cent.

1. 10 grams of salt in 100 grams of a mixture of salt and water is called a 10% salt solution.
2. 5 m$l$ of acid in 100 m$l$ of a mixture of water and acid is called a 5% acid solution.

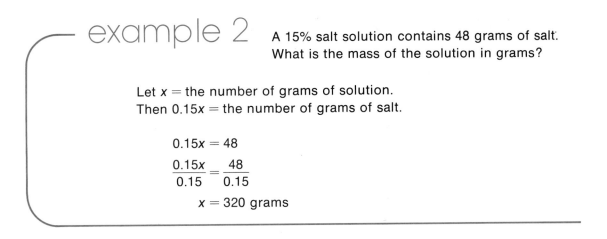

example 2

A 15% salt solution contains 48 grams of salt.
What is the mass of the solution in grams?

Let $x$ = the number of grams of solution.
Then $0.15x$ = the number of grams of salt.

$$0.15x = 48$$
$$\frac{0.15x}{0.15} = \frac{48}{0.15}$$
$$x = 320 \text{ grams}$$

## ORAL EXERCISES 8.7

*Tell how much of each ingredient is in each mixture.* (Example 1, Example 2)

1. 1 part concentrated orange juice and 3 parts water in 800 milliliters of mixture

2. 2 parts brown sugar and 3 parts white sugar in 75 grams of mixture

3. A 25% salt solution (mixture of salt and water) in 400 grams of mixture

4. 200 milliliters of a 4% acid solution (mixture of acid and water)

5. 1 part oxygen and 4 parts nitrogen in 500 cubic meters of air

6. 2 parts of chemical A, 3 parts of chemical B, and 5 parts of chemical C in 600 milliliters of mixture

*Tell the missing numeral or phrase.* (Example 2)

| | Per Cent Solution | Amount of Mixture | Amount of Salt |
|---|---|---|---|
| 7. | 10% | 60 grams | __?__ grams |
| 8. | 5% | $x$ kilograms | __?__ kilograms |
| 9. | 15% | $y$ milligrams | __?__ milligrams |
| 10. | 4% | $(100 - x)$ grams | __?__ grams |
| 11. | 20% | __?__ grams | 40 grams |
| 12. | 25% | __?__ grams | 10 grams |

*Tell the missing numeral or phrase.* (Example 2)

| | Per Cent Solution | Amount of Mixture | Amount of Acid | Amount of Water |
|---|---|---|---|---|
| 13. | 4% acid | 50 liters | __?__ liters | __?__ liters |
| 14. | 5% acid | x milliliters | __?__ milliliters | 0.95x milliliters |
| 15. | 9% acid | 600 milliliters | __?__ milliliters | __?__ milliliters |
| 16. | 3% acid | y grams | __?__ grams | __?__ grams |
| 17. | __?__ % acid | 20 liters | 5 liters | __?__ liters |
| 18. | __?__ % acid | 40 grams | __?__ grams | 28 grams |

## WRITTEN EXERCISES 8.7

**A** **Goal:** To write an equation for a word problem involving mixtures and then use it to solve the problem

**Sample Problem:** Dr. Lopez mixes a solution that is one part sulfur, two parts carbon, and four parts liquid. The mixture is 63 grams. How many grams of each ingredient did she use?

**Answer:** 9 grams of sulfur, 18 grams of carbon, 36 grams of liquid

*Write an answer to each question.* (Example 1, Example 2)

1. The nitrogen content of a fertilizer is 18%. How many kilograms of nitrogen are in a 40-kilogram bag of the fertilizer?

2. An acid solution is 5% pure acid. How much pure acid is in 200 milliliters of the solution?

3. Five kilograms of salt are mixed with water. There are 80 kilograms of mixture. How much water is used?

4. One liter of insect spray is mixed with water to get 23 liters of the mixture. How much water is used?

5. 100 milliliters of water and x milliliters of acid are mixed. What open phrase describes the amount of the mixture?

6. Three kilograms of salt are mixed with y kilograms of water. What open phrase describes the amount of the mixture?

7. 500 milliliters of liquid fertilizer are mixed with water to obtain w milliliters of the mixture. What open phrase describes the amount of water?

8. Water is mixed with x liters of a radiator coolant to get a mixture of 15 liters. What open phrase describes the amount of water?

*For each problem, (a) select a variable and show what it represents, (b) write open phrases that are needed, (c) write an equation to describe the problem, and (d) solve the problem. (Example 1, Example 2)*

**9.** A recipe for a special soap solution requires 1 part of palm-oil soap, 4 parts of glycerin, and 8 parts of pure water. Find how much of each ingredient is needed for 520 grams of the solution.

**10.** A copper alloy is 55 parts copper, 25 parts zinc, and 20 parts nickel. How much of each metal is needed for 25 kilograms of the alloy?

**11.** An 8% acid solution contains 152 milliliters of pure acid. Find the amount of the solution in milliliters.

**12.** A 6% salt solution contains 204 grams of salt. Find the amount of the solution in grams.

**13.** A grocer makes a blend of coffee by using 2 parts of Brand X, 5 parts of Brand Y, and 11 parts of Brand Z. How much of each brand is needed for 54 kilograms of the mixture?

**14.** A clerk in a store is preparing a mixture of nuts. She must use 8 parts of peanuts, 5 parts of almonds, and 3 parts of cashews. How much of each kind must be used for a mixture of 12.8 kilograms?

**B**

**EXAMPLE:** A 12% acid solution is mixed with a 5% acid solution. How many milliliters of each solution are needed to obtain 560 milliliters of a $7\frac{1}{2}$% solution?

**SOLUTION:**

| Per Cent Solution | Number of Milliliters | Amount of Pure Acid |
|---|---|---|
| 12% | $x$ | $0.12x$ |
| 5% | $560 - x$ | $0.05(560 - x)$ |
| $7\frac{1}{2}$% | 560 | $0.075(560)$ |

The sum of the amounts of pure acid in the 12% and 5% solutions equals the total amount of pure acid in the mixture.

**EQUATION:** $0.12x + 0.05(560 - x) = 0.075(560)$

**ANSWER:** 200 m$l$ of 12% solution, 360 m$l$ of 5% solution

**15.** A 5% acid solution is mixed with a 10% acid solution. How many milliliters of each solution are used to obtain 360 milliliters of an $8\frac{1}{3}$% solution?

**16.** A 25% salt solution is mixed with a 15% salt solution. How many milliliters of each solution are used to obtain 1600 milliliters of a $17\frac{1}{2}$% solution?

# Radiologist

Persons who operate X-ray equipment are called radiologic technologists or X-ray technicians. Some radiologic technologists work as radiation therapists. They use X-rays to assist physicians in treating patients with diseases such as cancer. Other radiologic technologists work in nuclear medicine.

A person can prepare to be an X-ray technician by completing a training program in X-ray technology. These programs are offered by hospitals, by medical schools at universities, by colleges and community colleges. Most are 24-month programs. All schools in X-ray technology require high school graduation for entrance. Most schools prefer students who have studied mathematics, physics, chemistry, biology, and typing in high school.

X-ray technicians must have a knowledge of what electricity is and how it works. The basic formula in electricity is Ohm's Law.

$$I = \frac{E}{R}$$

In this formula, E represents the number of volts (electrical pressure), R represents the number of ohms of resistance in the electrical circuit, and I represents the rate of current flow in amperes.

**EXAMPLE:** Find the number of amperes (amps) in a circuit of 115 volts with a resistance of 23 ohms.

**SOLUTION:** $I = \frac{E}{R}$

$I = \frac{115}{23}$

$I = 5$ amperes

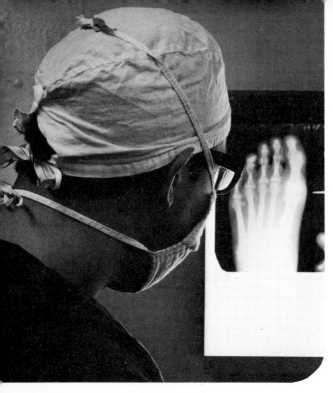

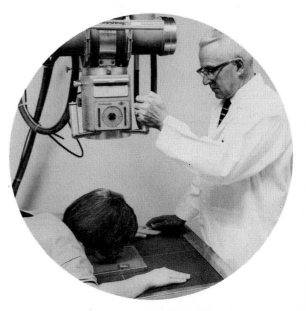

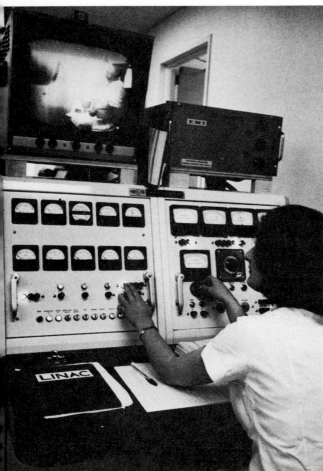

The photos prepared in the process of X-raying are called radiographs. An important factor in the quality of a radiograph is its density. Density refers to the amount of film blackening.

# CHAPTER SUMMARY

| | |
|---|---|
| **IMPORTANT TERMS** | Consecutive numbers *(p. 189)*       Liter *(p. 193)* <br> Consecutive even numbers *(p. 189)*      Milliliter *(p. 193)* <br> Consecutive odd numbers *(p. 189)*      Kiloliter *(p. 193)* <br> Cubic centimeter *(p. 192)*      Gram *(p. 193)* <br> Cubic decimeter *(p. 192)*      Milligram *(p. 193)* <br> Kilogram *(p. 193)* |

**IMPORTANT IDEAS**

*1.* The words <u>sum</u>, <u>total</u>, <u>plus</u>, <u>increased by</u>, and <u>more than</u> suggest the operation of addition.

*2.* The words <u>difference</u>, <u>less</u>, <u>less than</u>, <u>minus</u>, <u>decreased by</u>, and <u>diminished by</u> suggest the operation of subtraction.

*3.* The words <u>product</u>, <u>multiplied by</u>, <u>times</u>, <u>twice</u>, <u>doubled</u>, and <u>tripled</u> suggest the operation of multiplication.

*4.* The words <u>quotient</u> and <u>divided by</u> suggest the operation of division.

*5.* The following steps are recommended in solving word problems.
   *a.* Make a drawing of the problem if possible.
   *b.* Represent an unknown by a variable.
   *c.* Represent other unknowns by open phrases.
   *d.* Write an equation using the operations suggested.
   *e.* Solve the equation and find all the unknowns.

*6.* The formula $T = nc$ is used to compute the total cost, $T$, of $n$ items with $c$ representing the cost per item.

*7.* If $n$ represents a whole number, then $n + 1$ represents the next greater whole number.

*8.* If $n$ represents an odd whole number, then $n + 2$ represents the next greater odd whole number.

*9.* If $n$ represents an even whole number, then $n + 2$ represents the next greater even whole number.

*10.* 1 milliliter of water has a mass of one gram. 1 liter of water has a mass of 1000 grams or 1 kilogram.

# CHAPTER REVIEW

### SECTION 8.1

*Select a variable and write what it represents. Then write an open phrase.*

**1.** Twenty-three more than the number of stamps

**2.** The number of singers diminished by ten

**3.** Twelve less than the number of games

**4.** Five more than twice the number of teachers

*Write an equation that describes each word sentence.*

5. Twenty-seven is nineteen more than *n*.

6. Fourteen less *t* is equal to twelve.

7. Eighteen increased by three times *q* is fifty-one.

8. Twice *k* diminished by thirteen is thirty.

9. The quotient, *x* divided by ten, plus seven equals twenty-eight.

10. Fifty-six is three less than nine times *w*.

*For each problem, (a) select a variable and write what it represents, (b) write open phrases that are needed, (c) write an equation to describe the problem, and (d) solve the problem.*

11. In the girls' softball championship game the Braves scored three more runs than the Saints. The total number of runs scored in the game was 21. Find the number of runs scored by each team.

12. Jerry bought a back pack and a sleeping bag for a camping trip. The sleeping bag cost $14 less than the back pack. Find the cost of each item if the total cost was $62.

**SECTION 8.3**

13. The length of a rectangle is 5 centimeters more than three times the width. The perimeter is 122 centimeters. Find the length and width.

14. The perimeter of a triangle is 117 units. The length of the longest side is three times the length of the shortest side. The length of the third side is three more than twice the length of the shortest side. Find the lengths of the three sides.

**SECTION 8.4**

15. Dave saved nickels, dimes, and quarters to buy a tennis racquet. He had 12 more dimes than quarters, and 8 fewer nickels than twice the number of quarters. The total amount saved was $17.00. Find the number of each kind of coin.

16. Money from a class treasury was invested in savings accounts. One amount was invested at a rate of 5% simple interest. An amount twice as great was invested at 6%. The club earned $20.40 interest in one year on the investments. Find how much was invested at each rate.

**SECTION 8.5**

**17.** The sum of two consecutive odd whole numbers is 108. Find the two numbers.

**18.** The sum of three consecutive whole numbers is 192. Find the three numbers.

**SECTION 8.6**

*Use a proportion to solve for each unknown measure.*

**19.** $6.8 \text{ dm}^3 = x \text{ cm}^3$

**20.** $348 \text{ mm}^3 = x \text{ cm}^3$

**21.** $0.023 \text{ m}^3 = x \text{ cm}^3$

**22.** $0.42 \text{ } l = x \text{ m}l$

**23.** $2560 \text{ } l = x \text{ k}l$

**24.** $0.0381 \text{ kg} = x \text{ g}$

**SECTION 8.7**

*For each problem, (a) select a variable and write what it represents, (b) write open phrases that are needed, (c) write an equation to describe the problem, and (d) solve the problem.*

**25.** Sugar is composed of 12 parts carbon, 22 parts hydrogen, and 11 parts oxygen. How much carbon is in 180 grams of sugar?

**26.** A 6% acid solution contains 72 grams of acid. How many grams are in the solution?

# 9

# Rational Numbers

# 9.1 Integers

The number line in Figure 1 has whole-number coordinates.

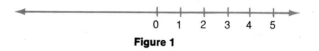

**Figure 1**

The points with coordinates 0 and 1 determine the length of a unit.

This unit is used to mark points to the left of 0 as in Figure 2.

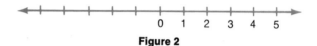

**Figure 2**

The first point to the left of 0 is labeled ⁻1. This coordinate is read "negative one." The coordinate of the next point is "negative two," the next "negative three," and so on. See Figure 3.

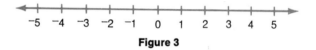

**Figure 3**

P-1    **What is the first coordinate to the left of ⁻4?   to the left of ⁻5?**

Numbers that are coordinates of points to the left of 0 are called **negative numbers.**

The arrows at each end of a number line indicate two important facts.

> 1. The line extends infinitely in both directions.
> 2. The pattern of coordinates continues infinitely in both directions.

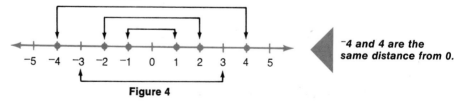

**Figure 4**

⁻4 and 4 are the same distance from 0.

The set of counting numbers {1, 2, 3, 4, 5, · · ·} is often called the set of **positive integers.**

The numbers that can be paired with the positive integers as shown in Figure 4 make up the set of **negative integers.**

This pairing is shown below in another way.

**Positive Integers:** 1 2 3 4 5 6

etc.

**Negative Integers:** ⁻1 ⁻2 ⁻3 ⁻4 ⁻5 ⁻6

> *0 is an integer but 0 is neither positive nor negative.*

P-2  **What negative integer is paired with 25?  What positive integer is paired with ⁻100?**

> The **set of integers** is made up of the positive integers, zero, and the negative integers.

The set of integers and four of its <u>subsets</u> are described below.

**Integers:**  {· · ·, ⁻3, ⁻2, ⁻1, 0, 1, 2, 3, · · ·}

**Positive Integers:**  {1, 2, 3, 4, 5, · · ·}

**Negative Integers:**  {· · ·, ⁻5, ⁻4, ⁻3, ⁻2, ⁻1}

**Even Integers:**  {· · ·, ⁻6, ⁻4, ⁻2, 0, 2, 4, 6, · · ·}

**Odd Integers:**  {· · ·, ⁻5, ⁻3, ⁻1, 1, 3, 5, · · ·}

> Set A is a **subset** of Set B if every element of A is an element of B.

P-3  **What set is shown by each graph below?**

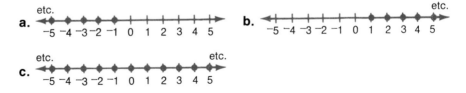

## ORAL EXERCISES 9.1

*Say each symbol in words.*

1. ⁻10

2. ⁻15

3. ⁻47

4. ⁻31

5. ⁻77

6. ⁻2

7. ⁻300

8. ⁻13

9. Count by ones starting with 5 and ending with ⁻3.

10. Count by ones starting with ⁻4 and ending with 7.

11. Count by ones starting with ⁻10 and ending with ⁻2.

12. Count by ones starting with ⁻3 and ending with ⁻12.

13. Count by twos starting with ⁻8 and ending with 10.

14. Count by twos starting with 4 and ending with ⁻12.

15. Count by threes starting with ⁻3 and ending with ⁻15.

16. Count by fives starting with ⁻30 and ending with 25.

*Say True or False.*

17. {negative integers} is a subset of {integers}.

18. {whole numbers} is a subset of {integers} .

19. {negative integers} is a subset of {whole numbers}.

20. {counting numbers} is a subset of {integers}.

21. {positive integers} is a subset of {whole numbers}.

22. {counting numbers} = {positive integers}.

23. {0} is a subset of {integers}.

24. {positive integers} is a subset of {negative integers}.

*Think of the two numbers as coordinates of points on a number line. Name the coordinate of the point on the right.*

25. ⁻4, 2    26. 0, ⁻8    27. ⁻35, 35    28. 19, 0    29. ⁻5, ⁻13    30. 17, ⁻8

## WRITTEN EXERCISES 9.1

**A**

**Goal:** To describe a subset of {integers} in word form, roster form, or by a number-line graph

**Sample Problem:** Write {negative odd integers} in roster form. Then graph the set.

**Answer:** {· · · , ⁻5, ⁻3, ⁻1};

*Write each set in roster form.*

1. {positive even integers}

2. {negative even integers}

3. {whole numbers}

4. {counting numbers}

5. {integers less than ⁻3}

6. {integers greater than ⁻5}

7. {integers greater than or equal to ⁻4}

8. {integers less than or equal to 2}

*Write a word description of each set that is graphed.* (P-3)

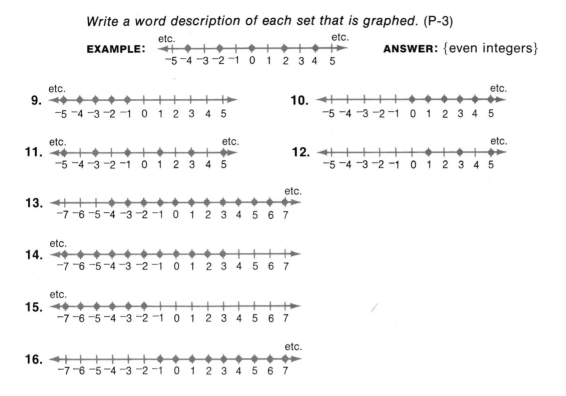

**EXAMPLE:**  etc. −5 −4 −3 −2 −1 0 1 2 3 4 5 etc.    **ANSWER:** {even integers}

9.  etc. −5 −4 −3 −2 −1 0 1 2 3 4 5

10.  −5 −4 −3 −2 −1 0 1 2 3 4 5 etc.

11.  etc. −5 −4 −3 −2 −1 0 1 2 3 4 5 etc.

12.  −5 −4 −3 −2 −1 0 1 2 3 4 5 etc.

13.  −7 −6 −5 −4 −3 −2 −1 0 1 2 3 4 5 6 7 etc.

14.  etc. −7 −6 −5 −4 −3 −2 −1 0 1 2 3 4 5 6 7

15.  etc. −7 −6 −5 −4 −3 −2 −1 0 1 2 3 4 5 6 7

16.  −7 −6 −5 −4 −3 −2 −1 0 1 2 3 4 5 6 7 etc.

*Write the numbers of each exercise in order from least to greatest.*

**EXAMPLE:** 5, $^-$2, 0, $^-$10, $^-$1    **ANSWER:** $^-$10, $^-$2, $^-$1, 0, 5

**17.** $^-$3, 1, 0, $^-$10, 7
**18.** 3, $^-$5, 2, $^-$6, 10
**19.** 12, $^-$9, 5, $^-$1, $^-$8

**20.** 4, $^-$12, 9, 7, $^-$8
**21.** $^-$19, $^-$23, $^-$11, $^-$5, $^-$31
**22.** $^-$27, $^-$8, $^-$13, $^-$39, $^-$2

**23.** $^-$56, 72, 0, 1, $^-$42, $^-$99
**24.** 12, $^-$8, $^-$37, 1, $^-$42, $^-$98

**25.** 19, $^-$26, $^-$29, $^-$101, $^-$88
**26.** 0, 25, $^-$35, $^-$17, 50, $^-$95

**27.** $^-$1024, $^-$2536, $^-$117, 28, 33
**28.** 48, $^-$1078, $^-$1206, $^-$1087, $^-$1, 29

*Draw graphs of the following sets.* (P-3)

**29.** {· · ·, $^-$4, $^-$3, $^-$2, $^-$1}
**30.** {1, 2, 3, 4, · · ·}

**31.** {· · ·, $^-$6, $^-$4, $^-$2, 0, 2, 4, 6, · · ·}
**32.** {· · ·, $^-$5, $^-$3, $^-$1, 1, 3, 5, · · ·}

**33.** {· · ·, $^-$7, $^-$5, $^-$3, $^-$1}
**34.** {2, 4, 6, 8, 10, · · ·}

**35.** {$^-$3, 0, 3, 6, · · ·}
**36.** {· · ·, $^-$6, $^-$4, $^-$2, 0, 2, 4}

**37.** {$^-$3, 0, 3, 6}
**38.** {$^-$6, $^-$4, $^-$2, 0, 2, 4}

# 9.2   Rational Numbers

**P-1**   **What rational numbers of arithmetic are graphed in Figure 1?**

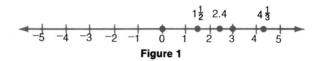

**Figure 1**

**P-2**   **How can each number of the graph be expressed as a quotient of two whole numbers?**

The point halfway between the points with coordinates 0 and ⁻1 has the coordinate ⁻($\frac{1}{2}$) as shown in Figure 2. The number ⁻($\frac{1}{2}$) is a *negative rational number.* It is read "negative one half."

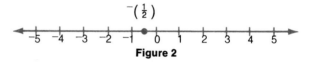

**Figure 2**

**P-3**   **Where is the point which has the negative rational number ⁻(1$\frac{1}{2}$) as its coordinate?**

The point with coordinate ⁻(2$\frac{1}{3}$) is one third of a unit to the left of the point with coordinate ⁻2. (See Figure 3.)

$$^{-}(\tfrac{11}{3})\ ^{-}(2\tfrac{1}{3})\ ^{-}(1\tfrac{1}{2})\ \ ^{-}(\tfrac{2}{3})$$

**Figure 3**

**P-4**   **How could you describe the location of ⁻($\frac{11}{3}$)?   of ⁻($\frac{2}{3}$)?**

Positive and negative rational numbers can be paired just as integers are paired.

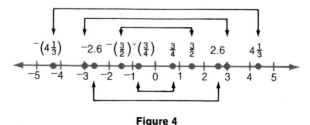

**Figure 4**

**P-5**   **What rational number is paired with ⁻(4$\frac{1}{3}$)?   with 2.6?   with 3?**

Rational numbers of arithmetic that are coordinates of points to the right of 0 are called **positive rational numbers.** The set consisting of 0 and the positive rational numbers is also called the **set of nonnegative rational numbers.**

> The **set of rational numbers** consists of the negative rational numbers, zero, and the positive rational numbers.

P-6 **How can you write 4 in fraction form? ⁻10? 0?**

> The set of integers is a subset of the set of rational numbers.

## ORAL EXERCISES 9.2

*Say each numeral in words.*

1. $^-\left(\frac{3}{4}\right)$

2. $^-3\frac{1}{4}$

3. $^-6.3$

4. $^-\left(\frac{15}{4}\right)$

5. $^-0.9$

6. $^-17$

7. $^-15\frac{7}{8}$

8. $^-\left(\frac{1}{8}\right)$

*Say* _True_ *or* _False_ *for each statement.*

9. {negative rational numbers} is a subset of {rational numbers}.

10. {positive rational numbers} is a subset of {rational numbers}.

11. {0} is a subset of {rational numbers}.

12. {integers} is a subset of {rational numbers}.

13. {negative rational numbers} is a subset of {negative integers}.

14. {positive integers} is a subset of {positive rational numbers}.

15. {whole numbers} is a subset of {positive rational numbers}.

16. {counting numbers} is a subset of {rational numbers}.

17. {rational numbers of arithmetic} = {positive rational numbers}.

18. {0} is a subset of {positive rational numbers}.

*Think of the two numbers as coordinates of points on a number line. Name the coordinate of the point on the right.*

**19.** $^-(\frac{1}{3})$ and $\frac{2}{5}$

**20.** $^-2\frac{1}{3}$ and $^-2$

**21.** $2\frac{1}{5}$ and 3

**22.** $^-3\frac{1}{4}$ and $^-4$

**23.** $^-4\frac{1}{3}$ and $\frac{1}{3}$

**24.** $\frac{7}{8}$ and $\frac{7}{16}$

**25.** $^-(\frac{7}{8})$ and $^-(\frac{7}{16})$

**26.** 0 and $^-(\frac{1}{5})$

**27.** $^-2\frac{3}{4}$ and $^-3\frac{1}{4}$

**28.** $^-1\frac{1}{3}$ and $^-1\frac{2}{3}$

**29.** $^-1.31$ and $^-1.32$

**30.** $^-1.30$ and $^-1.29$

**31.** $^-4.2$ and 0

**32.** 0 and 5.6

## WRITTEN EXERCISES 9.2

**A**

**Goal:** To describe a subset of {rational numbers} in roster form and by a number-line graph

**Sample Problem:** Write in roster form the subset of $\{^-(\frac{1}{5}), \frac{6}{3}, ^-2, \frac{0}{3}\}$ that contains integers. Then graph this subset.

**Answer:** $\{\frac{6}{3}, ^-2, \frac{0}{3}\}$;

*Write each subset of R in roster form.*

$$R = \{^-10, ^-(\tfrac{8}{2}), ^-2\tfrac{2}{3}, ^-(\tfrac{7}{4}), ^-0.1, 0, \tfrac{5}{8}, 3, \tfrac{13}{4}, \tfrac{15}{3}\}$$

**EXAMPLE:** {Elements of R that are even integers}    **ANSWER:** $\{^-10, ^-(\frac{8}{2}), 0\}$

**1.** {Elements of R that are rational numbers}

**2.** {Elements of R that are negative rational numbers}

**3.** {Elements of R that are integers}

**4.** {Elements of R that are nonnegative rational numbers}

**5.** {Elements of R that are whole numbers}

**6.** {Elements of R that are numbers of arithmetic}

**7.** {Elements of R that are nonnegative integers}

**8.** {Elements of R that are negative integers}

**9.** {Elements of R that are positive rational numbers}

**10.** {Elements of R that are counting numbers}

*Graph each set.* (P-3, P-4)

**11.** $\{^-(\frac{1}{2}), 3, ^-(\frac{9}{3}), 0, ^-(\frac{5}{2})\}$

**12.** $\{\frac{3}{4}, ^-1\frac{1}{4}, \frac{8}{4}, ^-2\frac{2}{3}\}$

**13.** $\{^-1.3, ^-3.6, ^-(\frac{3}{4}), \frac{3}{4}\}$

**14.** $\{4.7, 0, ^-0.6, ^-1.3, ^-5\}$

**15.** $\{\cdots, ^-3\frac{1}{2}, ^-2\frac{1}{2}, ^-1\frac{1}{2}, ^-(\frac{1}{2}), \frac{1}{2}, 1\frac{1}{2}, 2\frac{1}{2}, \cdots\}$

**16.** $\{\cdots, ^-(\frac{7}{2}), ^-(\frac{6}{2}), ^-(\frac{5}{2}), ^-(\frac{4}{2}), ^-(\frac{3}{2}), ^-(\frac{2}{2}), ^-(\frac{1}{2})\}$

*Think of the two numbers as coordinates of points on a number line. Write the coordinate of the point on the right.*

**17.** $^-(\frac{3}{4})$ and $\frac{1}{4}$

**18.** $\frac{5}{4}$ and $^-(\frac{1}{4})$

**19.** $^-3\frac{1}{2}$ and $^-3\frac{3}{4}$

**20.** $^-4\frac{3}{8}$ and $^-4\frac{1}{8}$

**21.** $^-(\frac{17}{4})$ and $^-(\frac{33}{8})$

**22.** $^-(\frac{11}{2})$ and $^-(\frac{23}{4})$

**23.** $^-0.62$ and $^-0.61$

**24.** $^-0.58$ and $^-0.59$

**25.** $^-3.8$ and $0$

**26.** $0$ and $2.3$

**C** *Think of the two numbers as coordinates of points on a number line. Write the coordinate of a point that is between two given points.*

**EXAMPLE:** $^-5$ and $^-5\frac{1}{2}$    **ANSWER:** $^-5\frac{1}{4}, ^-5.1, ^-5.2, ^-5\frac{3}{8}, ^-(\frac{41}{8})$ are a few possible answers.

**27.** $^-3$ and $^-4$

**28.** $^-5$ and $^-6$

**29.** $^-(\frac{1}{4})$ and $^-(\frac{1}{2})$

**30.** $^-(\frac{1}{2})$ and $^-(\frac{3}{4})$

**31.** $^-3\frac{1}{4}$ and $^-3\frac{1}{8}$

**32.** $^-2\frac{5}{8}$ and $^-2\frac{1}{4}$

**33.** $0$ and $^-(\frac{1}{16})$

**34.** $^-(\frac{1}{10})$ and $0$

*Think of the numbers as coordinates of points on a number line. Write the coordinates of the points in order from left to right.*

**EXAMPLE:** $\frac{5}{12}, ^-(\frac{5}{12}), \frac{12}{5}, ^-(\frac{12}{5})$

**ANSWER:** $^-(\frac{12}{5}), ^-(\frac{5}{12}), \frac{5}{12}, \frac{12}{5}$

**35.** $\frac{4}{11}, ^-(\frac{11}{4}), ^-(\frac{4}{11}), \frac{11}{4}$

**36.** $^-(\frac{3}{7}), \frac{7}{3}, \frac{3}{7}, ^-(\frac{7}{3})$

**37.** $\frac{6}{7}, ^-(\frac{5}{7}), \frac{5}{6}, ^-(\frac{5}{6}), ^-(\frac{6}{7}), \frac{5}{7}$

**38.** $^-(\frac{7}{8}), \frac{7}{9}, ^-(\frac{8}{9}), \frac{8}{9}, \frac{7}{8}, ^-(\frac{7}{9})$

**39.** $1.2, ^-1.2, ^-(\frac{4}{5}), \frac{7}{5}$

**40.** $3\frac{1}{2}, ^-3\frac{5}{16}, ^-3\frac{1}{2}, ^-3.4$

**41.** $^-4.6, 5\frac{1}{3}, ^-4\frac{2}{3}, ^-(\frac{14}{5})$

**42.** $^-2.5, ^-(\frac{13}{5}), 1.5, ^-(\frac{13}{4})$

# 9.3 Decimal Forms of Rational Numbers

**P-1**  **What decimal is a name for each of the following numbers?**

**a.** $\frac{1}{2}$   **b.** $\frac{3}{4}$   **c.** $^-1\frac{1}{5}$   **d.** $^-(\frac{3}{10})$   **e.** $4\frac{3}{5}$

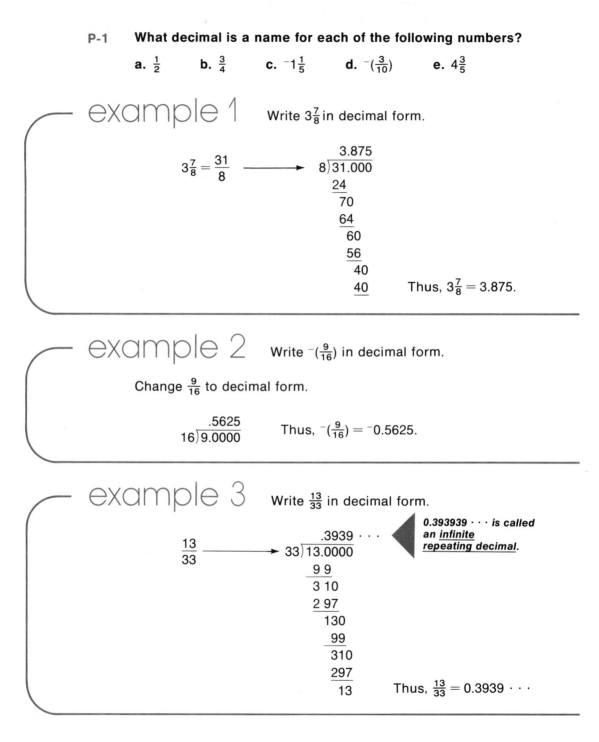

example 1   Write $3\frac{7}{8}$ in decimal form.

$$3\frac{7}{8} = \frac{31}{8} \longrightarrow$$

$$\begin{array}{r} 3.875 \\ 8\overline{)31.000} \\ \underline{24}\phantom{.000} \\ 70\phantom{00} \\ \underline{64}\phantom{00} \\ 60\phantom{0} \\ \underline{56}\phantom{0} \\ 40 \\ \underline{40} \end{array}$$

Thus, $3\frac{7}{8} = 3.875$.

example 2   Write $^-(\frac{9}{16})$ in decimal form.

Change $\frac{9}{16}$ to decimal form.

$$\begin{array}{r} .5625 \\ 16\overline{)9.0000} \end{array}$$

Thus, $^-(\frac{9}{16}) = ^-0.5625$.

example 3   Write $\frac{13}{33}$ in decimal form.

$$\frac{13}{33} \longrightarrow$$

$$\begin{array}{r} .3939 \cdots \\ 33\overline{)13.0000} \\ \underline{9\ 9}\phantom{.0000} \\ 3\ 10\phantom{000} \\ \underline{2\ 97}\phantom{000} \\ 130\phantom{0} \\ \underline{99}\phantom{0} \\ 310 \\ \underline{297} \\ 13 \end{array}$$

0.393939 · · · is called an _infinite_ _repeating decimal._

Thus, $\frac{13}{33} = 0.3939\ \cdots$

Every rational number can be represented as an infinite repeating decimal.

$$^-(\tfrac{1}{2}) = {}^-0.50000\cdots$$

$$\tfrac{2}{7} = 0.285714285714\cdots$$

## example 4

Write each of the following as an infinite repeating decimal.

**a.** 25   **b.** $^-(\tfrac{1}{4})$   **c.** $\tfrac{5}{8}$   **d.** $^-(\tfrac{18}{10})$

**a.** $25 = 25.000\cdots$       **b.** $^-(\tfrac{1}{4}) = {}^-0.25000\cdots$

**c.** $\tfrac{5}{8} = 0.625000\cdots$       **d.** $^-(\tfrac{18}{10}) = {}^-1.8000\cdots$

**P-2**   **Which is the greater number, 2.1718 or 2.17181?**

On a number line the point with coordinate 2.17181 is <u>to the right</u> of the point with coordinate 2.1718.

**P-3**   **If $^-1.813$ and $^-1.812$ are graphed on a number line, which point is to the right of the other?**

**P-4**   **Which number do you think is greater, $^-1.813$ or $^-1.812$?**

If a point with coordinate $x$ is to the right of a point with coordinate $y$ on a number line, then $x > y$.

## example 5

Write the following rational numbers in order from least to greatest.

$$^-(\tfrac{5}{4}) \qquad ^-5 \qquad ^-(\tfrac{5}{8}) \qquad 1\tfrac{3}{4} \qquad 0$$

Think of each number as the coordinate of a point.

Then write the coordinates in order from left to right.

$$^-5 \qquad ^-(\tfrac{5}{4}) \qquad ^-(\tfrac{5}{8}) \qquad 0 \qquad 1\tfrac{3}{4}$$

## ORAL EXERCISES 9.3

*Tell which number is greater in each pair.* (P-2, P-3, P-4)

**EXAMPLE:** $^-1.654$ and $^-1.653$
**ANSWER:** $^-1.653$

1. $^-1$ and 1

2. $^-3\frac{1}{2}$ and 2

3. 0 and $^-5$

4. 10 and 0

5. $^-3$ and $^-4$

6. 5.6 and $^-6.5$

7. 1.125 and 1.126

8. $^-1.125$ and $^-1.126$

9. 10 and $^-100$

10. $1\frac{3}{4}$ and $^-1\frac{3}{4}$

11. $2\frac{1}{8}$ and $^-3\frac{5}{8}$

12. $^-1.07$ and $^-1.06$

13. 2.1503 and 2.150

14. $^-4.316$ and $^-4.3162$

15. 0.1527 and 0.153

16. $8.131313 \cdots$ and 8.13

17. $^-2.5$ and $^-2.555 \cdots$

18. $^-0.187187187 \cdots$ and $^-0.187$

*Tell whether each statement is* <u>True</u> *or* <u>False</u>.

19. $^-6 < 5$

20. $^-8 > ^-2$

21. $1\frac{1}{2} = 1.5000 \cdots$

22. $2\frac{1}{4} = 2.25$

23. $^-1.6 < ^-1.666 \cdots$

24. $\frac{2}{3} = 0.666 \cdots$

25. $1.05 = 1.05000 \cdots$

26. $\frac{5}{8} < \frac{5}{16}$

27. $^-(\frac{5}{8}) < ^-(\frac{5}{16})$

28. $^-(\frac{15}{4}) > ^-(\frac{13}{4})$

29. $\frac{1}{3} = 0.333 \cdots$

30. $\frac{1}{3} < 0.3$

31. $3.14 = \frac{22}{7}$

32. $^-(\frac{2}{5}) > ^-(\frac{2}{3})$

33. $\frac{3}{4} = 0.7500$

## WRITTEN EXERCISES 9.3

**A** **Goal:** To change a rational number from fraction form to decimal form
**Sample Problem:** $^-(\frac{7}{11})$
**Answer:** $^-0.6363 \cdots$

*Write each number in decimal form.* (Example 1, Example 2, Example 3)

1. $^-(\frac{7}{2})$

2. $^-(\frac{9}{2})$

3. $2\frac{3}{4}$

4. $3\frac{1}{4}$

5. $\frac{3}{16}$

6. $\frac{5}{8}$

7. $^-(\frac{7}{9})$

8. $^-(\frac{5}{9})$

9. $^-1\frac{8}{11}$

10. $^-2\frac{5}{11}$

*Write as an infinite repeating decimal.* (Example 4)

**11.** 16  **12.** $^-(\frac{2}{5})$  **13.** 0  **14.** 1  **15.** $^-(\frac{7}{8})$  **16.** $^-(\frac{3}{4})$

*Write whether the inequality $a > b$ is True or False for each graph.*

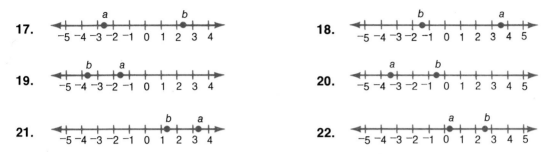

**17.**  
**18.**  
**19.**  
**20.**  
**21.**  
**22.**

*Use $>$ and $<$ to write two true inequalities for each pair of numbers.*

**EXAMPLE 1:** 1.87 and 1.88   **ANSWER:** $1.87 < 1.88$
$$1.88 > 1.87$$

**EXAMPLE 2:** $^-1.92$ and $^-1.93$   **ANSWER:** $^-1.92 > ^-1.93$
$$^-1.93 < ^-1.92$$

**23.** $^-5$ and 5

**24.** 10 and $^-10$

**25.** 0 and $^-3$

**26.** 0 and 5

**27.** $^-3\frac{1}{4}$ and $^-4\frac{1}{4}$

**28.** $^-1\frac{1}{5}$ and $^-2\frac{1}{10}$

**29.** $^-10.2$ and $^-9.6$

**30.** $^-8.9$ and $^-9.8$

**31.** $^-(\frac{1}{2})$ and $^-1$

**32.** $^-(\frac{3}{2})$ and $^-2$

**33.** 2.13 and 2.131

**34.** 5.671 and 5.67

**35.** $^-0.06$ and $^-0.003$

**36.** $^-0.09$ and $^-0.7$

**37.** $^-0.18$ and $^-0.181818\cdots$

**38.** $^-0.414141\cdots$ and $^-0.41$

**39.** $^-(\frac{7}{4})$ and $^-(\frac{7}{6})$

**40.** $^-(\frac{11}{4})$ and $^-(\frac{11}{2})$

*Write the numbers of each exercise in order from least to greatest.*
(Example 5)

**41.** $^-1\frac{1}{4}$, $^-1\frac{7}{8}$, $^-(\frac{1}{2})$, $^-0.6$

**42.** $^-2\frac{1}{8}$, $^-1.8$, $^-0.9$, $^-(\frac{4}{5})$

**43.** $^-(\frac{19}{8})$, $^-(\frac{23}{7})$, $^-(\frac{7}{16})$, $^-(\frac{7}{15})$

**44.** $^-(\frac{7}{4})$, $^-(\frac{15}{8})$, $^-(\frac{29}{8})$, $^-(\frac{29}{9})$

**45.** $^-2.3$, $^-2\frac{1}{3}$, $^-0.7$, $^-(\frac{15}{20})$, $^-2.13$

**46.** $^-1.8$, $^-1\frac{80}{99}$, $^-(\frac{3}{8})$, $^-0.37$, $^-1\frac{1}{3}$

## 9.4 Opposites

**P-1**  **How far apart are the points with coordinates 0 and 3?  the points with coordinates 0 and ⁻3?**

The point with coordinate zero is called the *origin*.

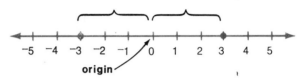

Numbers that are paired in the same way as 3 and ⁻3 are called *opposites.*

**P-2**  **What is the opposite of ⁻2½?  of 4⅓?**

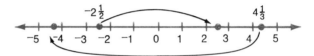

The dash symbol, −, means "the opposite of" a number.

## example 1

Read each of the following.

    **a.** −10    **b.** −(⁻3)    **c.** −⁻($\frac{3}{4}$)    **d.** −x

**a.** "−10" is read "**the opposite of** ten."
**b.** "−(⁻3)" is read "**the opposite of** negative three."
**c.** "−⁻($\frac{3}{4}$)" is read "**the opposite of** negative three fourths."
**d.** "−x" is read "**the opposite of** x."

Note that the symbol for "the opposite of" looks like the subtraction symbol. However, it does not refer to subtraction.

**P-3**  **What do you think is the opposite of 0?**

> Two numbers $x$ and $-x$ are *opposites* if their corresponding points on a number line are the same distance and in opposite directions from 0. The opposite of 0 is 0.

**P-4** **How would you read each of the following numerals?**

a. ⁻10    b. −10    c. −(⁻10)
d. −½    e. ⁻(½)    f. −⁻(½)

**P-5** **What number is the opposite of ⁻10?**

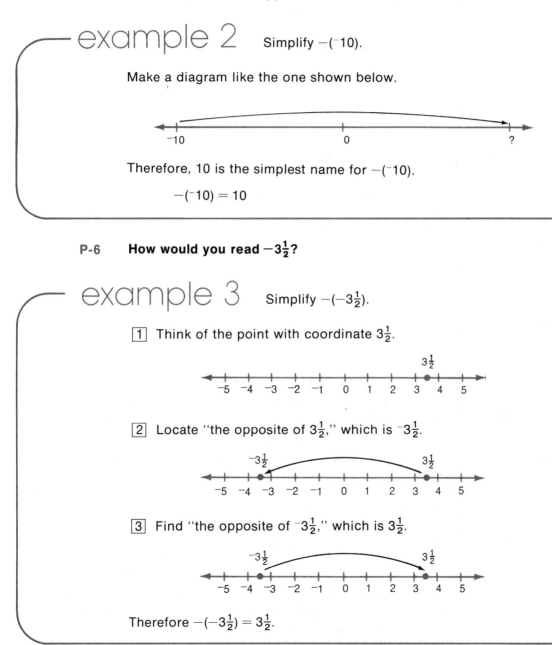

example 2    Simplify −(⁻10).

Make a diagram like the one shown below.

Therefore, 10 is the simplest name for −(⁻10).

$$-(^-10) = 10$$

**P-6** **How would you read** $-3\frac{1}{2}$**?**

example 3    Simplify $-(-3\frac{1}{2})$.

1 Think of the point with coordinate $3\frac{1}{2}$.

2 Locate "the opposite of $3\frac{1}{2}$," which is $^-3\frac{1}{2}$.

3 Find "the opposite of $^-3\frac{1}{2}$," which is $3\frac{1}{2}$.

Therefore $-(-3\frac{1}{2}) = 3\frac{1}{2}$.

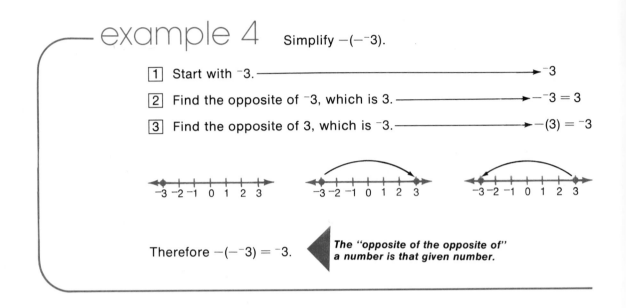

example 4    Simplify $-(-^-3)$.

1. Start with $^-3$. —————————————————→ $^-3$

2. Find the opposite of $^-3$, which is 3. ————————→ $-^-3 = 3$

3. Find the opposite of 3, which is $^-3$. ————————→ $-(3) = ^-3$

Therefore $-(-^-3) = ^-3$.    The "opposite of the opposite of" a number is that given number.

If $x$ is any number, then $-(-x) = x$.    $-(-^-6) = ^-6$

## ORAL EXERCISES 9.4

*Read each numeral.* (Example 1, P-4)

**EXAMPLE:** $-(-(-5))$    **ANSWER:** "The opposite of the opposite of the opposite of five"

**1.** $-12$

**2.** $-(^-7)$

**3.** $^-\left(\frac{5}{8}\right)$

**4.** $-\frac{5}{8}$

**5.** $-\left(^-\left(\frac{1}{2}\right)\right)$

**6.** $-^-\left(\frac{1}{2}\right)$

**7.** $-(-15)$

**8.** $-(-^-12)$

**9.** $-(-(^-12))$

**10.** $-(-(-100))$

**11.** $-3\frac{1}{2}$

**12.** $^-3\frac{1}{2}$

*Simplify.* (Example 2, Example 3, Example 4)

**13.** $-(^-8)$

**14.** $-(-13)$

**15.** $-\left(-\frac{3}{4}\right)$

**16.** $-^-\left(\frac{1}{3}\right)$

**17.** $-(-(-2))$

**18.** $-(-(^-6))$

**19.** $-(4 + 3)$

**20.** $-\left(-\left(^-2\frac{1}{2}\right)\right)$

**21.** $-(^-0.8)$

**22.** $-(-(^-1.9))$

**23.** $-[-(-(-15))]$

**24.** $-(-(-^-19))$

*Say True or False for each sentence.*

**25.** The opposite of a positive rational number is a negative rational number.

**26.** The opposite of a negative rational number is a negative rational number.

**27.** Each rational number has a different rational number as its opposite.

**28.** Each rational number has exactly one rational number as its opposite.

**29.** The opposite of the opposite of any rational number is a positive rational number.

**30.** The opposite of the opposite of any negative rational number is a positive rational number.

## WRITTEN EXERCISES 9.4

**A**  **Goal:** To write the simplest name of an opposite
**Sample Problem:** Simplify $-(-(-8))$.    **Answer:** ($^-8$)

*Simplify.* (Example 2, Example 3, Example 4)

**1.** $-(^-11)$

**2.** $-(^-35)$

**3.** $-(-22)$

**4.** $-(-13)$

**5.** $-(^-5.2)$

**6.** $-(^-3.9)$

**7.** $-(^-(\frac{7}{8}))$

**8.** $-(^-(\frac{1}{5}))$

**9.** $-(-^-25)$

**10.** $-(-^-17)$

**11.** $-(-(-8))$

**12.** $-(-(-19))$

**13.** $^-3\frac{1}{2}$

**14.** $^-8.7$

**15.** $-0$

**16.** $-(-0)$

**17.** $-(8+5)$

**18.** $-(13-7)$

**19.** $-(2\frac{1}{2}+\frac{1}{2})$

**20.** $-(3\frac{1}{4}+\frac{3}{4})$

**21.** $-(^-t)$

**22.** $-(-k)$

**23.** $-(-3x)$

**24.** $-(-5y)$

**25.** $-(-(-r))$

**26.** $-(-(-n))$

**27.** $-[-(-(-p))]$

**28.** $-[-(-(-a))]$

**B**  *Replace each variable by the given number. Then simplify.*

**EXAMPLE:** $-n$ if $n$ equals $^-25$    **SOLUTION:** $-n=-(^-25)$   or   $25$

**29.** $-(-n)$ if $n$ equals $^-2$

**30.** $-(-n)$ if $n$ equals $5$

**31.** $-t$ if $t$ equals $^-7$

**32.** $-k$ if $k$ equals $^-10$

**33.** $-m$ if $m$ equals $^-(\frac{1}{2})$

**34.** $-r$ if $r$ equals $^-0.9$

**35.** $-(-(-p))$ if $p$ equals $4$

**36.** $-(-(-y))$ if $y$ equals $^-15$

**37.** $-(-(-x))$ if $x$ equals $-\frac{1}{2}$

**38.** $-(-(-n))$ if $n$ equals $\frac{3}{4}$

**C**  *Write the truth number for each equation.*

**39.** $-x=\frac{1}{2}$

**40.** $-y=\frac{2}{3}$

**41.** $-a=^-(\frac{5}{2})$

**42.** $-t=-0.8$

*Rational Numbers  /  221*

# 9.5 Order Property of Opposites

The point with coordinate ⁻3 is to the left of the point with coordinate 7.

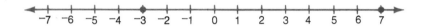

Therefore, the inequality ⁻3 < 7 is true.

**P-1** **What is another inequality for ⁻3 and 7?**

**P-2** **What is the opposite of ⁻3?  of 7?**

**P-3** **What do you think is true about the order of the opposites of ⁻3 and 7?**

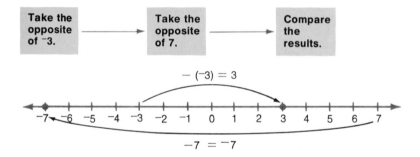

| Take the opposite of ⁻3. | Take the opposite of 7. | Compare the results. |

$$- (⁻3) = 3$$

$$-7 = ⁻7$$

Since 3 is to the right of ⁻7, the following inequalities are true.

$$3 > ⁻7 \qquad ⁻7 < 3$$

## example 1

Use the inequality below to form two true inequalities showing the order of the opposites of the two numbers.

$$⁻5 < ⁻2$$

1. Find the opposite of ⁻5. ────────→ 5

2. Find the opposite of ⁻2. ────────→ 2

3. Compare the results. ────────→ 5 > 2  or  2 < 5

## example 2

Write two inequalities showing the order of the opposites of 3 and 5.

$$3 < 5$$
$$-3 > -5$$
or $\quad -3 > -5$

$$5 > 3$$
$$-5 < -3$$
or $\quad -5 < -3$

▶ Find the opposites. Then compare them.

The results of Examples 1 and 2 are instances of the Order Property of Opposites.

> **Order Property of Opposites**
>
> For any rational numbers $x$ and $y$, if $x < y$, then $-x > -y$.
>
> $8\frac{1}{2} < 11\frac{1}{4}$
> $-8\frac{1}{2} > -11\frac{1}{4}$

This property can be extended to apply to the inequality symbols $>$, $\leq$, and $\geq$.

If $y > x$, then $-y < -x$.
If $x \leq y$, then $-x \geq -y$.
If $y \geq x$, then $-y \leq -x$.

**P-4**  **What two inequalities can you write using the opposites of the numbers in the inequalities below?**

   **a.** $5 > {}^-7$    **b.** $^-2 > {}^-3$    **c.** $3 \geq {}^-7$    **d.** $4 \leq 10$

## ORAL EXERCISES 9.5

*Tell an inequality using the opposites of the two given numbers.*
(Example 1, Example 2)

**EXAMPLE:** $5 > {}^-9$
**ANSWER:** $^-5 < 9$  or  $9 > {}^-5$

| | | | |
|---|---|---|---|
| **1.** $2 < 5$ | **2.** $^-3 > {}^-8$ | **3.** $^-1 < 7$ | **4.** $10 > 8$ |
| **5.** $^-7 < {}^-4$ | **6.** $0 < 9$ | **7.** $^-5 < 0$ | **8.** $5 > {}^-11$ |
| **9.** $0 > {}^-10$ | **10.** $15 > 0$ | **11.** $-7 > -9$ | **12.** $-({}^-3) < 8$ |
| **13.** $-5 < 5$ | **14.** $^-3 < -(-7)$ | **15.** $3\frac{1}{2} > {}^-(\frac{1}{2})$ | **16.** $^-(\frac{3}{4}) < {}^-(\frac{1}{4})$ |

## WRITTEN EXERCISES 9.5

**A**

**Goal:** To write an inequality using the opposites of two numbers

**Sample Problem:** $^-3.1 \geq ^-5.9$. Write two inequalities using the opposites of the two numbers.

**Answer:** $3.1 \leq 5.9$   or   $5.9 \geq 3.1$

(a) *Write an inequality using $<$ to show the order of the two numbers.*
(b) *Write an inequality using $>$ to show the order of their opposites.*
*Simplify where necessary.* (Example 1, Example 2)

**EXAMPLE:** $^-1; 7$     **ANSWERS:** (a) $^-1 < 7$; (b) $1 > ^-7$

**1.** $8; 3$
**2.** $17; 5$
**3.** $^-3; ^-10$
**4.** $^-1; ^-12$
**5.** $^-7; 5$

**6.** $^-10; 3$
**7.** $0; ^-7$
**8.** $^-12; 0$
**9.** $0; 8$
**10.** $12; 0$

**11.** $^-1\frac{1}{2}; ^-3\frac{1}{4}$
**12.** $^-5\frac{1}{8}; ^-7\frac{1}{4}$
**13.** $^-2.7; 3.3$
**14.** $5.2; ^-4.8$
**15.** $^-0.66; \frac{2}{3}$

**16.** $\frac{1}{3}; ^-0.33$
**17.** $-(^-3); -10$
**18.** $-17; -(^-8)$
**19.** $-(8 + 3);$
       $-(12 - 10)$
**20.** $-(8 + 7);$
       $-(15 - 10)$

*Write an inequality showing the order of the opposites of the two numbers.* (Example 1, Example 2)

**21.** $^-15 < 2$
**22.** $5 > ^-17$
**23.** $^-13 < ^-11$
**24.** $^-56 < ^-50$

**25.** $8 > 1$
**26.** $15 < 26$
**27.** $0 > -17$
**28.** $21 > 0$

**29.** $-(5\frac{1}{8}) < -(\frac{19}{4})$
**30.** $2\frac{5}{8} > -(\frac{11}{8})$
**31.** $^-2.8 \leq 0.7$
**32.** $3.4 \geq ^-3.4$

**33.** $^-5.2 \geq ^-8.3$
**34.** $^-10.3 \leq ^-7.9$
**35.** $-5 \leq -(^-7)$
**36.** $-(^-10) \geq ^-15$

**B**     *Write True or False for each sentence.*

**37.** If $-x > -y$, then $x > -y$.
**38.** If $-x < -y$, then $y > x$.

**39.** If $x > -y$, then $-x < y$.
**40.** If $-y < -x$, then $y < x$.

**41.** If $y > x$, then $-x > -y$.
**42.** If $x < y$, then $-x > -y$.

**43.** If $x \leq -y$, then $y \geq \div x$.
**44.** If $-y \geq -x$, then $y \leq x$.

**45.** If $-x \leq -y$, then $y \leq x$.
**46.** If $-(-x) \geq -y$, then $x \leq y$.

**C**     *Decide whether each number or its opposite is greater. Then write the greater number.*

**EXAMPLE:** $^-1.8$     **SOLUTION:** Opposite of $^-1.8$ is $1.8$.
                    **ANSWER:** $1.8$

**47.** $^-5$
**48.** $10$
**49.** $^-5\frac{1}{8}$
**50.** $-(^-6)$
**51.** $-(8 + 9)$
**52.** $-\frac{1}{4}$

# 9.6 Opposites and Truth Sets

**P-1** **What is the truth set of each sentence below if the domain is {0, 1, 2, 3, 4, 5}?**

**a.** $2x + 5 = 7$ **b.** $2x \leq 6$ **c.** $x + 1 < 5$

You have worked with sentences like these before.
They are called <u>open sentences</u>.

> An **open sentence** is a sentence with a variable.

**P-2** **What are some truth numbers of the following inequality if {rational numbers} is the domain?**

$$x < {}^-4\tfrac{1}{2}$$

All rational numbers less than $^-4\tfrac{1}{2}$ will make the inequality true. Here is one way of describing the truth set.

$$\{x: x < {}^-4\tfrac{1}{2}\}$$

◄ **Solution set** is
another name
for truth set.

This is read "the set of all rational numbers that are less than $^-4\tfrac{1}{2}$."

## example 1
Write the truth set of $-x > {}^-1$. The domain is $\{^-3, {}^-2, {}^-1, 0, 1, 2, 3\}$.

$$-x > {}^-1$$

☐1 Order Property of Opposites ⟶ $x < 1$

☐2 Write the truth set. ⟶ $\{^-3, {}^-2, {}^-1, 0\}$

## example 2
Write the truth set of $-x < 12$. The domain is {rational numbers}.

$$-x < 12$$

☐1 Order Property of Opposites ⟶ $x > {}^-12$

☐2 Write the truth set. ⟶ $\{x: x > {}^-12\}$

**P-3** What is the truth number of $-x = 3\frac{1}{2}$ if the domain is {rational numbers}?

You know that $x = ^-3\frac{1}{2}$ has the truth number $^-3\frac{1}{2}$. The number $^-3\frac{1}{2}$ is also the truth number of $-x = 3\frac{1}{2}$.

$$-x = 3\tfrac{1}{2}$$

---

**Equality Property of Opposites**

The equations $-x = a$ and $x = -a$ are equivalent.

$-x = 4\frac{1}{2}$

$x = ^-4\frac{1}{2}$

---

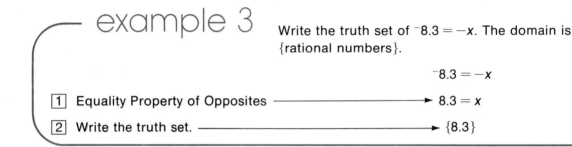

example 3    Write the truth set of $^-8.3 = -x$. The domain is {rational numbers}.

$$^-8.3 = -x$$

1. Equality Property of Opposites ⟶ $8.3 = x$

2. Write the truth set. ⟶ {8.3}

## ORAL EXERCISES 9.6

*Tell an open sentence that is equivalent to each open sentence. Use x instead of $-x$. (Step 1 of Example 1, Example 2, Example 3)*

**EXAMPLE:** $-x \leq 5$    **ANSWER:** $x \geq ^-5$

1. $-x < \frac{1}{4}$
2. $-x > ^-6$
3. $-x < ^-(\frac{1}{2})$
4. $3 \leq -x$

5. $^-10 \geq -x$
6. $^-(\frac{1}{3}) < -x$
7. $10 > -x$
8. $-x = 6.3$

9. $-x = ^-5\frac{1}{2}$
10. $-x \leq ^-(\frac{2}{3})$
11. $^-8.9 > -x$
12. $-x \geq 15$

*Tell the truth set. The domain is $\{^-3, ^-2, ^-1, 0, 1, 2, 3\}$. (P-1, Example 1)*

13. $-x > 2$
14. $-x < ^-1$
15. $-x = 3$

16. $-x = ^-2$
17. $-x > ^-1$
18. $-x < 2$

19. $-x \leq ^-2$
20. $-x \geq 3$
21. $0 < -x$

*Tell the truth set. The domain is {rational numbers}. (Example 2, Example 3)*

**EXAMPLE:** $-x \le -3\frac{1}{2}$    **ANSWER:** $\{x: x \ge 3\frac{1}{2}\}$

**SAY:** "The set of all rational numbers that are greater than or equal to $3\frac{1}{2}$"

**22.** $-x > 2$     **23.** $-x < -8$     **24.** $-x \ge -(\frac{1}{2})$     **25.** $-x \le 2.5$

**26.** $-x = -1.9$     **27.** $-x = 19$     **28.** $-x + 3 = 17$     **29.** $9 = -x + 4$

## WRITTEN EXERCISES 9.6

**A**

**Goal:** To solve an open sentence containing the opposite of an unknown number

**Sample Problem:** Write the truth set of $-r > 4.4$. The domain is {rational numbers}.

**Answer:** $\{r : r < -4.4\}$

*Write an open sentence that is equivalent to each open sentence. Use x instead of $-x$. (Step 1 of Example 1, Example 2, Example 3)*

**EXAMPLE:** $-x \ge -12$     **ANSWER:** $x \le 12$ (or $12 \ge x$)

**1.** $-x > 20$     **2.** $-x < 15$     **3.** $-x \le -27$     **4.** $-x \ge -19$

**5.** $-x < -4.2$     **6.** $-x > -6.8$     **7.** $-x = 3\frac{3}{4}$     **8.** $-x = 5\frac{1}{4}$

**9.** $-x = -(\frac{5}{8})$     **10.** $-x = -(\frac{7}{4})$     **11.** $12.9 \ge -x$     **12.** $14.5 \le -x$

**13.** $-(\frac{15}{8}) < -x$     **14.** $-(\frac{3}{4}) > -x$     **15.** $0 \le -x$     **16.** $-x \le 0$

*Write the truth set. The domain is $\{-5, -4, -3, -2, -1, 0, 1, 2, 3, 4, 5\}$. (P-1, Example 1)*

**17.** $-r > -1$     **18.** $-w < -4$     **19.** $-y < 3$     **20.** $-n > 4$

**21.** $-k \le -4$     **22.** $-a \le -1$     **23.** $-t = -3$     **24.** $-d = -5$

**25.** $-n + 1 = 4$     **26.** $-x + 3 = 5$     **27.** $-y + 2 \le 2$     **28.** $-p + 4 \ge 4$

*Write the truth set. The domain is {rational numbers}. (Example 2, Example 3)*

**29.** $-y > -6$     **30.** $-t < -13$     **31.** $-r \le \frac{1}{2}$     **32.** $-n \ge 1\frac{1}{2}$

**33.** $-w < -2.8$     **34.** $-y > -14.2$     **35.** $-x = \frac{28}{15}$     **36.** $-p = \frac{13}{4}$

**37.** $-0.9 = -a$     **38.** $-0.02 = -b$     **39.** $-2.7 \ge -k$     **40.** $6.3 \le -r$

# 9.7　Absolute Value

**P-1**　In Figure 1, what is the coordinate of point *A*?　of point *B*? of the origin?

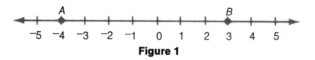

**Figure 1**

**P-2**　What is the distance of point *B* from the origin in Figure 1? of point *A* from the origin?

The distance from a point to the origin is the <u>absolute value</u> of the coordinate of the point. Thus, the absolute value of ⁻4 is 4. The absolute value of 3 is 3.

**P-3**　What is the absolute value of ⁻2.3?　of $3\frac{1}{2}$?

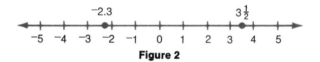

**Figure 2**

The absolute value of a number *x* may be represented as $|x|$.

---

The **absolute value** of a positive number equals that number. The absolute value of a negative number equals the opposite of that number. The absolute value of 0 equals 0.

$|4| = 4$

$|⁻4| = 4$

$|0| = 0$

---

| Number | Symbol for Absolute Value | Simplest Name for Absolute Value |
|---|---|---|
| ⁻6.7 | $|⁻6.7|$ | 6.7 |
| 13 | $|13|$ | 13 |
| 0 | $|0|$ | 0 |

**P-4**　What is the simplest name for each absolute value below?

　　**a.** $|5.2|$　　**b.** $|⁻4\frac{1}{2}|$　　**c.** $|⁻3| + |4|$　　**d.** $-(|10| \cdot |⁻6|)$

## ORAL EXERCISES 9.7

*Simplify.* (P-4)

**1.** $|10|$  **2.** $|^-8|$  **3.** $|1\frac{3}{4}|$  **4.** $|^-(\frac{7}{8})|$  **5.** $|0|$  **6.** $|-0|$

**7.** $|14.7|$  **8.** $|^-8.3|$  **9.** $|^-2\frac{1}{2}|$

**10.** $|^-2| + |3|$  **11.** $|^-2| + |^-3|$  **12.** $|^-5| + |^-6| + |9|$

*Say True or False.*

**13.** $|9| = 9$  **14.** $|^-3| < 3$  **15.** $|^-2| \geq 0$

**16.** $|^-(\frac{1}{2})| = \frac{1}{2}$  **17.** $|^-2| > |^-3|$  **18.** $|^-100| < 0$

## WRITTEN EXERCISES 9.7

**A**  **Goal:** To simplify a phrase containing absolute values
**Sample Problem:** Simplify $-(|^-7| - |^-4|)$.
**Answer:** $^-3$

*Simplify.* (P-4)

**1.** $|^-25|$  **2.** $|^-18|$  **3.** $|99|$  **4.** $|85|$  **5.** $|0|$  **6.** $|-0|$

**7.** $|12\frac{1}{2}|$  **8.** $|8\frac{3}{4}|$  **9.** $|^-7.6|$  **10.** $|^-10.3|$  **11.** $|8.6|$  **12.** $|0.9|$

**13.** $|0.2 + 0.7|$  **14.** $|1.3 + 4.5|$  **15.** $|^-3| + |10|$

**16.** $|7| + |^-13|$  **17.** $|^-2| + |^-11|$  **18.** $|^-5| + |^-16|$

**19.** $-(12 - |^-4|)$  **20.** $-(|^-8| - 5)$

**21.** $-(|^-3| \cdot |^-2|)$  **22.** $-(|7| \cdot |^-5|)$

**B**  *Write the truth set. The domain is* $\{^-5,\ ^-4,\ ^-3,\ ^-2,\ ^-1,\ 0,\ 1,\ 2,\ 3,\ 4,\ 5\}$.

**EXAMPLE:** $|x| < 5$  **ANSWER:** $\{^-4,\ ^-3,\ ^-2,\ ^-1,\ 0,\ 1,\ 2,\ 3,\ 4\}$

**23.** $|x| < 3$  **24.** $|x| < 4$  **25.** $|x| \leq 1$  **26.** $|x| \leq 2$

**27.** $|x| = 3$  **28.** $|x| = 5$  **29.** $|x| > 2$  **30.** $|x| > 3$

**C**  *x and y are coordinates of points on a number line. Write whether x or y is the greater number.*

**31.** $|y| < |x|$,
$y > 0, x > 0$

**32.** $|y| > |x|$,
$y < 0, x < 0$

**33.** $|x| > |y|$,
$x < 0, y < 0$

**34.** $|y| > |x|$,
$x > 0, y > 0$

# CHAPTER SUMMARY

| | | |
|---|---|---|
| **IMPORTANT TERMS** | Negative numbers *(p. 206)*<br>Negative integers *(p. 206)*<br>Positive integers *(p. 206)*<br>Integers *(p. 207)*<br>Even integers *(p. 207)*<br>Odd integers *(p. 207)*<br>Subset *(p. 207)*<br>Negative rational numbers *(p. 210)*<br>Positive rational numbers *(p. 211)* | Set of nonnegative rational<br>  numbers *(p. 211)*<br>Set of rational numbers *(p. 211)*<br>Infinite repeating decimal *(p. 214)*<br>Origin *(p. 218)*<br>Opposites *(p. 218)*<br>Open sentence *(p. 225)*<br>Absolute value *(p. 228)* |

**IMPORTANT IDEAS**

1. The number 0 is an integer, but 0 is neither positive nor negative.
2. The set of integers is a subset of the set of rational numbers.
3. Every rational number can be represented by an infinite repeating decimal.
4. If a point with coordinate $x$ is to the right of a point with coordinate $y$ on a number line, then $x > y$.
5. If $x$ is any number, then $-(-x) = x$.
6. *Order Property of Opposites:* For any rational numbers $x$ and $y$, if $x < y$, then $-x > -y$.
7. *Equality Property of Opposites:* The equations $-x = a$ and $x = -a$ are equivalent.

# CHAPTER REVIEW

### SECTION 9.1

*Write each set in roster form.*

1. {integers greater than $^-10$}
2. {integers less than 3}
3. {even integers less than or equal to $^-2$}
4. {odd integers greater than or equal to $^-16$}

*Write the numbers of each exercise in order from least to greatest.*

5. 5, $^-12$, $^-6$, 0, 13, $^-9$
6. 0, $^-1$, $^-7$, 19, $^-27$, $^-3$
7. $^-42$, 0, 54, $^-28$, $^-5$, $^-19$
8. 15, 0, $^-12$, $^-39$, 29, $^-47$

## SECTION 9.2

*Write each subset of set A in roster form.*

$$A = \{^-15, \, ^-(\tfrac{19}{2}), \, ^-(\tfrac{15}{3}), \, ^-3\tfrac{1}{4}, \, ^-0.3, \, 0, \, 1.7, \, 4, \, \tfrac{25}{4}\}$$

**9.** The subset of A containing all elements that are rational numbers

**10.** The subset of A containing all elements that are integers

**11.** The subset of A containing all elements that are negative integers

**12.** The subset of A containing all elements that are positive rational numbers

*Think of the two numbers as coordinates of points on a number line. Write the coordinate of the point on the right.*

**13.** $^-2.7$; $^-2.6$   **14.** $^-12.3$; $5.4$   **15.** $0$; $^-17.8$   **16.** $^-(\tfrac{5}{13})$; $^-(\tfrac{6}{13})$

## SECTION 9.3

*Write each number in decimal form.*

**17.** $^-(\tfrac{9}{4})$   **18.** $^-(\tfrac{13}{5})$   **19.** $^-2\tfrac{5}{8}$   **20.** $^-4\tfrac{3}{16}$   **21.** $\tfrac{4}{9}$   **22.** $\tfrac{3}{11}$

*Use $>$ and $<$ to write two true inequalities for each pair of numbers.*

**23.** $^-18$ and $18$   **24.** $23$ and $^-27$   **25.** $^-12.6$ and $^-14.5$

**26.** $^-5.003$ and $^-5.03$   **27.** $^-(\tfrac{10}{13})$ and $^-(\tfrac{1}{13})$   **28.** $^-(\tfrac{11}{8})$ and $^-(\tfrac{17}{8})$

## SECTION 9.4

*Simplify.*

**29.** $-\left(^-(\tfrac{1}{3})\right)$   **30.** $-(-\,^-14)$   **31.** $-(-g)$   **32.** $-(-(-h))$

## SECTION 9.5

*(a) Write an inequality using $<$ to show the order of the two numbers.*
*(b) Write an inequality using $>$ to show the order of their opposites.*
*Simplify where necessary.*

**33.** $^-15$ and $^-28$   **34.** $12$ and $^-3$   **35.** $4.2$ and $0.3$

**36.** $^-4\tfrac{1}{4}$ and $^-3\tfrac{3}{4}$   **37.** $^-13.5$ and $^-9.2$   **38.** $-(^-12)$ and $^-13$

*Write the truth set. The domain is $\{^-3, ^-2, ^-1, 0, 1, 2, 3\}$.*

**39.** $-t < ^-1$   **40.** $-r > 2$   **41.** $-x \geq ^-2$   **42.** $-y \leq ^-1$

**43.** $-x = ^-3$   **44.** $-y = ^-2$   **45.** $-x - 1 = ^-2$   **46.** $-n + 1 = 2$

*Write the truth set. The domain is {rational numbers}.*

**47.** $-n = 5.6$   **48.** $-w = ^-\left(\frac{3}{4}\right)$   **49.** $-x > ^-4.2$

**50.** $-t < ^-15$   **51.** $^-1.9 \leq -a$   **52.** $^-5\frac{1}{2} \geq -p$

## SECTION 9.7

*Simplify.*

**53.** $|8.6|$   **54.** $|^-13.9|$   **55.** $|0|$   **56.** $|-0|$

**57.** $|^-9| + |^-5|$   **58.** $|^-9| - |^-5|$   **59.** $|-(14.2 + 9.3)|$   **60.** $|-(15.1 + 6.9)|$

**61.** $(|^-4| \cdot |^-21|)$   **62.** $(|^-3| \cdot |^-4|)$   **63.** $-(|^-5| \cdot |^-2|)$   **64.** $-(|^-4| \cdot |^-7|)$

# 10

# Rational Numbers
# Addition

# 10.1  Sums of Integers

Maria, Mike, and Manuel Gonzales have a game called **Forward and Backward.** The game pieces are a board, a stack of cards, and a marker for each player.

| P | O | N | M | L | K |
|---|---|---|---|---|---|
| Q |   |   |   |   | J |
| R |   |   |   |   | I |
| S |   |   |   |   | H |
| T |   |   |   |   | G |
| U |   |   |   |   | F |
| V |   |   |   |   | E |
| W |   |   |   |   | D |
| X |   |   |   |   | C |
| Y | Z | START | A | B |

← Backward     Forward →

**Rules:**

1. Put a marker in the <u>Start</u> space.
2. Draw a card.
3. Follow instructions on the card.

The winner is the first player to reach **Z** after passing **M** in <u>either</u> direction.

The following examples show the players' moves in a game.

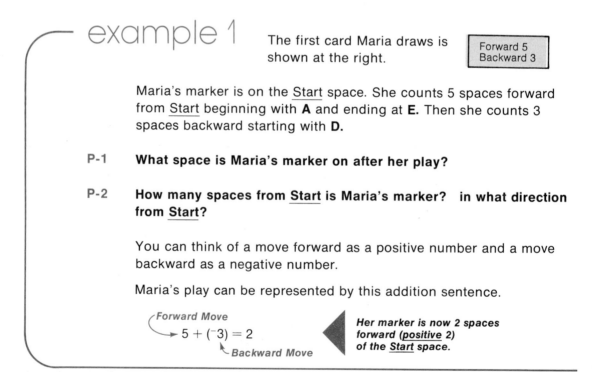

## example 1

The first card Maria draws is shown at the right.

> Forward 5
> Backward 3

Maria's marker is on the <u>Start</u> space. She counts 5 spaces forward from <u>Start</u> beginning with **A** and ending at **E.** Then she counts 3 spaces backward starting with **D.**

**P-1  What space is Maria's marker on after her play?**

**P-2  How many spaces from <u>Start</u> is Maria's marker?   in what direction from <u>Start</u>?**

You can think of a move forward as a positive number and a move backward as a negative number.

Maria's play can be represented by this addition sentence.

Forward Move
$$5 + (^-3) = 2$$
Backward Move

> Her marker is now 2 spaces forward (<u>positive</u> 2) of the <u>Start</u> space.

# example 2

Mike first draws the card shown at the right.

Backward 6
Forward 3

He first counts 6 spaces backward from <u>Start</u> beginning with **Z**.

**P-3** **What space is his marker on after the first move?**

**P-4** **How many spaces from <u>Start</u> is Mike's marker after the two moves? in what direction from <u>Start</u>?**

Mike's play is represented by this addition sentence.

$$(^-6) + 3 = {}^-3$$  *Mike lands 3 spaces backward from Start.*

# example 3

Manuel first draws the card shown at the right.

$$(^-2) + 7$$

**P-5** **What move does Manuel make as represented by $^-2$?**

**P-6** **What move does he make as represented by 7?**

His play is represented by the addition sentence below.

$$(^-2) + 7 = 5$$ *Manuel's marker is now on space E, 5 spaces forward of <u>Start</u>.*

# example 4

A marker in the Forward and Backward game is on **Q**. A player draws the card shown.

$$(^-3) + (^-4)$$

**P-7** **Where is the marker after the two moves?**

This play is described by this sentence.

$$(^-3) + (^-4) = {}^-7$$  *The marker is now on J.*

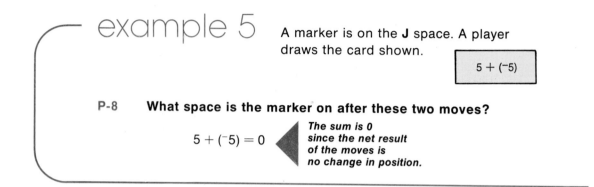

## example 5

A marker is on the **J** space. A player draws the card shown.

$$5 + (^-5)$$

**P-8**  **What space is the marker on after these two moves?**

$$5 + (^-5) = 0$$  ◀ **The sum is 0 since the net result of the moves is no change in position.**

## ORAL EXERCISES 10.1

*Tell an integer that is the result of two moves in the Forward and Backward game.* (Example 1, Example 2, Example 3, Example 4, Example 5)

1. Forward 5, Backward 4

2. Backward 2, Backward 4

3. Backward 1, Forward 8

4. Forward 2, Backward 9

5. Backward 10, Forward 7

6. Forward 7, Forward 4

7. $(^-8) + 6$

8. $(^-5) + (^-1)$

9. $9 + (^-9)$

10. $12 + (^-3)$

11. $(^-11) + 5$

12. $(^-6) + 0$

13. $(^-7) + 12$

14. $9 + 0$

15. $(^-6) + 6$

16. $(^-15) + 3$

17. $3 + (^-15)$

18. $(^-3) + 15$

19. $15 + (^-3)$

20. $(^-3) + (^-15)$

21. $(^-15) + (^-3)$

22. $14 + (^-5)$

23. $(^-11) + (^-6)$

24. $20 + (^-16)$

25. $(^-18) + 7$

26. $(^-10) + (^-12)$

27. $24 + (^-24)$

28. $(^-10) + 20$

29. $(^-19) + (^-5)$

30. $21 + (^-9)$

31. If you make two moves forward, are you ahead of or behind the space you left?

32. If you make two moves backward, are you ahead of or behind the space you left?

33. If you make one move forward and one move backward, what determines whether you are ahead of or behind the space you left?

34. If you add two positive numbers, is the sum positive or negative?

35. If you add two negative numbers, is the sum positive or negative?

36. If you add a positive number and a negative number, what determines whether the sum is positive or negative?

## WRITTEN EXERCISES 10.1

**A**    **Goal:** To add integers using forward and backward moves
**Sample Problem:** $^-12 + 7$    **Answer:** $^-5$

*Write an integer for each sum. Think of two moves in the Forward and
Backward game. (Example 1, Example 2, Example 3, Example 4, Example 5)*

**1.** $(^-6) + 4$

**2.** $(^-8) + 3$

**3.** $(^-4) + (^-5)$

**4.** $(^-6) + (^-7)$

**5.** $9 + (^-2)$

**6.** $12 + (^-6)$

**7.** $(^-8) + 8$

**8.** $(^-4) + 4$

**9.** $(^-9) + 0$

**10.** $(^-12) + 0$

**11.** $(^-5) + (^-11)$

**12.** $(^-3) + (^-12)$

**13.** $(^-12) + 7$

**14.** $(^-15) + 10$

**15.** $17 + (^-13)$

**16.** $21 + (^-16)$

**17.** $13 + (^-13)$

**18.** $18 + (^-18)$

**19.** $0 + (^-24)$

**20.** $0 + (^-16)$

**21.** $(^-14) + (^-11)$

**22.** $(^-16) + (^-9)$

**23.** $8 + (^-12)$

**24.** $11 + (^-15)$

**25.** $(^-14) + 8$

**26.** $(^-17) + 9$

**27.** $(^-7) + (^-8)$

**28.** $(^-6) + (^-9)$

**B**    *Think of x as an unknown move in the Forward and Backward game. Write
the truth number.*

**EXAMPLE:** $4 + x = ^-5$    **SOLUTION:** One move is 4 spaces forward. The marker
is 5 spaces back of the beginning space
after two moves. The second move must
be 9 spaces backward.
**ANSWER:** $x = ^-9$

**29.** $5 + x = 9$

**30.** $6 + x = 13$

**31.** $^-2 + x = ^-5$

**32.** $^-5 + x = ^-6$

**33.** $^-8 + x = ^-2$

**34.** $^-6 + x = ^-2$

**35.** $3 + x = ^-8$

**36.** $4 + x = ^-10$

**C**    *Solve each problem.*

**EXAMPLE:** A football team gains 19 yards
on one play and loses 12 yards
on the next play. Where is the
team's position after the two
plays?

**SOLUTION:** $19 + (^-12) = 7$
The team is 7 yards
forward of its position
before the two plays.

**37.** The temperature rose 11° from midnight to 3:00 p.m. It dropped 15°
from 3:00 p.m. to midnight. What
was the net change in 24 hours?

**38.** A small business lost $800 one
week and had a profit of $1200 the
next week. What was the net result
for the two weeks?

*Rational Numbers: Addition  /  237*

# 10.2 Number Line Addition

These are the rules for using a number line to add positive and negative numbers.

1. Start at the origin.

2. Move to the right for a positive number.

3. Move to the left for a negative number.

4. The sum is the coordinate of the point where the second move ends.

P-1 **What number describes the first move below? the second move?**

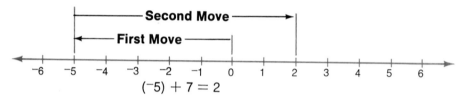

$$(^-5) + 7 = 2$$

P-2 **How do you show 4 by a move on a number line? How do you show ⁻8?**

example 1   Show $4 + (^-8)$ on a number line. Then add.

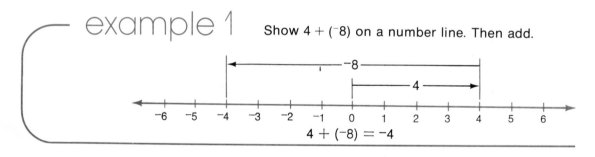

$$4 + (^-8) = ^-4$$

example 2   Show $(^-6) + 4$ on a number line. Then add.

The first move is 6 units to the left of the origin. The second move is 4 units to the right of the endpoint of the first move.

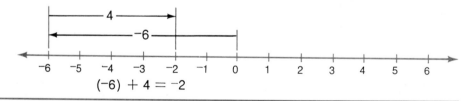

$$(^-6) + 4 = ^-2$$

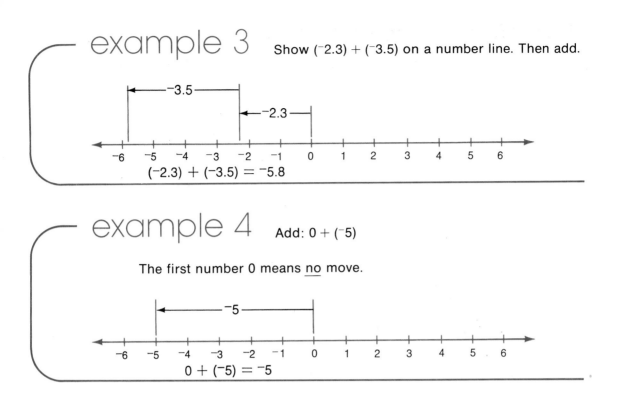

example 3    Show (⁻2.3) + (⁻3.5) on a number line. Then add.

(⁻2.3) + (⁻3.5) = ⁻5.8

example 4    Add: 0 + (⁻5)

The first number 0 means <u>no</u> move.

0 + (⁻5) = ⁻5

## ORAL EXERCISES 10.2

*Tell how you would show each sum on a number line. Then add.*
(Example 1, Example 2, Example 3, Example 4)

**1.** (⁻1) + 3

**2.** 4 + (⁻2)

**3.** (⁻3) + (⁻2)

**4.** 5 + (⁻5)

**5.** (⁻6) + 2

**6.** 1 + (⁻5)

**7.** (⁻10) + 0

**8.** 0 + (⁻7)

**9.** $4\frac{1}{2}$ + (⁻$2\frac{1}{4}$)

**10.** (⁻$1\frac{1}{2}$) + (⁻$3\frac{1}{2}$)

**11.** (⁻1.8) + (⁻3.2)

**12.** 5.6 + (⁻3.6)

**13.** (⁻3.8) + 1.3

**14.** 9.2 + (⁻4.7)

**15.** 4.9 + (⁻4.9)

**16.** (⁻0.8) + 0.8

*Tell what sum is shown by each number-line example.*

**17.**

**18.**

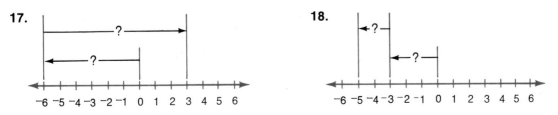

Tell what sum is shown by each number-line example.

**19.**

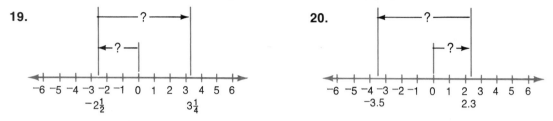

**20.**

## WRITTEN EXERCISES 10.2

**A**

**Goal:** To add numbers using a number line

**Sample Problem:** Show the sum $^-5 + 3$ on a number line. Then add.

**Answer:**

$$^-5 + 3 = ^-2$$

Show each sum on a number line. Then add. (Example 1, Example 2, Example 3, Example 4)

**1.** $(^-2) + (^-3)$

**2.** $(^-3) + (^-1)$

**3.** $^+2 + 4$

**4.** $3 + 3$

**5.** $(^-2) + 7$

**6.** $(^-3) + 6$

**7.** $5 + (^-9)$

**8.** $4 + (^-7)$

**9.** $0 + (^-6)$

**10.** $(^-5) + 0$

**11.** $(^-4) + 4$

**12.** $(^-3) + 3$

**13.** $(^-12) + 15$

**14.** $(^-9) + 17$

**15.** $(^-13) + (^-19)$

**16.** $(^-15) + (^-14)$

**17.** $22 + (^-18)$

**18.** $24 + (^-17)$

**19.** $\frac{1}{2} + (^-1\frac{1}{2})$

**20.** $2\frac{1}{2} + (^-4)$

**21.** $(^-2\frac{1}{2}) + (^-3\frac{1}{2})$

**22.** $(^-4\frac{1}{2}) + (^-1\frac{1}{2})$

**23.** $12.8 + (^-5.4)$

**24.** $9.6 + (^-6.3)$

**25.** $(^-8.7) + (^-5.6)$

**26.** $(^-5.9) + (^-6.3)$

**27.** $0 + (^-1.3)$

**28.** $0 + (^-5.2)$

**29.** $(^-19.3) + 19.3$

**30.** $(^-24.6) + 24.6$

**C**

Write _True_ or _False_ for each sentence.

**31.** $(^-4) + (^-3) = |^-4| + |^-3|$

**32.** $(^-4) + (^-3) = -(|^-4| + |^-3|)$

**33.** $(^-6) + 2 = |^-6| - |2|$

**34.** $(^-6) + 2 = -(|^-6| - |2|)$

**35.** $8 + (^-5) = |8| - |^-5|$

**36.** $8 + (^-5) = -(|8| - |^-5|)$

# 10.3  Rules for Addition

**P-1**  **What is the simplest name for each sum below?**

**a.** $5 + 10$    **b.** $(^-8) + (^-9)$    **c.** $2\frac{1}{2} + 1\frac{1}{2}$
**d.** $(^-1.4) + (^-3.2)$    **e.** $(^-100) + (^-300)$

**P-2**  **What can you say about the sum of two positive numbers? the sum of two negative numbers?**

Two negative numbers can be added without using a number line.

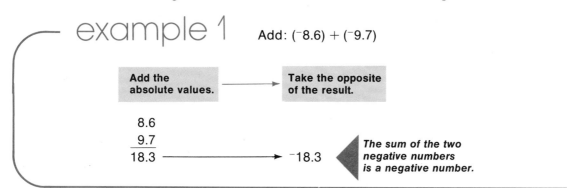

example 1     Add: $(^-8.6) + (^-9.7)$

| Add the absolute values. | → | Take the opposite of the result. |

$$\begin{array}{r} 8.6 \\ 9.7 \\ \hline 18.3 \end{array}$$

$18.3 \longrightarrow {}^-18.3$     ◀ *The sum of the two negative numbers is a negative number.*

---

**Sum of Two Positive Numbers**

Add as in arithmetic.     $3 + 4 = 7$

**Sum of Two Negative Numbers**

1. Add the absolute values.
2. Write the opposite of the result.     $(^-3) + (^-4) = {}^-7$

---

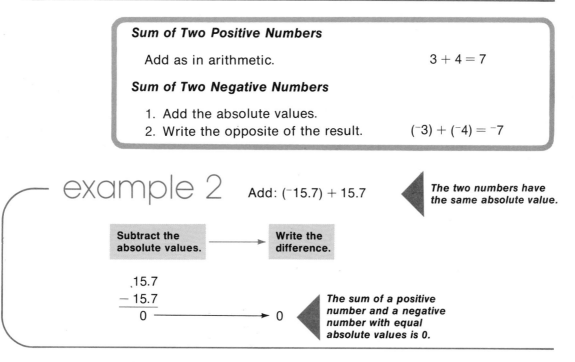

example 2     Add: $(^-15.7) + 15.7$     ◀ *The two numbers have the same absolute value.*

| Subtract the absolute values. | → | Write the difference. |

$$\begin{array}{r} 15.7 \\ - 15.7 \\ \hline 0 \end{array}$$

$0 \longrightarrow 0$     ◀ *The sum of a positive number and a negative number with equal absolute values is 0.*

**P-3**   What is the simplest name for each sum below?

|  | Group I |  | Group II |
|---|---|---|---|
| **a.** | $(^-3) + 8$ | **e.** | $(^-10) + 7$ |
| **b.** | $12 + (^-5)$ | **f.** | $12 + (^-18)$ |
| **c.** | $6\frac{1}{2} + (^-2\frac{1}{2})$ | **g.** | $(^-3\frac{1}{2}) + 1\frac{1}{4}$ |
| **d.** | $(^-1.3) + 7.4$ | **h.** | $2.4 + (^-6.5)$ |

**P-4**   How do the answers of Group I differ from the answers of Group II?

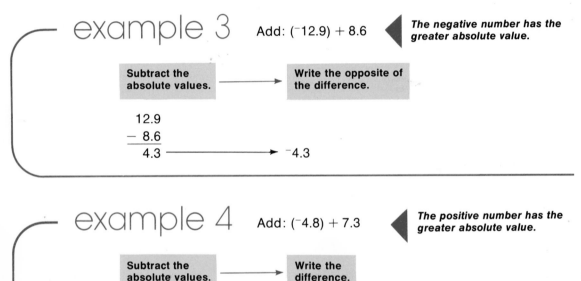

example 3   Add: $(^-12.9) + 8.6$   ◀ *The negative number has the greater absolute value.*

| Subtract the absolute values. | → | Write the opposite of the difference. |

$\begin{array}{r} 12.9 \\ -\ 8.6 \\ \hline 4.3 \end{array}$ ⟶ $^-4.3$

example 4   Add: $(^-4.8) + 7.3$   ◀ *The positive number has the greater absolute value.*

| Subtract the absolute values. | → | Write the difference. |

$\begin{array}{r} 7.3 \\ -\ 4.8 \\ \hline 2.5 \end{array}$ ⟶ $2.5$

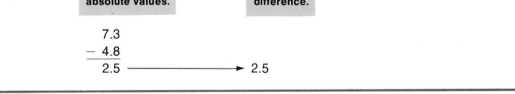

> *If the positive number has the greater absolute value:*
>
> 1. Subtract the absolute values.
> 2. Write the difference.
>
> *If the negative number has the greater absolute value:*
>
> 1. Subtract the absolute values.
> 2. Write the opposite of the difference.

Thus, you can see that the sum of a positive number and a negative number might be positive, negative, or zero. The sum depends on how the absolute values compare.

**P-5**  **What is the simplest name for each sum below?**

**a.** $(^-21) + 0$     **b.** $0 + 56$     **c.** $(^-5\frac{1}{2}) + 0$     ◄ *The sum of any number n and 0 is the number n.*

**d.** $0 + (^-13.8)$     **e.** $0.19 + 0$     **f.** $0 + \frac{7}{13}$

## ORAL EXERCISES 10.3

*Add.* (Example 1, Example 2, Example 3, Example 4, P-5)

**1.** $(^-40) + (^-20)$

**2.** $(^-10) + (^-62)$

**3.** $(^-30) + 20$

**4.** $50 + (^-80)$

**5.** $40 + (^-30)$

**6.** $(^-50) + 100$

**7.** $45 + (^-45)$

**8.** $(^-112) + 112$

**9.** $0 + (^-500)$

**10.** $(^-180) + 0$

**11.** $(^-87) + 85$

**12.** $59 + (^-56)$

**13.** $(^-48) + (^-12)$

**14.** $(^-8) + (^-92)$

**15.** $(^-0.8) + 0.5$

**16.** $(^-0.2) + (^-0.7)$

**17.** $0.47 + (^-0.32)$

**18.** $(^-0.98) + 0.53$

**19.** $(^-12.3) + (^-7.7)$

**20.** $(^-24.8) + (^-5.2)$

**21.** $47.8 + (^-42.3)$

**22.** $(^-90.7) + 10.7$

**23.** $15.4 + (^-4.8)$

**24.** $(^-24.1) + 19.5$

**25.** $(^-12.7) + (^-8.4)$

**26.** $(^-0.9) + 19.3$

**27.** $(^-117.8) + 0$

**28.** $0 + (^-576.6)$

**29.** $(^-86.93) + 86.93$

**30.** $8.012 + (^-8.012)$

## WRITTEN EXERCISES 10.3

Ⓐ   **Goal:** To add numbers using the addition rules
**Sample Problem:** $^-7 + ^-23$
**Answer:** $^-30$

*Add.* (Example 1, Example 2, Example 3, Example 4)

**1.** $600 + (^-300)$

**2.** $800 + (^-500)$

**3.** $(^-56) + (^-28)$

**4.** $(^-43) + (^-39)$

**5.** $(^-119) + 82$

**6.** $(^-138) + 73$

**7.** $71 + (^-47)$

**8.** $92 + (^-54)$

**9.** $(^-316) + (^-209)$

**10.** $(^-283) + (^-308)$

**11.** $432 + (^-376)$

**12.** $516 + (^-479)$

*Add.* (Example 1, Example 2, Example 3, Example 4)

13. $(^-863) + 709$

14. $(^-786) + 607$

15. $(^-10\frac{1}{8}) + (^-6\frac{3}{8})$

16. $(^-12\frac{5}{8}) + (^-9\frac{1}{8})$

17. $14\frac{3}{4} + (^-23\frac{1}{2})$

18. $18\frac{1}{2} + (^-31\frac{1}{4})$

19. $(^-5\frac{1}{4}) + 2\frac{3}{8}$

20. $(^-10\frac{5}{8}) + 7\frac{3}{4}$

21. $(^-12.9) + (^-8.3)$

22. $(^-16.4) + (^-9.9)$

23. $(^-38.6) + 22.3$

24. $(^-47.9) + 33.7$

25. $42.1 + (^-28.6)$

26. $53.2 + (^-37.8)$

27. $(^-0.83) + 0.83$

28. $(^-4.87) + 4.87$

29. $29.05 + (^-16.67)$

30. $31.02 + (^-19.76)$

31. $(^-3.162) + (^-5.079)$

32. $(^-0.057) + (^-0.408)$

33. $(^-12.8) + (^-12.8)$

34. $(^-33.9) + (^-33.9)$

35. $615 + (^-479)$

36. $705 + (^-538)$

37. $^-19.6 + (^-98 + 98)$

38. $^-43.6 + (^-127 + 127)$

39. $(^-39 + 57) + 86$

40. $(^-83 + 49) + 26$

**B**     *Solve each equation.*

**EXAMPLE:** $27 + x = ^-43$     **SOLUTION:** Think: What number must be added to 27 to get $^-43$?

$$27 + (^-70) = ^-43$$

Therefore, $x = ^-70$.

41. $19 + x = ^-13$

42. $23 + x = ^-9$

43. $^-15 + x = 57$

44. $^-34 + x = 26$

45. $^-38 + x = ^-12$

46. $^-56 + x = ^-16$

47. $^-11 + x = ^-83$

48. $^-24 + x = ^-58$

49. $^-16.3 + x = ^-16.3$

50. $29.8 + x = 0$

**C**     *Write True or False for each equation.*

51. $(^-14) + 9 = 9 + (^-14)$

52. $(^-33) + (^-28) = (^-28) + (^-33)$

53. $(^-120 + 140) + 30 = ^-120 + (140 + 30)$

54. $(30 + 40) + (^-50) = 30 + (^-40 + 50)$

# 10.4 Addition Properties of Rational Numbers

**P-1**   **What is the simplest name of each sum below?**

    **a.** $(^{-}45) + 0$      **b.** $(^{-}3\frac{1}{2}) + 0$      **c.** $(^{-}13.9) + 0$

> **Addition Property of Zero**
>
> For any rational number $a$,        $(^{-}3.2) + 0 = {}^{-}3.2$
>     $a + 0 = a.$

**P-2**   **What is the opposite of each of the following numbers?**

    **a.** $^{-}5\frac{3}{4}$      **b.** $0$      **c.** $0.47$      **d.** $^{-}600$    *Every rational number has exactly one opposite.*

**P-3**   **What is the simplest name for each sum?**

    **a.** $96 + (^{-}96)$      **b.** $10\frac{1}{2} + (^{-}10\frac{1}{2})$      **c.** $(^{-}3.8) + 3.8$

> **Addition Property of Opposites**
>
> For any rational number $a$,        $\frac{6}{1} + {}^{-}(\frac{6}{1}) = 0$
>     $a + (-a) = 0.$

**P-4**   **What sum is shown on each number line below?**

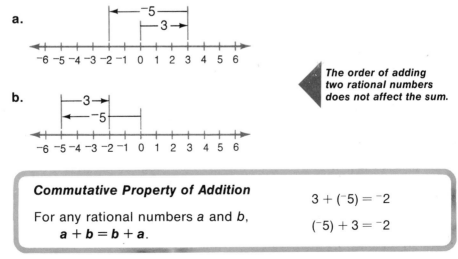

*The order of adding two rational numbers does not affect the sum.*

> **Commutative Property of Addition**
>
> For any rational numbers $a$ and $b$,      $3 + (^{-}5) = {}^{-}2$
>     $a + b = b + a.$                $(^{-}5) + 3 = {}^{-}2$

**P-5**   **What is the simplest name of ($^-$3 + 2) + 5?   of $^-$3 + (2 + 5)?**

($^-$3 + 2) + 5 means ($^-$1) + 5.      $^-$3 + (2 + 5) means ($^-$3) + 7.

Both phrases have the value 4.
Therefore, ($^-$3 + 2) + 5 = $^-$3 + (2 + 5).

◄ *The way in which numbers are grouped for addition does not affect the sum.*

---

**Associative Property of Addition**

For any rational numbers *a*, *b*, and *c*,
  **(a + b) + c = a + (b + c)**.

$8\frac{3}{16} + (2\frac{13}{16} + 4) = 15$

$(8\frac{3}{16} + 2\frac{13}{16}) + 4 = 15$

---

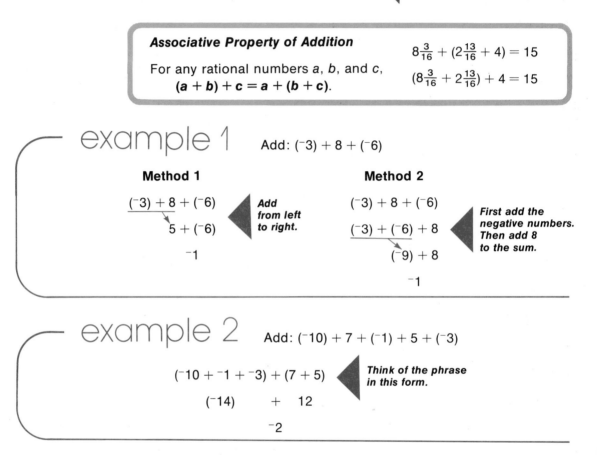

## example 1   Add: ($^-$3) + 8 + ($^-$6)

**Method 1**

($^-$3) + 8 + ($^-$6)

  5 + ($^-$6)

    $^-$1

◄ *Add from left to right.*

**Method 2**

($^-$3) + 8 + ($^-$6)

($^-$3) + ($^-$6) + 8

  ($^-$9) + 8

    $^-$1

◄ *First add the negative numbers. Then add 8 to the sum.*

## example 2   Add: ($^-$10) + 7 + ($^-$1) + 5 + ($^-$3)

($^-$10 + $^-$1 + $^-$3) + (7 + 5)

  ($^-$14)      +    12

        $^-$2

◄ *Think of the phrase in this form.*

---

Of course, you can also add the numbers from left to right.

($^-$10) + 7 + ($^-$1) + 5 + ($^-$3)

  $^-$3 + ($^-$1) + 5 + ($^-$3)

    ($^-$4) + 5 + ($^-$3)

      1 + ($^-$3)

        $^-$2

## ORAL EXERCISES 10.4

*Add. Simplify where necessary.* (P-5, Example 1, Example 2)

**1.** (⁻3) + 4 + 1

**2.** (⁻2) + (⁻3) + 6

**3.** (⁻1) + (⁻5) + (⁻3)

**4.** 4 + (⁻6) + (⁻2)

**5.** (⁻1) + (⁻1) + (⁻1)

**6.** (⁻2) + (⁻2) + (⁻2)

**7.** 12 + (⁻3) + 2

**8.** 9 + (⁻6) + 3

**9.** 4 + (⁻13) + 5

**10.** (⁻6) + 4 + (⁻8)

**11.** 10 + (⁻6) + 3

**12.** (⁻8) + 3 + (⁻1)

**13.** (⁻5) + 20 + (⁻10)

**14.** 30 + (⁻40) + 5

**15.** (⁻5) + (⁻10) + (⁻15)

**16.** 12 + (⁻5) + (⁻3)

**17.** 18 + (⁻15) + 7

**18.** (⁻14) + 7 + (⁻3)

## WRITTEN EXERCISES 10.4

**A**

**Goal:** To add three or more rational numbers
**Sample Problem:** 5.7 + (⁻6.3) + (⁻8.9)
**Answer:** ⁻9.5

*Add. Simplify where necessary.* (P-5, Example 1, Example 2)

**1.** (⁻8) + 6 + (⁻3)

**2.** (⁻12) + 5 + (⁻2)

**3.** 7 + (⁻13) + 8

**4.** 5 + (⁻12) + 13

**5.** (⁻6) + (⁻9) + (⁻14)

**6.** (⁻3) + (⁻9) + (⁻15)

**7.** (⁻35) + 25 + (⁻15)

**8.** (⁻40) + 15 + (⁻25)

**9.** (⁻6) + 9 + (⁻4) + 3

**10.** (⁻8) + 5 + (⁻3) + 7

**11.** (⁻12) + 7 + 13 + (⁻8)

**12.** (⁻10) + 9 + 14 + (⁻16)

**13.** (⁻6) + (⁻8) + (⁻11) + (⁻9)

**14.** (⁻8) + (⁻9) + (⁻13) + (⁻3)

**15.** 33 + (⁻29) + 16 + 13

**16.** 42 + (⁻56) + 16 + 19

**17.** 38 + (⁻43) + 19 + (⁻27)

**18.** 29 + (⁻37) + 23 + (⁻46)

**19.** (⁻8) + 9 + (⁻5) + (⁻2) + 16

**20.** (⁻12) + 14 + (⁻6) + (⁻5) + 20

**21.** $(⁻3\frac{1}{2}) + 5\frac{1}{2} + (⁻9\frac{1}{2}) + 3\frac{1}{2}$

**22.** $(⁻6\frac{1}{2}) + 2\frac{1}{2} + (⁻11\frac{1}{2}) + 8\frac{1}{2}$

**23.** $(⁻5\frac{1}{4}) + (⁻2\frac{3}{4}) + (⁻7\frac{3}{4}) + 4\frac{1}{4}$

**24.** $(⁻3\frac{3}{4}) + 6\frac{1}{4} + (⁻8\frac{1}{4}) + 2\frac{3}{4}$

**25.** 5.6 + (⁻3.2) + (⁻4.8) + 9.4

**26.** 8.6 + (⁻6.3) + 2.4 + (⁻7.7)

**27.** (⁻12.1) + (⁻8.8) + 14.7 + (⁻9.1)

**28.** (⁻8.6) + (⁻5.3) + 13.6 + (⁻7.6)

# 10.5 Simplest Names of Open Phrases

**P-1**    **What are some ways of finding the simplest name for this phrase?**

$$(^-2) + 3 + (^-4)$$

Here are two methods that could be used.

<table>
<tr><td align="center">**Method 1**</td><td align="center">**Method 2**</td></tr>
<tr><td>$(^-2) + 3 + (^-4) = (^-2 + 3) + (^-4)$</td><td>$(^-2) + 3 + (^-4) = (^-2 + {}^-4) + 3$</td></tr>
<tr><td align="center">$= \quad 1 + (^-4)$</td><td align="center">$= \quad (^-6) + 3$</td></tr>
<tr><td align="center">$= \quad {}^-3$</td><td align="center">$= \quad {}^-3$</td></tr>
</table>

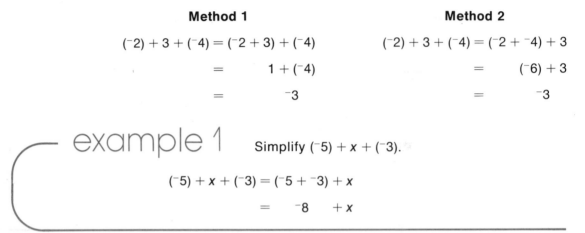

## example 1    Simplify $(^-5) + x + (^-3)$.

$$(^-5) + x + (^-3) = (^-5 + {}^-3) + x$$
$$= \quad {}^-8 \quad + x$$

By the Commutative Property of Addition, $(^-8) + x$ and $x + (^-8)$ name the same number. They are called <u>equivalent phrases</u>.

> **Equivalent phrases** are open phrases that have the same value when the variables are replaced by the same number.

**P-2**    **What is the simplest name for $12.3 + (^-9.6)$?**

## example 2    Simplify $12.3 + (^-9.6) + x + (^-4.8)$.

$$12.3 + (^-9.6) + x + (^-4.8) = 2.7 + x + (^-4.8)$$
$$= (2.7 + {}^-4.8) + x$$
$$= \quad (^-2.1) \quad + x$$

**P-3**    **In what other form can you write $(^-2.1) + x$ by use of the Commutative Property of Addition?**

**P-4    What does (−a) mean?**

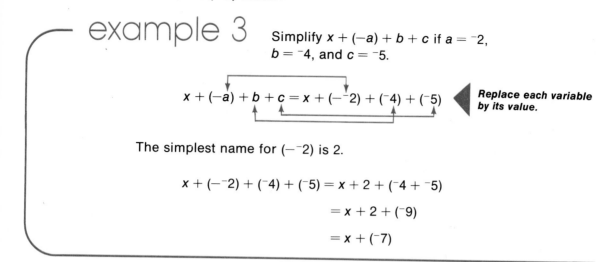

example 3    Simplify $x + (-a) + b + c$ if $a = {}^-2$, $b = {}^-4$, and $c = {}^-5$.

$$x + (-a) + b + c = x + (--2) + (^-4) + (^-5)$$

▸ Replace each variable by its value.

The simplest name for $(--2)$ is 2.

$$x + (--2) + (^-4) + (^-5) = x + 2 + (^-4 + {}^-5)$$
$$= x + 2 + (^-9)$$
$$= x + (^-7)$$

## ORAL EXERCISES 10.5

*Simplify.* (Example 1, Example 2, Example 3)

**1.** $^-2 + x + 5$

**2.** $7 + x + (^-3)$

**3.** $x + (^-4) + 9$

**4.** $(^-5) + x + 8$

**5.** $(^-10) + n + (^-7)$

**6.** $(^-12) + y + (^-6)$

**7.** $(^-2) + r + 8 + (^-3)$

**8.** $5 + (^-7) + t + 8$

**9.** $(^-8) + p + 8 + (^-12)$

**10.** $5 + n + (^-5) + 17$

**11.** $(^-1) + 9 + q + (^-5)$

**12.** $y + (^-8) + (^-5) + (^-7)$

**13.** $15.8 + a + (^-12.3)$

**14.** $(^-14.5) + b + 8.2$

**15.** $3\frac{1}{2} + (^-2\frac{1}{4}) + y$

**16.** $(^-1.9) + x + 2.3 + 1.9$

**17.** $a + (^-5) + x + (-a)$

**18.** $(^-5\frac{1}{8}) + x + 3\frac{3}{8}$

**19.** $x + (^-5)$ if $x = {}^-7$

**20.** $^-7 + (-x)$ if $x = 9$

**21.** $n + 18$ if $n = {}^-15$

**22.** $12 + (-y)$ if $y = {}^-12$

**23.** $^-13 + (-t)$ if $t = {}^-13$

**24.** $50 + r$ if $r = 13$

**25.** $x + a + b$ if $a = {}^-3$ and $b = {}^-4$

**26.** $x + (-a) + b$ if $a = {}^-5$ and $b = {}^-6$

## WRITTEN EXERCISES 10.5

**A**  **Goal:** To simplify open phrases containing positive and negative numbers

**Sample Problem:** $2\frac{1}{4} + (-3x) + {}^-5\frac{1}{2} + x$

**Answer:** $-3\frac{1}{4} + (-2x)$

*Simplify.* (Example 1, Example 2)

**1.** $(^-2) + x + 7$

**2.** $(^-5) + x + 12$

**3.** $13 + x + (^-19)$

**4.** $9 + x + (^-17)$

**5.** $(^-5) + (^-6) + x$

**6.** $(^-15) + (^-3) + x$

**7.** $(^-42) + x + (^-19)$

**8.** $(^-26) + x + (^-19)$

**9.** $5.2 + x + (^-4.1)$

**10.** $9.8 + x + (^-5.3)$

**11.** $(^-8.2) + x + 3.7$

**12.** $(^-8.7) + x + 3.9$

**13.** $2 + x + (^-9) + (^-1)$

**14.** $5 + x + (^-3) + (^-1)$

**15.** $23 + (^-45) + x + (^-19)$

**16.** $28 + (^-37) + x + (^-12)$

**17.** $\frac{5}{8} + x + {}^-(\frac{3}{8})$

**18.** $^-(\frac{3}{11}) + x + {}^-(\frac{5}{11})$

**19.** $(^-6\frac{1}{4}) + 2\frac{3}{4} + x + (^-5\frac{3}{4})$

**20.** $(^-10\frac{3}{4}) + 3\frac{1}{4} + x + (^-4\frac{1}{4})$

**21.** $4.2 + (^-3.8) + x + (^-7.9)$

**22.** $7.3 + (^-4.8) + x + (^-1.9)$

**23.** $k + x + (^-28) + (-x)$

**24.** $r + x + (^-28) + (-r)$

**25.** $(^-91.6) + x + 0.9 + 91.6$

**26.** $(^-113.8) + x + 3.7 + 113.8$

**27.** $36 + (^-59) + t + x + (^-63) + (-t)$

**28.** $45 + (^-29) + y + x + (^-78) + (-y)$

*Simplify each phrase for the given values of a, b, and c.* (Example 3)

**29.** $x + a + b + (-c)$
$a = {}^-12, b = 14, c = {}^-5$

**30.** $x + a + (-b) + c$
$a = 9, b = {}^-13, c = {}^-16$

**31.** $a + (-b) + x + (-c)$
$a = 32, b = {}^-27, c = 19$

**32.** $(-a) + b + x + c$
$a = {}^-29, b = {}^-12, c = 42$

**33.** $c + x + (-a) + (-b)$
$a = {}^-5.8, b = {}^-2.3, c = {}^-4.7$

**34.** $b + x + (-c) + (-a)$
$a = {}^-9.1, b = {}^-6.2, c = {}^-4.4$

**35.** $r + (-a) + (-b) + s + c$
$a = {}^-10\frac{1}{4}, b = 6\frac{1}{2}, c = {}^-4\frac{1}{4}$

**36.** $m + a + (-b) + n + (-c)$
$a = {}^-12\frac{1}{2}, b = {}^-7\frac{3}{4}, c = 16\frac{1}{4}$

**C**

**37.** $-(a + b) + x + (-c)$
$a = {}^-9, b = 14, c = {}^-12$

**38.** $-(a + c) + x + b$
$a = 36, b = {}^-16, c = {}^-27$

**39.** $-(a + (-b) + {}^-c)) + x$
$a = {}^-60, b = {}^-70, c = 85$

**40.** $-(b + c + (-a)) + x$
$a = {}^-35, b = {}^-65, c = 25$

# 10.6 Opposite of a Sum

In the first line of the table below, $a$ is replaced by 5 and $b$ is replaced by 8.

**P-1**     **What value should replace $(-a)$?  $(-b)$?**

| $-(a+b)$ | $(-a)+(-b)$ |
|---|---|
| $-(5+8)=-(13)$ | $(-5)+(-8)=({}^-5)+({}^-8)$ |
| $={}^-13$ | $={}^-13$ |
| $-({}^-12+6)=-({}^-6)$ | $(-({}^-12))+(-6)=(12)+({}^-6)$ |
| $=6$ | $=6$ |
| $-({}^-7+{}^-10)=-({}^-17)$ | $(-({}^-7))+(-({}^-10))=(7)+(10)$ |
| $=17$ | $=17$ |
| $-(7.7+{}^-4.3)=-(3.4)$ | $(-7.7)+(-({}^-4.3))=({}^-7.7)+(4.3)$ |
| $={}^-3.4$ | $={}^-3.4$ |

The phrase $-(a+b)$ is the <u>opposite of the sum</u> $(a+b)$.

These examples suggest the <u>Property of the Opposite of a Sum</u>.

---

**Property of the Opposite of a Sum**

For any two rational numbers $a$ and $b$,
$$-(a+b)=(-a)+(-b).$$

---

## example 1

Write $-({}^-5+7)$ in the form $(-a)+(-b)$. Use simplest names for $(-a)$ and $(-b)$.

Compare $-({}^-5+7)$ with $-(a+b)$.

$$-(a+b)=(-a)+(-b)$$
$$-({}^-5+7)=\left(-({}^-5)\right)+(-7)$$
$$=\quad 5\ +({}^-7)$$

---

The Property of the Opposite of a Sum can be applied to a sum of several numbers.

$$-(a + b + c) \text{ is equivalent to } (-a) + (-b) + (-c).$$
$$-(a + b + c + d) \text{ is equivalent to } (-a) + (-b) + (-c) + (-d).$$
$$-(a + b + c + \cdots) \text{ is equivalent to } (-a) + (-b) + (-c) + \cdots.$$

example 2   Write a phrase equivalent to the following one.

$$-(^-7 + x + 12 + (-y))$$

1  Take the opposite of each number or variable. $\longrightarrow$ $-(^-7 + x + 12 + (-y)) = -(^-7) + (-x) + (-12) + -(-y)$

2  Simplify. $\longrightarrow$ $= 7 + (-x) + (^-12) + y$

example 3   Solve the following equation. First write an equivalent equation involving $x$.

$$^-5 = ^-3 + (-x)$$

1  Equality Property of Opposites $\longrightarrow$ $-(^-5) = -(^-3 + (-x))$

2  Property of the Opposite of a Sum $\longrightarrow$ $-(^-5) = -(^-3) + -(-x)$

3  Simplify. $\longrightarrow$ $5 = 3 + x$

4  Subtraction Property of Equality $\longrightarrow$ $5 - 3 = 3 + x - 3$

5  Simplify. $\longrightarrow$ $2 = x$

or   $x = 2$

## ORAL EXERCISES 10.6

Use $-(a + b) = (-a) + (-b)$ to say each phrase in another way. (Example 1, Example 2)

**EXAMPLE:** $-(5 + (-x))$     **ANSWER:** $(^-5) + x$   ("Negative 5 plus x")

**1.** $-(5 + 9)$      **2.** $-(10 + ^-3)$      **3.** $-(^-5 + ^-8)$      **4.** $-(^-9 + 4)$

**5.** $-(^-0.8 + ^-0.7)$      **6.** $-(^-0.05 + ^-0.17)$      **7.** $-(x + ^-3)$      **8.** $-((-y) + 4)$

**9.** $-(8.2 + (-n))$      **10.** $-(t + ^-1\frac{1}{4})$      **11.** $-(^-12 + (-r) + s)$

**12.** $-(p + ^-6.3 + (-q))$      **13.** $-(r + ^-5 + (-s) + (-t))$      **14.** $-((-k) + (-n) + ^-5\frac{1}{2} + t)$

For each equation, tell an equivalent equation involving x. (Steps 1, 2, and 3 of Example 3)

**EXAMPLE:** $3 = -(^-8 + (-x))$     **ANSWER:** $3 = 8 + x$

**15.** $-x = -(5 + ^-3)$

**16.** $-x = -(^-7 + ^-2)$

**17.** $5 = 3 + (-x)$

**18.** $^-2 = -(5 + (-x))$

**19.** $-x = ^-7 + 5$

**20.** $-x = ^-10 + ^-19$

**21.** $^-1 = ^-7 + (-x)$

**22.** $12 = ^-5 + (-x)$

**23.** $-((-x) + 3.8) = ^-5.2$

## WRITTEN EXERCISES 10.6

**A**     **Goal:** To use the Property of the Opposite of a Sum
**Sample Problem:** Solve the equation $^-13 + (-x) = ^-27$
**Answer:** $x = 14$

Use $-(a + b) = (-a) + (-b)$ to write each phrase in another way. (Example 1, Example 2)

**EXAMPLE:** $-(14.7 + ^-9.5)$     **ANSWER:** $^-14.7 + 9.5$

**1.** $-(^-19 + 12)$

**2.** $-(^-24 + 17)$

**3.** $-(12.9 + ^-6.5)$

**4.** $-(15.8 + ^-3.7)$

**5.** $-(^-0.6 + ^-0.7)$

**6.** $-(^-0.04 + ^-0.17)$

**EXAMPLE:** $-((-x) + ^-13 + 27)$     **ANSWER:** $x + 13 + (^-27)$

**7.** $-(r + ^-26)$

**8.** $-(t + ^-58)$

**9.** $-((-m) + 19)$

**10.** $-((-x) + 24)$

**11.** $-(^-17 + r + (-s))$

**12.** $-((-t) + ^-33 + k)$

**13.** $-(^-8.2 + x + (-y))$

**14.** $-(^-12.6 + (-m) + n)$

**15.** $-(24 + (-c) + ^-18)$

**16.** $-(92 + (-p) + ^-47)$

**17.** $-(r + (-s) + -(-t) + w)$

**18.** $-(k + -(-n) + m + (-p))$

Solve each equation. (Example 3)

**19.** $-x = -(^-12 + 15)$

**20.** $-x = -(17 + ^-23)$

**21.** $^-2 + (-x) = ^-5$

**22.** $(-x) + (^-24) = ^-40$

**23.** $^-6.2 + (-x) = ^-9.7$

**24.** $^-16.3 + (-x) = ^-23.6$

**25.** $^-130 = (-x) + (^-56) + 25$

**26.** $^-225 = (-x) + (^-42) + 18$

**B**     Use $(-a) + (-b) = -(a + b)$ to write each phrase in another way.

**EXAMPLE:** $^-6 + (-t)$     **ANSWER:** $-(6 + t)$

**27.** $x + (^-5)$

**28.** $y + (^-13.8)$

**29.** $(-x) + 13 + y$

**30.** $-m + 28 + n$

**31.** $(-p) + (-q) + (^-96)$

**32.** $(-r) + (-s) + (^-128)$

**33.** $x + (^-5.8) + 6.2 + (-y)$

**34.** $m + (^-16.3) + 4.8 + (-n)$

**35.** $(-k) + (-n) + (-r) + (-q) + 28$

**36.** $(-a) + (-b) + (-c) + (-d) + 76$

# 10.7 Problems in Addition

**P-1** **Which word phrases below can be described by positive numbers? by negative numbers?**

**a.** A temperature of 20° below zero    **b.** A loss of $75

**c.** A fall of 6 degrees in temperature    **d.** A gain of 7 kilograms

**e.** A deficiency of 7.6 centimeters in rainfall

**f.** An increase of $2\frac{1}{4}$ points in a stock price

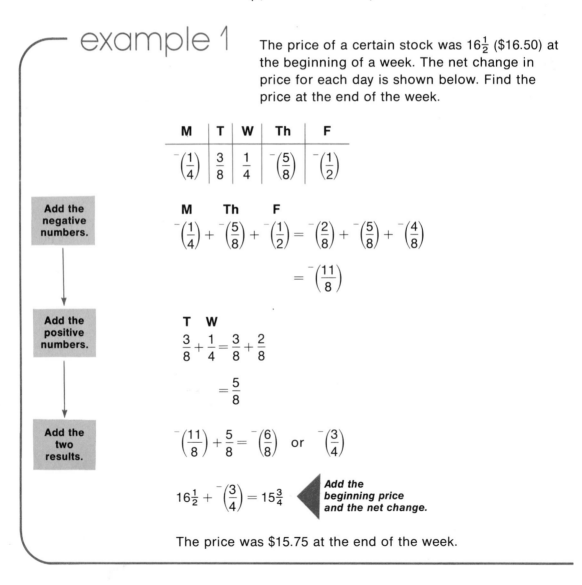

example 1    The price of a certain stock was $16\frac{1}{2}$ ($16.50) at the beginning of a week. The net change in price for each day is shown below. Find the price at the end of the week.

| M | T | W | Th | F |
|---|---|---|---|---|
| $^-\left(\dfrac{1}{4}\right)$ | $\dfrac{3}{8}$ | $\dfrac{1}{4}$ | $^-\left(\dfrac{5}{8}\right)$ | $^-\left(\dfrac{1}{2}\right)$ |

**Add the negative numbers.**

$$\begin{array}{ccc} \text{M} & \text{Th} & \text{F} \end{array}$$

$$^-\left(\frac{1}{4}\right) + {}^-\left(\frac{5}{8}\right) + {}^-\left(\frac{1}{2}\right) = {}^-\left(\frac{2}{8}\right) + {}^-\left(\frac{5}{8}\right) + {}^-\left(\frac{4}{8}\right)$$

$$= {}^-\left(\frac{11}{8}\right)$$

**Add the positive numbers.**

$$\begin{array}{cc} \text{T} & \text{W} \end{array}$$

$$\frac{3}{8} + \frac{1}{4} = \frac{3}{8} + \frac{2}{8}$$

$$= \frac{5}{8}$$

**Add the two results.**

$$^-\left(\frac{11}{8}\right) + \frac{5}{8} = {}^-\left(\frac{6}{8}\right) \quad \text{or} \quad {}^-\left(\frac{3}{4}\right)$$

$$16\frac{1}{2} + {}^-\left(\frac{3}{4}\right) = 15\frac{3}{4} \quad \blacktriangleleft \quad \textit{Add the beginning price and the net change.}$$

The price was $15.75 at the end of the week.

# example 2

The excess of rainfall in a city is shown as a positive number. The deficiency is represented as a negative number. Find the net excess or deficiency for a six month period.

| Sept. | Oct. | Nov. | Dec. | Jan. | Feb. |
|-------|------|------|------|------|------|
| 2.7 cm | ⁻0.8 cm | ⁻2.9 cm | ⁻3.4 cm | 1.8 cm | 4.1 cm |

1 Add the negative amounts. ────────▶ $(^-0.8) + (^-2.9) + (^-3.4) = ^-7.1$

2 Add the positive amounts. ────────▶ $2.7 + 1.8 + 4.1 = 8.6$

3 Add the two results. ────────▶ $(^-7.1) + 8.6 = 1.5$

There was an excess of 1.5 centimeters of rainfall.

# example 3

A zoo keeper keeps a record of the mass of a chimpanzee each week. He records the increase or decrease each week for five weeks. Find the net increase or decrease in mass.

| 1 | 2 | 3 | 4 | 5 |
|---|---|---|---|---|
| ⁻2.1 kg | 1.3 kg | ⁻0.9 kg | ⁻1.3 kg | 0.7 kg |

Add the negative numbers. ───▶ Add the positive numbers. ───▶ Add the two results.

$$
\begin{array}{l}
^-2.1 \\
^-0.9 \\
\underline{^-1.3} \\
^-4.3
\end{array}
\qquad
\begin{array}{l}
1.3 \\
\underline{0.7} \\
2.0
\end{array}
\qquad
(^-4.3) + 2.0 = ^-2.3
$$

There was a loss of 2.3 kilograms.

## ORAL EXERCISES 10.7

*For each word phrase, tell a numerical phrase that is a sum. Then tell its value and what the value means.*

**EXAMPLE:** A loss of $36 and     **NUMERICAL PHRASE:** $(^-36) + 14$
a profit of $14                         **VALUE:** $^-22$
                                            **MEANING:** Loss of $22

1. A drop of 3.2° in temperature followed by a drop of 1.4°

2. An increase of $0.24 in the price of an item followed by a decrease of $0.35 in price

3. A decline of $2\frac{3}{4}$ points in a stock price followed by a decline of $1\frac{1}{2}$ points

4. A descent of 30 meters by a scuba diver followed by an ascent of 5 meters

5. A loss of 16 yards by a football player on one play and a gain of 13 yards on the next play

6. A score of 3 under par by a golfer one day and a 5 over par score the next day

7. A profit of $15,000 by a business for the first 6 months of a year and a loss of $6,000 for the second 6 months

8. An excess of 5.2 centimeters of rainfall one month and a deficiency of 2.9 centimeters of rainfall the next month

9. An increase of 500 meters in a plane's altitude followed by a decrease of 800 meters

10. A decrease of 4.8 kilograms followed by a decrease of 2.7 kilograms

11. A decrease in sales of $1200 one week and an increase of $800 the following week

12. A decrease in speed of 16 kilometers per hour followed by a decrease of 9 kilometers per hour

13. Successive losses of 15 yards, 12 yards, and 8 yards by a football team

14. Successive declines in population of 1200 persons, 2500 persons, and 2800 persons

15. Scores of 6 over par, 2 under par, 3 over par, and 3 under par by a golfer on four successive days

16. Ship on a course moving 20 kilometers south, 26 kilometers north, and 14 kilometers south

17. Ship moving 15.3 kilometers east, 12.8 kilometers west, and 7.5 kilometers west

18. Losses of $28 and $34 followed by a gain of $76

**19.** Gains of $2\frac{1}{4}$ points and $1\frac{1}{2}$ points in stock prices followed by a loss of $2\frac{3}{4}$ points

**20.** Going up 28 floors in an elevator, going down 11 floors, and then going down 15 floors

## WRITTEN EXERCISES 10.7

**A**
**Goal:** To solve word problems using positive and negative numbers
**Sample Problem:** While scuba diving, Ida May descended 53 meters and then rose 37 meters. How far from the surface was she then?
**Answer:** She was 16 meters below the surface.

*Solve each problem by adding positive and negative numbers.* (Example 1, Example 2, Example 3)

**1.** The enrollment in a school showed the following gains *(G)* or losses *(L)* over a five-year period. Find the net gain or loss for the five years.

| 1969 | 1970 | 1971 | 1972 | 1973 |
|------|------|------|------|------|
| 158*(G)* | 192*(G)* | 129*(G)* | 33*(L)* | 96*(L)* |

**2.** A car dealer records the increase *(I)* or decrease *(D)* in the number of cars sold each month as compared with the previous year's sales. Find the net increase or decrease for the six-month period shown below.

| Jan. | Feb. | March | April | May | June |
|------|------|-------|-------|-----|------|
| 28*(D)* | 5*(I)* | 12*(D)* | 19*(I)* | 27*(I)* | 35*(D)* |

**3.** The price of certain stock was $35\frac{1}{4}$ at the beginning of a week. The net change in price is shown for each day. Find the price at the end of the week.

| M | T | W | Th | F |
|---|---|---|----|---|
| $-1\frac{1}{4}$ | $\frac{3}{4}$ | $-\left(\frac{7}{8}\right)$ | $\frac{1}{4}$ | $-\left(\frac{5}{8}\right)$ |

**4.** The price of certain stock was $67\frac{3}{8}$ at the beginning of a week. The net change in price is shown for each day. Find the price at the end of the week.

| M | T | W | Th | F |
|---|---|---|----|---|
| $\frac{7}{8}$ | $-\left(\frac{3}{4}\right)$ | $-2\frac{1}{2}$ | $\frac{5}{8}$ | $1\frac{1}{8}$ |

*Solve each problem.*

5. The excess *(E)* or deficiency *(D)* of rainfall for a city is shown for each of six weeks. Find the net excess or deficiency for the six-week period.

| 1 | 2 | 3 | 4 | 5 | 6 |
|---|---|---|---|---|---|
| 1.5 cm*(E)* | 0.8 cm*(D)* | 2.3 cm*(D)* | 1.2 cm*(E)* | 3.5 cm*(D)* | 0.4 cm*(E)* |

6. The excess *(E)* or deficiency *(D)* of rainfall for a city is shown for each of six months. Find the net excess or deficiency for the six-month period.

| 1 | 2 | 3 | 4 | 5 | 6 |
|---|---|---|---|---|---|
| 4.8 cm*(E)* | 1.7 cm*(E)* | 5.9 cm*(E)* | 0.9 cm*(D)* | 1.3 cm*(E)* | 7.2 cm*(D)* |

7. A business shows the following increase *(I)* or decrease *(D)* in sales for six months as compared with the same six-month period of the previous year. Find the net increase or decrease for the six-month period.

**Jan.** $36,000 *(I)*       **Feb.** $18,000 *(D)*       **March** $25,000 *(D)*
**April**  $8500 *(I)*       **May**   $1300 *(I)*       **June**  $12,500 *(D)*

8. The population of a city shows the following increases *(I)* and decreases *(D)* over a five-year period. Find the net increase or decrease for the five years.

| 1969 | 1970 | 1971 | 1972 | 1973 |
|---|---|---|---|---|
| 5200*(I)* | 3600*(I)* | 1500*(D)* | 4700*(D)* | 2400*(I)* |

9. A football coach asks each player to report for training camp at a certain weight. The first seven players he checks are over *(O)* or under *(U)* their weights as shown. Find the net amount by which the seven players are over or under the desired weights.

| Player | 1 | 2 | 3 | 4 | 5 | 6 | 7 |
|---|---|---|---|---|---|---|---|
| Weight | 6.3*(O)* | 1.8*(U)* | 2.5*(U)* | 2.9*(O)* | 2.9*(O)* | 3.6*(U)* | 0.7*(U)* |

10. A woman has $840 in a checking account at the beginning of a month. During the first week she makes the following deposits (D) and withdrawals (W). Find the balance of her account at the end of the week.

$19.40(W), $208.72 (W), $87.12(D), $56.70(W), $150(D), $306.87(W), $96.22(W), $210.50(D)

**B**    *Write an equation and solve for the unknown number.*

11. The opposite of an unknown number increased by ⁻16 equals ⁻52.

12. The opposite of the sum of an unknown number and ⁻10 equals ⁻94.

13. The opposite of an unknown number equals ⁻19.3 increased by 27.4.

14. The opposite of an unknown number equals the opposite of the sum of 12.5 and ⁻19.2.

**C**    *An __average__ of two or more measures can be computed by first adding the measures and then dividing by the number of measures.*

**EXAMPLE:** The low temperatures for five days are shown. Find the average low temperature for the five-day period to one decimal place.

| M | T | W | Th | F |
|---|---|---|----|---|
| ⁻2.6° | ⁻12.1° | ⁻5.8° | ⁻9.4° | ⁻4.7° |

**SOLUTION:** $\dfrac{(^-2.6) + (^-12.1) + (^-5.8) + (^-9.4) + (^-4.7)}{5} = \dfrac{^-34.6}{5}$

$$\approx {}^-6.9°$$

15. The following temperatures are the low temperatures for a city for each of six months. Find the average low temperature for those months to the nearest degree. (Hint: The sum of the low temperatures is a negative number. Therefore, the average low temperature is a negative number.)

| Nov. | Dec. | Jan. | Feb. | March | April |
|------|------|------|------|-------|-------|
| ⁻5.3° | ⁻10.7° | ⁻21.4° | ⁻18.3° | ⁻2.7° | 4.3° |

16. A football player makes the following gains or losses of yards in a football game. Find the average number of yards he gained or lost. Express to one decimal place.

15-yard gain, 3-yard loss, 23-yard gain, 6-yard gain, 18-yard loss, 1-yard loss, 7-yard gain, 12-yard loss

# Nurse

Persons who work in the nursing field may be registered nurses, licensed practical nurses, nurses aides, orderlies, or attendants. There are essentially three ways a person may qualify to be a registered nurse.

1. Complete four years of work leading to a bachelor's degree in a nursing program at a college or university.

2. Complete two years of work leading to an associate degree in a junior college or a community college.

3. Complete three years of training leading to a diploma in the nursing school of a hospital or independent school.

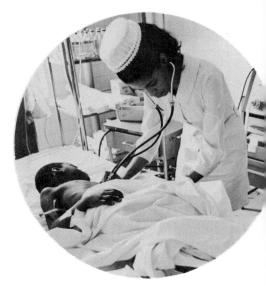

Registered nurses work in hospitals, doctors' offices, or in industry. They also work with public health agencies or as nurse educators.

One major responsibility of a registered nurse is to give medicine to patients under a doctor's direction. To do this a nurse must have a knowledge of measurement and be able to use proportions in calculations.

**EXAMPLE:** A doctor wants a patient to have 25 milligrams of a medicine per dose. A solution is available which has 500 milligrams of the medicine in 10 milliliters of solution. How many milliliters of solution should a nurse measure for each dose?

**SOLUTION:** Let $x$ = the number of milliliters

$$\frac{25}{x} = \frac{500}{10}$$

$$500x = 10(25)$$

$$500x = 250$$

$$x = 0.5$$

The nurse measures 0.5 m$\ell$ for each dose.

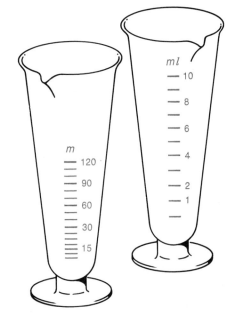

*A minim glass is used for measuring medicine. Both a minim scale and a metric scale are shown on most minim glasses. A minim is about the same as a drop.*

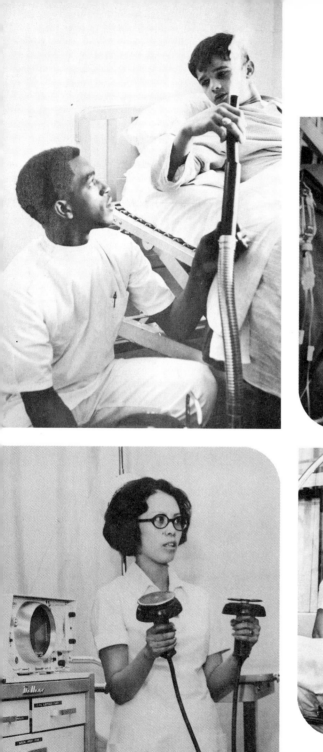

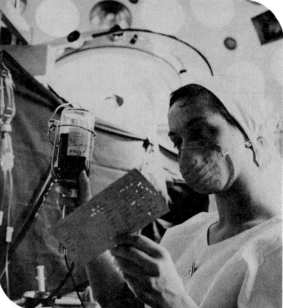

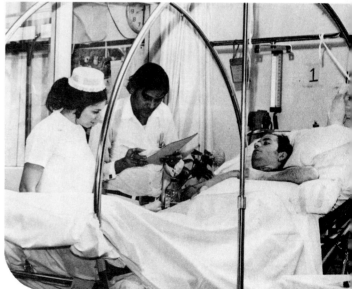

# CHAPTER SUMMARY

**IMPORTANT TERM**    Equivalent phrases *(p. 248)*

**IMPORTANT IDEAS**

1. Addition of two positive numbers: Add as in arithmetic.

2. Steps in adding two negative numbers:
   a. Add the absolute values.
   b. Write the opposite of the result.

3. The sum of a positive number and a negative number with equal absolute values is 0.

4. Steps in adding a positive number and a negative number having unequal absolute values:
   *If the positive number has the greater absolute value:*
   a. Subtract the absolute values.
   b. Write the difference.
   *If the negative number has the greater absolute value:*
   a. Subtract the absolute values.
   b. Write the opposite of the difference.

5. *Addition Property of Zero:* For any rational number $a$, $a + 0 = a$.

6. Every rational number has exactly one opposite.

7. *Addition Property of Opposites:* For any rational number $a$, $a + (-a) = 0$.

8. *Commutative Property of Addition:* For any rational numbers $a$ and $b$, $a + b = b + a$.

9. *Associative Property of Addition:* For any rational numbers $a$, $b$, and $c$, $(a + b) + c = a + (b + c)$.

10. *Property of the Opposite of a Sum:* For any two rational numbers $a$ and $b$, $-(a + b) = (-a) + (-b)$.

# CHAPTER REVIEW

### SECTION 10.1

*Write an integer for each sum.*

1. $(^-12) + 18$
2. $14 + (^-21)$
3. $(^-13) + (^-9)$
4. $(^-15) + (^-16)$
5. $(^-26) + 26$
6. $(^-23) + 0$
7. $6 + (^-23)$
8. $19 + (^-17)$

*Solve each problem.*

9. A man makes a deposit of $1200 in his checking account. Then he withdraws $850. What was the net change in his checking account balance?

10. During the year 43 new students enrolled in a school and 69 students transferred to other schools. What was the net effect on enrollment?

### SECTION 10.2

*Show each sum on a number line. Then add.*

11. $(^-4) + 9$

12. $5 + (^-7)$

13. $(^-2\frac{1}{2}) + (^-1\frac{1}{2})$

14. $4.7 + (^-4.7)$

15. $(^-42) + 19$

16. $26 + (^-37)$

17. $56 + (^-29)$

18. $(^-17) + 43$

19. $\frac{3}{4} + (^-1\frac{1}{4})$

20. $2\frac{3}{4} + (^-3\frac{1}{2})$

21. $(-12.8) + (^-9.6)$

22. $(^-8.3) + (^-13.9)$

### SECTION 10.3

*Add.*

23. $(^-48) + (^-57)$

24. $(^-39) + (^-78)$

25. $72 + (^-59)$

26. $(^-6.3) + 89$

27. $(^-16.3) + 24.9$

28. $33.7 + (^-24.8)$

29. $413 + (^-608)$

30. $(^-724) + 596$

### SECTION 10.4

*Add. Simplify where necessary.*

31. $(^-12) + 17 + (^-8)$

32. $(^-16) + 23 + (^-11)$

33. $(^-21) + (^-19) + (^-27)$

34. $(^-18) + (^-25) + (^-37)$

35. $(^-13) + 27 + (^-16) + (^-9)$

36. $(^-20) + (^-33) + 24 + (^-17)$

37. $(^-42.7) + (^-18.3) + 19.6 + (^-5.9)$

38. $34.6 + (^-22.3) + (^-19.6) + 12.5$

39. $6\frac{1}{4} + (^-5\frac{1}{2}) + (^-2\frac{3}{4}) + (\frac{3}{4})$

40. $3\frac{3}{4} + (^-2\frac{1}{4}) + (^-1\frac{3}{4}) + \frac{1}{2}$

### SECTION 10.5

*Simplify.*

41. $(^-16) + x + 9$

42. $24 + x + (^-19)$

43. $(^-35) + x + (^-16)$

44. $(^-42) + (^-16) + x$

*Simplify.*

**45.** $0.9 + (^-12.8) + x + (^-5.6)$

**46.** $(^-0.4) + 5.3 + x + (^-14.6)$

**47.** $42 + r + (^-14) + x + (-r)$

**48.** $t + (^-47) + x + (^-35) + (-t)$

*Simplify each phrase for the given values of a, b, and c.*

**49.** $x + (-a) + b + c$
$a = ^-5.2, b = 14.8, c = ^-10.7$

**50.** $x + a + (-b) + (-c)$
$a = 27.3, b = ^-19.4, c = 23.8$

### SECTION 10.6

*Use $-(a + b) = (-a) + (-b)$ to write each phrase in another way.*

**51.** $-(^-19 + t)$

**52.** $-((-x) + 7)$

**53.** $-(^-13 + (-r) + s)$

**54.** $-((-w) + ^-15 + (-q))$

**55.** $-(k + (-t) + n + (-r))$

**56.** $-((-p) + (^-16.3) + g + (-y))$

### SECTION 10.7

*Solve each problem by adding positive and negative numbers.*

**57.** A magazine company shows a record of new subscriptions and canceled subscriptions each month. The report for four months is shown below. Find the net gain or loss of subscriptions for four months.

|  | Jan. | Feb. | March | April |
|---|---|---|---|---|
| **New Subscriptions** | 1358 | 1512 | 496 | 1116 |
| **Canceled Subscriptions** | 1217 | 1176 | 893 | 1135 |

**58.** Mary Smith's checking account shows the following deposits *(D)* and withdrawals *(W)* in one week. Find the net increase or decrease in her account balance.

$123.19*(W)*, $87.52*(W)*, $20.62*(W)*, $162.48*(D)*,
$5.83*(W)*, $47.63*(W)*, $62.86*(D)*, $96.49*(W)*

# 11

# Rational Numbers
# Multiplication

# 11.1 Products of Positive and Negative Numbers

P-1 **How does the answer to each multiplication problem below compare with the one before it?**

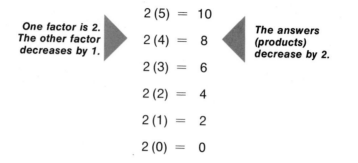

One factor is 2. The other factor decreases by 1.

$2(5) = 10$

$2(4) = 8$

$2(3) = 6$

$2(2) = 4$

$2(1) = 2$

$2(0) = 0$

The answers (products) decrease by 2.

P-2 **If the same pattern continues, what is each missing numeral below?**

$2(^-1) = \underline{\ ?\ }$

$2(^-2) = \underline{\ ?\ }$

$2(^-3) = \underline{\ ?\ }$

Since the answers decrease by 2 at each step, you would expect the answer after 0 to be $^-2$, and the one after $^-2$ to be $^-4$, and so forth.

$2(^-1) = {}^-2$

$2(^-2) = {}^-4$

$2(^-3) = {}^-6$

P-3 **What do you think should be the answer to each product below?**

**a.** $2(^-4)$     **b.** $2(^-5)$     **c.** $2(^-6)$

P-4 **How can you describe the pattern of the answers below?**

| a | b | c |
|---|---|---|
| $3(5) = 15$ | $6(5) = 30$ | $10(2\frac{1}{2}) = 25$ |
| $3(4) = 12$ | $6(4) = 24$ | $10(\ 2\ ) = 20$ |
| $3(3) = 9$ | $6(3) = 18$ | $10(1\frac{1}{2}) = 15$ |

The pattern is shown again on the next page and extended further.

|  | a | | b | | c |
|---|---|---|---|---|---|

|        a              |        b              |            c                |
|-----------------------|-----------------------|-----------------------------|
| $3(5) = 15$           | $6(5) = 30$           | $10(2\frac{1}{2}) = 25$     |
| $3(4) = 12$           | $6(4) = 24$           | $10(2) = 20$                |
| $3(3) = 9$            | $6(3) = 18$           | $10(1\frac{1}{2}) = 15$     |
| $3(2) = 6$            | $6(2) = 12$           | $10(1) = 10$                |
| $3(1) = 3$            | $6(1) = 6$            | $10(\frac{1}{2}) = 5$       |
| $3(0) = 0$            | $6(0) = 0$            | $10(0) = 0$                 |
| $3(^-1) = \underline{\ ?\ }$ | $6(^-1) = \underline{\ ?\ }$ | $10(^-\frac{1}{2}) = \underline{\ ?\ }$ |
| $3(^-2) = \underline{\ ?\ }$ | $6(^-2) = \underline{\ ?\ }$ | $10(^-1) = \underline{\ ?\ }$ |
| $3(^-3) = \underline{\ ?\ }$ | $6(^-3) = \underline{\ ?\ }$ | $10(^-1\frac{1}{2}) = \underline{\ ?\ }$ |

**P-5**  **If the same pattern continues, what is the missing numeral in each product above?**

The first two columns illustrate the pattern for multiplying positive and negative integers. The third column illustrates the pattern for multiplying positive and negative rational numbers.

## example 1    Multiply: $(^-12.8)(3)$

Follow these steps to find the product of a positive number and a negative number.

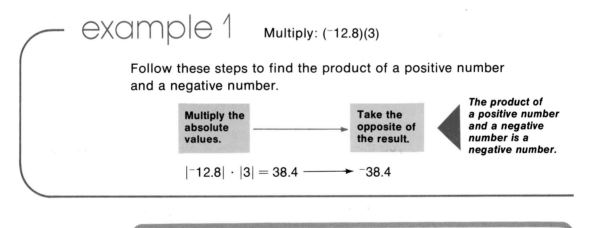

| Multiply the absolute values. | → | Take the opposite of the result. | ◀ | The product of a positive number and a negative number is a negative number. |

$|^-12.8| \cdot |3| = 38.4 \longrightarrow\ ^-38.4$

> The product of a positive rational number and a negative rational number is a negative rational number.
>
> $6 \cdot\ ^-4 =\ ^-24$

**P-6**  **What is the answer for each of these?**

**a.** $8(^-5)$     **b.** $(^-4)9$     **c.** $\frac{1}{2}(^-12)$     **d.** $^-2(2.3)$

**P-7** **What is the answer for each of these?**

**a.** $(^-3.5)0$     **b.** $0 \times 11\frac{2}{5}$     **c.** $0(^-9\frac{3}{8})$     **d.** $-\pi \cdot 0$

You know that the product of zero and any number is zero. Thus, this property must be true for rational numbers.

---

**Multiplication Property of Zero**

For any rational number $a$,
   $a \cdot 0 = 0$.

$0 \cdot {}^-4 = 0$

$^-2.6 \cdot 0 = 0$

---

**P-8** **What is the answer for each of these?**

**a.** $(0)(^-5.7)$     **b.** $(^-3\frac{1}{2})(0)$     **c.** $(\frac{15}{8})(0)$

## ORAL EXERCISES 11.1

*Multiply. Simplify where necessary.* (P-6, P-7, P-8, Example 1)

**1.** $^-1(6)$     **2.** $3(^-2)$     **3.** $4(^-5)$

**4.** $^-7(8)$     **5.** $^-7(4)$     **6.** $^-8(9)$

**7.** $7(^-6)$     **8.** $5(^-5)$     **9.** $^-4(8)$

**10.** $6(^-4)$     **11.** $^-9(3)$     **12.** $3(^-8)$

**13.** $^-12(4)$     **14.** $2(^-7)$     **15.** $4(^-11)$

**16.** $^-6(7)$     **17.** $^-2(9)$     **18.** $6(^-9)$

**19.** $9(^-4)$     **20.** $^-11(3)$     **21.** $^-4(0)$

**22.** $0(^-19)$     **23.** $0(^-4\frac{1}{2})$     **24.** $(^-8.3)0$

**25.** $\frac{1}{2}(^-8)$     **26.** $\frac{1}{3}(^-12)$     **27.** $^-(\frac{1}{2})16$

**28.** $^-(\frac{1}{4})12$     **29.** $^-2(4.1)$     **30.** $^-1(5.9)$

**31.** $2.2(^-3)$     **32.** $1.2(^-5)$     **33.** $7(^-7)$

**34.** $^-9(9)$     **35.** $0(^-19.6)$     **36.** $(7)9$

**37.** $(11)(6)$     **38.** $(^-2\frac{1}{2})(20)$     **39.** $1\frac{1}{4}(^-24)$

**40.** $(^-0.6)(12)$     **41.** $(^-400)3$     **42.** $^-4(250)$

# WRITTEN EXERCISES 11.1

**A**

**Goal:** To multiply a positive rational number and a negative rational number
**Sample Problem:** $(0.6)(^-4)$
**Answer:** $^-2.4$

*Multiply. Simplify where necessary.* (P-6, P-7, P-8, Example 1)

**1.** $^-3(4)$

**2.** $^-5(6)$

**3.** $7(^-5)$

**4.** $4(^-7)$

**5.** $^-6(5)$

**6.** $^-4(9)$

**7.** $^-9(7)$

**8.** $^-7(6)$

**9.** $9(^-6)$

**10.** $8(^-4)$

**11.** $12(^-8)$

**12.** $12(^-7)$

**13.** $8(^-8)$

**14.** $6(^-6)$

**15.** $^-9(6)$

**16.** $^-8(12)$

**17.** $\frac{1}{2}(^-14)$

**18.** $\frac{1}{2}(^-12)$

**19.** $^-(\frac{1}{2})(28)$

**20.** $^-(\frac{1}{2})(36)$

**21.** $\frac{1}{3}(^-15)$

**22.** $\frac{1}{3}(^-21)$

**23.** $^-(\frac{1}{4})(24)$

**24.** $^-(\frac{1}{4})(40)$

**25.** $^-3(5.2)$

**26.** $^-4(2.8)$

**27.** $(^-8.6)(7)$

**28.** $(^-10.3)(8)$

**29.** $(^-0.6)(28)$

**30.** $(^-0.8)(19)$

**31.** $(^-1.3)(0.3)$

**32.** $(^-3.7)(0.4)$

**33.** $^-(\frac{1}{4})(\frac{2}{5})$

**34.** $^-(\frac{2}{3})(\frac{6}{7})$

**35.** $0(^-236)$

**36.** $0(^-98)$

**37.** $12(^-35)$

**38.** $15(^-42)$

**39.** $(^-22)(29)$

**40.** $(^-34)(27)$

**41.** $600(^-5)$

**42.** $^-350(6)$

**C**

**EXAMPLE:** $^-5(^-12 + 21)$   **SOLUTION:** $^-5(^-12 + 21) = ^-5(9)$
$$= ^-45$$

**43.** $^-4(17 + ^-5)$

**44.** $^-6(^-13 + 18)$

**45.** $9(^-30 + 24)$

**46.** $12(^-23 + 19)$

**47.** $^-10(4 \cdot 5)$

**48.** $^-16(\frac{1}{2} \cdot 8)$

**49.** $(7 \cdot ^-2)3$

**50.** $(^-4 \cdot 2)9$

*Write True or False.*

**51.** $3(^-4 + ^-8) = 3(^-4) + 3(^-8)$

**52.** $(^-5\frac{1}{2} + ^-1\frac{1}{2})3 = (^-5\frac{1}{2})3 + (^-1\frac{1}{2})3$

**53.** $(^-8 + ^-7)4 = (^-8)4 + (^-7)4$

**54.** $2\frac{1}{2}(^-6 + ^-3\frac{1}{2}) = 2\frac{1}{2}(^-6) + 2\frac{1}{2}(^-3\frac{1}{2})$

**55.** $5(^-9 + ^-3) = ^-5(9) + ^-5(3)$

**56.** $(^-4 + 2)10 = (^-4)10 + 2(10)$

# 11.2 Product of Two Negative Numbers

P-1    **How does the answer to each multiplication problem below compare with the one above it?**

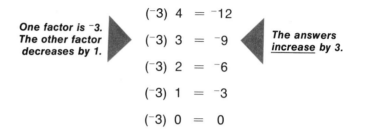

*One factor is ⁻3. The other factor decreases by 1.*

$$(^-3)\ 4 = {}^-12$$
$$(^-3)\ 3 = {}^-9$$
$$(^-3)\ 2 = {}^-6$$
$$(^-3)\ 1 = {}^-3$$
$$(^-3)\ 0 = 0$$

*The answers* <u>*increase*</u> *by 3.*

P-2    **What is the next greater number after 0 in the pattern of answers?**

P-3    **If the same pattern of answers continues, what is each missing numeral below?**

$$(^-3)(^-1) = \underline{\ ?\ }$$
$$(^-3)(^-2) = \underline{\ ?\ }$$
$$(^-3)(^-3) = \underline{\ ?\ }$$
$$(^-3)(^-4) = \underline{\ ?\ }$$

Since the answers <u>increase</u> by 3 at each step, you would expect the answer after 0 to be 3, the answer after 3 to be 6, and so forth.

$$(^-3)(^-1) = 3$$
$$(^-3)(^-2) = 6$$
$$(^-3)(^-3) = 9$$
$$(^-3)(^-4) = 12$$

P-4    **What do you think should be the answer to each product below?**

     **a.** $(^-3)(^-5)$      **b.** $(^-3)(^-6)$      **c.** $(^-3)(^-7)$

P-5    **How can you describe the two factors in the examples shown on the following page?**

P-6    **How can you describe the pattern of the answers in each example?**

|        a        |        b        |         c         |
| :-------------: | :-------------: | :---------------: |
| $^-4(5) = {}^-20$ | $^-5(5) = {}^-25$ | $^-10(2.5) = {}^-25$ |
| $^-4(4) = {}^-16$ | $^-5(4) = {}^-20$ | $^-10(2.0) = {}^-20$ |
| $^-4(3) = {}^-12$ | $^-5(3) = {}^-15$ | $^-10(1.5) = {}^-15$ |
| $^-4(2) = {}^-8$  | $^-5(2) = {}^-10$ | $^-10(1.0) = {}^-10$ |
| $^-4(1) = {}^-4$  | $^-5(1) = {}^-5$  | $^-10(0.5) = {}^-5$  |
| $^-4(0) = 0$      | $^-5(0) = 0$      | $^-10(0) = 0$        |
| $^-4(^-1) = \underline{\ ?\ }$ | $^-5(^-1) = \underline{\ ?\ }$ | $^-10(^-0.5) = \underline{\ ?\ }$ |
| $^-4(^-2) = \underline{\ ?\ }$ | $^-5(^-2) = \underline{\ ?\ }$ | $^-10(^-1.0) = \underline{\ ?\ }$ |
| $^-4(^-3) = \underline{\ ?\ }$ | $^-5(^-3) = \underline{\ ?\ }$ | $^-10(^-1.5) = \underline{\ ?\ }$ |

**P-7**  **What is the missing numeral in each product above?**

The first two columns illustrate the pattern for multiplying two negative integers. The third column illustrates the pattern for multiplying two rational numbers.

**P-8**  **What is the answer for each product below?**

**a.** $(^-7)(^-8)$     **b.** $^-(\frac{1}{2})(^-12)$     **c.** $(^-3)(^-4.1)$     **d.** $(^-0.6)(^-7)$

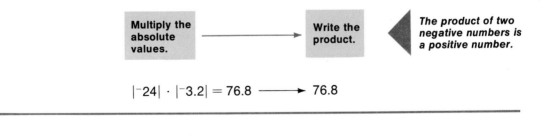

example 1    Multiply: $(^-24)(^-3.2)$

Follow these steps to find the product of two negative numbers.

| Multiply the absolute values. | ⟶ | Write the product. | ◀ | The product of two negative numbers is a positive number. |

$|^-24| \cdot |^-3.2| = 76.8 \longrightarrow 76.8$

> The product of two negative rational numbers is a positive rational number.
>
> $^-6 \cdot {}^-4 = 24$

## ORAL EXERCISES 11.2

*Multiply. Simplify where necessary. (Example 1)*

1. $(^-7)(^-5)$
2. $(^-4)(^-8)$
3. $(^-1)(^-9)$
4. $(^-3)(^-6)$

5. $(^-5)(^-9)$
6. $(^-8)(^-3)$
7. $(^-10)(^-8)$
8. $(^-11)(^-4)$

9. $(^-6)(^-6)$
10. $(^-9)(^-8)$
11. $(^-6)(^-3)$
12. $(^-7)(^-2)$

13. $(^-12)(^-2)$
14. $(^-6)(^-9)$
15. $(^-8)(^-4)$
16. $(^-9)(^-4)$

17. $(^-3)(^-2.2)$
18. $(^-1.4)(^-2)$
19. $(^-0.9)(^-3)$
20. $(^-5)(^-1.2)$

21. $^-(\frac{1}{2})(^-14)$
22. $^-(\frac{1}{3})(^-18)$
23. $^-(\frac{3}{4})(^-12)$
24. $(^-32) \cdot {}^-(\frac{1}{4})$

25. $(7)(^-9)$
26. $(^-8)(6)$
27. $(^-12)(5)$
28. $(10)(^-7)$

29. $^-(\frac{1}{2})(^-6.4)$
30. $^-(\frac{1}{3})(^-9.6)$
31. $(^-4.2)(\frac{1}{7})$
32. $^-(\frac{1}{5})(3.5)$

## WRITTEN EXERCISES 11.2

**A**  **Goal:** To multiply two negative rational numbers
**Sample Problem:** $^-(\frac{1}{5})(^-15)$
**Answer:** 3

*Multiply. Simplify where necessary. (Example 1)*

1. $(^-6)(^-4)$
2. $(^-5)(^-7)$
3. $(^-3)(^-8)$
4. $(^-4)(^-9)$

5. $(^-12)(^-7)$
6. $(^-8)(^-12)$
7. $(^-9)(^-8)$
8. $(^-6)(^-9)$

9. $(^-16)(^-8)$
10. $(^-14)(^-9)$
11. $(^-18)(^-7)$
12. $(^-24)(^-8)$

13. $(^-0.6)(^-18)$
14. $(^-0.8)(^-24)$
15. $(^-20.3)(^-5.6)$
16. $(^-48)(^-12.7)$

17. $(16)(^-8)$
18. $(21)(^-11)$
19. $(^-30)(^-40)$
20. $(^-50)(^-70)$

21. $(^-120)(3)$
22. $(^-150)(4)$
23. $(^-0.2)(^-0.7)$
24. $(^-0.4)(^-0.9)$

25. $(\frac{2}{5})(^-40)$
26. $(\frac{3}{5})(^-30)$
27. $(^-1\frac{2}{5})(^-2\frac{3}{4})$
28. $(^-2\frac{4}{5})(^-3\frac{1}{2})$

**C**  **EXAMPLE:** $^-4(12 + {}^-15)$
**SOLUTION:** $^-4(12 + {}^-15) = {}^-4(^-3) = 12$

29. $^-12(^-19 + 12)$
30. $^-20(4 + {}^-15)$
31. $(18 + {}^-26) \cdot {}^-(\frac{1}{2})$

32. $^-8(^-9 \cdot 5)$
33. $(^-7 + {}^-11)(^-4)$
34. $(^-6)(^-9) + (^-6)(14)$

35. $^-(\frac{1}{2})(16 \cdot 7)$
36. $(^-3)(^-6 + 8)$
37. $(^-5)(4) + (^-4)(4)$

# 11.3 Multiplication and Rational Numbers

**P-1**  **What is the answer for each of the following?**

**a.** $(1)(^-2.7)$  **b.** $(1)(0)$  **c.** $^-(\frac{3}{4})(1)$

| | |
|---|---|
| ***Multiplication Property of One*** | $1(^-2.6) = ^-2.6$ |
| For any rational number $a$, $1(a) = a$. | $^-(\frac{2}{3}) \cdot 1 = ^-(\frac{2}{3})$ |

**P-2**  **What is the answer for each of the following?**

**a.** $(^-9)(7)$  **b.** $(7)(^-9)$

**c.** $(^-8)(^-5)$  **d.** $(^-5)(^-8)$

◄ *The order of multiplying two rational numbers does not affect the product.*

| | |
|---|---|
| ***Commutative Property of Multiplication*** | $(^-2)(3) = ^-6$ |
| For any rational numbers $a$ and $b$, $ab = ba$. | $3(^-2) = ^-6$ |

**P-3**  **Which of the following are examples of the Commutative Property of Multiplication?**

**a.** $(^-5.6)(7) = (^-6.5)(7)$

**b.** $(^-1\frac{1}{4})(^-2\frac{1}{2}) = (^-2\frac{1}{2})(^-1\frac{1}{4})$

**c.** $(^-5 \cdot 6)(^-7 + 8) = (^-7 + 8)(^-5 \cdot 6)$

**d.** $(^-7 \cdot 8)(^-5) = (^-7)(8 \cdot ^-5)$

**P-4**  **What is the answer for $(^-3 \cdot 4)2$?  for $^-3(4 \cdot 2)$?**

$(^-3 \cdot 4)2$ means $(^-12)2$.
$^-3(4 \cdot 2)$ means $^-3(8)$.

◄ *The way in which numbers are grouped for multiplication does not affect the product.*

Both phrases have the simplest name $^-24$. Therefore, $(^-3 \cdot 4)2 = ^-3(4 \cdot 2)$ is true.

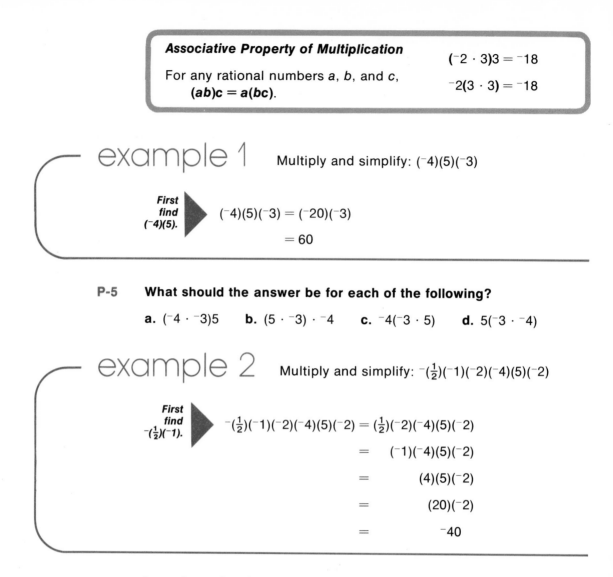

**Associative Property of Multiplication**

For any rational numbers $a$, $b$, and $c$,
$(ab)c = a(bc)$.

$(^-2 \cdot 3)3 = ^-18$

$^-2(3 \cdot 3) = ^-18$

## example 1

Multiply and simplify: $(^-4)(5)(^-3)$

**First find $(^-4)(5)$.**

$(^-4)(5)(^-3) = (^-20)(^-3)$

$= 60$

**P-5** **What should the answer be for each of the following?**

**a.** $(^-4 \cdot {}^-3)5$     **b.** $(5 \cdot {}^-3) \cdot {}^-4$     **c.** $^-4(^-3 \cdot 5)$     **d.** $5(^-3 \cdot {}^-4)$

## example 2

Multiply and simplify: $^-(\frac{1}{2})(^-1)(^-2)(^-4)(5)(^-2)$

**First find $^-(\frac{1}{2})(^-1)$.**

$^-(\frac{1}{2})(^-1)(^-2)(^-4)(5)(^-2) = (\frac{1}{2})(^-2)(^-4)(5)(^-2)$

$= (^-1)(^-4)(5)(^-2)$

$= (4)(5)(^-2)$

$= (20)(^-2)$

$= {}^-40$

**P-6** **Is each product below positive or negative?**

**a.** $(^-1)(^-46)(^-19)(^-27)(^-83)$

**b.** $(^-5)(7)(^-2)(^-86)(^-57)$

**c.** $(^-1)(^-1)(^-1)(^-1)(^-1)(^-1)(^-1)$

A product with an even number of negative factors is positive.
A product with an odd number of negative factors is negative.

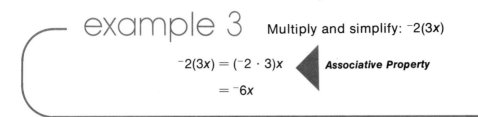

example 3   Multiply and simplify: $^-2(3x)$

$$^-2(3x) = (^-2 \cdot 3)x \qquad \text{Associative Property}$$
$$= ^-6x$$

## ORAL EXERCISES 11.3

*Multiply. Simplify where necessary.* (Example 1, Example 2, Example 3)

1. $(^-2)(3)(^-2)$
2. $(^-1)(5)(2)$
3. $(^-1)(^-2)(^-3)$
4. $(^-2)(^-2)(^-2)$
5. $(6)(\frac{1}{3})(^-5)$
6. $(^-1)(8)(^-3)$
7. $(^-5)(2)(^-4)$
8. $(6)(^-2)(3)$
9. $(^-0.5)(^-8)(3)$
10. $(0)(^-5)(^-6)$
11. $^-(\frac{1}{2}) \cdot \, ^-(\frac{4}{5})(^-1)$
12. $(0.9)(^-5)(1)$
13. $(^-2)(^-2)(^-2)(^-2)$
14. $(^-3)(2)(^-3)(^-2)$
15. $(^-1)(^-1)(^-1)(^-1)(^-1)$
16. $(^-4)(2)(^-3)(\frac{1}{2})$
17. $(^-5)(^-2)(^-3)(\frac{1}{3})$
18. $(^-4)(^-2)(\frac{1}{4})(^-3)$
19. $^-5(4a)$
20. $^-6(^-3r)$
21. $8(^-3t)$
22. $5x(^-6)$
23. $^-8y(7)$
24. $^-7n(^-4)$

## WRITTEN EXERCISES 11.3

**A**   **Goal:** To multiply with three or more rational numbers and variables
**Sample Problem:** $(^-3)(2)(^-\frac{1}{3}x)$
**Answer:** $2x$

*Multiply. Simplify where necessary.* (Example 1)

1. $(7)(^-3)(2)$
2. $(8)(^-5)(3)$
3. $(^-4)(^-6)(^-2)$
4. $(^-3)(^-5)(^-4)$

*Multiply. Simplify where necessary.* (Example 1, Example 2, Example 3)

**5.** $(^-6)(3)(^-5)$　　　　　　　　　　　　**6.** $(^-8)(1)(^-6)$

**7.** $(12)(^-3)(^-5)$　　　　　　　　　　　**8.** $(15)(^-2)(^-4)$

**9.** $(^-19)(^-1)(2)$　　　　　　　　　　**10.** $(^-24)(3)(^-1)$

**11.** $^-(\frac{1}{2})(12)(^-5)$　　　　　　　　**12.** $^-(\frac{1}{2})(20)(^-8)$

**13.** $^-(\frac{1}{4})(^-5)(^-8)$　　　　　　　**14.** $^-(\frac{1}{3})(^-7)(^-9)$

**15.** $(^-15)(^-11) \cdot ^-(\frac{2}{3})$　　　　　　**16.** $(^-20)(^-12) \cdot ^-(\frac{3}{4})$

**17.** $(^-1.2)(^-3)(4)$　　　　　　　　**18.** $(^-2.3)(^-4)(3)$

**19.** $(0.3)(^-1.4)(^-1)(2)$　　　　　**20.** $(0.5)(^-1.8)(^-1)(3)$

**21.** $(^-2)(^-1)(5)(^-1)(^-1)$　　　　**22.** $(^-3)(4)(^-1)(^-1)(^-1)$

**23.** $^-(\frac{2}{3})(\frac{3}{4}) \cdot ^-(\frac{2}{5})$　　　　　　　**24.** $^-(\frac{3}{5})(\frac{5}{12}) \cdot ^-(\frac{4}{7})$

**25.** $(^-1\frac{1}{2})(^-1\frac{1}{3})(^-3\frac{1}{2})$　　　　**26.** $(^-1\frac{1}{4})(^-1\frac{3}{5})(^-4\frac{1}{2})$

**27.** $(^-40)(^-3)(^-2)(^-1)(^-1)$　　**28.** $(^-20)(^-7)(^-3)(^-1)(^-1)$

**29.** $(^-15) \cdot ^-(\frac{1}{2}) \cdot ^-(\frac{1}{5})(^-16)$　　**30.** $(^-21) \cdot ^-(\frac{1}{4}) \cdot ^-(\frac{1}{3})(^-28)$

**31.** $^-4(8n)$　　　　**32.** $^-6(5b)$　　　　**33.** $12(^-4k)$　　　　**34.** $15(^-3t)$

**35.** $^-8(^-7x)$　　　**36.** $^-9(^-6p)$　　　**37.** $\frac{1}{2}(^-24y)$　　　**38.** $\frac{1}{3}(^-27m)$

**39.** $^-(\frac{1}{4})(^-32a)$　　**40.** $^-(\frac{1}{5})(^-40q)$　　**41.** $(^-19t)5$　　　**42.** $(^-16x)6$

**B**　　*Write the simplest name for each phrase.*

**EXAMPLE:** $(^-4) + (^-5)^2$

**SOLUTION:** $(^-4) + (^-5)^2 = (^-4) + 25$
$= 21$

**43.** $(^-2)^2 + (^-5)$　　　**44.** $(^-3)^2 + (^-10)$　　　**45.** $(^-1)^2 + 2(^-3)$　　　**46.** $^-5(7) + (^-5)^2$

**47.** $-(3^2)$　　　　　　**48.** $-(4^2)$　　　　　　**49.** $-(^-5)^2$　　　　　　**50.** $-(^-6)^2$

**51.** $(^-2)^3$　　　　　　**52.** $(^-1)^3$　　　　　　**53.** $5(^-3)^2$　　　　　　**54.** $3(^-2)^3$

**55.** $(^-6)^2 + 8(^-5) + 17$　　　　　　　　**56.** $^-3(8) + (^-7)^2 + (^-15)$

**57.** $(^-5)^2 + 6(^-3) + 48 + (^-4)$　　　　**58.** $(^-2)^2 + 8(^-2) + (^-9) + 32$

**59.** $(^-3)^3 + (^-81) + (^-4)^2$　　　　　　**60.** $64 + (^-4)^3 + (^-2)^3 + 8$

# 11.4 Distributive Property

**P-1**  **Which phrases below are products?  which are sums?**

     **a.** $2(^-6 + 9)$      **b.** $3(^-5) + (^-7)(^-5)$      **c.** $5y + {}^-2(7)$

     **d.** $(x + 7)(^-5)$      **e.** $(^-10 + r) + s$      **f.** $^-4w(^-9t)$

---

**Distributive Property**

For any rational numbers $a$, $b$, and $c$,
1. $a(b + c) = ab + ac$, and
2. $(b + c)a = ba + ca$.

$2(^-4 + 3) = 2(^-4) + 2(3)$

$(x + 3)4 = x(4) + 3(4)$

---

## example 1
     Multiply and simplify: $^-3(2x + 5)$

Use the Distributive Property.

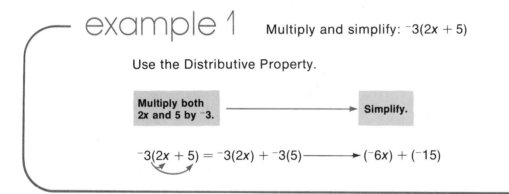

| Multiply both 2x and 5 by ⁻3. | → | Simplify. |

$$^-3(2x + 5) = {}^-3(2x) + {}^-3(5) \longrightarrow (^-6x) + (^-15)$$

---

**P-2**  **What factor is common to ⁻2x and ⁻2y?**

## example 2
     Write $(^-2x) + (^-2y)$ as a product.

Compare $(^-2x) + (^-2y)$ with the right side of $a(b + c) = ab + ac$.

$$a\,b + a\,c = a\,(b + c)$$
$$(^-2x) + (^-2y) = {}^-2(x + y)$$

Writing a phrase of the form $ab + ac$ in the form $a(b + c)$ is called **factoring**.

**P-3**  **What factors are common to ⁻5rx and ⁻5x?**

## example 3   Factor ⁻5rx + ⁻5x.

$$^-5rx + {}^-5x = (^-5x)r + (^-5x)1$$

Compare this phrase with $ab + ac$. Write it in the form $a(b + c)$.

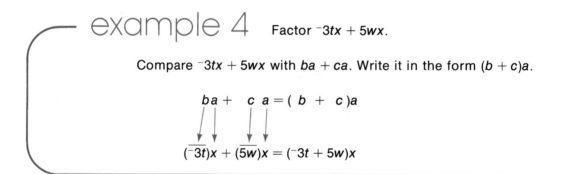

$$(^-5x)r + (^-5x)1 = {}^-5x(r + 1)$$

**P-4**  **What factor is common to ⁻3tx and 5wx?**

## example 4   Factor ⁻3tx + 5wx.

Compare $^-3tx + 5wx$ with $ba + ca$. Write it in the form $(b + c)a$.

$$ba + ca = (b + c)a$$

$$(^-3t)x + (5w)x = (^-3t + 5w)x$$

## example 5   Multiply and simplify: $(^-3t)(^-5t)$

Think of $(^-3t)(^-5t)$ in the form $(^-3)(t)(^-5)(t)$. Then use the Commutative and Associative Properties of Multiplication.

$$(^-3t)(^-5t) = (^-3)(t)(^-5)(t)$$
$$= (^-3 \cdot {}^-5)(t \cdot t)$$
$$= (15)t \cdot t$$
$$= 15t^2$$

**P-5**  **What is the simplest name for $(^-3x)(^-8x)$?**

example 6   Multiply and simplify: $^-3x(^-8x + 5)$

First use the Distributive Property.

$$^-3x(^-8x + 5) = (^-3x)(^-8x) + (^-3x)5$$
$$= (^-3 \cdot \ ^-8)(x \cdot x) + (^-3 \cdot 5)x$$
$$= \quad 24x^2 \quad + (^-15x)$$

## ORAL EXERCISES 11.4

*Multiply by use of the Distributive Property. Tell the simplest name.*
*(Example 1, Example 6)*

**EXAMPLE:** $4a(^-2x + 3)$
**ANSWER:** $^-8ax + 12a$

**1.** $^-2(x + 5)$  **2.** $(a + 3)(^-6)$  **3.** $^-1(n + \ ^-3)$
**4.** $^-3(x + \ ^-8)$  **5.** $(2x + 3)(^-5)$  **6.** $^-5(^-3x + 1)$
**7.** $^-3r(r + \ ^-2)$  **8.** $2t(^-5t + 7)$  **9.** $\frac{1}{2}k(^-4k + 10)$

*Say each sum as a product. (Example 2, Example 3, Example 4)*

**EXAMPLE:** $4(^-7x) + 4(y)$
**ANSWER:** $4(^-7x + y)$   Say, "Four times the quantity
negative seven x plus y."

**10.** $^-3y + \ ^-3x$  **11.** $a(^-5) + b(^-5)$  **12.** $^-10(r) + \ ^-10(7)$
**13.** $k(8) + \ ^-5(8)$  **14.** $^-4(t) + \ ^-4(1)$  **15.** $rx + \ ^-6x$
**16.** $5ax + \ ^-3x$  **17.** $(^-12ny) + (^-12nx)$  **18.** $(^-12m) + (^-12)$
**19.** $^-2kx + k$  **20.** $5r + \ ^-5s$  **21.** $^-3tm + 3tn$

*Multiply. Simplify where necessary. (Example 1, Example 5, Example 6)*

**22.** $^-3r(2r + \ ^-1)$  **23.** $^-5(8x)$  **24.** $^-7(^-9y)$
**25.** $(2x)(^-7x)$  **26.** $^-3t(^-7t + 5)$  **27.** $(^-2ay)(3y)$
**28.** $(^-3xy)(^-10xy)$  **29.** $(^-4y + \ ^-3)(^-5y)$  **30.** $\frac{1}{5}(^-5x)$

# WRITTEN EXERCISES 11.4

**A**  **Goals:** To multiply and to factor using the Distributive Property
**Sample Problems: a.** $^-12n(^-3n + 5)$   **b.** $^-7ax + 9bx$
**Answers: a.** $36n^2 + ^-60n$   **b.** $(^-7a + 9b)x$

*Multiply. Simplify where necessary. (Example 1, Example 5, Example 6)*

1. $^-2(8a + ^-5)$
2. $^-3(10x + ^-6)$
3. $^-5(^-3r + ^-7)$

4. $^-4(^-7n + ^-9)$
5. $(5 + 3x)(^-7)$
6. $(5a + ^-3)(^-5)$

7. $\frac{1}{4}(12x + ^-4)$
8. $\frac{1}{3}(^-15y + 6)$
9. $(6 + ^-9x)\frac{1}{3}$

10. $(15y + 10)\frac{1}{5}$
11. $x(^-5 + 2x)$
12. $y(3 + ^-2y)$

13. $(^-3a + ^-2)2a$
14. $(5r + ^-3)3r$
15. $^-3n(2n + ^-5)$

16. $^-5t(^-3t + 1)$
17. $\frac{1}{2}a(4a + ^-2)$
18. $\frac{1}{3}x(^-21x + ^-15)$

*Factor each phrase. (Example 2, Example 3, Example 4)*

19. $(^-7)x + (^-7)y$
20. $(^-15)a + (^-15)b$

21. $t(^-8) + s(^-8)$
22. $p(^-11) + q(^-11)$

23. $^-8.6r + ^-8.6s$
24. $^-3.7m + ^-3.7n$

25. $(^-12)0.5 + (3y)0.5$
26. $(13)0.8 + (^-4g)0.8$

27. $5rw + (^-5rx)$
28. $9kn + (^-9kt)$

29. $5ax + (^-6ay)$
30. $ab + (^-5a)$

31. $25p + 25(^-1q)$
32. $^-18x + ^-18(^-1y)$

33. $5m + ^-5n$
34. $8r + ^-8s$

35. $^-3xm + 3my$
36. $8rt + (^-8tw)$

37. $13a(^-3x) + 13a(1)$
38. $5s(^-6) + (^-1)(^-6)$

**B**  **EXAMPLE:** $^-3rs + 3rt$   **ANSWER:** $^-3r(s + ^-1t)$   or   $3r(^-1s + t)$

39. $4x + 20$
40. $3k + 18$
41. $^-5r + (^-15)$

42. $^-5ax + a$
43. $t + (^-3rt)$
44. $2st + ^-6s$

45. $^-3wz + 12z$
46. $^-6m + 9n$
47. $8ap + ^-12q$

# 11.5 Special Properties

**P-1**  **What is the simplest name for each product below?**

**a.** $(^-1)(3)$  **b.** $(^-1)(^-0.3)$

**c.** $(^-1)(^-4)$  **d.** $(^-1)(150)$

**e.** $(^-1)(\frac{3}{4})$  **f.** $(^-1)(^-2\frac{1}{2})$

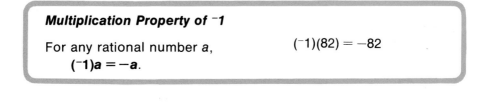

*Multiplying a number by $^-1$ is the same as taking the opposite of the number.*

---

**Multiplication Property of $^-1$**

For any rational number $a$,
   $(^-1)a = -a$.

$(^-1)(82) = -82$

---

You know that $-(a + b)$ and $(-a) + (-b)$ are equivalent phrases. This fact and the fact that $^-1(a + b)$ and $-(a + b)$ are also equivalent phrases lead to the following property.

---

**Product of $^-1$ and a Sum of Numbers**

For any rational numbers $a$ and $b$,
   $^-1(a + b) = (-a) + (-b)$.

$^-1(3 + 8) = (-3) + (-8)$

---

Here are two special properties of multiplication of rational numbers.

---

For any rational numbers $a$ and $b$,

1. $(-a)(b) = -ab$, and
2. $(-a)(-b) = ab$.

$(-5)(4) = -20$

$(-5)(-4) = 20$

---

**P-2**  **What is the simplest name of each product below based on these properties?**

**a.** $(m)(-n)$  **b.** $(-s)(-t)$  **c.** $(^-3)(-x)$  **d.** $(2)(^-4)(-n)(^-1)$

The phrase $-ab$ will be used as the simplest name for $-(ab)$, $(-a)(b)$, and $(a)(-b)$. Also, $ab$ is the simplest name for $(-a)(-b)$.

**P-3**    **What is the simplest name for $(-t)(k)$? for $(r)(-s)(t)$? for $(-r)(-s)$?**

## example 1    Multiply and simplify: $(^-3)(-x)(^-5)(-z)$

1. Commutative and Associative
   Properties of Multiplication ─────────→ $(^-3)(-x)(^-5)(-z) = (^-3 \cdot {}^-5)(-x \cdot -z)$

2. Simplify. ─────────────────────────────→ $= 15xz$

## example 2    Write an equivalent phrase having the least number of opposite or negative symbols.

$$-(^-5 + p + (-q))$$

1. Multiplication Property of $^-1$ ────→ $-(^-5 + p + (-q)) = {}^-1(^-5 + p + (-q))$

2. Property of the Product of $^-1$
   and a Sum of Numbers ──────────────────→ $= -(^-5) + (-p) + {}-(-q)$

3. Simplify. ──────────────────────────────→ $= \quad 5 \ + (-p) + \quad q$

## example 3    Multiply and simplify: $-x(^-3 + 4x)$

Use the Distributive Property.

> **Multiply each term by $-x$.** ─────────────→ **Simplify.**

$$-x(^-3 + 4x) = -x(^-3) + {}-x(4x) \longrightarrow 3x + {}^-4x^2$$

## ORAL EXERCISES 11.5

*Tell the name of an equivalent phrase based on $(^-1)a = -a$.* (P-1)

1. $^-1 \cdot y$          2. $h(^-1)$          3. $-t$          4. $^-1(-r)$

5. $(-x)(^-1)$          6. $^-1(n + 5)$          7. $-(y + {}^-3)$          8. $(^-1)(x + y + 10)$

Tell the name of an equivalent phrase based on
$^-1(a + b) = (-a) + (-b)$.

**9.** $^-1(x + 7)$        **10.** $^-1(-r + 8)$        **11.** $^-1(s + {}^-5)$

**12.** $^-1(-n + {}^-6)$        **13.** $(-k + 10)(^-1)$        **14.** $(-m) + (^-9)$

**15.** $(-p) + 13$        **16.** $g + (-h)$        **17.** $^-1(w + (-x) + y)$

Simplify each product. (P-2, P-3, Example 1)

**18.** $5(-t)$        **19.** $k(-q)$        **20.** $(-z)w$

**21.** $(-c)(-d)$        **22.** $(^-6)(-t)$        **23.** $(^-5m)(-n)$

# WRITTEN EXERCISES 11.5

**A**

**Goal:** To multiply and simplify phrases using the multiplication properties
of rational numbers

**Sample Problems: a.** $-((-x)^2 + (^-5)(-x))$    **b.** $^-3a(4a + (-b))$
**Answers: a.** $-x^2 + {}^-5x$    **b.** $^-12a^2 + 3ab$

Multiply and simplify. (P-2, P-3, Example 1)

**1.** $(^-12)(-y)$        **2.** $(^-18)(-k)$        **3.** $(^-2)(r)(-r)$

**4.** $(^-5)(s)(-s)$        **5.** $(^-3m)(-n)(p)$        **6.** $(^-8x)(-y)(z)$

**7.** $(3p)(^-2q)(-p)(-q)$        **8.** $(^-4m)(n)(-m)(^-5n)$        **9.** $(^-5p^2)(-p)(t)$

**10.** $(^-4n)(-n^2)(s)$        **11.** $(^-7s^2)(t)(^-3s)$        **12.** $(8q)(r^2)(^-2q)$

Write an equivalent phrase having the least number of opposite or
negative symbols. (Example 2)

**13.** $^-1(^-6 + a)$        **14.** $^-1((-b) + 7)$        **15.** $-(^-4 + x)$

**16.** $-(5 + (-x))$        **17.** $-(^-12 + (-k) + (-t))$        **18.** $-(-r + s + {}^-5)$

Multiply and simplify. (Example 3)

**19.** $-x(y + {}^-2)$        **20.** $-y(a + {}^-5)$        **21.** $^-2a(-b + 5)$

**22.** $^-8m(-n + 7)$        **23.** $(-m + n)(^-2a)$        **24.** $(^-3y + 7)(-y)$

**25.** $^-5r(-r + {}^-3)$        **26.** $^-10q(-q + {}^-4)$        **27.** $4st(^-2s + (-t))$

**28.** $7mn(^-5p + (-n))$        **29.** $^-8r(-p + q + {}^-7)$        **30.** $^-6x(-y + z + {}^-9)$

# 11.6 Adding Like Terms

**P-1**   **What is the simplest name for $2x + 3x$?**

A phrase such as $2x + 3x$ with two terms is called a **binomial**. In any phrase involving addition the terms are separated by the addition symbol $+$.

The terms of the phrase $2x^2 + 3y + (^-5)$ are $2x^2$, $3y$, and $^-5$.

**P-2**   **What are the terms of $10 + (-a) + (^-5b^2)$?**

**P-3**   **What <u>like terms</u> are in each of the following phrases?**

    **a.**  $^-2x^2 + ^-3y + 5z + 3x^2 + ^-8$

    **b.**  $^-3ax^2 + 5a^2x + (-ax^2) + ^-3a^2x + ^-6$

*Like terms* have the same variables and the same power for each variable.

## example 1   Simplify $7x + (^-3x)$.

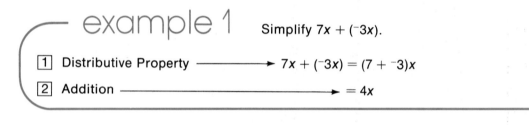

   1.  Distributive Property ⟶ $7x + (^-3x) = (7 + ^-3)x$

   2.  Addition ⟶ $= 4x$

**P-4**   **What numerical factor does the term $3x$ have?**

**P-5**   **What numerical factor is implied in the term $(-x)$?**

## example 2   Simplify $3x + (-x)$.

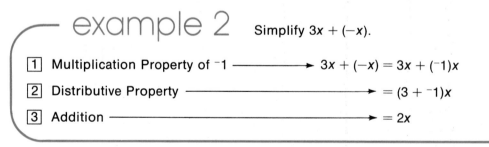

   1.  Multiplication Property of $^-1$ ⟶ $3x + (-x) = 3x + (^-1)x$

   2.  Distributive Property ⟶ $= (3 + ^-1)x$

   3.  Addition ⟶ $= 2x$

These examples suggest the rule for adding like terms.

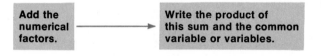

| Add the numerical factors. | ⟶ | Write the product of this sum and the common variable or variables. |

**P-6** What are the like terms in $2x^2 + (^-1.2x) + (-x^2) + (^-0.5x)$?

example 3  Add like terms: $2x^2 + (^-1.2x) + (-x^2) + (^-0.5x)$

$$2x^2 + (^-1.2x) + (-x^2) + (^-0.5x) = 2x^2 + (-x^2) + (^-1.2x) + (^-0.5x)$$

$$= \quad x^2 \quad + \quad (^-1.7x)$$

## ORAL EXERCISES 11.6

*Tell the like terms in each phrase. (P-3)*

1. $3x + (^-5y) + (^-4x) + 7$

2. $5ab + (^-3ac) + (-ab) + (^-5bc)$

3. $5m^2n + (-m^2n + ^-3) + mn + (^-4mn)$

4. $^-3pq + 2pq^2 + ^-5p^2q + (-pq)$

5. $(^-1.7apq) + (^-2.3p^2q) + (-p^2q) + 8.3pq$

6. $12rs^2 + (^-3\frac{1}{4}rs^2) + (^-1.9rs^2) + 6r^2s$

*Add like terms and simplify. (Example 1, Example 2, Example 3)*

7. $5m + ^-2m$

8. $r + ^-4r$

9. $^-6x^2 + ^-2x^2$

10. $6t + (-t)$

11. $^-5rs + 4rs$

12. $-ab + ^-7ab$

13. $y + (^-3) + 4y$

14. $^-10p + x + ^-3p$

15. $^-15a^2b + 9a^2b$

16. $2w + (^-3w) + (^-5w)$

17. $6a^2 + (-a^2) + (^-3a^2)$

18. $12ab + (^-3ab) + (^-5ab)$

19. $(^-3xy) + (^-6xy) + (-xy)$

20. $5m + 2n + (-m) + 3n$

21. $5.9t^2 + (^-1.9t^2)$

22. $(^-1\frac{1}{2}rt) + (^-2\frac{1}{2}rt)$

23. $4x^2 + (^-3x) + (-x) + (^-3)$

24. $y^2 + (^-12y) + 7y + 8$

25. $5ab^2 + (-a^2b) + (-ab^2) + 3a^2b$

26. $2.4st + (^-0.8st) + (^-0.5st)$

27. $5r + 3s + (^-7t) + (-s)$

28. $3x^3 + 4x^2 + (^-5x) + x + ^-6$

## WRITTEN EXERCISES 11.6

**A**

**Goal:** To add like terms

**Sample Problem:** $6a^2b + (^-5a^2b) + (^-6ab)$

**Answer:** $a^2b + (^-6ab)$

*Add like terms and simplify.* (Example 1, Example 2, Example 3)

**1.** $4k + ^-11k$

**2.** $6t + ^-15t$

**3.** $^-17r + 6r$

**4.** $^-13s + 9s$

**5.** $^-8.6p + ^-4.7p$

**6.** $^-3.9q + ^-5.6q$

**7.** $12rw + ^-5rw$

**8.** $16pq + ^-7pq$

**9.** $^-36a^2 + a^2$

**10.** $^-28n^2 + n^2$

**11.** $19r^2s + (-r^2s)$

**12.** $27xy^2 + (-xy^2)$

**13.** $4y + (^-9) + 13y$

**14.** $6m + (^-13) + 15m$

**15.** $1.6k + 13 + (^-2.9k)$

**16.** $2.8w + 7 + (^-4.1w)$

**17.** $^-5m + 14 + (^-9) + 8m$

**18.** $15y + (^-4) + 13 + (^-3y)$

**19.** $12g + (^-18g) + (-g)$

**20.** $(^-13h) + 11h + (-h)$

**21.** $1.9x^2 + (^-0.4x^2) + (^-12.3x^2)$

**22.** $2.5r^2 + (^-6.9x^2) + (^-1.4x^2)$

**23.** $6.3t + (-t) + 8.3 + (^-1.9)$

**24.** $4.9r + 1.7 + (-r) + (^-3.2)$

**25.** $4m^2n + (^-3mn^2) + (^-13m^2n) + 5mn$

**26.** $12pq^2 + (-p^2q) + (^-5pq) + 13p^2q$

**27.** $23x + (-y) + (^-38x) + 25y + (^-6)$

**28.** $31s + (^-43t) + (-t) + (^-27s) + 14$

**29.** $5x^2 + (^-19x) + (^-8) + (-x^2) + (^-15x) + 22$

**30.** $^-7y^2 + 23y + (^-1) + (-y^2) + (^-41y) + (^-19)$

**B**

Use the Property of the Opposite of a Sum. Then add like terms and simplify.

**EXAMPLE:** $3x + (^-2y) + -(-x + 7y)$

**SOLUTION:** $3x + (^-2y) + x + (^-7y) = 3x + x + (^-2y) + (^-7y)$
$$= 4x + (^-9y)$$

**31.** $-(2a + ^-4b) + 3b + ^-9a$

**32.** $-(5r + (-s)) + (^-4r) + 8s$

**33.** $2x^2 + (^-3x) + -(9x^2 + 4x)$

**34.** $^-9xy + 7 + -((-xy) + 19)$

**35.** $14p + (^-3q) + -(8q + (-p) + ^-13)$

**36.** $^-24m + 19 + -(^-7m + (-n) + 24)$

**37.** $8x + (^-4y) + -(4x + (^-9y) + (-y^2))$

**38.** $9m + (^-6n) + -(n^2 + -(n^2 + (-n)) + 5)$

# 11.7 Product of Two Binomials

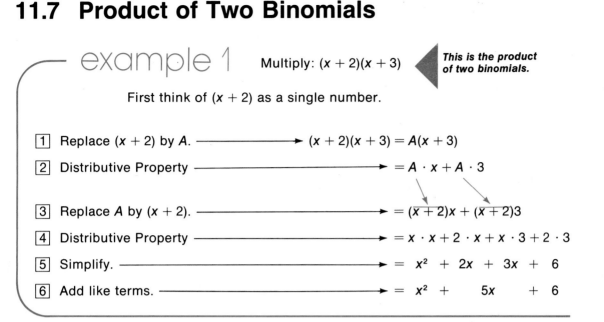

example 1    Multiply: $(x + 2)(x + 3)$ ◀ **This is the product of two binomials.**

First think of $(x + 2)$ as a single number.

| | | |
|---|---|---|
| ☐1 | Replace $(x + 2)$ by $A$. ⟶ | $(x + 2)(x + 3) = A(x + 3)$ |
| ☐2 | Distributive Property ⟶ | $= A \cdot x + A \cdot 3$ |
| ☐3 | Replace $A$ by $(x + 2)$. ⟶ | $= (x + 2)x + (x + 2)3$ |
| ☐4 | Distributive Property ⟶ | $= x \cdot x + 2 \cdot x + x \cdot 3 + 2 \cdot 3$ |
| ☐5 | Simplify. ⟶ | $= x^2 + 2x + 3x + 6$ |
| ☐6 | Add like terms. ⟶ | $= x^2 + \phantom{xx} 5x \phantom{xx} + 6$ |

P-1    **How many terms are in the phrase of Step ☐6 in Example 1?**

A phrase of <u>three</u> terms is called a **_trinomial._**

Note how the terms of $x^2 + 5x + 6$ can be easily determined.

1. $x^2$ is the product of the first terms.

$$(x + 2)(x + 3) = \mathbf{x^2} + 5x + 6$$

2. $5x$ is the sum of the products of the outside terms and the inside terms.

$$(x + 2)(x + 3) = x^2 + \mathbf{5x} + 6$$

3. 6 is the product of the last terms.

$$(x + 2)(x + 3) = x^2 + 5x + \mathbf{6}$$

The word **FOIL** may help you remember the method.

F suggests the product of the **f**irst terms.
O suggests the product of the **o**utside terms.
I suggests the product of the **i**nside terms.
L suggests the product of the **l**ast terms.

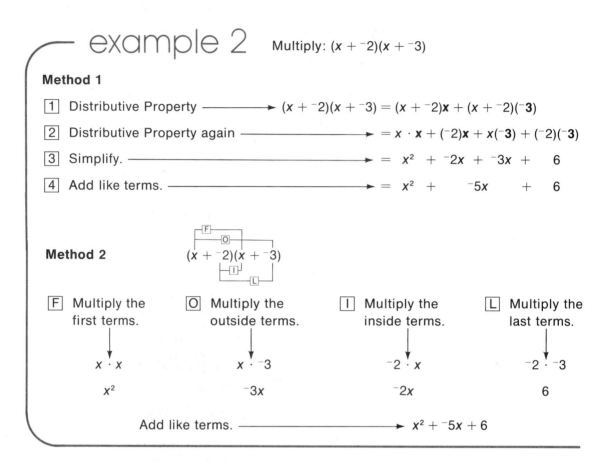

## example 2   Multiply: $(x + {}^-2)(x + {}^-3)$

**Method 1**

1. Distributive Property ⟶ $(x + {}^-2)(x + {}^-3) = (x + {}^-2)x + (x + {}^-2)({}^-\mathbf{3})$

2. Distributive Property again ⟶ $= x \cdot x + ({}^-2)x + x({}^-\mathbf{3}) + ({}^-2)({}^-\mathbf{3})$

3. Simplify. ⟶ $= x^2 + {}^-2x + {}^-3x + 6$

4. Add like terms. ⟶ $= x^2 + {}^-5x + 6$

**Method 2**

$(x + {}^-2)(x + {}^-3)$

| F | Multiply the first terms. | O | Multiply the outside terms. | I | Multiply the inside terms. | L | Multiply the last terms. |
|---|---|---|---|---|---|---|---|
| | $x \cdot x$ | | $x \cdot {}^-3$ | | ${}^-2 \cdot x$ | | ${}^-2 \cdot {}^-3$ |
| | $x^2$ | | ${}^-3x$ | | ${}^-2x$ | | 6 |

Add like terms. ⟶ $x^2 + {}^-5x + 6$

The phrase $(x + y)^2$ is the square of the binomial $(x + y)$.

$(x + y)^2$ means $(x + y)(x + y)$.

**P-2**   **What is the product of the first terms in $(x + y)(x + y)$?   of the last terms?**

**P-3**   **What is the product of the outside terms?   of the inside terms?**

**P-4**   **What is the sum of the like terms?**

$(x + y)^2 = x^2 + 2xy + y^2$

In a similar way, a trinomial that is the square of $(x + -y)$ may be obtained.

$(x + -y)^2 = x^2 + (-xy) + (-xy) + (-y)^2$

**P-5**    What is the sum of the like terms?

**P-6**    What is the simplest name of $(-y)^2$?

$$(x + -y)^2 = x^2 + (^-2xy) + y^2$$

> The square of a binomial equals the square of the first term plus twice the product of the two terms plus the square of the second term.
>
> $$(a + b)^2 = a^2 + 2ab + b^2$$
> $$(x + ^-3)^2 = x^2 + (^-6x) + 9$$

**P-7**    What is the square of 2x?   of 3?

## example 3    Square the binomial: $(2x + 3)^2$

$$(2x + 3)^2 = (2x)^2 + 2(2x)(3) + 3^2$$
$$= 4x^2 + 12x + 9$$

## ORAL EXERCISES 11.7

*Tell a trinomial in simplest form for each product.* (Example 1, Example 2)

1. $(x + 2)(x + 4) = x \cdot x + 4 \cdot x + 2 \cdot x + 2 \cdot 4$
2. $(y + ^-1)(y + 5) = y \cdot y + 5 \cdot y + ^-1 \cdot y + (^-1)(5)$
3. $(t + 2)(t + ^-3) = t \cdot t + ^-3 \cdot t + 2 \cdot t + 2(^-3)$
4. $(n + ^-1)(n + ^-2) = n \cdot n + ^-2 \cdot n + ^-1 \cdot n + (^-1)(^-2)$
5. $(r + ^-3)(r + 7) = r \cdot r + 7 \cdot r + ^-3 \cdot r + (^-3)(7)$
6. $(2a + 3)(a + ^-5) = 2a \cdot a + ^-5(2a) + 3 \cdot a + 3(^-5)$
7. $(3k + 1)(2k + ^-1) = 3k \cdot 2k + ^-1(3k) + 1(2k) + 1(^-1)$
8. $(2w + ^-3)(2w + ^-3) = 2w \cdot 2w + ^-3(2w) + ^-3(2w) + (^-3)(^-3)$
9. $(x + 1)(x + 4)$               10. $(x + 2)(x + ^-1)$
11. $(x + ^-3)(x + ^-2)$          12. $(x + ^-1)(x + ^-5)$
13. $(x + 3)(x + 10)$             14. $(x + ^-5)(x + 1)$
15. $(x + ^-2)(x + ^-6)$          16. $(x + ^-10)(x + 5)$

*Use the special rule to square each binomial and simplify.* (Example 3)

**EXAMPLE:** $(x + {}^-2)^2$     **SOLUTION:** $x^2 + 2({}^-2)(x) + ({}^-2)^2$
**ANSWER:** $x^2 + {}^-4x + 4$

**17.** $(x + 1)^2$      **18.** $(x + 2)^2$      **19.** $(x + {}^-1)^2$      **20.** $(x + 3)^2$

**21.** $(a + 5)^2$      **22.** $(r + {}^-3)^2$      **23.** $(t + 10)^2$      **24.** $(y + {}^-5)^2$

## WRITTEN EXERCISES 11.7

**Ⓐ** **Goal:** To multiply and then simplify two binomials
**Sample Problem:** $(a + 6)(a + {}^-3)$
**Answer:** $a^2 + 3a + {}^-18$

*Multiply and simplify.* (Example 1, Example 2)

**1.** $(x + 1)(x + 2)$      **2.** $(x + 1)(x + 3)$      **3.** $(t + {}^-1)(t + {}^-3)$

**4.** $(w + {}^-1)(w + {}^-2)$      **5.** $(y + {}^-1)(y + 2)$      **6.** $(r + {}^-1)(r + 3)$

**7.** $(n + 1)(n + {}^-3)$      **8.** $(m + 1)(m + {}^-2)$      **9.** $(x + 2)(x + 5)$

**10.** $(x + 3)(x + 4)$      **11.** $(a + {}^-2)(a + {}^-5)$      **12.** $(g + {}^-3)(g + {}^-4)$

**13.** $(k + {}^-3)(k + 4)$      **14.** $(q + {}^-2)(q + 5)$      **15.** $(y + 2)(y + {}^-5)$

**16.** $(s + 3)(s + {}^-4)$      **17.** $(2x + 5)(x + 2)$      **18.** $(2x + 3)(x + 2)$

**19.** $(2x + 3)(x + {}^-2)$            **20.** $(2x + {}^-5)(x + 2)$

*Square each binomial and simplify.* (Example 3)

**21.** $(y + 6)^2$      **22.** $(r + 4)^2$      **23.** $(t + {}^-8)^2$      **24.** $(n + {}^-6)^2$

**25.** $(d + 9)^2$      **26.** $(k + 11)^2$      **27.** $(w + {}^-12)^2$      **28.** $(s + {}^-8)^2$

**29.** $(2t + 1)^2$      **30.** $(3r + 1)^2$      **31.** $(4m + {}^-2)^2$      **32.** $(4q + {}^-3)^2$

**Ⓑ** *Multiply and simplify.*

**33.** $(2x + 5)(3x + 1)$            **34.** $(4x + 3)(2x + 1)$

**35.** $(3x + {}^-2)(4x + 3)$            **36.** $(5x + {}^-1)(3x + 2)$

**37.** $(4x + {}^-5)(3x + {}^-4)$            **38.** $(5x + {}^-2)(4x + {}^-3)$

**39.** $(5x + 6)(2x + {}^-5)$            **40.** $(10x + {}^-3)(5x + 8)$

## CHAPTER SUMMARY

| IMPORTANT TERMS | Factoring *(p. 277)* | Like terms *(p. 284)* |
|---|---|---|
| | Binomial *(p. 284)* | Trinomial *(p. 287)* |

**IMPORTANT IDEAS**

1. The product of a positive rational number and a negative rational number is a negative rational number.

2. The product of two negative rational numbers is a positive rational number.

3. A product with an even number of negative factors is positive. A product with an odd number of negative factors is negative.

4. *Multiplication Property of Zero:* For any rational number $a$, $a \cdot 0 = 0$.

5. *Multiplication Property of One:* For any rational number $a$, $1(a) = a$.

6. *Commutative Property of Multiplication:* For any rational numbers $a$ and $b$, $ab = ba$. (The order of multiplying two rational numbers does not affect the product.)

7. *Associative Property of Multiplication:* For any rational numbers $a$, $b$, and $c$, $(ab)c = a(bc)$. (The way in which numbers are grouped for multiplication does not affect the product.)

8. *Distributive Property:* For any rational numbers $a$, $b$, and $c$, $a(b + c) = ab + ac$ and $(b + c)a = ba + ca$.

9. *Multiplication Property of ⁻1:* For any rational number $a$, $(^-1)a = -a$.

10. *Product of ⁻1 and a Sum of Numbers:* For any rational numbers $a$ and $b$, $^-1(a + b) = (-a) + (-b)$.

11. For any rational numbers $a$ and $b$, $(-a)b = -ab$ and $(-a)(-b) = ab$.

## CHAPTER REVIEW

### SECTION 11.1

*Multiply. Simplify where necessary.*

1. $(^-12)(9)$  2. $(14)(^-10)$  3. $(^-0.8)(2.6)$  4. $(4.3)(^-5.4)$

5. $\frac{1}{4}(^-24)$  6. $^-(\frac{2}{3})(51)$  7. $(340)(^-11)$  8. $(^-3.9)(272)$

### SECTION 11.2

*Multiply. Simplify where necessary.*

9. $(^-15)(^-8)$  10. $(^-24)(^-14)$  11. $(^-0.6)(45)$  12. $(^-30)(^-70)$

13. $(^-5.2)(^-6.8)$  14. $^-(\frac{1}{4})(^-28)$  15. $^-(\frac{3}{4}) \cdot {}^-(\frac{4}{9})$  16. $(^-1\frac{3}{8})(^-1\frac{3}{11})$

## SECTION 11.3

*Multiply and simplify.*

**17.** $(9)(^-12)(5)$      **18.** $(^-15)(8)(^-12)$      **19.** $(^-6)(^-17)(^-9)$      **20.** $(^-0.4)(^-8)(5)$

**21.** $(^-4)(^-5)(^-3)(^-8)$      **22.** $(^-18)(^-1)(^-1)(^-2)(^-1)$      **23.** $9(^-15k)$      **24.** $^-12(^-11n)$

## SECTION 11.4

*Multiply. Simplify where necessary.*

**25.** $^-12(3r + {}^-2)$      **26.** $(^-4t + {}^-9)(^-15)$      **27.** $\frac{1}{2}(^-8s + {}^-15)$

**28.** $y(^-9y + 12)$      **29.** $^-8x(3x + {}^-9)$      **30.** $^-6k(^-5p + {}^-8q)$

*Factor.*

**31.** $^-19r + {}^-19s$      **32.** $m(^-25) + n(^-25)$      **33.** $5t(1.8) + (^-12)1.8$

**34.** $^-13rs + 9rt$      **35.** $12an + (^-12nk)$      **36.** $15t(^-2y) + 15t(^-1)$

## SECTION 11.5

*Multiply. Simplify where necessary.*

**37.** $(^-20)(-n)$      **38.** $(^-8)(t)(-t)$      **39.** $(^-12a)(-b)(-c)$      **40.** $(^-5p)(q)(-q)(-p)$

**41.** $-t(r + {}^-10)$      **42.** $^-15p(-q + 5)$      **43.** $^-12w(-w + {}^-6)$      **44.** $^-4xy(-z + 8)$

## SECTION 11.6

*Add like terms. Simplify where necessary.*

**45.** $12n + {}^-7n$      **46.** $^-22p + {}^-18p$      **47.** $^-4.2ab + 13.6ab$

**48.** $5.9xy + {}^-15.3xy$      **49.** $27pq^2 + (-pq^2)$      **50.** $19r + (^-15) + (^-27r)$

## SECTION 11.7

*Multiply. Simplify where necessary.*

**51.** $(r + 5)(r + 3)$      **52.** $(t + {}^-4)(t + {}^-5)$      **53.** $(x + {}^-8)(x + 5)$

**54.** $(y + 10)(y + {}^-7)$      **55.** $(x + {}^-9)^2$      **56.** $(2n + {}^-3)^2$

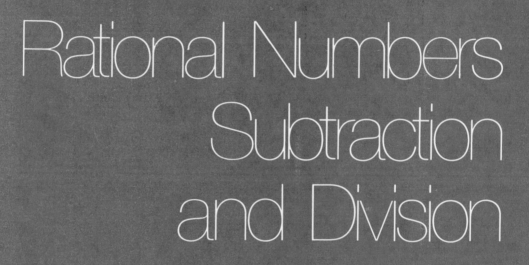

# 12

## Rational Numbers
## Subtraction
## and Division

# 12.1 Meaning of Subtraction

**P-1**   **What is the simplest name for each <u>difference</u> below?**

*A phrase involving subtraction is called a <u>difference</u>.*

      **a.** $19 - 15$      **b.** $5\frac{1}{2} - 5\frac{1}{2}$      **c.** $8.6 - 3.1$

**P-2**   **What is the simplest name for $12 - 9$?   for $12 + (^-9)$?**

Thus, $12 - 9 = 12 + (^-9)$.

> If $a$ and $b$ are any rational numbers, then $a - b = a + (-b)$.
> To subtract $b$ from $a$, add the opposite of $b$ to $a$.

**P-3**   **What is the simplest name for each difference in the table?**

| Difference | | Sum |
|---|:---:|---|
| $8 - 13$ | $=$ | $8 + (^-13)$ |
| $12 - (^-4)$ | $=$ | $12 + 4$ |
| $(^-5.4) - (^-2.3)$ | $=$ | $(^-5.4) + 2.3$ |
| $(^-11.3) - (^-15.8)$ | $=$ | $(^-11.3) + 15.8$ |
| $0 - 23$ | $=$ | $0 + (^-23)$ |
| $0 - (^-19)$ | $=$ | $0 + 19$ |
| $(^-0.8) - (^-0.8)$ | $=$ | $(^-0.8) + 0.8$ |

**P-4**   **What is the opposite of 12?**

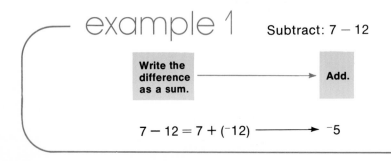

example 1    Subtract: $7 - 12$

Write the difference as a sum. ⟶ Add.

$7 - 12 = 7 + (^-12) \longrightarrow {}^-5$

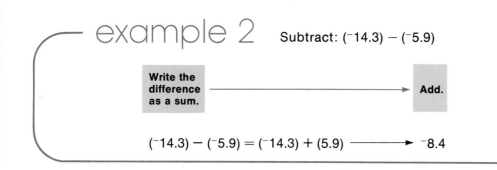

example 2    Subtract: $(^-14.3) - (^-5.9)$

| Write the difference as a sum. | ⟶ | Add. |

$$(^-14.3) - (^-5.9) = (^-14.3) + (5.9) \longrightarrow {}^-8.4$$

**P-5**    **What is the simplest name for each difference below?**

**a.** $3 - 9$    **b.** $(^-11) - 7$    **c.** $(^-6) - (^-13)$

**d.** $r - s$    **e.** $r - (^-s)$

---

Summary of the "Dash" symbol:

1. In $a - b$, the dash means subtraction.
   The phrase $a - b$ is read "$a$ minus $b$" or "$a$ less $b$."
2. In $a + (^-b)$, the dash means "the opposite of."
   The phrase $a + (^-b)$ is read "$a$ plus the opposite of $b$."
3. The dash is also used to indicate a negative number.
   The numeral $^-5$ is a name for the number "negative five."

---

**P-6**    **How do you read $a - (^-b)$?**

## ORAL EXERCISES 12.1

*Say each phrase as a sum.* (P-3)

**EXAMPLE:** $12 - (^-15)$    **ANSWER:** "Twelve plus the opposite of negative fifteen"

**1.** $14 - 5$                    **2.** $2 - 9$

**3.** $5 - (^-14)$             **4.** $(^-6) - 8$

**5.** $16 - (^-7)$            **6.** $(^-1) - (^-10)$

**7.** $0 - 17$                **8.** $0 - (^-8)$

**9.** $n - 19$               **10.** $r - (^-23)$

*Simplify.* (Example 1, Example 2, P-5)

**11.** $5 - 8$

**12.** $3 - 13$

**13.** $0 - 15$

**14.** $4 - (^-5)$

**15.** $12 - (^-4)$

**16.** $(^-14) - 3$

**17.** $(^-9) - 11$

**18.** $(^-6) - (^-3)$

**19.** $(^-4) - (^-10)$

**20.** $0 - (^-40)$

**21.** $13 - (^-13)$

**22.** $13 - 13$

**23.** $(^-13) - (^-13)$

**24.** $3\frac{1}{2} - (^-2\frac{1}{2})$

**25.** $(^-7\frac{3}{4}) - (^-2\frac{1}{2})$

**26.** $8.4 - (^-3.2)$

**27.** $(^-2.6) - 3.1$

**28.** $(^-0.8) - (^-0.9)$

**29.** $14 - (-y)$

**30.** $n - (^-27)$

## WRITTEN EXERCISES 12.1

**A**    **Goal:** To write a difference as a sum and then add
**Sample Problem:** $(^-8) - 2$
**Answer:** $(^-8) + (^-2); \ ^-10$

*Write as a sum. Then simplify.* (Example 1, Example 2, P-5)

**1.** $15 - 11$

**2.** $22 - 17$

**3.** $19 - 26$

**4.** $16 - 24$

**5.** $18 - (^-7)$

**6.** $20 - (^-12)$

**7.** $24 - (^-29)$

**8.** $31 - (^-39)$

**9.** $(^-13) - (^-5)$

**10.** $(^-21) - (^-7)$

**11.** $(^-9) - (^-23)$

**12.** $(^-11) - (^-25)$

**13.** $0 - 24$

**14.** $0 - 16$

**15.** $0 - (^-36)$

**16.** $0 - (^-50)$

**17.** $0.9 - (^-4.8)$

**18.** $0.5 - (^-7.6)$

**19.** $0.24 - 0.93$

**20.** $0.53 - 0.87$

**21.** $(^-13.9) - 9.5$

**22.** $(^-17.3) - 8.9$

**23.** $52 - (-k)$

**24.** $65 - (-t)$

**25.** $0 - (-w)$

**26.** $0 - (-p)$

**27.** $r - (^-8.6)$

**28.** $y - (^-19.3)$

**B**    *Write each problem as a difference. Then write it as a sum and add.*

**EXAMPLE:** Find a number that is $^-7$ less than 19.

**SOLUTION:** $19 - (^-7) = 19 + 7$
$= 26$

**29.** Subtract $^-15$ from 17.

**30.** Subtract $^-24$ from 11.

**31.** Find a number that is $^-12$ less 23.

**32.** Find a number that is $^-14$ less 3.

**33.** Find a number that is 16 less than 7.

**34.** Find a number that is 25 less than 19.

**35.** Find how much greater $^-6$ is than $^-21$.

**36.** Find how much greater $^-12$ is than $^-35$.

**37.** Find "negative eighteen less twenty-seven."

**38.** Find "negative twenty-one less negative fourteen."

# 12.2 Subtraction Practice

**P-1**  **How do you say the following true sentence?**

$$-10 = {}^{-}10$$

It will no longer be necessary to use the raised dash to name negative numbers. The "opposite" symbol will be used.

◀ *You can say either "negative 10" or "the opposite of 10" for −10.*

> The simplest name of a negative number is considered to be a numeral preceded by the "opposite" symbol.
>
> "−10" is the simplest name for "negative ten."

**P-2**  **What is the simplest name of each phrase below?**

**a.** $(-3) + (-4)$      **b.** $(-5)(6)$      **c.** $1.3 - 2.5$

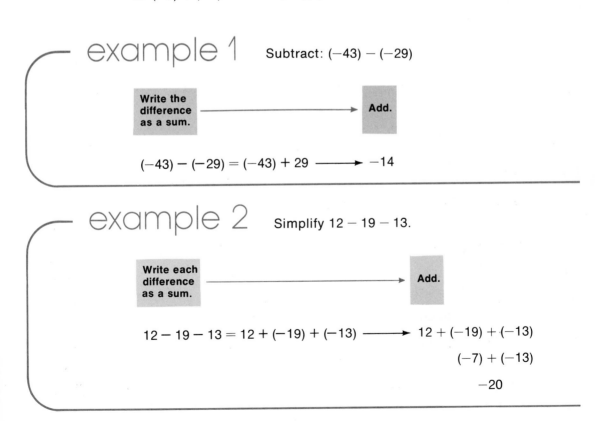

## example 1    Subtract: $(-43) - (-29)$

**Write the difference as a sum.** ⟶ **Add.**

$$(-43) - (-29) = (-43) + 29 \longrightarrow -14$$

## example 2    Simplify $12 - 19 - 13$.

**Write each difference as a sum.** ⟶ **Add.**

$$12 - 19 - 13 = 12 + (-19) + (-13) \longrightarrow 12 + (-19) + (-13)$$
$$(-7) + (-13)$$
$$-20$$

**P-3**  How can you write $27 - 45$ as a sum?  $-45 - 31$ as a sum?

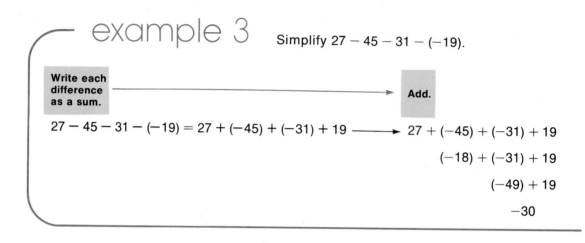

example 3  Simplify $27 - 45 - 31 - (-19)$.

| Write each difference as a sum. | → | Add. |

$$27 - 45 - 31 - (-19) = 27 + (-45) + (-31) + 19 \longrightarrow 27 + (-45) + (-31) + 19$$
$$(-18) + (-31) + 19$$
$$(-49) + 19$$
$$-30$$

example 4  The low temperature on a winter day was $-20.3°C$. It rose to a high temperature of $-4.9°C$. How much greater was the high temperature than the low temperature?

You subtract the lower temperature, $-20.3°$, from the higher temperature, $-4.9°$.

$$(-4.9) - (-20.3) = (-4.9) + 20.3$$
$$= 15.4$$

**The high temperature was 15.4 degrees greater.**

## ORAL EXERCISES 12.2

*Simplify.* (Example 1, Example 2, Example 3)

**1.** $8 - (-5)$    **2.** $6 - (-12)$    **3.** $(-9) - 11$    **4.** $0 - (-18)$

**5.** $12 - (-12)$    **6.** $(-25) - (-25)$    **7.** $2 - 13$    **8.** $\left(-\frac{7}{8}\right) - \frac{1}{8}$

**9.** $\frac{3}{4} - \left(-\frac{1}{4}\right)$    **10.** $8.7 - (-3.2)$    **11.** $(-1.7) - 2.3$    **12.** $(-2.4) - (-5.9)$

**13.** $21 - (-3.2)$    **14.** $(-26) - (-29)$    **15.** $11 - 16 + 5$    **16.** $14 - 20 - 6$

**17.** $30 - 50 + 5$    **18.** $-12 + 7 - 19$    **19.** $-1 - 2 - 3 - 4$    **20.** $\frac{3}{8} - \frac{7}{8} - 6 + 2\frac{1}{2}$

*Tell a phrase to describe each problem.* (First phrase in Example 4)

**21.** How much greater is −18 than −37?

**22.** How much less is −14.2 than −12.9?

**23.** How much less is a temperature of −16°C than a temperature of 20°C?

**24.** How much greater is a temperature of −5.3°C than a temperature of −25.8°C?

## WRITTEN EXERCISES 12.2

**A**  **Goal:** To simplify numerical phrases involving subtraction
**Sample Problem:** $6 - 9 - (-4)$
**Answer:** 1

*Subtract.* (Example 1)

**1.** $15 - (+9)$

**2.** $11 - (+7)$

**3.** $12 - (+24)$

**4.** $14 - (-30)$

**5.** $(-28) - 17$

**6.** $(-21) - 43$

**7.** $17 - 26$

**8.** $22 - 31$

**9.** $0 - 10\frac{1}{4}$

**10.** $0 - 8\frac{1}{2}$

**11.** $(-29) + (+17)$

**12.** $(-34) - (+23)$

**13.** $(-27) - (-56)$

**14.** $(-22) - (+49)$

**15.** $(-8\frac{3}{8}) - \frac{7}{8}$

**16.** $(-12\frac{3}{4}) - 2\frac{1}{4}$

**17.** $3\frac{1}{2} - 7\frac{3}{4}$

**18.** $5\frac{5}{8} - 13\frac{7}{8}$

**19.** $14.3 - 19.8$

**20.** $20.2 - 33.7$

**21.** $(-0.9) - (-0.7)$

**22.** $(-0.4) - (-0.8)$

**23.** $13.46 - 15.42$

**24.** $19.87 - 20.93$

*Simplify.* (Example 2, Example 3)

**25.** $12 - 29 + 6$

**26.** $20 - 43 + 13$

**27.** $-14 - (-12) - 18$

**28.** $-21 - (-15) - 24$

**29.** $-8 - 13 - 24 - 2 - 5$

**30.** $-5 - 10 - 3 - 18 - 1$

**31.** $-8.5 - 1.8 - 4.1 - 9.6 - 7.1$

**32.** $-12.3 + 2.9 - 4.8 - 5.7 + 6.9$

**33.** $-0.6 - (-4.9) + 1.6 - (-4.3)$

**34.** $-1.7 - (-0.4) + 8.3 - (-5.6)$

*Work the problem by writing a phrase involving subtraction.* (Example 4)

**35.** The net number of yards gained by one football player in a game was −16. The net number of yards gained by another player was 27. How many more yards did the player with 27 yards gain than the player with −16 yards?

*Work each problem by writing a phrase involving subtraction.* (Example 4)

**36.** One golfer has a score of $-2$ (2 below par) and another golfer has a score of $-5$. How much greater is the score of $-2$ than the score of $-5$?

**37.** The record low temperature for a city is $-30.1°C$. Last year the city's low temperature was $-25.8°C$. How much less is the record temperature than last year's low temperature?

**38.** The low temperature for a city on a winter day was $-5.7°C$. The high temperature for the same day was $-1.4°C$. How much less was the low temperature than the high temperature?

**C**   *Write the simplest names for the two differences in Exercises 39–42.*

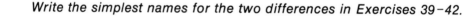

**39.** $5 - 2$ and $2 - 5$

**40.** $8 - (-3)$ and $(-3) - 8$

**41.** $3 - (10 - 6)$ and $(3 - 10) - 6$

**42.** $(12 - 5) - 1$ and $12 - (5 - 1)$

**43.** Write <u>Yes</u> or <u>No</u> to show whether subtraction is a commutative operation.

**44.** Write <u>Yes</u> or <u>No</u> to show whether subtraction is an associative operation.

**45.** What property is illustrated by the following true sentence?
$$5 + (-2) = (-2) + 5$$

**46.** What property is illustrated by the following true sentence?
$$(3 + -10) + -6 = 3 + (-10 + -6)$$

# 12.3  Subtraction in Open Phrases

**P-1**   **How can you express $5x - 2x$ as a sum?**

**P-2**   **What is the simplest name for $5x + (-2x)$?**

example 1   Simplify $9n - 12 - 4n$.

$$9n - 12 - 4n = 9n + (-12) + (-4n)$$
$$= 5n + (-12)$$
$$= 5n - 12 \qquad \blacktriangleleft \quad \text{$5n + (-12)$ and $5n - 12$ are equivalent phrases.}$$

The phrase $5n - 12$ is a simpler name than $5n + (-12)$ because it uses fewer symbols.

example 2   Simplify $7 + x - 10 - 5x$.

1. Write it as a sum. $\longrightarrow$ $7 + x - 10 - 5x = 7 + x + (-10) + (-5x)$

2. Commutative and Associative Properties of Addition $\longrightarrow$ $= (x + -5x) + (7 + -10)$

3. Add. $\longrightarrow$ $= \quad (-4x) \quad + \quad (-3)$

4. Simplify. $\longrightarrow$ $= \quad -4x - 3$

example 3   Simplify $5 - x - 2$.

**Method 1**

$$5 - x - 2 = 5 + (-x) + (-2)$$
$$= (5 + -2) + (-x)$$
$$= \quad 3 \quad + (-x)$$
$$= \quad 3 - x$$

**Method 2**

$$5 - x - 2 = 5 + (-x) + (-2)$$
$$= (-x) + (5 + -2)$$
$$= (-x) + \quad 3$$
$$= -x + 3 \qquad \blacktriangleleft \quad \text{$3 - x$ and $-x + 3$ are equivalent.}$$

**P-3** What does the following sentence tell you about subtraction and the Commutative Property?

$$8 - 5 \neq 5 - 8$$

**P-4** What does the following sentence tell you about subtraction and the Associative Property?

$$(8 - 5) - 1 \neq 8 - (5 - 1)$$

Thus, the Commutative Property and the Associative Property do <u>not</u> apply to subtraction.

**P-5** How do you write $-(3x + 7)$ as a sum?

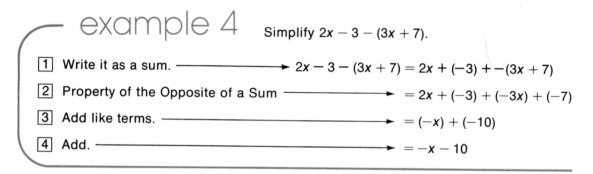

example 4   Simplify $2x - 3 - (3x + 7)$.

1. Write it as a sum. $\longrightarrow$ $2x - 3 - (3x + 7) = 2x + (-3) + -(3x + 7)$

2. Property of the Opposite of a Sum $\longrightarrow$ $= 2x + (-3) + (-3x) + (-7)$

3. Add like terms. $\longrightarrow$ $= (-x) + (-10)$

4. Add. $\longrightarrow$ $= -x - 10$

## ORAL EXERCISES 12.3

*Simplify.* (Example 1, Example 2, Example 3, Example 4)

1. $x - (-2)$     2. $x + (-3)$     3. $5x - 2x$

4. $3x - 2x$     5. $4x - 9x$     6. $5x - x$

7. $6x - 5x$     8. $x - 9x$     9. $-8x - x$

10. $5 + x - 3$     11. $3 + x - 10$     12. $x - 5 - 3x$

13. $12 - 3x - 9$     14. $5 - x - 6$     15. $5 + (x - 3)$

16. $5 - (3 - x)$     17. $5 - (x - 3)$     18. $5 - (x + 3)$

19. $2x + 6 - x - 5$     20. $x - 5 - 3x - 7$     21. $-x - 1 - 2x - 3$

22. $x^2 - 5 - x^2 - 2$     23. $-3r + 4s - 7r - s$     24. $12m - n - 23m - 4n$

25. $y^2 - 7 - 2y^2$     26. $p^2 - 8 - p^2 + 5$     27. $9g - 8s^2 + 2s^2 - 4g$

## WRITTEN EXERCISES 12.3

**A**

**Goal:** To simplify open phrases involving subtraction
**Sample Problem:** $7 - 2x - 10$
**Answer:** $-2x - 3$

*Simplify.* (Example 1, Example 2, Example 3, Example 4)

1. $5x - (-7)$

2. $8a - (-12)$

3. $13y - 9y$

4. $20x - 13x$

5. $4a - a$

6. $8t + t$

7. $w + 5w$

8. $r - 10r$

9. $4n - 5n$

10. $11y - 12y$

11. $3x - 5 - 2x$

12. $5k - 7 - 4k$

13. $-8p + 3 - 2p$

14. $-3s + 7 - 12s$

15. $14t - 3t - 17t$

16. $11r - 5r - 18r$

17. $-4.3m - 1.8 + 3.9m$

18. $9.6n - 3.4 - 11.2n$

19. $2a - 3 - 5a - 8$

20. $5t - 1 - 9t - 5$

21. $-3\frac{1}{4}w - \frac{1}{2} + 6\frac{1}{2}w - \frac{3}{4}$

22. $-7\frac{5}{8}h - \frac{5}{8} - \frac{7}{8} + 3\frac{3}{8}h$

23. $0.8w - 1.5w - 3.9w$

24. $1.3t - 4.3t - 7.8t$

25. $3x - (10 - x)$

26. $4y - (15 - y)$

27. $5 - (r + 3)$

28. $12 - (q + 7)$

29. $(n + 2) - (3n - 5)$

30. $(y - 1) - (4y + 5)$

31. $5x - (8x - x)$

32. $3a - (5a - 9a)$

**B**

33. $-19.3n^2 - 8.7n - 9.2 + 8.9n^2 - 4.5n - 5.8$

34. $-0.8r^2 + 12.6r - 1.9r - 13.6 - 6.3r - 12.7r^2$

35. $23y - 15z - (19z - 5y + 28)$

36. $37k - 65g - (-48k + 19g - 43)$

37. $(19y^2 - 24y - 18) - (-y^2 + 13y - 27)$

38. $(-42t^2 + 34t - 29) - (5t^2 - 27t - 13)$

# 12.4 Special Properties of Subtraction

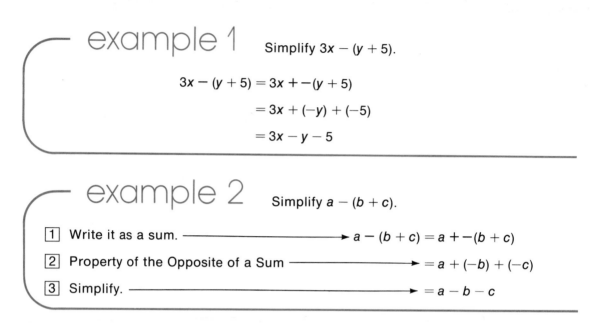

example 1    Simplify $3x - (y + 5)$.

$$3x - (y + 5) = 3x + -(y + 5)$$
$$= 3x + (-y) + (-5)$$
$$= 3x - y - 5$$

example 2    Simplify $a - (b + c)$.

1  Write it as a sum. ————————————→ $a - (b + c) = a + -(b + c)$

2  Property of the Opposite of a Sum ————————→ $= a + (-b) + (-c)$

3  Simplify. ————————————————————→ $= a - b - c$

**P-1**    **What is the simplest name for each phrase below?**

   **a.** $3x - (2y + 5)$    **b.** $8n - (-y + 9)$

example 3    Simplify $a - (b - c)$.

$$a - (b - c) = a + -(b + -c)$$
$$= a + (-b) + c$$
$$= a - b + c$$

**P-2**    **What is the simplest name for each phrase below?**

   **a.** $4t - (w - 9)$    **b.** $-3m - (16 - 4n)$

> For any rational numbers $a$, $b$, and $c$,
>
> 1.  $a - (b + c) = a - b - c$, and
> 2.  $a - (b - c) = a - b + c$.

These special properties can be extended to apply to phrases such as the ones below.

$$a - (b + c - d - e) = a - b - c + d + e$$

$$(a - b) - (c + d - e) = a - b - c - d + e$$

**P-3** **What is the simplest name for $3(9 - 4)$?   for $3 \cdot 9 - 3 \cdot 4$?**

Both phrases equal 15 as shown below.

| $3(9 - 4)$ | $3 \cdot 9 - 3 \cdot 4$ |
|:---:|:---:|
| $3(5)$ | $27 - 12$ |
| $15$ | $15$ |

The sentence $3(9 - 4) = 3 \cdot 9 - 3 \cdot 4$ suggests the Distributive Property for subtraction.

> **Distributive Property (Multiplication over Subtraction)**
>
> For any rational numbers $a$, $b$, and $c$,
>
> 1. $a(b - c) = ab - ac$, and
>
> 2. $(b - c)a = ba - ca$.

**P-4** **How can you write the following product as a difference?**

$$3r(2r - 5)$$

Use the Distributive Property.

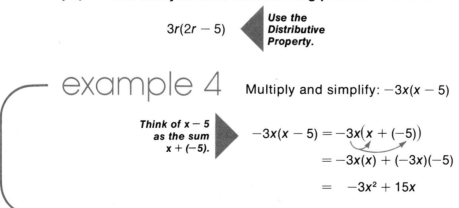

example 4   Multiply and simplify: $-3x(x - 5)$

Think of $x - 5$ as the sum $x + (-5)$.

$$-3x(x - 5) = -3x(x + (-5))$$
$$= -3x(x) + (-3x)(-5)$$
$$= -3x^2 + 15x$$

The Distributive Property can also be applied to general sums and differences.

$$2(x^2 + 3x + 5) = 2x^2 + 6x + 10$$

$$3(x^2 - 5x - 10) = 3x^2 - 15x - 30$$

$$-5r(4r - 3s - 2t + 9) = -20r^2 + 15rs + 10rt - 45r$$

## ORAL EXERCISES 12.4

*Simplify.* (Example 1, Example 2, Example 3, P-2)

**1.** $r - (s + 7)$

**2.** $12 - (p - q)$

**3.** $-6 - (-m + n)$

**4.** $-1 - (t - r)$

**5.** $p - (9 - q)$

**6.** $n - (-7 + k)$

**7.** $5 - (x - y + 7)$

**8.** $p - (-q + r - s - 8)$

**9.** $(a + b) - (2a - b)$

**10.** $(m - n) - (m + n)$

*Simplify.* (P-4, Example 4)

**EXAMPLE:** $-8(2r - 3s + 5)$
**ANSWER:** $-16r + 24s - 40$

**11.** $2(x - y)$

**12.** $3(x - 2)$

**13.** $5(2x - 3)$

**14.** $(a - 3)3$

**15.** $(r - 2)r$

**16.** $(x - 5)2x$

**17.** $\frac{1}{2}(2a - 6)$

**18.** $\frac{1}{3}(3x - 3)$

**19.** $-8(x - y)$

**20.** $-4(3x - 2)$

**21.** $(-x + 7)(-x)$

**22.** $-2y(y - 5)$

**23.** $3(-t - 1)$

**24.** $2(-3r - \frac{1}{2})$

**25.** $2(x - y - 3)$

**26.** $3(x + y - 5)$

**27.** $-5(2r - 3s - 4)$

**28.** $-3m(-3m + 5n - 8)$

## WRITTEN EXERCISES 12.4

**A**     **Goal:** To simplify open phrases that involve subtracting a sum or difference
**Sample Problem:** $5 - (x - 3)$
**Answer:** $8 - x$

*Simplify.* (Example 1, Example 2, Example 3, P-2)

1. $12 - (t - 5)$          2. $15 - (n - 8)$

3. $r - (6r - 3)$          4. $w - (9w - 5)$

5. $-8 - (12y + 9)$          6. $-6 - (13p + 14)$

7. $5k - (17 - k)$          8. $20q - (12 - q)$

9. $13s - (19 - 13s)$          10. $15m - (24 - 15m)$

11. $4.9a - (-2.6 + 6.2a)$          12. $11.6s - (-9.8 + 15.7s)$

13. $5\frac{1}{2}m - (-m + \frac{1}{4})$          14. $2\frac{3}{4}n - (-n + 1\frac{1}{2})$

15. $(y + 0.9) - (23y - 0.7)$          16. $(r - 1.7) - (17r - 5.3)$

17. $(4t - 16) - (-13 + 9t)$          18. $(31 - 5w) - (-12w + 24)$

19. $(12.8r - 1.9) - (-1.9 + 12.8r)$          20. $(14.7 - 72.3t) - (-72.3t + 14.7)$

21. $18 - (23x + 15 - 19x)$          22. $25 - (-16m - 12 + 9m)$

23. $(s^2 + 5) - (9s^2 - 8s - 7)$          24. $(r^2 + 8r - 12) - (3r^2 - 7r)$

*Multiply. Simplify where necessary.* (P-4, Example 4)

      **EXAMPLE:** $-8t(3t - 4)$      **ANSWER:** $-24t^2 + 32t$

25. $5(r - 8)$          26. $9(n - 7)$

27. $8(7y - 6)$          28. $11(4t - 9)$

29. $-3a(2a - 7)$          30. $-6p(3p - 5)$

31. $(-w + 16)(-3)$          32. $(-r + 14)(-2)$

33. $-\frac{1}{2}(-12x + 8)$          34. $-\frac{1}{4}(-8q + 20)$

35. $(0.7 - 1.3k)(-0.5)$          36. $(0.9 - 3.2n)(-0.7)$

37. $-1(2r - 3s - \ldots)$          38. $-1(-5a + 2b - 4c)$

39. $-5x(-2x^2 + 4x - 7)$          40. $-8w(-w^2 + 9w - 4)$

# 12.5 Reciprocals

**P-1** **What is the simplest name for each product below?**

    **a.** $(\frac{4}{3})(\frac{3}{4})$      **b.** $(-\frac{1}{4})(-\frac{4}{1})$      **c.** $(-\frac{10}{1})(-\frac{1}{10})$      **d.** $(-0.2)(-5)$

The two factors of each product are called <u>reciprocals</u>.

> Two numbers are **reciprocals** of each other     $(\frac{2}{3})(1\frac{1}{2}) = 1$
> if their product is 1.                 $(-\frac{1}{4})(-4) = 1$

**P-2** **What is the truth set of each sentence below?**

    **a.** $1(x) = 1$      **b.** $-1(x) = 1$      **c.** $0(x) = 1$

Since the truth set of **c** is empty, 0 has no reciprocal.

**P-3** **What is the reciprocal of 1? of −1?**

**P-4** **What is the reciprocal of each number below?**

    **a.** 5      **b.** $\frac{1}{2}$      **c.** $\frac{5}{4}$      **d.** $\frac{7}{8}$

| Number | Reciprocal |
|--------|-----------|
| 5 or $\frac{5}{1}$ | $\frac{1}{5}$ |
| $\frac{1}{2}$ | $\frac{2}{1}$ or 2 |
| $\frac{5}{4}$ | $\frac{4}{5}$ |
| $\frac{7}{8}$ | $\frac{8}{7}$ or $1\frac{1}{7}$ |

*The reciprocal of a positive number in fraction form can be named by interchanging the numerator and the denominator.*

**P-5** **What is the simplest name for each of these products?**

    **a.** $(-\frac{3}{4})(-\frac{4}{3})$      **b.** $(-10)(-\frac{1}{10})$      **c.** $(-\frac{3}{2})(-\frac{2}{3})$

**P-6** **What is the reciprocal of $-\frac{3}{4}$? of −10? of $-\frac{3}{2}$?**

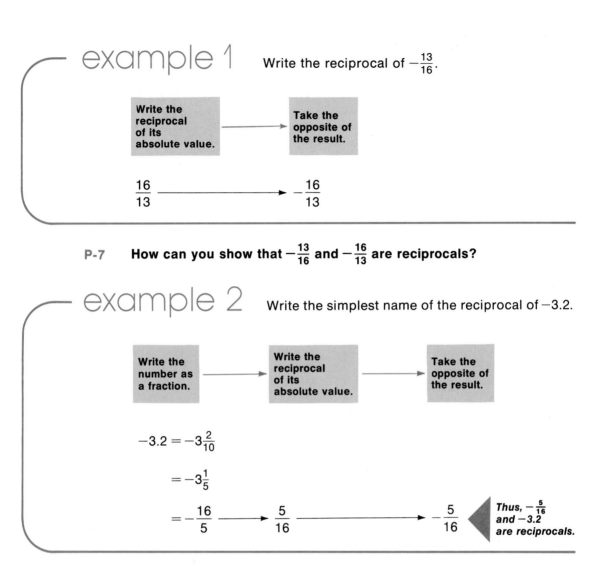

example 1　　Write the reciprocal of $-\frac{13}{16}$.

| Write the reciprocal of its absolute value. | Take the opposite of the result. |
|---|---|

$$\frac{16}{13} \longrightarrow -\frac{16}{13}$$

**P-7**　**How can you show that $-\frac{13}{16}$ and $-\frac{16}{13}$ are reciprocals?**

example 2　　Write the simplest name of the reciprocal of $-3.2$.

| Write the number as a fraction. | Write the reciprocal of its absolute value. | Take the opposite of the result. |
|---|---|---|

$$-3.2 = -3\frac{2}{10}$$

$$= -3\frac{1}{5}$$

$$= -\frac{16}{5} \longrightarrow \frac{5}{16} \longrightarrow -\frac{5}{16}$$

Thus, $-\frac{5}{16}$ and $-3.2$ are reciprocals.

## ORAL EXERCISES 12.5

*Tell the reciprocal of each number. Simplify where necessary.* (P-4, P-6, Example 1, Example 2)

**1.** 7　　　　**2.** $-12$　　　**3.** $\frac{2}{5}$　　　　**4.** $-\frac{1}{4}$　　　**5.** $\frac{8}{3}$　　　**6.** $-\frac{5}{6}$

**7.** $-\frac{12}{12}$　　　**8.** $-\frac{12}{3}$　　　**9.** $-1\frac{1}{2}$　　　**10.** $\frac{23}{1}$　　　**11.** $\frac{25}{25}$　　　**12.** 0.2

**13.** $-0.1$　　　　　　**14.** $t$ if $t \neq 0$　　　　　**15.** $\frac{1}{r}$ if $r \neq 0$

**16.** $\frac{n}{n}$ if $n \neq 0$　　　**17.** $\frac{a}{b}$ if $a \neq 0, b \neq 0$　　　**18.** $\frac{2r}{3s}$ if $r \neq 0, s \neq 0$

## WRITTEN EXERCISES 12.5

**A**   **Goal:** To write the simplest name for the reciprocal of a rational number
**Sample Problem:** $-7.2$   **Answer:** $-\frac{5}{36}$

*Write the reciprocal. Simplify where necessary.* (P-4, P-6, Example 1, Example 2)

**1.** 14

**2.** 20

**3.** $-4$

**4.** $-8$

**5.** $\frac{1}{3}$

**6.** $\frac{1}{6}$

**7.** $-\frac{1}{12}$

**8.** $-\frac{1}{7}$

**9.** $\frac{5}{8}$

**10.** $\frac{9}{16}$

**11.** $-\frac{11}{12}$

**12.** $-\frac{5}{8}$

**13.** $5\frac{1}{4}$

**14.** $3\frac{3}{8}$

**15.** $-2\frac{5}{8}$

**16.** $-3\frac{3}{4}$

**17.** 0.7

**18.** 0.9

**19.** $-4.1$

**20.** $-3.6$

**21.** $-\frac{12}{6}$

**22.** $-\frac{18}{3}$

**23.** $-\frac{25}{25}$

**24.** $-\frac{39}{39}$

**25.** $\frac{1}{k}$ if $k \neq 0$

**26.** $\frac{1}{3n}$ if $n \neq 0$

**27.** $\frac{r}{2s}$ if $r \neq 0, s \neq 0$

**28.** $\frac{p}{q}$ if $p \neq 0, q \neq 0$

**B**   *Solve each equation.*

**EXAMPLE:** $-\frac{2}{3}(-2x) = 1$   **SOLUTION:** $-\frac{2}{3}(-2x) = 1$
$$\frac{4}{3}x = 1$$
$$x = \frac{3}{4}$$

**29.** $\frac{3}{5}x = 1$

**30.** $\frac{12}{11}y = 1$

**31.** $(-5)(-2x) = 1$

**32.** $(-7)(-2a) = 1$

**33.** $(-x)(5) = 1$

**34.** $(3)(-y) = 1$

**C**   *Multiply each phrase by a number to get x as the product. Then write the number.*

**EXAMPLE:** $\frac{7}{4}x$   **SOLUTION:** $(\frac{7}{4}x)\frac{4}{7} = (\frac{7}{4} \cdot \frac{4}{7})x$   **ANSWER:** $\frac{4}{7}$
$$= (1)x$$
$$= x$$

**35.** $\frac{1}{4}x$

**36.** $\frac{2}{3}x$

**37.** $-3x$

**38.** $-10x$

**39.** $-\frac{1}{5}x$

**40.** $-\frac{1}{2}x$

**41.** $\frac{9}{4}x$

**42.** $3\frac{1}{2}x$

**43.** $-1.6x$

**44.** $-3.1x$

# 12.6 Meaning of Division

**P-1** **What is the simplest name for each <u>quotient</u> below?**

**a.** $86 \div (-43)$    **b.** $(-6.2) \div (-6.2)$    **c.** $3 \div 5$

*A phrase involving division is called a <u>quotient</u>.*

**P-2** **What is the simplest name for $8 \div 4$?   for $8 \cdot \frac{1}{4}$?**

Thus, $8 \div 4 = 8 \cdot \frac{1}{4}$.

> If $a$ and $b$ are any rational numbers, $b \neq 0$, then $a \div b = a \cdot \frac{1}{b}$.
> To divide $a$ by $b$, multiply $a$ by the reciprocal of $b$.

**P-3** **What is the reciprocal of $-3$?**

example 1    Divide: $\frac{12}{-3}$

*"$\frac{12}{-3}$" means "12 ÷ (−3)."*

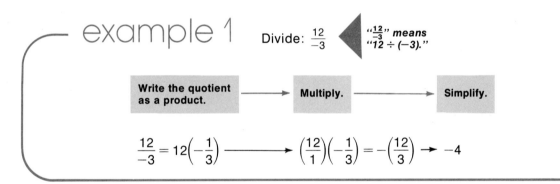

| Write the quotient as a product. | → | Multiply. | → | Simplify. |

$$\frac{12}{-3} = 12\left(-\frac{1}{3}\right) \longrightarrow \left(\frac{12}{1}\right)\left(-\frac{1}{3}\right) = -\left(\frac{12}{3}\right) \rightarrow -4$$

**P-4** **What is the reciprocal of $-6$?**

example 2    Divide: $\frac{-24}{-6}$

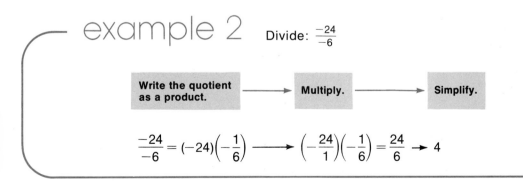

| Write the quotient as a product. | → | Multiply. | → | Simplify. |

$$\frac{-24}{-6} = (-24)\left(-\frac{1}{6}\right) \longrightarrow \left(-\frac{24}{1}\right)\left(-\frac{1}{6}\right) = \frac{24}{6} \rightarrow 4$$

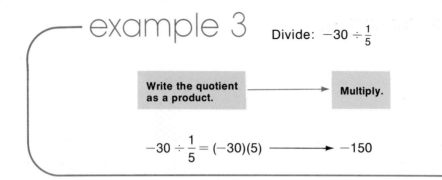

## example 3

Divide: $-30 \div \frac{1}{5}$

| Write the quotient as a product. | ⟶ | Multiply. |

$$-30 \div \frac{1}{5} = (-30)(5) \longrightarrow -150$$

---

### Division of Positive and Negative Rational Numbers

1. If a positive number is divided by a positive number, the quotient is a positive number.
2. If a positive number is divided by a negative number, the quotient is a negative number.
3. If a negative number is divided by a negative number, the quotient is a positive number.
4. If a negative number is divided by a positive number, the quotient is a negative number.

---

**P-5**    **What is the simplest name for each quotient?**

**a.** $\frac{36}{-4}$    **b.** $\frac{-36}{4}$    **c.** $\frac{-36}{-4}$

## ORAL EXERCISES 12.6

*Say each quotient as a product.* (Step 1 of Example 1, Example 2, Example 3)

**EXAMPLE:** $\frac{9}{-4}$    **ANSWER:** $9\left(-\frac{1}{4}\right)$; "Nine times negative one-fourth"

**1.** $\frac{-7}{2}$    **2.** $\frac{4}{-9}$    **3.** $\frac{-5}{-6}$    **4.** $\frac{10}{3}$

**5.** $\frac{13}{-7}$    **6.** $\frac{-19}{5}$    **7.** $\frac{-15}{-3}$    **8.** $10 \div (-4)$

**9.** $(-11) \div (-5)$    **10.** $(-23) \div 12$    **11.** $(-12) \div \frac{3}{4}$    **12.** $20 \div (-\frac{2}{3})$

**13.** $(-19) \div (-\frac{1}{2})$    **14.** $-2 \div \frac{1}{4}$    **15.** $\frac{25}{-5}$    **16.** $\frac{-28}{7}$

## WRITTEN EXERCISES 12.6

**A**

**Goal:** To divide by rational numbers

**Sample Problem:** $60 \div \left(-\frac{5}{6}\right)$

**Answer:** $-72$

*Write each quotient as a product.* (Step 1 of Example 1, Example 2, Example 3)

**EXAMPLE:** $14 \div \left(-\frac{3}{4}\right)$  **ANSWER:** $14\left(-\frac{4}{3}\right)$

1. $\frac{12}{-5}$  

2. $\frac{8}{-4}$  

3. $\frac{2}{-3}$  

4. $\frac{5}{-8}$

5. $\frac{-5}{-6}$  

6. $\frac{-4}{-7}$  

7. $\frac{13}{4}$  

8. $\frac{11}{3}$

9. $(-18) \div 9$  

10. $(-23) \div 10$  

11. $20 \div (-12)$  

12. $40 \div (-7)$

13. $(-21) \div (-8)$  

14. $(15) \div (-11)$  

15. $(-2) \div (-19)$  

16. $3 \div (-14)$

17. $(-8) \div \left(-\frac{3}{5}\right)$  

18. $(-3) \div \left(-\frac{5}{4}\right)$  

19. $(-11) \div \frac{2}{3}$  

20. $10 \div \left(-\frac{5}{4}\right)$

*Divide.* (Example 1, Example 2, Example 3, P-5)

21. $\frac{-48}{8}$  

22. $\frac{-54}{6}$  

23. $\frac{72}{-9}$  

24. $\frac{56}{-8}$

25. $\frac{-120}{-12}$  

26. $\frac{-99}{-11}$  

27. $\frac{25}{-2}$  

28. $\frac{14}{-4}$

29. $\frac{-27}{6}$  

30. $\frac{-21}{5}$  

31. $42 \div (-6)$  

32. $63 \div (-9)$

33. $(-33) \div (-11)$  

34. $(-49) \div (-7)$  

35. $(-20) \div 5$  

36. $(-32) \div 8$

37. $\frac{-27}{-27}$  

38. $\frac{-18}{-18}$  

39. $(-6) \div \left(-\frac{1}{2}\right)$  

40. $(-8) \div \left(-\frac{1}{3}\right)$

**B**  **EXAMPLE:** $(-15) \div 2\frac{1}{2}$  **SOLUTION:** $(-15) \div 2\frac{1}{2} = (-15) \div \left(\frac{5}{2}\right)$

$$= (-15)\left(\frac{2}{5}\right)$$

$$= -6$$

41. $(-18) \div 4\frac{1}{2}$  

42. $(-21) \div 3\frac{1}{2}$

43. $(-27) \div \left(-2\frac{1}{4}\right)$  

44. $(-33) \div \left(-1\frac{3}{8}\right)$

45. $\left(-\frac{3}{4}\right) \div 4\frac{1}{2}$  

46. $\left(-\frac{4}{5}\right) \div 1\frac{3}{5}$

*Rational Numbers: Subtraction and Division* / **313**

# 12.7 Special Properties of Division

**P-1** **What is the simplest name for each product?**

**a.** $12\left(\dfrac{1}{12}\right)$     **b.** $-5\left(\dfrac{1}{-5}\right)$     **c.** $-\dfrac{2}{3}\left(\dfrac{1}{-\frac{2}{3}}\right)$     **d.** $1.3\left(\dfrac{1}{1.3}\right)$

> The reciprocal of any nonzero rational number $a$ can be represented by $\dfrac{1}{a}$.

**P-2** **What is the simplest name for each product?**

**a.** $-3\left(\dfrac{1}{-3}\right)$     **b.** $-3\left(-\dfrac{1}{3}\right)$

You know that $\dfrac{1}{-3}$ and $-\dfrac{1}{3}$ are both names for the reciprocal of $-3$.

> For any rational number $a$, except 0,
> $$-\dfrac{1}{a} = \dfrac{1}{-a}.$$

The following special properties of division are useful.

> For any rational numbers $a$ and $b$, $b \neq 0$,
> 1. $\dfrac{-a}{b} = -\dfrac{a}{b}$     2. $\dfrac{a}{-b} = -\dfrac{a}{b}$     3. $\dfrac{-a}{-b} = \dfrac{a}{b}.$

**P-3** **What are two other names for each quotient?**

**a.** $\dfrac{-3}{4}$     **b.** $\dfrac{5}{-12}$     **c.** $\dfrac{-2}{-(x-3)},\ x \neq 3$

The form $-\dfrac{a}{b}$ is the simplest name rather than $\dfrac{-a}{b}$ or $\dfrac{a}{-b}$. Also, the form with the fewest "dash" symbols is considered the simplest. Thus, $\dfrac{a}{b}$ is the simplest name rather than $\dfrac{-a}{-b}$.

**P-4**  What is the simplest name for each quotient below?

a. $\dfrac{-5}{13}$    b. $\dfrac{5}{-13}$    c. $\dfrac{-5}{-13}$    d. $\dfrac{-m}{-n}, n \neq 0$

**P-5**  What is the simplest name of $\dfrac{t}{-7}$?

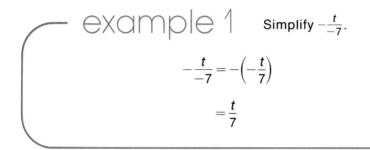

example 1    Simplify $-\dfrac{t}{-7}$.

$$-\dfrac{t}{-7} = -\left(-\dfrac{t}{7}\right)$$
$$= \dfrac{t}{7}$$

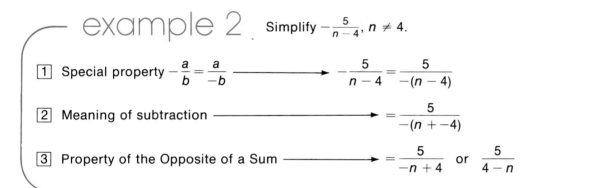

example 2 . Simplify $-\dfrac{5}{n-4}$, $n \neq 4$.

1 Special property $-\dfrac{a}{b} = \dfrac{a}{-b}$ ⟶ $-\dfrac{5}{n-4} = \dfrac{5}{-(n-4)}$

2 Meaning of subtraction ⟶ $= \dfrac{5}{-(n+-4)}$

3 Property of the Opposite of a Sum ⟶ $= \dfrac{5}{-n+4}$ or $\dfrac{5}{4-n}$

## ORAL EXERCISES 12.7

*Tell two other names for each quotient.* (P-3)

**EXAMPLE:** $\dfrac{11}{-13}$    **ANSWER:** $\dfrac{-11}{13}$ ; $-\dfrac{11}{13}$

1. $\dfrac{-5}{7}$    2. $\dfrac{14}{-17}$    3. $-\dfrac{7}{10}$    4. $\dfrac{-n}{8}$    5. $\dfrac{t}{-5}$    6. $-\dfrac{k}{4}$

7. $\dfrac{w-5}{-6}$    8. $-\dfrac{s+7}{3}$    9. $\dfrac{r}{-s}, s \neq 0$    10. $\dfrac{m+n}{-p}, p \neq 0$

11. $-\dfrac{a-b}{c}, c \neq 0$    12. $\dfrac{-(y-6)}{10}$    13. $\dfrac{-15}{-(r-8)}, r \neq 8$    14. $-\dfrac{y-5}{-6}$

*Rational Numbers: Subtraction and Division*   /   **315**

*Simplify. (P-4, P-5, Example 1, Example 2)*

**15.** $-\dfrac{-3}{7}$  **16.** $-\dfrac{-2}{-11}$  **17.** $-\dfrac{1}{-13}$  **18.** $\dfrac{-9}{-13}$  **19.** $-\dfrac{28}{-7}$  **20.** $-\dfrac{-26}{-13}$

**21.** $-\dfrac{-36}{9}$  **22.** $\dfrac{-49}{-7}$  **23.** $-\dfrac{x}{-y}, \; y \neq 0$  **24.** $-\dfrac{-x}{-y}, \; y \neq 0$

**25.** $\dfrac{-a}{-b}, \; b \neq 0$  **26.** $-\dfrac{x+2}{-5}$  **27.** $-\dfrac{-(x+y)}{a}, \; a \neq 0$  **28.** $-\dfrac{6}{n-1}, \; n \neq 1$

## WRITTEN EXERCISES 12.7

**A**    **Goal:** To simplify quotients

**Sample Problems: a.** $-\dfrac{-3}{-5}$  **b.** $\dfrac{-(x-5)}{7}$

**Answers: a.** $-\dfrac{3}{5}$  **b.** $\dfrac{-x+5}{7}$

*Write two other names for each quotient. (P-3)*

**1.** $\dfrac{-8}{13}$  **2.** $\dfrac{-12}{19}$  **3.** $\dfrac{5}{-11}$  **4.** $\dfrac{4}{-9}$

**5.** $-\dfrac{17}{18}$  **6.** $-\dfrac{6}{11}$  **7.** $\dfrac{-k}{8}$  **8.** $\dfrac{-w}{16}$

**9.** $-\dfrac{t}{-12}$  **10.** $-\dfrac{q}{-16}$  **11.** $\dfrac{-(x+3)}{5}$  **12.** $\dfrac{-(w+1)}{16}$

**13.** $\dfrac{t+6}{-2}$  **14.** $\dfrac{p+5}{-3}$  **15.** $-\dfrac{r}{s}, \; s \neq 0$  **16.** $-\dfrac{t}{w}, \; w \neq 0$

**17.** $-\dfrac{n-3}{2}$  **18.** $-\dfrac{k-8}{5}$  **19.** $-\dfrac{4}{x-2}, \; x \neq 2$  **20.** $-\dfrac{6}{a-8}, \; a \neq 8$

*Simplify. (P-4, P-5, Example 1, Example 2)*

**21.** $-\dfrac{-4}{15}$  **22.** $-\dfrac{-6}{19}$  **23.** $-\dfrac{2}{-11}$  **24.** $-\dfrac{3}{-16}$  **25.** $\dfrac{-5}{-9}$  **26.** $\dfrac{-4}{-17}$

**27.** $\dfrac{a}{-b}, \; b \neq 0$  **28.** $\dfrac{-r}{s}, \; s \neq 0$  **29.** $\dfrac{-(x+3)}{10}$  **30.** $\dfrac{-(y+6)}{11}$

**31.** $-\dfrac{a-5}{3}$  **32.** $-\dfrac{r-6}{5}$  **33.** $\dfrac{t-4}{-9}$  **34.** $\dfrac{s-3}{-5}$

**35.** $-\dfrac{1}{k-3}, \; k \neq 3$  **36.** $-\dfrac{1}{t-5}, \; t \neq 5$  **37.** $-\dfrac{56}{-7}$  **38.** $-\dfrac{-48}{16}$

**C**    *Simplify.*

**39.** $\dfrac{3}{7} + \dfrac{-1}{7}$  **40.** $\dfrac{4}{5} - \dfrac{-2}{5}$  **41.** $\dfrac{3}{11} + \dfrac{5}{-11}$  **42.** $\dfrac{9}{13} - \dfrac{-5}{13}$

**43.** $\dfrac{5}{x+y} - \dfrac{-2}{x+y}, \; x+y \neq 0$  **44.** $\dfrac{-4}{t} - \dfrac{-8}{t}, \; t \neq 0$

# 12.8  Division Practice

You know that a rational number can be divided by a rational number.

**P-1**  **What is the reciprocal of $-\frac{8}{3}$?**

example 1    Divide and simplify: $\frac{2}{3} \div \left(-\frac{8}{3}\right)$

You first express the quotient as a product.

$$\frac{2}{3} \div \left(-\frac{8}{3}\right) = \frac{2}{3}\left(-\frac{3}{8}\right)$$

$$= -\frac{\overset{1}{\cancel{2}}}{\cancel{3}} \cdot \frac{\overset{1}{\cancel{3}}}{\cancel{8}}$$

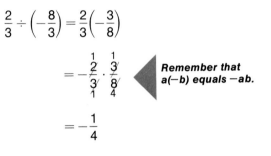 *Remember that a(−b) equals −ab.*

$$= -\frac{1}{4}$$

**P-2**  **What is the reciprocal of $-3\frac{1}{3}$?**

example 2    Divide and simplify: $\left(-\frac{5}{6}\right) \div \left(-3\frac{1}{3}\right)$

$$\left(-\frac{5}{6}\right) \div \left(-3\frac{1}{3}\right) = \left(-\frac{5}{6}\right) \div \left(-\frac{10}{3}\right)$$

$$= \left(-\frac{5}{6}\right)\left(-\frac{3}{10}\right)$$

$$= \frac{\overset{1}{\cancel{5}}}{\underset{2}{\cancel{6}}} \cdot \frac{\overset{1}{\cancel{3}}}{\underset{2}{\cancel{10}}}$$

*Remember that (−a)(−b) = ab.*

$$= \frac{1}{4}$$

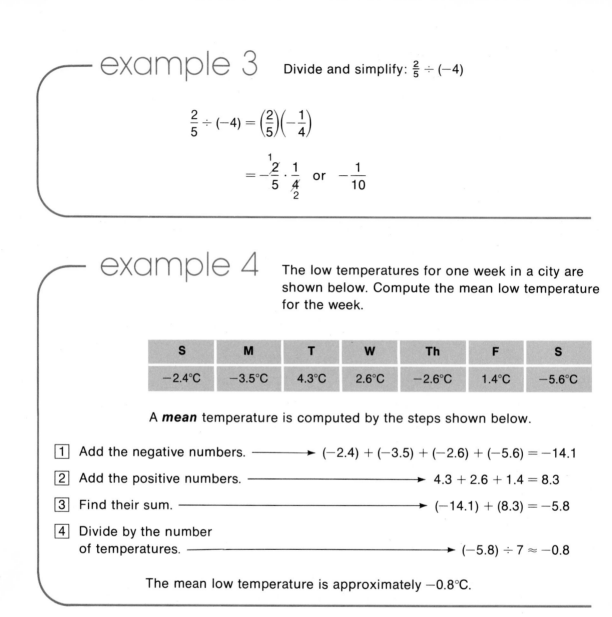

example 3    Divide and simplify: $\frac{2}{5} \div (-4)$

$$\frac{2}{5} \div (-4) = \left(\frac{2}{5}\right)\left(-\frac{1}{4}\right)$$

$$= -\frac{\overset{1}{2}}{5} \cdot \frac{1}{\underset{2}{4}} \quad \text{or} \quad -\frac{1}{10}$$

example 4    The low temperatures for one week in a city are shown below. Compute the mean low temperature for the week.

| S | M | T | W | Th | F | S |
|---|---|---|---|---|---|---|
| −2.4°C | −3.5°C | 4.3°C | 2.6°C | −2.6°C | 1.4°C | −5.6°C |

A **mean** temperature is computed by the steps shown below.

1 Add the negative numbers. ⟶ $(-2.4) + (-3.5) + (-2.6) + (-5.6) = -14.1$

2 Add the positive numbers. ⟶ $4.3 + 2.6 + 1.4 = 8.3$

3 Find their sum. ⟶ $(-14.1) + (8.3) = -5.8$

4 Divide by the number of temperatures. ⟶ $(-5.8) \div 7 \approx -0.8$

The mean low temperature is approximately −0.8°C.

## ORAL EXERCISES 12.8

*Simplify.* (Example 1, Example 2, Example 3)

1. $\frac{-54}{9}$

2. $\frac{-80}{-10}$

3. $\frac{63}{-9}$

4. $-\frac{-42}{-6}$

5. $56 \div (-8)$

6. $(-72) \div 12$

7. $(-72) \div (-9)$

8. $(-90) \div 9$

**9.** $(-3) \div \frac{1}{4}$       **10.** $5 \div (-\frac{1}{3})$       **11.** $(-10) \div (-\frac{1}{2})$       **12.** $4 \div (-\frac{2}{3})$

**13.** $(-6) \div \frac{3}{5}$       **14.** $(-8) \div (-\frac{4}{3})$       **15.** $\frac{1}{2} \div (-\frac{3}{2})$       **16.** $(-\frac{1}{4}) \div (-\frac{3}{4})$

**17.** $(-\frac{1}{5}) \div \frac{3}{10}$       **18.** $(-\frac{3}{8}) \div (-\frac{5}{8})$       **19.** $(-\frac{7}{4}) \div \frac{9}{4}$       **20.** $\frac{11}{8} \div (-\frac{11}{4})$

## WRITTEN EXERCISES 12.8

**A**

**Goal:** To solve problems involving division of rational numbers by rational numbers

**Sample Problem:** Find the mean temperature for $-4.5°$, $6.9°$, $-5.2°$, $8.3°$, $1.0°$, $-7.7°$

**Answer:** $-0.2°$

*Divide. Simplify where necessary.* (Example 1, Example 2, Example 3)

**1.** $\frac{-96}{12}$       **2.** $\frac{-121}{11}$       **3.** $\frac{-132}{-11}$       **4.** $\frac{-144}{-12}$       **5.** $\frac{91}{-7}$       **6.** $\frac{126}{-9}$

**7.** $(-14) \div 4$       **8.** $(-27) \div 6$       **9.** $23 \div (-3)$       **10.** $37 \div (-5)$

**11.** $(-42) \div (-8)$       **12.** $(-74) \div (-10)$       **13.** $(-6) \div \frac{1}{3}$       **14.** $(-12) \div \frac{1}{5}$

**15.** $9 \div (-\frac{1}{4})$       **16.** $8 \div (-\frac{1}{6})$       **17.** $(-14) \div (-\frac{1}{2})$       **18.** $(-21) \div (-\frac{1}{2})$

**19.** $8 \div (-\frac{4}{3})$       **20.** $10 \div (-\frac{2}{5})$       **21.** $(-16) \div \frac{8}{5}$       **22.** $(-12) \div \frac{6}{5}$

**23.** $(-20) \div (-\frac{4}{7})$       **24.** $(-15) \div (-\frac{5}{8})$       **25.** $\frac{1}{4} \div (-\frac{5}{4})$       **26.** $\frac{1}{3} \div (-\frac{7}{3})$

**27.** $(-\frac{8}{9}) \div (-\frac{4}{3})$       **28.** $(-\frac{4}{5}) \div (-\frac{8}{5})$       **29.** $1\frac{1}{2} \div (-2\frac{1}{4})$       **30.** $1\frac{3}{4} \div (-1\frac{1}{8})$

*Compute the mean temperature.* (Example 4)

**31.** $-6.2°$, $-4.1°$, $1.9°$, $3.8°$, $-2.4°$, $5.2°$       **32.** $10.1°$, $6.5°$, $-4.8°$, $-2.6°$, $1.6°$, $-3.6°$

*The net loss or gain of a stock is shown for each of five days. Find the average loss or gain per day. (Hint: Average as used here is the same as mean.)*

**EXAMPLE:** $\frac{5}{8}$, $-2\frac{1}{4}$, $-\frac{1}{2}$, $1\frac{7}{8}$, $-\frac{1}{2}$

**SOLUTION:** $\frac{5}{8} + 1\frac{7}{8} = 2\frac{1}{2}$

$(-2\frac{1}{4}) + (-\frac{1}{2}) + (-\frac{1}{2}) = -3\frac{1}{4}$

$(-3\frac{1}{4}) + 2\frac{1}{2} = -\frac{3}{4}$

$(-\frac{3}{4}) \div 5 = -\frac{3}{20}$

**33.** $-\frac{7}{8}$, $1\frac{1}{2}$, $\frac{3}{4}$, $-1\frac{1}{8}$, $-\frac{5}{8}$       **34.** $\frac{3}{4}$, $-1\frac{1}{8}$, $-\frac{5}{8}$, $1\frac{1}{8}$, $-\frac{7}{8}$

# Automobile Mechanic

It is estimated that there are over 700,000 persons working as automobile mechanics in the United States. A person interested in becoming an automobile mechanic should take auto shop courses in high school as well as science and mathematics courses. It is recommended that a person participate in an apprenticeship program in order to prepare to be fully qualified. Apprenticeship programs include classroom instruction as well as on-the-job training.

Automobile mechanics must be able to read tables that show such things as tune-up specifications. (See the facing page.) Note that in this table most measures are in inches. However, displacement is given in both cubic centimeters and cubic inches.

*Displacement* is the total volume of all the engine's cylinders. The diameter of an engine cylinder is called the *bore*. The distance the piston moves is called the *stroke*. The following formula relates bore, stroke, and displacement.

$$\text{Displacement} = \pi\left(\frac{\text{Bore}}{2}\right)^2 (\text{Stroke}) (\text{Number of cylinders})$$

$$D = \pi\left(\frac{b}{2}\right)^2 (s) (n)$$

**EXAMPLE:** A certain 4-cylinder engine has a bore of 84 mm and a stroke of 84.4 mm. Compute its displacement in cubic centimeters.

**SOLUTION:** 84 mm = 8.4 cm; 84.4 mm = 8.44 cm
Use $\pi = 3.14$; $b = 8.4$ cm; $s = 8.44$ cm; $n = 4$.

$$D = 3.14\left(\frac{8.4}{2}\right)^2 (8.44)(4)$$

$$D = 3.14(17.64)(8.44)(4)$$

$$D = 1870 \text{ cubic centimeters}$$

# TUNE-UP SPECIFICATIONS

When analyzing compression test results, look for uniformity among cylinders, rather than specific pressures.

| Year and Model | Engine Cu in. Displacement | SPARK PLUGS Type | SPARK PLUGS Gap (in.) | DISTRIBUTOR Point Dwell (deg) | DISTRIBUTOR Point Gap (in.) | IGNITION TIMING (deg) MT | IGNITION TIMING (deg) AT | Intake Valve Opens (deg) | Fuel Pump Pressure (psi) | IDLE SPEED (rpm) MT | IDLE SPEED (rpm) AT | VALVE CLEAR. (in.)① In | VALVE CLEAR. (in.)① Ex |
|---|---|---|---|---|---|---|---|---|---|---|---|---|---|
| 1970-1971 Super 90 | 107.5 (1,760 cc) | Ch N3 | 0.016-0.020 | 47-53 | 0.016 | 9A @ 950 rpm② | — | 6B | 3 | 950 | — | 0.006 | 0.012 |
| 1972 Super 90 | 107.5 (1,760 cc) | Ch N8Y | 0.024-0.030 | 47-53 | 0.016 | 9A @ 950 rpm② | — | 5B | 3 | 950 | — | 0.008 | 0.016 |
| 1970-1971 100 LS | 107.5 (1,760 cc) | Ch N7Y | 0.023-0.029 | 47-53 | 0.016 | 9A @ 950 rpm③ | 9A @ 950 rpm③ | 5B | 3.6 | 850-1000 | 850-1000 | 0.008 | 0.016 |
| 1972 100 100 LS | 114.2 (1,871 cc) | Ch N8Y | 0.024-0.030 ④ | 47-53 | 0.016 | 8A @ idle③ | 8A @ idle③ | 5B | 3.6 | 850-1000 | 850-1000 | 0.008 | 0.016 |
| 1973 100 100 LS 100 GL | 114.2 (1,871 cc) | Ch N7Y | 0.036-0.039 | 47-53 | 0.016 | 8A @ idle⑤ | 8A @ idle⑥ | 5B | 3.6 | 850-1000 | 850-1000 | 0.008 | 0.016 |

**NOTE:** % of CO at idle should be 1.0 for all 100, 100 LS, and 100 GL, 1.5 for 1970-1971 Super 90, and 1.0 for 1972 Super 90.

*Modern electronic tune-up equipment consists of various kinds of testing devices with dials and scales that a mechanic must be able to read and interpret.*

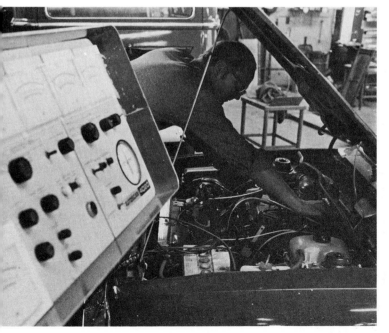

# CHAPTER SUMMARY

| **IMPORTANT TERMS** | Difference *(p. 294)* | Quotient *(p. 311)* |
| | Reciprocal *(p. 308)* | Mean *(p. 318)* |

**IMPORTANT IDEAS**

1. If $a$ and $b$ are any rational numbers, then $a - b = a + (-b)$. To subtract $b$ from $a$, add the opposite of $b$ to $a$.

2. The simplest name of a negative number is a numeral preceded by the "opposite" symbol.

3. For any rational numbers $a$, $b$, and $c$,
$a - (b + c) = a - b - c$ and $a - (b - c) = a - b + c$.

4. *Distributive Property (Multiplication over Subtraction):*
For any rational numbers $a$, $b$, and $c$,
$a(b - c) = ab - ac$ and $(b - c)a = ba - ca$.

5. If $a$ and $b$ are any rational numbers, $b \neq 0$, then $a \div b = a \cdot \dfrac{1}{b}$.
To divide $a$ by $b$, multiply $a$ by the reciprocal of $b$.

6. If a positive number is divided by a positive number, the quotient is a positive number.

7. If a positive number is divided by a negative number, the quotient is a negative number.

8. If a negative number is divided by a negative number, the quotient is a positive number.

9. If a negative number is divided by a positive number, the quotient is a negative number.

10. The reciprocal of any nonzero rational number $a$ can be represented by $\dfrac{1}{a}$.

11. For any rational number $a$, except 0, $-\dfrac{1}{a} = \dfrac{1}{-a}$.

12. For any rational numbers $a$ and $b$, $b \neq 0$,
$\dfrac{-a}{b} = -\dfrac{a}{b}$ and $\dfrac{a}{-b} = -\dfrac{a}{b}$ and $\dfrac{-a}{-b} = \dfrac{a}{b}$.

# CHAPTER REVIEW

**SECTION 12.1**

*Write each difference as a sum. Then simplify.*

**1.** $18 - 25$ **2.** $23 - 37$

**3.** $15 - (^-8)$ **4.** $24 - (^-5)$

**5.** $(^-13) - (^-18)$

**6.** $(^-17) - (^-19)$

**7.** $(^-9) - 24$

**8.** $(^-14) - 31$

**9.** $5.8 - 12.3$

**10.** $11.9 - 13.2$

### SECTION 12.2

*Simplify.*

**11.** $-36 - 19$

**12.** $-48 - 13$

**13.** $35 - (-17)$

**14.** $24 - (-28)$

**15.** $(-56) - (-18)$

**16.** $(-47) - (-39)$

**17.** $26 - 39 - (-5)$

**18.** $19 - (-17) - 47$

**19.** $4.7 - 8.3 - 5.7 + 2.9 - 1.6$

**20.** $-12.3 + 8.9 - 1.7 + 4.7 - 0.8$

### SECTION 12.3

*Simplify.*

**21.** $12r - r$

**22.** $24t - t$

**23.** $3w - 12w$

**24.** $8k - 23k$

**25.** $-13n + 17 - 5n$

**26.** $22p - 19 - 31p$

**27.** $x - 5 + 13 - 5x$

**28.** $y + 19 - 8 - 15y$

**29.** $13 - (4x - 16)$

**30.** $28 - (5m - 19)$

### SECTION 12.4

*Simplify.*

**31.** $(2w + 1.3) - (8w - 3.6)$

**32.** $(5t - 2.9) - (3t + 5.3)$

**33.** $29 - (15p - 19 + 13p)$

**34.** $36 - (8r + 23 - 15r)$

**35.** $(2x^2 - 7) - (x^2 + 8x - 3)$

**36.** $(5a^2 - 12a + 6) - (a^2 + 4a - 8)$

*Multiply. Simplify where necessary.*

**37.** $12(5n - 4)$

**38.** $-6(-3n + 7)$

**39.** $-9t(-3t + 8)$

**40.** $7p(8p - 6)$

**41.** $(3r^2 - 7r + 2)(-3r)$

**42.** $(-5w^2 + 3w - 6)(-4w)$

## SECTION 12.5

*Write the reciprocal. Simplify where necessary.*

**43.** $-\frac{1}{8}$   **44.** $-\frac{1}{15}$   **45.** $4\frac{1}{3}$   **46.** $6\frac{7}{8}$   **47.** $-5.3$   **48.** $-4.8$

**49.** $-6\frac{1}{2}$   **50.** $-7\frac{1}{4}$   **51.** $-\frac{56}{7}$   **52.** $-\frac{81}{9}$   **53.** $-\frac{14}{14}$   **54.** $-\frac{23}{23}$

## SECTION 12.6

*Write each quotient as a product.*

**55.** $\frac{-13}{19}$   **56.** $\frac{15}{-29}$   **57.** $(-5) \div (-23)$

**58.** $(-14) \div (-\frac{5}{8})$   **59.** $3r \div (-\frac{3}{4})$   **60.** $(-5n) \div (-\frac{5}{8})$

*Divide.*

**61.** $\frac{64}{-4}$   **62.** $\frac{-63}{7}$   **63.** $\frac{-25}{-4}$   **64.** $\frac{-27}{-8}$

**65.** $(-24) \div 8$   **66.** $36 \div (-12)$   **67.** $(-9) \div \frac{1}{4}$   **68.** $(-7) \div (-\frac{1}{3})$

## SECTION 12.7

*Simplify.*

**69.** $-\frac{8}{-17}$   **70.** $-\frac{-11}{18}$   **71.** $\frac{-3}{-16}$   **72.** $\frac{-8}{-25}$

**73.** $\frac{q-5}{-6}$   **74.** $-\frac{4-t}{8}$   **75.** $-\frac{-108}{-9}$   **76.** $-\frac{-144}{-12}$

## SECTION 12.8

*Divide. Simplify where necessary.*

**77.** $(-15) \div \frac{5}{3}$   **78.** $(-20) \div (-\frac{4}{5})$   **79.** $(-\frac{7}{4}) \div -10\frac{1}{2}$   **80.** $\frac{3}{8} \div (-2\frac{1}{4})$

**81.** $2\frac{1}{4} \div (-1\frac{1}{8})$   **82.** $(-3\frac{1}{4}) \div 1\frac{5}{8}$   **83.** $(4\frac{1}{3}) \div (-1\frac{1}{6})$   **84.** $(5\frac{1}{3}) \div (-2\frac{1}{6})$

# REVIEW EXERCISES FOR CHAPTERS 7-12

*Write the simplest name for each ratio. (Section 7.1)*

**1.** 14 to 32      **2.** $\frac{21}{49}$      **3.** $k$ to $t$      **4.** $q$ to $p$

*Solve each proportion. (Section 7.2)*

**5.** $\frac{3}{7} = \frac{x}{28}$      **6.** $\frac{9}{x} = \frac{6}{22}$      **7.** $\frac{y}{14} = \frac{8}{21}$      **8.** $\frac{35}{21} = \frac{10}{n}$

*Write each number as a per cent. Use a proportion. (Section 7.3)*

**9.** $\frac{3}{16}$      **10.** $\frac{1}{8}$      **11.** $\frac{13}{60}$      **12.** $\frac{59}{80}$

*Write a proportion. Then solve it. (Section 7.4)*

**13.** 40% of 92 is $t$.   **14.** 55% of 108 is $r$.   **15.** 72 is 12% of $n$.   **16.** 120 is 15% of $b$.

*Write a product for each word phrase. (Section 7.5)*

**17.** 74% of $t$ dimes   **18.** 38% of $k$ hours   **19.** $a$% of 2400 pupils   **20.** $p$% of $4400

*Write an open phrase that represents the interest on each investment. (Section 7.6)*

**21.** $r$ dollars at 5% for 2 years      **22.** $x$ dollars at 8% for 9 months

*Compute the discount and the net price for each item. (Section 7.7)*

**23.** A book listed at $14 is reduced 20%.      **24.** A dress listed at $28 is reduced 15%.

*Choose a variable and show what it represents. Then write an open phrase. (Section 8.1)*

**25.** The number of days decreased by seven      **26.** The number of sailboats increased by eight

*For each problem, (a) select a variable and show what it represents, (b) write open phrases that are needed, (c) write an equation to describe the problem, and (d) solve the problem. (Sections 8.2 through 8.5)*

**27.** Kim caught eight more fish than her father. Together they caught 22 fish. How many fish did each person catch?

**28.** The distance from St. Louis to Atlanta is 177 kilometers less than the distance from Atlanta to Miami. The distance from St. Louis to Miami through Atlanta is 1727 kilometers. Find the distance from St. Louis to Atlanta.

**29.** The width of a rectangle is 8 centimeters less than the length. The perimeter is 192 centimeters. Find the length and width.

**30.** The length of the shortest side of a triangle is 4 meters less than the length of the longest side. The length of the third side is 9 meters less than twice the length of the longest side. The perimeter is 15 meters. Find the length of each side.

**31.** The junior class sold adult tickets for $0.75 and student tickets for $0.50 for the school play. The number of adult tickets sold was twenty more than twice the number of student tickets. The total sales were $815.00. How many tickets of each kind were sold?

**32.** A collection of half-dollars, quarters, dimes, and nickels is worth $14.95. There are twice as many quarters as half-dollars. There are three more than twice as many dimes as half-dollars. The number of nickels is seven less than the number of half-dollars. Find the number of each kind of coin.

**33.** The sum of three consecutive odd numbers is 189. Find the three numbers.

**34.** The sum of three consecutive even numbers is 270. Find the three numbers.

*Write a proportion to solve for each unknown measure. (Section 8.6)*

**35.** $0.00216 \text{ m}^3 = x \text{ cm}^3$

**36.** $0.0927 \text{ cm}^3 = y \text{ mm}^3$

*For each problem, (a) select a variable and write what it represents, (b) write open phrases that are needed, (c) write an equation to describe the problem, and (d) solve the problem. (Section 8.7)*

**37.** An alloy of gold is 50 parts gold, 35 parts copper, and 15 parts silver. How much of each metal is needed for 1500 grams of the alloy?

**38.** A 12% salt solution is mixed with a 20% salt solution to obtain 800 liters of a 17% solution. Find the amount of each solution.

*Write each set in roster form. (Section 9.1)*

**39.** {integers greater than 3}

**40.** {integers greater than or equal to $^-5$}

*Think of the two numbers as coordinates of points on a number line. Write the coordinate of the point on the right. (Section 9.2)*

**41.** $^-5.02$ and $^-5.16$

**42.** 0 and $^-0.29$

*Write each number in decimal form. (Section 9.3)*

**43.** $^-\left(\dfrac{19}{4}\right)$

**44.** $3\frac{1}{8}$

**45.** $\dfrac{4}{33}$

**46.** $^-\left(\dfrac{5}{11}\right)$

*Simplify.* (Section 9.4)

**47.** $-(^-27)$  **48.** $-(^-4.9)$  **49.** $-(-(^-12))$  **50.** $-(-(^-37))$

*Write an inequality showing the order of the opposites of the two numbers.* (Section 9.5)

**51.** $4 > ^-11$  **52.** $^-19 < 7$  **53.** $^-14.6 < -(^-8.4)$  **54.** $-(^-8.3) > ^-2.7$

*Write the truth set. The domain is* $\{^-3, ^-2, ^-1, 0, 1, 2, 3\}$. (Section 9.6)

**55.** $-x > 2$  **56.** $-x \geq 3$  **57.** $-x \leq ^-2$  **58.** $-x < 0$

*Simplify.* (Section 9.7)

**59.** $|^-13.8|$  **60.** $|^-7\frac{1}{4}|$  **61.** $|^-5| + |12|$  **62.** $|5.8| + |^-3.2|$

*Write an integer for each sum.* (Section 10.1)

**63.** $(^-14) + 17$  **64.** $18 + (^-11)$  **65.** $(^-13) + (^-19)$  **66.** $(^-16) + (^-23)$

*Show each sum on a number line. Then add.* (Section 10.2)

**67.** $(^-4) + 8$  **68.** $5 + (^-9)$  **69.** $(^-2) + (^-4)$  **70.** $(^-3) + (^-3)$

*Add.* (Section 10.3 and Section 10.4)

**71.** $243 + (^-164)$  **72.** $(^-68) + (^-127)$

**73.** $(^-16) + 24 + (^-18)$  **74.** $(^-34) + 27 + (^-16)$

*Simplify.* (Section 10.5)

**75.** $(^-28) + x + 11 + (^-12)$  **76.** $22 + (^-29) + x + (^-9)$

*Use* $-(a + b) = (-a) + (-b)$ *to write each phrase in another way.* (Section 10.6)

**77.** $-(^-78 + x)$  **78.** $-((-t) + ^-16)$

*Solve each problem by adding positive and negative numbers.* (Section 10.7)

**79.** A business showed the following record of profit *(P)* and loss *(L)* over a four-week period. Find the net profit or loss for the period.

  1: $1250*(P)*   2: $865*(P)*   3: $240*(L)*   4: $710*(L)*

**80.** The initial price of a certain stock was $16\frac{1}{2}$. The net change in price is shown for each day. Find the final price.

  **Mon:** $^-2\frac{3}{8}$   **Tues:** $\frac{3}{4}$   **Wed:** $1\frac{1}{2}$   **Thurs:** $^-\left(\frac{1}{4}\right)$   **Fri:** $3\frac{1}{8}$

*Multiply. Simplify where necessary.* (Sections 11.1 through 11.5)

**81.** $(8)(^-2.5)$    **82.** $(12)(^-4.3)$    **83.** $(^-4)(3.1)$    **84.** $(^-5)(4.2)$

**85.** $(^-10.8)(^-24)$    **86.** $(^-0.4)(^-42)$    **87.** $(^-20)(^-8)(^-30)$    **88.** $(^-40)(^-4)(^-10)$

**89.** $^-8(6q + 8)$    **90.** $^-12(7 + {}^-5p)$    **91.** $(-a + 3b)(^-7k)$    **92.** $(-x + 12y)(^-3t)$

*Add like terms.* (Section 11.6)

**93.** $^-5.3w + {}^-8.9w$    **94.** $^-24pq + 19pq$

*Multiply. Simplify where necessary.* (Section 11.7)

**95.** $(n + 11)(n + {}^-12)$    **96.** $(y + {}^-9)(y + 10)$

*Write each difference as a sum. Then add.* (Section 12.1)

**97.** $24 - 35$    **98.** $8.6 - 10.2$    **99.** $(^-16) - (^-28)$    **100.** $(^-26) - (^-19)$

*Subtract.* (Section 12.2)

**101.** $27.6 - (-30.4)$    **102.** $14.9 - (-17.6)$

*Simplify.* (Section 12.3)

**103.** $17k - 29k - k$    **104.** $-31r + 3r - 15r$

*Multiply. Simplify where necessary.* (Section 12.4)

**105.** $-10t(5t - 9)$    **106.** $-14q(5 - r)$

*Write the reciprocal. Simplify where necessary.* (Section 12.5)

**107.** $-\frac{1}{19}$    **108.** $-102$    **109.** $-7\frac{1}{8}$    **110.** $1.3$

*Divide.* (Section 12.6)

**111.** $\frac{-168}{14}$    **112.** $\frac{165}{-15}$    **113.** $\frac{-33}{-6}$    **114.** $\frac{-50}{-8}$

*Simplify.* (Section 12.7)

**115.** $-\frac{9}{-16}$    **116.** $-\frac{-5}{17}$    **117.** $-\frac{-(-1)}{-6}$    **118.** $-\frac{11}{-(-15)}$

*Divide. Simplify where necessary.* (Section 12.8)

**119.** $-10 \div \frac{2}{5}$    **120.** $18 \div \left(-\frac{3}{4}\right)$    **121.** $\left(-\frac{9}{4}\right) \div \left(-\frac{1}{8}\right)$    **122.** $\left(-\frac{7}{8}\right) \div \left(-\frac{1}{4}\right)$

# 13

## Rational Numbers
## Solving Equations

# 13.1 Addition and Subtraction Properties

The Addition and Subtraction Properties of Equality for numbers of arithmetic also apply to rational numbers.

**P-1**   What number can you add to each side of $x - \frac{1}{4} = -5\frac{1}{2}$ to get an equivalent equation with only $x$ on one side?

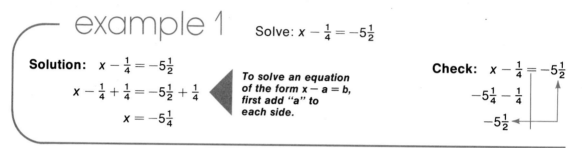

## example 1

Solve: $x - \frac{1}{4} = -5\frac{1}{2}$

**Solution:**   $x - \frac{1}{4} = -5\frac{1}{2}$

$x - \frac{1}{4} + \frac{1}{4} = -5\frac{1}{2} + \frac{1}{4}$

$x = -5\frac{1}{4}$

*To solve an equation of the form x − a = b, first add "a" to each side.*

**Check:**   $x - \frac{1}{4} = -5\frac{1}{2}$

$-5\frac{1}{4} - \frac{1}{4}$

$-5\frac{1}{2}$

**P-2**   What number can you subtract from each side of $x + 4.7 = 1.8$ to get an equivalent equation with only $x$ on one side?

## example 2

Solve: $x + 4.7 = 1.8$

**Solution:**   $x + 4.7 = 1.8$

$x + 4.7 - 4.7 = 1.8 - 4.7$

$x = -2.9$

*To solve an equation of the form x + a = b, first subtract "a" from each side.*

**Check:**   $x + 4.7 = 1.8$

$-2.9 + 4.7$

$1.8$

## example 3

Solve: $-x + 28 = 16$

$-x + 28 = 16$                    **Check**

1. Subtract 28 from each side. ——→ $-x + 28 - 28 = 16 - 28$         $-x + 28 = 16$

2. Simplify. ——————————————→ $-x = -12$            $-12 + 28$

3. Equality Property of Opposites ——→ $x = 12$              $16$

Note that any rational number $a$ can be eliminated from $x + a = b$ by adding the opposite of $a$ to each side. This is the same as subtracting $a$ from each side.

## ORAL EXERCISES 13.1

Tell an equivalent equation that is the first step in solving each equation.
(P-1, P-2)

**EXAMPLE:** $2.1 = 4.3 + x$     **ANSWER:** $2.1 - 4.3 = 4.3 + x - 4.3$

**1.** $x + 18 = 7$

**2.** $x - 24 = 20$

**3.** $x + 5 = -22$

**4.** $x - 18 = -30$

**5.** $x - \frac{3}{4} = -4\frac{1}{2}$

**6.** $x + 3.2 = 0.9$

**7.** $28 = -17 + x$

**8.** $-15 = 12 + x$

**9.** $-12.8 = x - 3.9$

**10.** $\frac{3}{4} = \frac{7}{8} + x$

**11.** $15.6 = -0.9 + x$

**12.** $-8.7 = x - 4.8$

**13.** $43 - x = 24$

**14.** $-19 - x = 49$

**15.** $-56 = 27 - x$

## WRITTEN EXERCISES 13.1

**A**

**Goal:** To solve an equation by using the Addition and Subtraction Properties of Equality for rational numbers
**Sample Problem:** Solve $6.2 - x = 7.8$.
**Answer:** $-1.6$

Solve and check each equation. Show all steps. (Examples 1, 2, 3)

**1.** $x - 14 = 25$

**2.** $x - 9 = 17$

**3.** $x - 24 = -15$

**4.** $x - 18 = -13$

**5.** $x + 29 = 16$

**6.** $x + 35 = 27$

**7.** $x + 8 = -19$

**8.** $x + 12 = -23$

**9.** $x + 9.4 = 5.1$

**10.** $x + 13.7 = 8.6$

**11.** $x - 5\frac{3}{4} = -3\frac{1}{4}$

**12.** $x - 8\frac{1}{2} = -5\frac{1}{4}$

**13.** $14.8 + x = 12.3$

**14.** $22.9 + x = 15.4$

**15.** $-29 = x - 47$

**16.** $-18 = x - 34$

**17.** $-0.7 = -1.6 + x$

**18.** $-0.5 = -3.8 + x$

**19.** $5\frac{3}{4} = x + 3\frac{1}{4}$

**20.** $10\frac{1}{2} = x + 4\frac{3}{8}$

**21.** $15 - x = 23$

**22.** $32 - x = 47$

**23.** $28 - x = 19$

**24.** $47 - x = 18$

**25.** $48.3 = 27.5 - x$

**26.** $33.4 = 22.9 - x$

**27.** $-19.5 = 8.7 - x$

**28.** $-27.4 = 11.9 - x$

**29.** $\frac{5}{12} = -\frac{13}{12} - x$

**30.** $\frac{7}{8} = -\frac{15}{8} - x$

**C**     Write an equivalent equation by simplifying each side.

**31.** $3x - 8 - 2x = 9 - 13$

**32.** $5x + 3 - 6x = -16 + 9$

**33.** $8x + 12 - 9x = -15 - 17$

**34.** $-16 + x + 25 = -32 + 18$

# 13.2 Like Terms in Equations

P-1  **What is the simplest name for $-13 + 27$?  for $-x + 19 + 2x$?**

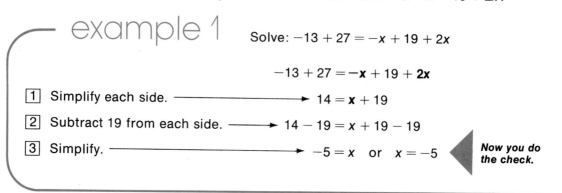

example 1    Solve: $-13 + 27 = -x + 19 + 2x$

$$-13 + 27 = -x + 19 + 2x$$

1  Simplify each side. ⟶ $14 = x + 19$

2  Subtract 19 from each side. ⟶ $14 - 19 = x + 19 - 19$

3  Simplify. ⟶ $-5 = x$  or  $x = -5$

**Now you do the check.**

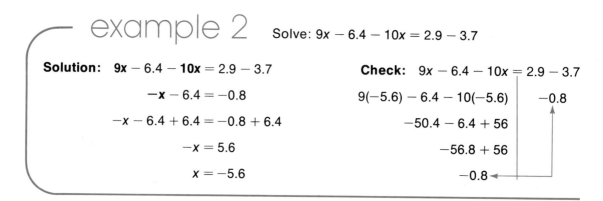

example 2    Solve: $9x - 6.4 - 10x = 2.9 - 3.7$

**Solution:**  $9x - 6.4 - 10x = 2.9 - 3.7$

$$-x - 6.4 = -0.8$$

$$-x - 6.4 + 6.4 = -0.8 + 6.4$$

$$-x = 5.6$$

$$x = -5.6$$

**Check:**  $9x - 6.4 - 10x = 2.9 - 3.7$

$9(-5.6) - 6.4 - 10(-5.6)$ | $-0.8$

$-50.4 - 6.4 + 56$

$-56.8 + 56$

$-0.8$

P-2  **What equivalent phrase do you get for $-3(2x + 5)$ by use of the Distributive Property?**

example 3    Solve: $-3(2x + 5) + 7x = 23 - 37$

**Solution:**  $-3(2x + 5) + 7x = 23 - 37$

$$-6x - 15 + 7x = -14$$

$$x - 15 = -14$$

$$x - 15 + 15 = -14 + 15$$

$$x = 1$$

**Check:**  $-3(2x + 5) + 7x = 23 - 37$

$-3(2 \cdot 1 + 5) + 7 \cdot 1$ | $-14$

$-3(7) + 7$

$-21 + 7$

$-14$

## ORAL EXERCISES 13.2

*Tell the simplest name for each phrase.* (P-1, P-2)

**1.** $6x + 13 - 5x$

**2.** $-7x + 18 + 6x$

**3.** $-12x - 8 + 13x$

**4.** $-12.3 + x + 9.4$

**5.** $0.3x - 20 + 0.7x$

**6.** $-22x + 35 + 21x$

**7.** $\frac{1}{2}(2x + 10) - 11$

**8.** $\frac{1}{4}(8x - 12) - x$

**9.** $16x + 29 - 33 - 15x$

*Tell an equivalent equation that is the first step in solving each equation.*
*(First step of Example 1, Example 2, and Example 3)*

**10.** $4x - 10 - 3x = 4 - 9$

**11.** $-19 + x + 13 = -1 - 12$

**12.** $\frac{1}{4}x + 6 + \frac{3}{4}x = -6 - 5$

**13.** $20 - 25 = 12x - 3 - 13x$

**14.** $3x - 4x + 5.1 = -4.2 - 1.8$

**15.** $x - 5 - 4x + 2x = 9 - 15$

**16.** $2(x + 3) - x = 19$

**17.** $-3(x + 4) + 4x = -8 - 7$

## WRITTEN EXERCISES 13.2

**A.**

**Goal:** To solve an equation involving like terms
**Sample Problem:** Solve $0.5 = 4(x - 0.1) - 5x$.
**Answer:** $-0.9$

*Solve and check each equation. Show all steps.* (Example 1, Example 2,
Example 3)

**1.** $6x - 19 - 5x = -16 + 13$

**2.** $-12x - 23 + 13x = 18 - 25$

**3.** $2x + 14 - 3x = 17 - 24$

**4.** $4x + 17 - 5x = 12 - 19$

**5.** $5.6 - 8.3 = -4.2x + 2.6 + 5.2x$

**6.** $7.9 - 10.4 = -8.1x + 3.3 + 9.1x$

**7.** $3x + 12x - 16x + 2 = -18 - 5$

**8.** $7x - 17x + 9x + 5 = -23 - 14$

**9.** $-8\frac{1}{4} + 6\frac{1}{2} = 4\frac{1}{4}x - 6x + 2\frac{3}{4}x$

**10.** $4\frac{3}{4} - 9\frac{1}{4} = 3\frac{5}{8}x - 11x + 8\frac{3}{8}x$

**11.** $3(x - 4) - 2x = -27 + 19$

**12.** $4(x - 5) - 3x = -33 + 12$

**13.** $-14.7 + 6.9 = -5(x - 2) + 4x$

**14.** $12.8 - 17.3 = -10(x - 1) + 9x$

**15.** $x - (5 + 2x) = 47 - 58$

**16.** $3x - (4x + 9) = 35 - 43$

**17.** $12 - (x - 13) = -26 + 15$

**18.** $27 - (-17 + x) = 13 - 28$

**19.** $5.2x - 6.8 - 5.2x = 7.1 - (x + 12.3)$

**20.** $12.9x - 14.3 - 12.9x = 11.6 - (x + 14.2)$

# 13.3 More Equations

**P-1** How can you eliminate the variable from the right side of $12 - 4x = 27 - 3x$?

**P-2** What equivalent equation is formed if you add $3x$ to each side of $12 - 4x = 27 - 3x$?

## example 1  Solve: $12 - 4x = 27 - 3x$

$$12 - 4x = 27 - 3x$$

1 Addition Property of Equality ⟶ $12 - 4x + 3x = 27 - 3x + 3x$

2 Simplify. ⟶ $12 - x = 27$

3 Subtraction Property of Equality ⟶ $12 - x - 12 = 27 - 12$

4 Simplify. ⟶ $-x = 15$

5 Equality Property of Opposites ⟶ $x = -15$  **Now you do the check.**

**P-3** What is the simplest name for $5x - (3x + 7)$?  for $6 + 3x - 14$?

## example 2  Solve: $5x - (3x + 7) = 6 + 3x - 14$

Write the simplest name for each side first.

**Solution:**

$$5x - (3x + 7) = 6 + 3x - 14$$
$$5x - 3x - 7 = 3x - 8$$
$$2x - 7 = 3x - 8$$
$$2x - 7 - 2x = 3x - 8 - 2x$$
$$-7 = x - 8$$
$$-7 + 8 = x - 8 + 8$$
$$1 = x \quad \text{or} \quad x = 1$$

**Check:**

$$5x - (3x + 7) = 6 + 3x - 14$$

| $5(1) - (3 \cdot 1 + 7)$ | $6 + 3 \cdot 1 - 14$ |
|---|---|
| $5 - (3 + 7)$ | $6 + 3 - 14$ |
| $5 - 10$ | $9 - 14$ |
| $-5$ | $-5$ |

## ORAL EXERCISES 13.3

*Tell two different steps you can take to eliminate the variable from one side of each equation.*

**EXAMPLE:** $5x - 4 = 6x + 7$     **ANSWER:** Subtract $5x$ or $6x$ from each side.

**1.** $12x + 3 = 11x - 6$

**2.** $10 - 3x = -4x - 6$

**3.** $-x + 7 = 12 - 2x$

**4.** $5.6x - 1.8 = 4.6x + 2.3$

**5.** $\frac{3}{4} - \frac{1}{2}x = 1\frac{1}{4} + \frac{1}{2}x$

**6.** $\frac{1}{3}x - \frac{7}{2} = -\frac{2}{3}x + \frac{9}{4}$

*Tell what value you get for the phrase on each side. Then say* Yes *or* No *to tell whether the given value of x is a truth number.* (Check of Example 2)

**7.** $4x - 3 = 3x + 5$ if $x$ equals 8

**8.** $-x + 10 = 14 - 2x$ if $x$ equals 4

**9.** $5 - 3x = -4x - 2$ if $x$ equals $-7$

**10.** $2x + 6 = x - 4$ if $x$ equals 10

**11.** $\frac{1}{2}x + 8 = 6 - \frac{1}{2}x$ if $x$ equals 2

**12.** $-\frac{3}{4}x - 2 = \frac{1}{4}x + 6$ if $x$ equals $-8$

## WRITTEN EXERCISES 13.3

evens

**A**

**Goal:** To solve an equation in which the variable appears on both sides
**Sample Problem:** Solve $6.2 + 14.7x = 13.7x - 3.8$.     **Answer:** $-10$

*Solve and check each equation. Show all steps.* (Example 1, Example 2)

**1.** $x - 5 = 2x + 7$

**2.** $3x + 2 = 2x - 11$

**3.** $8 - 3x = -4x - 2$

**4.** $-9x - 3 = 12 - 10x$

**5.** $-24x - 5 = 12 - 23x$

**6.** $7 - 14x = -15x - 16$

**7.** $0.2x - 1.7 = 4.9 - 0.8x$

**8.** $3.4 - 0.6x = 0.4x - 5.9$

**9.** $\frac{3}{8}x - 6 = -\frac{5}{8}x + 10$

**10.** $-\frac{3}{4}x + 3 = \frac{1}{4}x - 5$

**11.** $\frac{5}{4}x + 1 = \frac{1}{4}x - 7$

**12.** $-\frac{4}{3}x + 2 = 14 - \frac{1}{3}x$

**13.** $3x - (x - 3) = x - 7$

**14.** $-4x - (7 - x) = 4 - 2x$

**15.** $10x - 5 - 12x = 10 - x$

**16.** $-2x + 5 - 5x = 8 - 6x$

**17.** $-3(2x - 1) + x = 5 - 4x$

**18.** $5(-x + 3) + 2x = -2x + 7$

**19.** $3x - 7 - 8x = -17 + 9 - 4x$

**20.** $12x - 4 - 9x = 6 - 4x$

**21.** $1.8x + 2.6 = -5.8 + 2.8x$

**22.** $4.9 - 6.5x = -7.5x - 2.2$

# 13.4 Multiplication and Division Properties

The Multiplication and Division Properties of Equality for numbers of arithmetic also apply to rational numbers.

**P-1** **What equivalent equation is formed by multiplying each side of the following equation by 2?**

$$\tfrac{1}{2}x = -3$$

**P-2** **What equivalent equation is formed by dividing each side of the following equation by $-4$?**

$$-4x = 28$$

**P-3** **What equivalent equation is formed by multiplying each side of $\frac{x}{12} = -9$ by 12?**

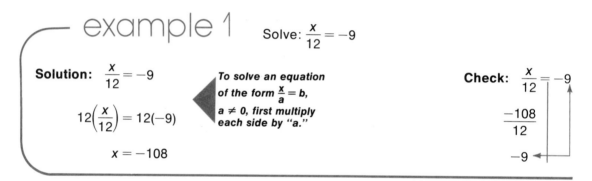

## example 1     Solve: $\dfrac{x}{12} = -9$

**Solution:** $\dfrac{x}{12} = -9$

$12\left(\dfrac{x}{12}\right) = 12(-9)$

$x = -108$

To solve an equation of the form $\frac{x}{a} = b$, $a \neq 0$, first multiply each side by "$a$."

**Check:** $\dfrac{x}{12} = -9$

$\dfrac{-108}{12}$

$-9$

**P-4** **What equivalent equation is formed by dividing each side of $-4x = 15$ by $-4$?**

## example 2     Solve: $-4x = 15$

**Solution:** $-4x = 15$

$\dfrac{-4x}{-4} = \dfrac{15}{-4}$

$x = -3\tfrac{3}{4}$

To solve an equation of the form $ax = b$, $a \neq 0$, first divide each side by "$a$."

**Check:** $-4x = 15$

$-4(-3\tfrac{3}{4})$

$-4(-\tfrac{15}{4})$

$15$

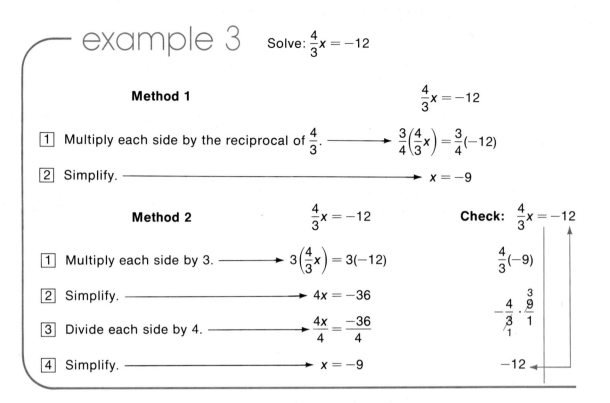

# example 3    Solve: $\frac{4}{3}x = -12$

**Method 1**                                        $\frac{4}{3}x = -12$

① Multiply each side by the reciprocal of $\frac{4}{3}$. ⟶ $\frac{3}{4}\left(\frac{4}{3}x\right) = \frac{3}{4}(-12)$

② Simplify. ⟶ $x = -9$

**Method 2**    $\frac{4}{3}x = -12$         **Check:** $\frac{4}{3}x = -12$

① Multiply each side by 3. ⟶ $3\left(\frac{4}{3}x\right) = 3(-12)$    $\frac{4}{3}(-9)$

② Simplify. ⟶ $4x = -36$

③ Divide each side by 4. ⟶ $\frac{4x}{4} = \frac{-36}{4}$    $-\frac{4}{3} \cdot \frac{\overset{3}{\cancel{9}}}{1}$

④ Simplify. ⟶ $x = -9$    $-12$

Any nonzero rational number $a$ can be eliminated from $ax = b$ by multiplying each side by the reciprocal of $a$. This is the same as dividing by $a$.

## ORAL EXERCISES 13.4

*Tell an equivalent equation that is the first step in solving each equation.* (First step of Example 1, Example 2, and Example 3)

**EXAMPLE:** $-5x = 20$    **ANSWER:** $\frac{-5x}{-5} = \frac{20}{-5}$

**1.** $12x = -48$

**2.** $-8x = -72$

**3.** $-6x = 42$

**4.** $-2.8x = 5.6$

**5.** $\frac{x}{4} = -7$

**6.** $\frac{x}{-3} = -19$

**7.** $10 = \frac{x}{-7}$

**8.** $-13 = \frac{x}{5}$

**9.** $-\frac{1}{3}x = 5$

*Tell an equivalent equation that is the first step in solving each equation.*
*(First step of Example 1, Example 2, and Example 3)*

**10.** $-\dfrac{1}{4}x = -6$

**11.** $\dfrac{2}{3}x = -12$

**12.** $-\dfrac{5}{2}x = 35$

**13.** $\dfrac{-7x}{4} = 21$

**14.** $-9 = \dfrac{3x}{5}$

**15.** $\dfrac{5}{8} = -\dfrac{5}{2}x$

*Tell the truth number of each equation.*

**16.** $-\dfrac{3}{4}\left(-\dfrac{4}{3}x\right) = -8$

**17.** $\dfrac{5}{4}\left(\dfrac{4}{5}x\right) = 2$

**18.** $5\left(\dfrac{x}{5}\right) = 5(-3)$

**19.** $-6\left(\dfrac{x}{-6}\right) = (-6)(-2)$

**20.** $\dfrac{-12x}{-12} = \dfrac{36}{-12}$

**21.** $\dfrac{4x}{4} = \dfrac{-18}{4}$

## WRITTEN EXERCISES 13.4

**A**

**Goal:** To solve an equation by using the Multiplication and Division
Properties of Equality for rational numbers
**Sample Problem:** Solve $-1\frac{1}{4}x = -\frac{5}{12}$.
**Answer:** $\frac{1}{3}$

*Solve and check each equation. Show all steps. (Example 1, Example 2,
Example 3)*

**1.** $4x = 32$

**2.** $6x = 18$

**3.** $-3x = 21$

**4.** $-7x = 28$

**5.** $-9x = -72$

**6.** $-11x = -77$

**7.** $17 = -\frac{1}{2}x$

**8.** $14 = -\frac{1}{3}x$

**9.** $\dfrac{x}{6} = -19$

**10.** $\dfrac{x}{12} = -8$

**11.** $-\dfrac{x}{3.8} = -7$

**12.** $-\dfrac{x}{4.3} = -12$

**13.** $-\frac{11}{4}x = 33$

**14.** $-\frac{9}{8}x = 27$

**15.** $-29 = 6x$

**16.** $34 = -8x$

**17.** $-\frac{5}{4}x = -35$

**18.** $-\frac{8}{7}x = -24$

**19.** $4x = -\frac{2}{5}$

**20.** $6x = -\frac{3}{8}$

**21.** $-1.2x = 8.76$

**22.** $-2.6x = 12.74$

**23.** $1\frac{3}{4}x = -\frac{7}{8}$

**24.** $-1\frac{7}{8}x = \frac{5}{16}$

**C**

**25.** $2x - 7 = -15$

**26.** $-3x + 4 = -14$

**27.** $-19 + 7 = -4x + 6$

**28.** $16 - 5x - 28 = -58 + 14$

**29.** $\frac{2}{3}x - 10 = 3 - 19$

**30.** $12 - \frac{3}{4}x = 21 - 39$

# 13.5 Equations with Combined Operations

**P-1** **What equivalent equation is formed if you subtract 11 from each side of $3x + 11 = 5$?**

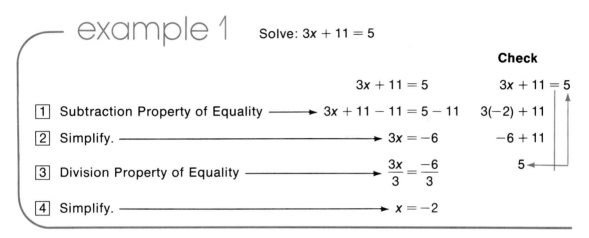

## example 1 Solve: $3x + 11 = 5$

|   |   |   | **Check** |
|---|---|---|---|
|   | $3x + 11 = 5$ | | $3x + 11 = 5$ |
| 1 Subtraction Property of Equality ⟶ | $3x + 11 - 11 = 5 - 11$ | | $3(-2) + 11$ |
| 2 Simplify. ⟶ | $3x = -6$ | | $-6 + 11$ |
| 3 Division Property of Equality ⟶ | $\dfrac{3x}{3} = \dfrac{-6}{3}$ | | $5$ |
| 4 Simplify. ⟶ | $x = -2$ | | |

**P-2** **Which property was used first in the solution of Example 1?**

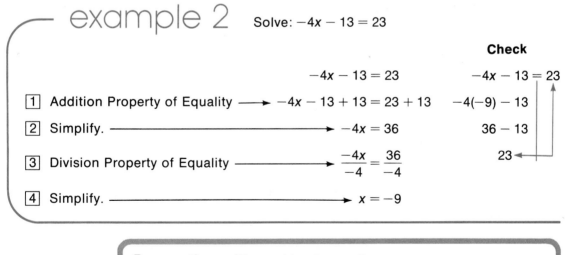

## example 2 Solve: $-4x - 13 = 23$

|   |   |   | **Check** |
|---|---|---|---|
|   | $-4x - 13 = 23$ | | $-4x - 13 = 23$ |
| 1 Addition Property of Equality ⟶ | $-4x - 13 + 13 = 23 + 13$ | | $-4(-9) - 13$ |
| 2 Simplify. ⟶ | $-4x = 36$ | | $36 - 13$ |
| 3 Division Property of Equality ⟶ | $\dfrac{-4x}{-4} = \dfrac{36}{-4}$ | | $23$ |
| 4 Simplify. ⟶ | $x = -9$ | | |

---

For equations with combined operations:

1. Use the Addition or Subtraction Property of Equality first.
2. Then use the Multiplication or Division Property of Equality.

$$\frac{x}{-6} + 19 = 12$$

$$\frac{x}{-6} = -7$$

$$x = 42$$

---

# example 3

Ten times a number is increased by 28. The result equals −32. What is the number?

Let $n$ = the unknown number.

$$10n + 28 = -32$$

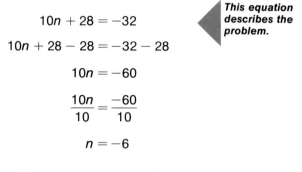 This equation describes the problem.

$$10n + 28 - 28 = -32 - 28$$

$$10n = -60$$

$$\frac{10n}{10} = \frac{-60}{10}$$

$$n = -6$$

**Check:** "Ten times a number is increased by 28. The result equals −32."

$$10(-6) = -60 \qquad (-60) + 28 = -32$$

# example 4

The length of a rectangle is 3 centimeters greater than the width. The perimeter is 50 centimeters. What are the length and width?

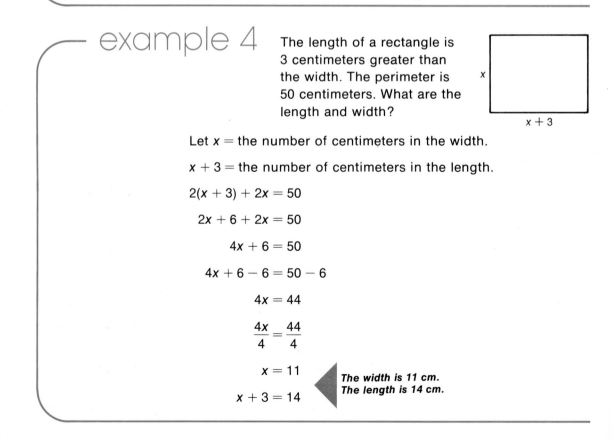

Let $x$ = the number of centimeters in the width.

$x + 3$ = the number of centimeters in the length.

$$2(x + 3) + 2x = 50$$

$$2x + 6 + 2x = 50$$

$$4x + 6 = 50$$

$$4x + 6 - 6 = 50 - 6$$

$$4x = 44$$

$$\frac{4x}{4} = \frac{44}{4}$$

$$x = 11$$

The width is 11 cm.
The length is 14 cm.

$$x + 3 = 14$$

## ORAL EXERCISES 13.5

*Tell the equivalent equation you get as the first step in solving each equation.* (First step of Example 1 and Example 2)

**1.** $3x + 2 = 5$

**2.** $-2x + 8 = 12$

**3.** $4x - 6 = -19$

**4.** $7x - 1 = 15$

**5.** $12 = 8 - 3x$

**6.** $-13 = 5x + 7$

**7.** $5.8 = 12.4 - 2x$

**8.** $-3.9 = 3x - 1.2$

**9.** $\dfrac{x}{3} - 5 = -19$

**10.** $\dfrac{x}{4} + 7 = -5$

**11.** $6x + 1.9 = -3.5$

**12.** $-9x + 0.3 = 12.6$

**13.** $-\dfrac{3}{5}x - 1\dfrac{2}{3} = 4\dfrac{1}{3}$

**14.** $12 = \dfrac{x}{-1.3} + 15$

**15.** $-3\dfrac{1}{2} = \dfrac{x}{-2} - 8\dfrac{1}{4}$

**16.** $4x + 3 - 5x = -18 + 13$

**17.** $-3x + 6 + 6x = 15 - 24$

**18.** $-3(x - 4) - 7 = -25 - 3$

**19.** $5x - (8 - x) = 3 - 21$

**20.** $-13 - 5(2 - 4x) = 43 - 6$

**21.** $-(18 + 5) = -4(x - 3) - 7$

## WRITTEN EXERCISES 13.5

**A**

**Goal:** To solve an equation by use of more than one property of equality

**Sample Problem:** Solve $\dfrac{1}{2}(2x - 6) = 4x + 9$.

**Answer:** $-4$

*Solve and check each equation. Show all steps.* (Example 1, Example 2)

**1.** $4x + 13 = -7$

**2.** $3x + 12 = -15$

**3.** $5x - 6 = -16$

**4.** $6x - 7 = -43$

**5.** $\dfrac{x}{4} + 19 = 16$

**6.** $\dfrac{x}{8} + 24 = 21$

**7.** $\dfrac{x}{-6} - 14 = -21$

**8.** $\dfrac{x}{-5} - 19 = -25$

**9.** $24 - 8x = 36$

**10.** $17 - 6x = 32$

**11.** $7.2 = 13.8 - 2x$

**12.** $5.3 = 14.9 - 3x$

**13.** $-\dfrac{3}{4}x + 12 = -15$

**14.** $14 - \dfrac{5}{8}x = -26$

**15.** $22 - \dfrac{x}{7} = 17$

**16.** $33 - \dfrac{x}{9} = 25$

**17.** $-6x - 7.8 = 19.2$

**18.** $-4x - 3.6 = 12.0$

*Solve and check each equation. Show all steps.* (Example 1, Example 2)

**19.** $2x - 7 - 5x = 3 - 19$

**20.** $3x - 12 - 7x = 7 - 27$

**21.** $5x - (12 - x) = 6 - 34$

**22.** $6x - (15 - 2x) = 4 - 39$

**23.** $-8 - 13 = -3(2x - 7)$

**24.** $-9 + 31 = -4(3x + 2)$

**25.** $-\frac{1}{4}(8x - 12) - 2x = 12 - 28$

**26.** $-\frac{1}{3}(6x - 9) - x = 9 - 23$

*For each problem, (a) select a variable and show what it represents, (b) write open phrases that are needed, (c) write an equation to describe the problem, and (d) solve the problem.* (Example 3, Example 4)

**27.** One number is 10 less than another number and their sum is $-6$. What are the numbers?

**28.** One number is 12 more than another number and their sum is $-18$. What are the numbers?

**29.** The length of a rectangle is 2 decimeters more than the width. The perimeter is 44 decimeters. What are the length and width? (See the figure at the left below.)

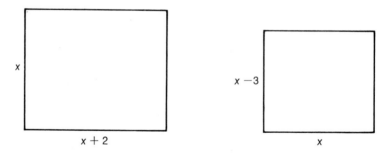

**30.** The width of a rectangle is 3 centimeters less than the length. The perimeter is 106 centimeters. What are the length and width? (See the figure at the right above.)

**B**

**31.** The sum of two numbers is 4. Twice the greater number less four times the lesser number equals 29. What are the two numbers? (Hint: Let $n$ and $4 - n$ represent the numbers.)

**32.** The sum of two numbers is 8. Four times the greater number increased by 8 times the lesser number equals 23. What are the two numbers? (Hint: Let $n$ and $8 - n$ represent the numbers.)

**33.** The sum of two numbers is 6. Three times the greater equals eight more than twice the lesser. What are the two numbers? (Hint: Let $n$ and $6 - n$ represent the two numbers.)

# 13.6  Practice in Solving Equations

**P-1**  **What equivalent equation is formed by subtracting 2x from each side of $5x + 7 = 2x - 8$?**

## example 1    Solve: $5x + 7 = 2x - 8$

**Solution:**

$$5x + 7 = 2x - 8$$

$$5x + 7 - 2x = 2x - 8 - 2x$$

$$3x + 7 = -8$$

$$3x + 7 - 7 = -8 - 7$$

$$3x = -15$$

$$\frac{3x}{3} = \frac{-15}{3}$$

$$x = -5$$

**Check:**  $5x + 7 = 2x - 8$

| $5(-5) + 7$ | $2(-5) - 8$ |
|---|---|
| $-25 + 7$ | $-10 - 8$ |
| $-18$ | $-18$ |

**P-2**  **What equivalent phrase do you get for $-3(4x + 2) + 5x$ by use of the Distributive Property?**

## example 2    Solve: $-3(4x + 2) + 5x = x - (9 + 4x)$

**Solution:**

$$-3(4x + 2) + 5x = x - (9 + 4x)$$

$$-12x - 6 + 5x = x - 9 - 4x$$

$$-7x - 6 = -3x - 9$$

$$-7x - 6 + 3x = -3x - 9 + 3x$$

$$-4x - 6 = -9$$

$$-4x - 6 + 6 = -9 + 6$$

$$-4x = -3$$

$$\frac{-4x}{-4} = \frac{-3}{-4}$$

$$x = \frac{3}{4}$$

**Check:**  $-3(4x + 2) + 5x = x - (9 + 4x)$

| $-3(4 \cdot \frac{3}{4} + 2) + 5 \cdot \frac{3}{4}$ | $\frac{3}{4} - (9 + 4 \cdot \frac{3}{4})$ |
|---|---|
| $-3(3 + 2) + \frac{15}{4}$ | $\frac{3}{4} - (9 + 3)$ |
| $-15 + 3\frac{3}{4}$ | $\frac{3}{4} - 12$ |
| $-11\frac{1}{4}$ | $-11\frac{1}{4}$ |

**P-3** What open phrase represents "three less than twice an unknown number"? "12 less three times the same number"?

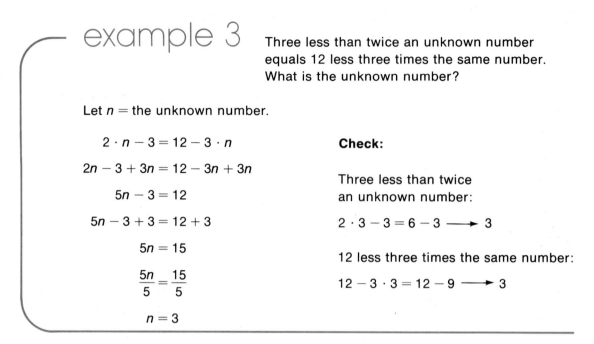

example 3

Three less than twice an unknown number equals 12 less three times the same number. What is the unknown number?

Let $n =$ the unknown number.

$$2 \cdot n - 3 = 12 - 3 \cdot n$$

$$2n - 3 + 3n = 12 - 3n + 3n$$

$$5n - 3 = 12$$

$$5n - 3 + 3 = 12 + 3$$

$$5n = 15$$

$$\frac{5n}{5} = \frac{15}{5}$$

$$n = 3$$

**Check:**

Three less than twice an unknown number:

$$2 \cdot 3 - 3 = 6 - 3 \longrightarrow 3$$

12 less three times the same number:

$$12 - 3 \cdot 3 = 12 - 9 \longrightarrow 3$$

## ORAL EXERCISES 13.6

*Tell two different steps you can take to eliminate the variable from one side of each equation.*

**EXAMPLE:** $4x - 1 = 4 - 2x$    **ANSWER:** Add $2x$ to each side or subtract $4x$ from each side.

**1.** $4 - x = 6 - 5x$

**2.** $\frac{1}{2}x + 3 = \frac{1}{4}x - 2$

**3.** $9 + 3x = 6 - 2x$

**4.** $12 + 6x = 9x + 15$

**5.** $14 + x = 13 - 3x$

**6.** $2.8 + 0.5x = 3.7 - 4.5x$

**7.** $20x - 6 = 18x + 4$

**8.** $12 - \frac{3}{4}x = \frac{5}{4}x - 15$

**9.** $-13 - 3x = 27 - 5x$

*Tell the equivalent equation you get as the first step in solving each equation.* (First step of Example 1 and Example 2)

**10.** $3(5 - 2x) - x = 3 - 2x - 10$

**11.** $3x - x - 5x = 4x - 12 - 8x$

**12.** $3x - (5 - x) = 5 - x - 19$

**13.** $-5(2x - 3) + 3x = 4x - x$

**14.** $12 - x - 3x = \frac{1}{2}(2 - 4x) + 3x$

**15.** $(8 - 3x)5 = -4(2x - 3)$

## WRITTEN EXERCISES 13.6

**A**
**Goal:** To solve an equation with the variable on both sides
**Sample Problem:** $2x - 3 = 5x + 7$
**Answer:** $-3\frac{1}{3}$

*Solve and check each equation. Show all steps.* (Example 1, Example 2)

**1.** $6x + 8 = 2x - 12$

**2.** $8x + 3 = 5x - 18$

**3.** $4x - 3 = 15 - 2x$

**4.** $8 - 5x = 3x - 24$

**5.** $-3x - 8 = 7 - x$

**6.** $6 - 4x = -6x - 9$

**7.** $\frac{1}{2}x - 16 = 14 - \frac{3}{2}x$

**8.** $\frac{1}{4}x - 12 = 28 - \frac{7}{4}x$

**9.** $6.7 - 1.8x = 3.7x - 9.8$

**10.** $8.4x - 2.9 = -13.1x + 14.3$

**11.** $-3(2x - 3) = 4(5 - x)$

**12.** $2(5 - 3x) = -4(x + 4)$

**13.** $3x - (5 + x) = -4x - 6 + 9x$

**14.** $2x + 8 - 7x = 12 - (3x - 1)$

**15.** $4x - 5(x + 2) = 6 - 3(3 - x)$

**16.** $13 - 2(3x - 3) = -5x + 3(x - 1)$

**17.** $(x - 3) - (2x + 2) = 5 + 2x - 19$

**18.** $x - 6 - 6x = (2x - 1) - (5x - 3)$

**19.** $-\frac{3}{4}(16x - 12) = \frac{2}{3}(18 - 9x)$

**20.** $\frac{5}{4}(12 - 8x) = -\frac{4}{3}(9x - 21)$

*For each problem, (a) select a variable and show what it represents, (b) write open phrases that are needed, (c) write an equation to describe the problem, and (d) solve the problem.* (Example 3)

**21.** The sum of two numbers is 12. Three times the lesser number is decreased by 4. The result equals the greater number. What are the numbers? (Hint: Let $n$ and $12 - n$ represent the two numbers.)

**22.** The sum of two numbers is 16. Twice the lesser number is increased by 1. The result equals three times the difference of the greater number less 19. What are the two numbers? (Hint: Let $n$ and $16 - n$ represent the two numbers.)

**B**

**23.** The length of a rectangle is 5 centimeters greater than the width. In a triangle, the length of the shortest side equals the width of the rectangle. The length of the longest side is three times the length of the shortest side. The length of the third side is 6 centimeters more than the length of the shortest side. The perimeter of the rectangle equals the perimeter of the triangle. Find the lengths of the sides of the rectangle and the triangle.

# 13.7 Equations with Two Truth Numbers

**P-1**   **What is the left side of $(x + 2)(x - 3) = 0$ if $x$ is replaced by $-2$?   by 3?**

This equation has $-2$ and 3 as truth numbers.

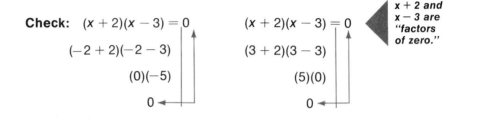

**Check:**   $(x + 2)(x - 3) = 0$          $(x + 2)(x - 3) = 0$

$\quad\quad\quad (-2 + 2)(-2 - 3)$          $(3 + 2)(3 - 3)$

$\quad\quad\quad\quad\quad (0)(-5)$          $(5)(0)$

$\quad\quad\quad\quad\quad\quad 0$          $0$

$x + 2$ and $x - 3$ are "factors of zero."

---

**Factors of Zero Property**

For any rational numbers $a$ and $b$, if $ab = 0$, then $a = 0$ or $b = 0$.

$ab = 0$

$(x - 5)(x + 2) = 0$

$x - 5 = 0$ or $x + 2 = 0$

---

## example 1   Solve: $(x + 4)(x - 7) = 0$

Write the equivalent *or* sentence by the Factors of Zero Property.

$\quad\quad x + 4 = 0 \quad or \quad x - 7 = 0$

$\quad\quad\quad x = -4 \quad\quad\quad\quad x = 7$

The truth numbers of $(x + 4)(x - 7) = 0$ are $-4$ and 7.

## example 2   Solve: $x(x - \frac{3}{2}) = 0$

$\quad\quad x(x - \frac{3}{2}) = 0$

$\quad\quad x = 0 \quad or \quad x - \frac{3}{2} = 0$

$\quad\quad x = 0 \quad\quad\quad\quad x = \frac{3}{2}$

The truth numbers are 0 and $\frac{3}{2}$.

**P-2**    What equivalent *or* sentence can be written for $(2x - 5)(4x + 1) = 0$?

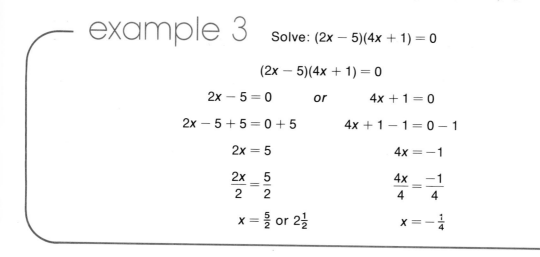

example 3    Solve: $(2x - 5)(4x + 1) = 0$

$$(2x - 5)(4x + 1) = 0$$

| | | |
|---|---|---|
| $2x - 5 = 0$ | *or* | $4x + 1 = 0$ |
| $2x - 5 + 5 = 0 + 5$ | | $4x + 1 - 1 = 0 - 1$ |
| $2x = 5$ | | $4x = -1$ |
| $\dfrac{2x}{2} = \dfrac{5}{2}$ | | $\dfrac{4x}{4} = \dfrac{-1}{4}$ |
| $x = \frac{5}{2}$ or $2\frac{1}{2}$ | | $x = -\frac{1}{4}$ |

**P-3**    How can you write $2x^2 - 6x$ as a product in simplest form?

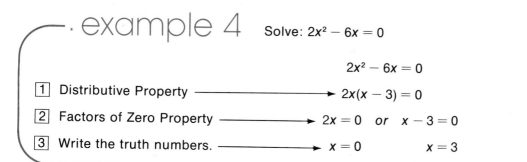

example 4    Solve: $2x^2 - 6x = 0$

$$2x^2 - 6x = 0$$

1. Distributive Property $\longrightarrow$ $2x(x - 3) = 0$
2. Factors of Zero Property $\longrightarrow$ $2x = 0$  or  $x - 3 = 0$
3. Write the truth numbers. $\longrightarrow$ $x = 0$        $x = 3$

## ORAL EXERCISES 13.7

*Tell the truth number or numbers of each equation.* (Example 1, Example 2, Example 3)

1. $(x + 11)(x - 5) = 0$
2. $(x - 6)(x - 10) = 0$
3. $(x + 2)(x + 13) = 0$
4. $(x - \frac{1}{2})(x + 18) = 0$
5. $(x - 6)(x - 6) = 0$
6. $(x + \frac{3}{4})(x - \frac{1}{8}) = 0$
7. $x(x - \frac{5}{4}) = 0$
8. $3x(x + 10.3) = 0$
9. $(x - 5.9)(x + 0.8) = 0$
10. $(2x - 1)(x + 4) = 0$
11. $(2x + 3)(5x - 1) = 0$
12. $-5(x - \frac{7}{4}) = 0$

*Factor the phrase on the left side of each equation.* (Step 1 of Example 4)

**EXAMPLE:** $3x^2 + 6x = 0$     **ANSWER:** $3x(x + 2) = 0$

**13.** $2x - 4 = 0$

**14.** $-6x^2 + 3x = 0$

**15.** $5x^2 + 15x = 0$

**16.** $-4x^2 - 12x = 0$

**17.** $1.6x^2 - 4.8x = 0$

**18.** $\frac{1}{2}x^2 + \frac{1}{4}x = 0$

## WRITTEN EXERCISES 13.7

**A**     **Goal:** To solve an equation with two truth numbers
**Sample Problem:** Solve $2x^2 - 6x = 0$.
**Answer:** 0 and 3

*Write the truth number or numbers of each equation.* (Examples 1, 2, 3)

**1.** $(x + 1)(x + 2) = 0$

**2.** $(x + 3)(x + 5) = 0$

**3.** $(x - 2)(x + 5) = 0$

**4.** $(x - 1)(x + 6) = 0$

**5.** $(x - 3)(x - 2) = 0$

**6.** $(x - 5)(x - 3) = 0$

**7.** $(n + 5)(n - 5) = 0$

**8.** $(a + 10)(a - 10) = 0$

**9.** $(y + \frac{1}{2})(y - 3) = 0$

**10.** $(r - 5)(r + \frac{1}{3}) = 0$

**11.** $(x + 3.5)(x - 1.7) = 0$

**12.** $(x - 8.2)(x - 5.3) = 0$

**13.** $5(n - 3) = 0$

**14.** $-3(x - 12) = 0$

**15.** $-10(2x + 3) = 0$

**16.** $6(3x - 2) = 0$

**17.** $n(n - 1) = 0$

**18.** $x(x + 3) = 0$

**19.** $(2x + 5)(x - 5) = 0$

**20.** $(3x - 2)(x + 3) = 0$

*Factor the left side of each equation. Then write the truth numbers.*
(Example 4)

**21.** $3x^2 - 12x = 0$

**22.** $2x^2 + 12x = 0$

**23.** $12x^2 + 4x = 0$

**24.** $-9x^2 - 3x = 0$

**25.** $2.3x^2 - 9.2x = 0$

**26.** $0.8x^2 + 4.8x = 0$

**27.** $\frac{1}{2}x^2 - \frac{1}{8}x = 0$

**28.** $\frac{1}{4}x^2 - \frac{1}{8}x = 0$

**29.** $-15x^2 + 20x = 0$

**30.** $-8x^2 - 10x = 0$

# CHAPTER SUMMARY

**IMPORTANT IDEAS**

1. The Addition, Subtraction, Multiplication, and Division Properties of Equality for numbers of arithmetic also apply to rational numbers.

2. To solve an equation of the form $x - a = b$, first add $a$ to each side.

3. To solve an equation of the form $x + a = b$, first subtract $a$ from each side.

4. Any rational number $a$ can be eliminated from $x + a = b$ by adding the opposite of $a$ to each side. This is the same as subtracting $a$ from each side.

5. To solve an equation of the form $\frac{x}{a} = b$, $a \neq 0$, first multiply each side by $a$.

6. To solve an equation of the form $ax = b$, $a \neq 0$, first divide each side by $a$.

7. Any nonzero rational number $a$ can be eliminated from $ax = b$ by multiplying each side by the reciprocal of $a$. This is the same as dividing by $a$.

8. For equations with combined operations:
   a. Use the Addition or Subtraction Property of Equality first.
   b. Then use the Multiplication or Division Property of Equality.

9. *Factors of Zero Property:* For any rational numbers $a$ and $b$, if $ab = 0$, then $a = 0$ *or* $b = 0$.

# CHAPTER REVIEW

*Solve and check each equation. Show all steps.*

**SECTION 13.1**

1. $x - 33 = -19$

2. $x - 47 = -28$

3. $x + 29 = -15$

4. $x + 36 = -18$

5. $-1.8 = 3.2 + x$

6. $4.7 = 8.1 + x$

7. $1\frac{3}{4} = 3\frac{1}{2} - x$

8. $-5\frac{7}{8} = 8\frac{1}{8} - x$

**SECTION 13.2**

9. $12x - 14 - 13x = 13 - 21$

10. $-5 - 18 = 8x + 9 - 9x$

11. $2.4x - 4.7x + 1.3x = 13 - 21$

12. $-3.8x - 11.9 + 2.8x = 8.5 - 13.9$

13. $-2(x - 4) + x - 3 = 5 - 19$

14. $3(2x - 3) - 5x + 4 = -4 - 12$

15. $42 - (29 - 3x) - 4x + 8 = -28 - 6$

16. $19 - 33 = 4x - (7 - x) - 6x$

*Solve and check each equation. Show all steps.*

### SECTION 13.3

**17.** $3x - 8 = 4x - 17$

**18.** $12 - 6x = -5x - 8$

**19.** $7.4 - 0.6x = -1.9 + 0.4x$

**20.** $0.9x - 13.3 = -5.9 - 0.1x$

**21.** $-4(x - 8) + 3x = 17 - 2x$

**22.** $27 - 4x = 8(3 - x) + 5x$

**23.** $-\frac{3}{4}x + 2\frac{3}{4} = -5\frac{1}{2} + \frac{1}{4}x$

**24.** $-3\frac{1}{4} - \frac{5}{8}x = \frac{3}{8}x - 5\frac{3}{4}$

### SECTION 13.4

**25.** $8x = -46$

**26.** $-12x = 69$

**27.** $-\dfrac{x}{4.6} = -7$

**28.** $-\dfrac{x}{1.9} = 12$

**29.** $-\frac{7}{2}x = 49$

**30.** $\frac{8}{3}x = -72$

**31.** $1\frac{9}{16}x = -1\frac{3}{5}$

**32.** $-1\frac{7}{8}x = -3\frac{1}{5}$

### SECTION 13.5

**33.** $6x + 15 = -9$

**34.** $4x - 27 = -19$

**35.** $\dfrac{x}{8} - 23 = -26$

**36.** $\dfrac{x}{12} + 15 = 9$

**37.** $13 - (3x + 5) + x = 5 - 29$

**38.** $x - (13 + 4x) - 3 = 16 - 29$

### SECTION 13.6

**39.** $4x - 6 = 7x + 9$

**40.** $10x + 5 = 6x - 19$

**41.** $-7(3 - x) + 3x = 2(4x + 3)$

**42.** $6(3 - 2x) - 12 = -4(5x - 4)$

*Find the unknown numbers.*

**43.** Five times an unknown number is decreased by 8. The result equals 14 decreased by three times the same number.

**44.** From twice an unknown number the sum of the number and 8 is subtracted. The result equals 9 less than three times the unknown number.

### SECTION 13.7

*Write the truth number or numbers of each equation.*

**45.** $(x - 1.6)(x - 2.9) = 0$

**46.** $(x - 3.7)(x - 12.5) = 0$

**47.** $12x^2 - 9x = 0$

**48.** $-14x^2 - 2x = 0$

# 14

# Real Numbers

# 14.1 Meaning of Square Root

**P-1**  **What is the square of each of the following numbers?**

**a.** 3       **b.** $-3$

The numbers 3 and $-3$ are <u>square roots</u> of 9.

$$(3)(3) = 9 \qquad (-3)(-3) = 9$$

| | |
|---|---|
| A **square root** of a number is one of the two equal factors of the number. | $3^2 = 9$<br>$(-3)^2 = 9$ |

**P-2**  **What are two square roots of each of the following?**

**a.** 16       **b.** $\frac{4}{9}$       **c.** 0.36

The **radical** symbol $\sqrt{\phantom{x}}$ represents a <u>positive</u> square root, and $-\sqrt{\phantom{x}}$ represents a <u>negative</u> square root. The number under the radical symbol is the **radicand.**

$\sqrt{16}$ is the radical. 16 is the radicand.

$$\sqrt{16} = 4 \qquad \sqrt{\frac{4}{9}} = \frac{2}{3} \qquad \sqrt{0.36} = 0.6$$

$$-\sqrt{16} = -4 \qquad -\sqrt{\frac{4}{9}} = -\frac{2}{3} \qquad -\sqrt{0.36} = -0.6$$

*Every positive number has both a positive and a negative square root.*

**P-3**  **What two equal factors does 0 have?**

**P-4**  **How many square roots does 0 have?**      $\sqrt{0} = 0$

The number 49 is a <u>perfect square</u> because it is the square of 7. The number 1 is a <u>perfect square</u> because it is the square of 1.

| | |
|---|---|
| A **perfect square** is a number that is the square of a whole number. | $49 = 7^2$<br>$1 = 1^2$ |

**P-5**  **Which of the following are perfect squares?**

**a.** 25       **b.** 17       **c.** 10       **d.** 36       **e.** 121

## example 1

Simplify $\sqrt{\dfrac{25}{49}}$. Refer to the Table of Squares below.

$\dfrac{5}{7} \cdot \dfrac{5}{7} = \dfrac{25}{49}$. Therefore, $\dfrac{5}{7}$ is the simplest name for $\sqrt{\dfrac{25}{49}}$.

### Table of Squares

| Number | Square | Number | Square |
|--------|--------|--------|--------|
| 0 | 0 | 8 | 64 |
| 1 | 1 | 9 ←——→ | 81 |
| 2 | 4 | 10 | 100 |
| 3 | 9 | 11 | 121 |
| 4 | 16 | 12 | 144 |
| 5 ←——→ | 25 | 13 | 169 |
| 6 | 36 | 14 | 196 |
| 7 ←——→ | 49 | 15 | 225 |

## example 2

Simplify $-\sqrt{0.81}$. ◄ *Simplify means to write the simplest name.*

From the table, $\sqrt{81} = 9$. Therefore, $(0.9)(0.9) = 0.81$.
The simplest name is $-0.9$.

## ORAL EXERCISES 14.1

*Tell the square of each number.* (P-1)

**1.** 8     **2.** $-6$     **3.** 12     **4.** $\dfrac{1}{3}$   $\frac{1}{9}$    **5.** $-\dfrac{2}{3}$   $\frac{4}{9}$    **6.** $\dfrac{5}{6}$   $\frac{25}{36}$

**7.** $-\dfrac{7}{8}$   $\frac{49}{64}$    **8.** 0.4     **9.** $-1.2$     **10.** 0.15     **11.** $1\dfrac{1}{2}$   $\frac{9}{4}$    **12.** $-2\dfrac{1}{4}$   $\frac{81}{16}$

*Tell two square roots.* (P-2)

**13.** 49     **14.** $\dfrac{1}{25}$     **15.** $\dfrac{36}{49}$     **16.** 0.64     **17.** 0.49

**18.** 121     **19.** 0.09     **20.** $2\dfrac{1}{4}$     **21.** 1.69     **22.** 2.25

*Simplify.* (Example 1, Example 2)

**23.** $\sqrt{100}$      **24.** $-\sqrt{81}$      **25.** $\sqrt{196}$      **26.** $-\sqrt{225}$

**27.** $\sqrt{\dfrac{16}{49}}$      **28.** $\sqrt{\dfrac{25}{121}}$      **29.** $\sqrt{2.25}$      **30.** $-\sqrt{1.96}$

## WRITTEN EXERCISES 14.1

**A**

**Goal:** To find the square roots and the square of a number
**Sample Problem:** Write the square roots and the square of $\frac{1}{4}$.
**Answer:** $\frac{1}{2}$ and $-\frac{1}{2}$ (square roots); $\frac{1}{16}$ (square)

*Write the square of each number.* (P-1)

**1.** 12      **2.** 14      **3.** $-10$      **4.** $-7$      **5.** 16

**6.** 18      **7.** $-17$      **8.** $-19$      **9.** $\frac{1}{7}$      **10.** $\frac{1}{6}$

**11.** $-\frac{2}{9}$      **12.** $-\frac{3}{8}$      **13.** $\frac{5}{21}$      **14.** $\frac{7}{24}$      **15.** 1.8

**16.** 1.7      **17.** 0.12      **18.** 0.14      **19.** $-0.08$      **20.** $-0.07$

*Write the two square roots of each number.* (P-2)

**21.** 144      **22.** 169      **23.** 225      **24.** 196      **25.** $\frac{1}{64}$

**26.** $\frac{1}{81}$      **27.** $\frac{169}{49}$      **28.** $\frac{144}{25}$      **29.** 0.04      **30.** 0.16

*Simplify.* (Example 1, Example 2)

**31.** $-\sqrt{1}$      **32.** $\sqrt{0}$      **33.** $\sqrt{36}$      **34.** $\sqrt{64}$

**35.** $-\sqrt{100}$      **36.** $-\sqrt{121}$      **37.** $\sqrt{0.49}$      **38.** $\sqrt{0.25}$

**39.** $\sqrt{\dfrac{4}{49}}$      **40.** $\sqrt{\dfrac{9}{100}}$      **41.** $-\sqrt{\dfrac{225}{81}}$      **42.** $\sqrt{\dfrac{121}{64}}$

**43.** $-\sqrt{1.21}$      **44.** $-\sqrt{1.44}$      **45.** $\sqrt{0.0036}$      **46.** $-\sqrt{0.0169}$

**C**

*The prime factorizations of some numbers are shown. Write* <u>Yes</u> *or* <u>No</u> *to show whether each number is a perfect square.*

**47.** $180 = 2 \cdot 2 \cdot 3 \cdot 3 \cdot 5$          **48.** $324 = 2 \cdot 2 \cdot 3 \cdot 3 \cdot 3 \cdot 3$

**49.** $400 = 2 \cdot 2 \cdot 2 \cdot 2 \cdot 5 \cdot 5$          **50.** $288 = 2 \cdot 2 \cdot 2 \cdot 2 \cdot 2 \cdot 3 \cdot 3$

**51.** $468 = 2 \cdot 2 \cdot 3 \cdot 3 \cdot 13$          **52.** $484 = 2 \cdot 2 \cdot 11 \cdot 11$

**53.** $504 = 2 \cdot 2 \cdot 2 \cdot 3 \cdot 3 \cdot 7$          **54.** $1800 = 2 \cdot 2 \cdot 2 \cdot 3 \cdot 3 \cdot 5 \cdot 5$

# 14.2 Irrational Numbers

Note the pattern below.

$$(\sqrt{4})^2 = (2)^2 = 4 \qquad (\sqrt{9})^2 = (3)^2 = 9$$
$$(-\sqrt{4})^2 = (-2)^2 = 4 \qquad (-\sqrt{9})^2 = (-3)^2 = 9$$

> For any number $a$,
>
> 1. $(\sqrt{a})^2 = a$,  and  2. $(-\sqrt{a})^2 = a$.

**P-1**  **What is the square of each number below?**

**a.** $\sqrt{64}$      **b.** $-\sqrt{49}$      **c.** $\sqrt{5}$      **d.** $-\sqrt{5}$

These sentences suggest that the positive square root of 5 is between 2 and 3. Also, the negative square root of 5 is between $-2$ and $-3$.

$$(2)^2 = 4 \qquad\qquad (-2)^2 = 4$$
$$(\sqrt{5})^2 = 5 \qquad\qquad (-\sqrt{5})^2 = 5$$
$$(3)^2 = 9 \qquad\qquad (-3)^2 = 9$$

*The square roots of 5 cannot be integers.*

Further, there is no rational number, $\dfrac{a}{b}$, which when squared equals 5.

The only whole numbers that have rational square roots are perfect squares. For example, $\sqrt{36}$ is a rational number since $\sqrt{36} = 6$.

> Any whole number that is not a perfect square has an <u>irrational</u> square root.

The numbers $\sqrt{5}$ and $-\sqrt{5}$ are <u>irrational numbers</u>.

**P-2**  **Which of the following numbers are rational?  irrational?**

**a.** $\sqrt{15}$      **b.** $\sqrt{4}$      **c.** $\sqrt{81}$      **d.** $\sqrt{27}$

You know that rational numbers can be written as repeating decimals. Thus, **nonrepeating decimals** are irrational numbers. $\sqrt{5}$ is a nonrepeating decimal. $\sqrt{5} = 2.23607 \cdots$.

$\sqrt{2}$, $\sqrt{3}$, $\sqrt{6}$, $\sqrt{7}$, etc., are also nonrepeating decimals.

$$\sqrt{2} = 1.41421 \cdots \qquad \sqrt{6} = 2.44948 \cdots$$

$$\sqrt{3} = 1.73205 \cdots \qquad \sqrt{7} = 2.64575 \cdots$$

◀ **The three dots mean the decimals are nonending.**

> A nonrepeating decimal always represents an irrational number.
>
> $4.5678910111213 \cdots$
> $-3.141592653 \cdots = -\pi$

**P-3** **Which of the following are rational? irrational?**

**a.** $0.747474 \cdots$      **b.** $6.328328 \cdots$      **c.** $\pi$

**d.** $8.0000 \cdots$      **e.** $1.0101101110 \cdots$      **f.** $5.1999 \cdots$

Numbers such as $-4$, $\sqrt{5}$, $-\frac{1}{2}$, $0$, $1$, $\sqrt{2}$, $\pi$, and $\frac{17}{4}$ are <u>real numbers</u>.

> The set of **real numbers** is the set containing all the rational numbers and all the irrational numbers. **Real numbers** are the numbers which can be written as infinite decimals, either repeating or nonrepeating.

Every point on a number line has a real number for a coordinate.

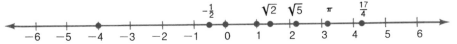

Thus, a number line is often called a **real-number line.**

## ORAL EXERCISES 14.2

*Tell the square of each number.* (P-1)

**1.** $\sqrt{7}$      **2.** $-\sqrt{11}$      **3.** $\sqrt{18}$      **4.** $-\sqrt{26}$      **5.** $\sqrt{36}$

**6.** $-\sqrt{49}$      **7.** $\sqrt{\frac{1}{2}}$      **8.** $\sqrt{\frac{2}{3}}$      **9.** $-\sqrt{\frac{11}{8}}$      **10.** $\sqrt{1000}$

*Say* <u>Rational</u> *or* <u>Irrational</u> *to describe each number.* (P-2, P-3)

**11.** $\sqrt{64}$      **12.** $\sqrt{12}$      **13.** $-\sqrt{23}$      **14.** $\frac{3}{5}$

**15.** $19$      **16.** $-4.3$      **17.** $5\frac{1}{8}$      **18.** $3.14$

**19.** $\sqrt{48}$     **20.** $-\sqrt{121}$     **21.** $-\sqrt{130}$     **22.** $-\sqrt{0}$

**23.** $\sqrt{\dfrac{9}{16}}$     **24.** $-\dfrac{1}{\sqrt{9}}$     **25.** $\dfrac{\sqrt{81}}{\sqrt{25}}$     **26.** $-\sqrt{\dfrac{9}{5}}$

**27.** $0.215115111511115 \cdots$     **28.** $-3.420420042000 \cdots$

**29.** $5.637637637 \cdots$     **30.** $-0.383838 \cdots$

## WRITTEN EXERCISES 14.2

**A**

**Goal:** To identify a real number as either rational or irrational
**Sample Problems: a.** $\sqrt{81}$     **b.** $0.7127137147157 \cdots$
**Answers: a.** rational     **b.** irrational

*Write the square of each number.* (P-1)

**1.** $\sqrt{15}$     **2.** $\sqrt{24}$     **3.** $-\sqrt{13}$     **4.** $-\sqrt{19}$     **5.** $\sqrt{\dfrac{1}{3}}$

**6.** $\sqrt{\dfrac{3}{7}}$     **7.** $-\sqrt{208}$     **8.** $-\sqrt{529}$     **9.** $\sqrt{64}$     **10.** $-\sqrt{81}$

*Write Rational or Irrational to describe each number.* (P-2, P-3)

**11.** $\sqrt{100}$     **12.** $\sqrt{15}$     **13.** $-\sqrt{22}$     **14.** $\sqrt{144}$

**15.** $\dfrac{4}{9}$     **16.** $-\dfrac{12}{5}$     **17.** $-2\dfrac{3}{8}$     **18.** $5\dfrac{1}{4}$

**19.** $-28$     **20.** $37$     **21.** $\sqrt{1}$     **22.** $\sqrt{0}$

**23.** $\sqrt{\dfrac{25}{36}}$     **24.** $-\sqrt{\dfrac{49}{4}}$     **25.** $-\sqrt{\dfrac{3}{4}}$     **26.** $\sqrt{\dfrac{5}{6}}$

**27.** $\dfrac{1}{\sqrt{25}}$     **28.** $-\dfrac{1}{\sqrt{81}}$     **29.** $0.087$     **30.** $\pi$

**31.** $3.142142142 \cdots$     **32.** $0.4040040004 \cdots$

**33.** $-0.5151151115 \cdots$     **34.** $-3.6666 \cdots$

**C**     *Simplify.*

**EXAMPLE:** $(\sqrt{25})(\sqrt{17})$     **ANSWER:** $5\sqrt{17}$

**35.** $(\sqrt{16})(\sqrt{3})$     **36.** $(\sqrt{9})(\sqrt{5})$     **37.** $(\sqrt{37})(\sqrt{10})$

**38.** $(\sqrt{4})(\sqrt{2})$     **39.** $(-\sqrt{49})(-\sqrt{13})$     **40.** $(-\sqrt{100})(\sqrt{23})$

# 14.3 Simplifying Radicals

## example 1

Write each product below as a radical.

a. $\sqrt{4} \cdot \sqrt{25}$    b. $\sqrt{9} \cdot \sqrt{16}$

a. **Answer:** $\sqrt{4} \cdot \sqrt{25} = \sqrt{100}$

**Check:**    $2 \cdot 5$    | 10

10              |

b. **Answer:** $\sqrt{9} \cdot \sqrt{16} = \sqrt{144}$

**Check:**    $3 \cdot 4$    | 12

12              |

Example 1 suggests the following property.

> **Product Property of Radicals**
>
> For any nonnegative numbers $a$ and $b$,    $\sqrt{5} \cdot \sqrt{3} = \sqrt{15}$
> $\sqrt{a} \cdot \sqrt{b} = \sqrt{ab}$.

A product like $\sqrt{5} \cdot \sqrt{3}$ is read "radical 5 times radical 3."

◀ **Remember!**
$\sqrt{5}$ **is a radical.**
5 **is a radicand.**

**P-1**  **How can each radical below be written as a product of two radicals?**

a. $\sqrt{3 \cdot 11}$    b. $\sqrt{5 \cdot 13}$    c. $\sqrt{29 \cdot 31}$

**P-2**  **How can each product below be written as one radical?  What is the simplest name?**

a. $\sqrt{5} \cdot \sqrt{8}$    b. $\sqrt{6} \cdot \sqrt{7}$    c. $\sqrt{8} \cdot \sqrt{9}$

## example 2    Simplify $\sqrt{18}$.

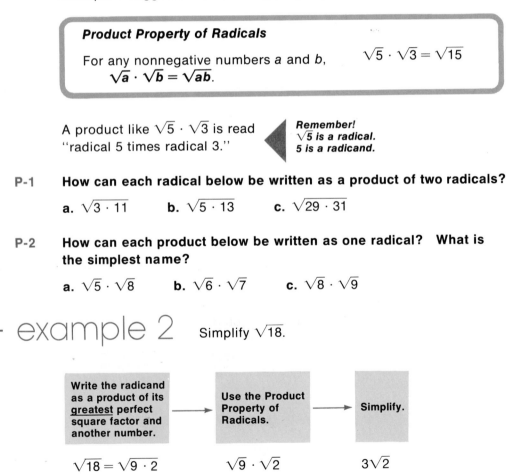

| Write the radicand as a product of its **greatest** perfect square factor and another number. | → | Use the Product Property of Radicals. | → | Simplify. |

$\sqrt{18} = \sqrt{9 \cdot 2}$    $\sqrt{9} \cdot \sqrt{2}$    $3\sqrt{2}$

> A radical is in simplest form if the radicand has no perfect square factor other than 1.
>
> $\sqrt{14}$, $2\sqrt{5}$, $\sqrt{33}$

**P-3** **Which of the following are in simplest form?**

   **a.** $\sqrt{20}$     **b.** $\sqrt{15}$     **c.** $\sqrt{34}$     **d.** $\sqrt{27}$

**P-4** **What perfect square, besides 1, is a factor of 20?**

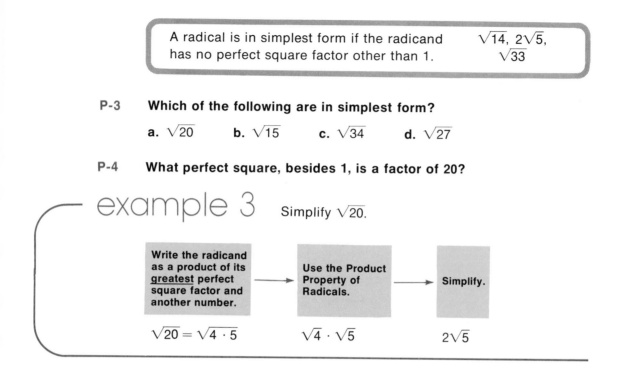

example 3   Simplify $\sqrt{20}$.

| Write the radicand as a product of its **greatest** perfect square factor and another number. | → | Use the Product Property of Radicals. | → | Simplify. |

$$\sqrt{20} = \sqrt{4 \cdot 5} \qquad \sqrt{4} \cdot \sqrt{5} \qquad 2\sqrt{5}$$

**P-5** **What is the greatest perfect square factor of 48?**

example 4   Simplify $\sqrt{48}$.

$$\sqrt{48} = \sqrt{16 \cdot 3}$$
$$= \sqrt{16} \cdot \sqrt{3}$$
$$= 4\sqrt{3}$$

You do not have to use the **greatest** perfect square factor. It takes more steps, though, if you do not.

$$\sqrt{48} = \sqrt{4 \cdot 12}$$
$$= 2\sqrt{12}$$
$$= 2\sqrt{4 \cdot 3}$$
$$= 2\sqrt{4} \cdot \sqrt{3}$$
$$= 2 \cdot 2\sqrt{3}$$
$$= 4\sqrt{3}$$

◀ *4 is a perfect square.*
*$\sqrt{12}$ can be simplified.*

## ORAL EXERCISES 14.3

*Tell one radical for each product. (Example 1, P-2)*

1. $\sqrt{2} \cdot \sqrt{6}$
2. $\sqrt{3} \cdot \sqrt{5}$
3. $\sqrt{7} \cdot \sqrt{5}$
4. $\sqrt{6} \cdot \sqrt{11}$
5. $\sqrt{4} \cdot \sqrt{7}$
6. $\sqrt{6} \cdot \sqrt{6}$
7. $\sqrt{9} \cdot \sqrt{10}$
8. $\sqrt{12} \cdot \sqrt{5}$

*Say each radical as a product of two radicals. (P-1, Second step of Example 2, Example 3, Example 4)*

**EXAMPLE:** $\sqrt{2 \cdot 9}$   **ANSWER:** $\sqrt{2} \cdot \sqrt{9}$

9. $\sqrt{3 \cdot 7}$
10. $\sqrt{5 \cdot 9}$
11. $\sqrt{2 \cdot 13}$
12. $\sqrt{5 \cdot 6}$
13. $\sqrt{11 \cdot 3}$
14. $\sqrt{10}$
15. $\sqrt{15}$
16. $\sqrt{35}$

*Simplify. (Last two steps of Example 2 and Example 3)*

17. $\sqrt{4 \cdot 7}$
18. $\sqrt{9 \cdot 3}$
19. $\sqrt{9 \cdot 5}$
20. $\sqrt{16 \cdot 2}$
21. $\sqrt{2 \cdot 36}$
22. $\sqrt{5 \cdot 25}$
23. $\sqrt{4 \cdot 13}$
24. $\sqrt{17 \cdot 16}$

## WRITTEN EXERCISES 14.3

**A**   **Goal:** To use the Product Property of Radicals to simplify a radical or a product of radicals

**Sample Problems:** Simplify   **a.** $\sqrt{6} \cdot \sqrt{15}$   **b.** $\sqrt{72}$.

**Answers: a.** $3\sqrt{10}$   **b.** $6\sqrt{2}$

*Write one radical for each product. (Example 1, P-2)*

1. $\sqrt{2} \cdot \sqrt{7}$
2. $\sqrt{3} \cdot \sqrt{11}$
3. $\sqrt{5} \cdot \sqrt{9}$
4. $\sqrt{6} \cdot \sqrt{9}$
5. $\sqrt{8} \cdot \sqrt{7}$
6. $\sqrt{10} \cdot \sqrt{7}$
7. $\sqrt{12} \cdot \sqrt{3}$
8. $\sqrt{5} \cdot \sqrt{11}$
9. $\sqrt{11} \cdot \sqrt{11}$
10. $\sqrt{13} \cdot \sqrt{13}$
11. $\sqrt{3} \cdot \sqrt{8}$
12. $\sqrt{7} \cdot \sqrt{9}$

*Simplify each product. (P-2, Third step of Example 2, Example 3, Example 4)*

13. $\sqrt{9} \cdot \sqrt{33}$
14. $\sqrt{16} \cdot \sqrt{35}$
15. $\sqrt{25} \cdot \sqrt{37}$
16. $\sqrt{36} \cdot \sqrt{17}$
17. $\sqrt{7} \cdot \sqrt{49}$
18. $\sqrt{23} \cdot \sqrt{64}$
19. $\sqrt{7} \cdot \sqrt{121}$
20. $\sqrt{5} \cdot \sqrt{169}$

*Simplify each radical. (Example 2, Example 3, Example 4)*

21. $\sqrt{9 \cdot 15}$
22. $\sqrt{4 \cdot 22}$
23. $\sqrt{26 \cdot 16}$
24. $\sqrt{38 \cdot 25}$
25. $\sqrt{81 \cdot 35}$
26. $\sqrt{121 \cdot 77}$
27. $\sqrt{24}$
28. $\sqrt{28}$
29. $\sqrt{45}$
30. $\sqrt{32}$
31. $\sqrt{80}$
32. $\sqrt{75}$

# 14.4 Sums and Differences

Radicals such as $2\sqrt{7}$ and $3\sqrt{7}$ are <u>like radicals</u> because they have equal radicands.

> Square root radicals with equal radicands are *like radicals.*
>
> $2\sqrt{7}$ and $3\sqrt{7}$
>
> $5\sqrt{8}$ and $-2\sqrt{8}$

**P-1**  **Which of the following are like radicals?**

**a.** $2\sqrt{12}$  **b.** $-\sqrt{5}$  **c.** $\sqrt{10}$  **d.** $\sqrt{12}$

**e.** $5\sqrt{5}$  **f.** $\sqrt{5}$  **g.** $7\sqrt{10}$  **h.** $3\sqrt{6}$

Properties of rational numbers also apply to irrational numbers.

## example 1   Add: $2\sqrt{5} + 6\sqrt{5}$

1  Distributive Property ⟶ $2\sqrt{5} + 6\sqrt{5} = (2 + 6)\sqrt{5}$

2  Simplify. ⟶ $= 8\sqrt{5}$

*Adding $2\sqrt{5}$ and $6\sqrt{5}$ is like adding 2x and 5x.*

## example 2   Subtract: $12\sqrt{14} - 5\sqrt{14}$

1  $12\sqrt{14} - 5\sqrt{14} = (12 - 5)\sqrt{14}$

2  $= 7\sqrt{14}$

*Use the Distributive Property.*

Radicals such as $\sqrt{2}$ and $\sqrt{8}$ do not appear to be like radicals. However, simplifying $\sqrt{8}$ shows otherwise.

$$\sqrt{8} = \sqrt{4 \cdot 2}$$
$$= \sqrt{4} \cdot \sqrt{2}$$
$$= 2\sqrt{2}$$

**P-2**  **What is the simplest name for $5\sqrt{2} + \sqrt{8}$?**

**P-3**    **What is the greatest perfect square factor of 12?**

example 3    Subtract: $5\sqrt{12} - \sqrt{3}$

$$5\sqrt{12} - \sqrt{3} = 5\sqrt{4 \cdot 3} - \sqrt{3}$$
$$= 5\sqrt{4} \cdot \sqrt{3} - \sqrt{3}$$
$$= 5 \cdot 2\sqrt{3} - \sqrt{3}$$
$$= 10\sqrt{3} - \sqrt{3} \quad \blacktriangleleft \quad \textbf{Think of } \sqrt{3} \text{ as } 1\sqrt{3}.$$
$$= 9\sqrt{3}$$

**P-4**    **What is the greatest square factor of 18?    of 12?**

example 4    Add and subtract. Then simplify.
$$\sqrt{18} + \sqrt{12} - 5\sqrt{3} - \sqrt{2}$$

$$\sqrt{18} = \sqrt{9 \cdot 2} \qquad\qquad \sqrt{12} = \sqrt{4 \cdot 3}$$
$$= 3\sqrt{2} \qquad\qquad\qquad = 2\sqrt{3}$$

$$\sqrt{18} + \sqrt{12} - 5\sqrt{3} - \sqrt{2} = 3\sqrt{2} + 2\sqrt{3} - 5\sqrt{3} - \sqrt{2}$$
$$= (3\sqrt{2} - \sqrt{2}) + (2\sqrt{3} - 5\sqrt{3})$$
$$= \qquad 2\sqrt{2} - 3\sqrt{3}$$

## ORAL EXERCISES 14.4

*Simplify.* (Example 1, Example 2, Example 3, Example 4)

**1.** $6\sqrt{2} + 8\sqrt{2}$

**2.** $7\sqrt{3} + \sqrt{3}$

**3.** $9\sqrt{5} - 6\sqrt{5}$

**4.** $10\sqrt{5} - \sqrt{5}$

**5.** $3\sqrt{11} + 12\sqrt{11}$

**6.** $3\sqrt{7} - 5\sqrt{7}$

**7.** $\sqrt{15} - 3\sqrt{15}$

**8.** $4\sqrt{6} + 13\sqrt{6}$

**9.** $7\sqrt{13} - 6\sqrt{13}$

**10.** $6\sqrt{23} - \sqrt{23}$

**11.** $4\sqrt{2} + 7\sqrt{2} + \sqrt{2}$

**12.** $6\sqrt{3} - 2\sqrt{3} + 5\sqrt{3}$

**13.** $8\sqrt{5} - \sqrt{5} - 2\sqrt{5}$

**14.** $-12\sqrt{7} + \sqrt{7} - 3\sqrt{7}$

**15.** $5\sqrt{11} - 9\sqrt{11} + 3\sqrt{11}$

**16.** $\frac{1}{2}\sqrt{3} + \frac{3}{2}\sqrt{3}$

**17.** $\frac{5}{4}\sqrt{5} - \frac{1}{4}\sqrt{5}$

**18.** $\frac{1}{4}\sqrt{7} + \frac{1}{2}\sqrt{7} - \sqrt{7}$

**19.** $\sqrt{12} + 5\sqrt{3}$

**20.** $9\sqrt{2} + \sqrt{8}$

**21.** $-\sqrt{12} + 2\sqrt{12} - \sqrt{12}$

## WRITTEN EXERCISES 14.4

**A**
    **Goal:** To add or subtract with radicals
    **Sample Problem:** $2\sqrt{3} + 5\sqrt{12}$
    **Answer:** $12\sqrt{3}$

*Add or subtract. Simplify where necessary.* (Example 1, Example 2, Example 3, Example 4)

**1.** $5\sqrt{2} + 11\sqrt{2}$

**2.** $4\sqrt{3} + 6\sqrt{3}$

**3.** $13\sqrt{5} + \sqrt{5}$

**4.** $\sqrt{7} + 12\sqrt{7}$

**5.** $10\sqrt{6} - 7\sqrt{6}$

**6.** $16\sqrt{10} - 9\sqrt{10}$

**7.** $14\sqrt{11} - \sqrt{11}$

**8.** $21\sqrt{15} - \sqrt{15}$

**9.** $5\sqrt{10} - 7\sqrt{10}$

**10.** $8\sqrt{6} - 13\sqrt{6}$

**11.** $2\sqrt{3} + \sqrt{3} + 5\sqrt{3}$

**12.** $\sqrt{5} + 3\sqrt{5} + 4\sqrt{5}$

**13.** $3\sqrt{6} - \sqrt{6} + 4\sqrt{6}$

**14.** $5\sqrt{2} - \sqrt{2} + 2\sqrt{2}$

**15.** $-7\sqrt{10} + 3\sqrt{10} - 5\sqrt{10}$

**16.** $-3\sqrt{11} + 5\sqrt{11} - 6\sqrt{11}$

**17.** $\frac{7}{2}\sqrt{6} + \frac{3}{2}\sqrt{6} - \frac{1}{2}\sqrt{6}$

**18.** $-\frac{1}{4}\sqrt{7} + \frac{7}{4}\sqrt{7} + \frac{3}{4}\sqrt{7}$

**19.** $\sqrt{18} + 5\sqrt{2}$

**20.** $\sqrt{20} + 6\sqrt{5}$

**21.** $2\sqrt{18} + \sqrt{8}$

**22.** $\sqrt{27} + 3\sqrt{12}$

**23.** $3\sqrt{6} - \sqrt{24}$

**24.** $3\sqrt{7} - \sqrt{28}$

**B**

**25.** $\sqrt{63} + \sqrt{27} - \sqrt{45}$

**26.** $\sqrt{48} - \sqrt{12} + \sqrt{27}$

**27.** $\sqrt{8} + \sqrt{50} + \sqrt{18}$

**28.** $\sqrt{72} + \sqrt{18} - \sqrt{50}$

# 14.5 Products

The rules for the operations on rational numbers also apply to irrational numbers.

## example 1

Multiply and simplify: $-3(4\sqrt{2})$

1. Associative Property of Multiplication $\longrightarrow$ $-3(4\sqrt{2}) = (-3 \cdot 4)\sqrt{2}$
2. Simplify. $\longrightarrow$ $= -12\sqrt{2}$

**P-1** What one radical equals $\sqrt{6} \cdot \sqrt{10}$? (Use the Product Property of Radicals.)

## example 2

Multiply and simplify: $(-\sqrt{6})(\sqrt{10})$

1. $(-a)(b) = -(ab)$ $\longrightarrow$ $(-\sqrt{6})(\sqrt{10}) = -(\sqrt{6} \cdot \sqrt{10})$
2. Product Property of Radicals $\longrightarrow$ $= -\sqrt{60}$
3. Write 60 as a product of two factors, one of which is the greatest perfect square factor of 60. $\longrightarrow$ $= -\sqrt{4 \cdot 15}$
4. Simplify. $\longrightarrow$ $= -2\sqrt{15}$

**P-2** What is the greatest perfect square factor of 20? of 27?

## example 3

Multiply and simplify: $(\sqrt{20})(\sqrt{27})$

$$(\sqrt{20})(\sqrt{27}) = (\sqrt{4 \cdot 5})(\sqrt{9 \cdot 3})$$

◀ *First simplify each radical.*

$$= (2\sqrt{5}) \cdot (3\sqrt{3})$$
$$= (2 \cdot 3)(\sqrt{5} \cdot \sqrt{3})$$
$$= 6\sqrt{15}$$

**P-3** What is the simplest name for each product below?

**a.** $(4\sqrt{5})(3\sqrt{7})$     **b.** $(5\sqrt{3})(4\sqrt{7})$     **c.** $\sqrt{8} \cdot \sqrt{3}$

**P-4** What is the approximate value of $\sqrt{15}$ from the following table?

| $n$ | $n^2$ | $\sqrt{n}$ | $n$ | $n^2$ | $\sqrt{n}$ |
|---|---|---|---|---|---|
| 1 | 1 | 1.000 | 14 | 196 | 3.742 |
| 2 | 4 | 1.414 | 15 | 225 | 3.873 |
| 3 | 9 | 1.732 | 16 | 256 | 4.000 |
| 4 | 16 | 2.000 | 17 | 289 | 4.123 |
| 5 | 25 | 2.236 | 18 | 324 | 4.243 |
| 6 | 36 | 2.449 | 19 | 361 | 4.359 |
| 7 | 49 | 2.646 | 20 | 400 | 4.472 |
| 8 | 64 | 2.828 | 21 | 441 | 4.583 |
| 9 | 81 | 3.000 | 22 | 484 | 4.690 |
| 10 | 100 | 3.162 | 23 | 529 | 4.796 |
| 11 | 121 | 3.317 | 24 | 576 | 4.899 |
| 12 | 144 | 3.464 | 25 | 625 | 5.000 |
| 13 | 169 | 3.606 | 26 | 676 | 5.099 |

**P-5** What is the simplest name for $19^2$?

**P-6** What is the simplest name for $\sqrt{361}$? for $\sqrt{676}$?

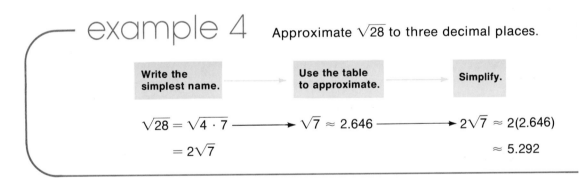

example 4    Approximate $\sqrt{28}$ to three decimal places.

| Write the simplest name. | → | Use the table to approximate. | → | Simplify. |
|---|---|---|---|---|

$\sqrt{28} = \sqrt{4 \cdot 7}$ ⟶ $\sqrt{7} \approx 2.646$ ⟶ $2\sqrt{7} \approx 2(2.646)$

$\qquad = 2\sqrt{7}$ $\qquad\qquad\qquad\qquad\qquad\qquad\qquad \approx 5.292$

## ORAL EXERCISES 14.5

*Simplify.* (Example 1, Example 2, Example 3, P-3)

**1.** $-5(4\sqrt{3})$

**2.** $-7(-8\sqrt{5})$

**3.** $10(-7\sqrt{6})$

**4.** $-\frac{1}{2}(12\sqrt{10})$

**5.** $(\sqrt{6})(\sqrt{7})$

**6.** $(-\sqrt{2})(\sqrt{13})$

**7.** $(\sqrt{5})(-\sqrt{11})$

**8.** $(-\sqrt{7})(-\sqrt{10})$

**9.** $(-3\sqrt{7})(4\sqrt{2})$

**10.** $(5\sqrt{2})(-4\sqrt{3})$

**11.** $(\sqrt{2})(\sqrt{6})$

**12.** $(\sqrt{6})(\sqrt{3})$

*Refer to a table to tell each value.* (P-4, P-5, P-6)

**13.** $16^2$  **14.** $22^2$  **15.** $\sqrt{361}$  **16.** $-\sqrt{625}$  **17.** $-\sqrt{324}$

**18.** $\sqrt{289}$  **19.** $\sqrt{10}$  **20.** $\sqrt{19}$  **21.** $-\sqrt{26}$  **22.** $-\sqrt{6}$

## WRITTEN EXERCISES 14.5

**A**

**Goal:** To multiply with radicals
**Sample Problem:** $(-4\sqrt{5})(5\sqrt{10})$
**Answer:** $-100\sqrt{2}$

*Multiply. Simplify where necessary.* (Example 1, Example 2, Example 3, P-3)

**1.** $-12(6\sqrt{5})$  **2.** $-8(9\sqrt{10})$  **3.** $15(-8\sqrt{7})$

**4.** $14(-6\sqrt{13})$  **5.** $-\frac{3}{4}(-24\sqrt{2})$  **6.** $-\frac{3}{8}(-32\sqrt{3})$

**7.** $(\sqrt{13})(\sqrt{5})$  **8.** $(\sqrt{13})(\sqrt{19})$  **9.** $(-\sqrt{6})(\sqrt{11})$

**10.** $(\sqrt{5})(-\sqrt{7})$  **11.** $(-\sqrt{10})(-\sqrt{23})$  **12.** $(-\sqrt{17})(-\sqrt{11})$

**13.** $(-3\sqrt{5})(4\sqrt{2})$  **14.** $(-5\sqrt{7})(9\sqrt{3})$  **15.** $(10\sqrt{10})(-\frac{1}{4}\sqrt{3})$

**16.** $(6\sqrt{11})(-\frac{3}{4}\sqrt{2})$  **17.** $(\sqrt{12})(5\sqrt{2})$  **18.** $(\sqrt{20})(4\sqrt{3})$

**19.** $(\sqrt{10})(\sqrt{2})$  **20.** $(-\sqrt{2})(\sqrt{14})$  **21.** $(-\sqrt{18})(\sqrt{20})$

**22.** $(\sqrt{24})(-\sqrt{27})$  **23.** $(-\sqrt{28})(-\sqrt{50})$  **24.** $(-\sqrt{28})(-\sqrt{45})$

**Goal:** To approximate square roots using a table
**Sample Problem:** Approximate $\sqrt{44}$ to three decimal places.
**Answer:** 6.634

*Use a table to approximate each square root to three decimal places.*
(Example 4)

**25.** $\sqrt{20}$  **26.** $\sqrt{24}$  **27.** $\sqrt{50}$  **28.** $\sqrt{45}$

**29.** $\sqrt{48}$  **30.** $\sqrt{80}$  **31.** $\sqrt{72}$  **32.** $\sqrt{98}$

**B**

**33.** $\sqrt{108}$  **34.** $\sqrt{88}$  **35.** $\sqrt{200}$  **36.** $\sqrt{180}$  **37.** $\sqrt{128}$  **38.** $\sqrt{243}$

**EXAMPLE:** $\sqrt{30}$   **SOLUTION:** $\sqrt{30} = \sqrt{5} \cdot \sqrt{6}$
$$\approx (2.236)(2.449)$$
$$\approx 5.476$$

**39.** $\sqrt{34}$  **40.** $\sqrt{66}$  **41.** $\sqrt{39}$  **42.** $\sqrt{46}$  **43.** $\sqrt{42}$  **44.** $\sqrt{57}$

# 14.6 Quotients

P-1    **What is the simplest name for each of these products?**

    **a.** $(\frac{2}{3})(\frac{2}{3})$     **b.** $(\frac{3}{4})(\frac{3}{4})$     **c.** $(\frac{5}{7})(\frac{5}{7})$

These values tell you the following sentences are true.

$$\sqrt{\frac{4}{9}} = \frac{2}{3} \qquad \sqrt{\frac{9}{16}} = \frac{3}{4} \qquad \sqrt{\frac{25}{49}} = \frac{5}{7}$$

P-2    **What is the simplest name for each of these quotients?**

    **a.** $\dfrac{\sqrt{4}}{\sqrt{9}}$     **b.** $\dfrac{\sqrt{9}}{\sqrt{16}}$     **c.** $\dfrac{\sqrt{25}}{\sqrt{49}}$

These examples illustrate the following property.

> **Quotient Property of Radicals**
>
> For any nonnegative number $a$ and any positive number $b$,   $\sqrt{\dfrac{a}{b}} = \dfrac{\sqrt{a}}{\sqrt{b}}.$     $\sqrt{\dfrac{4}{9}} = \dfrac{\sqrt{4}}{\sqrt{9}}$

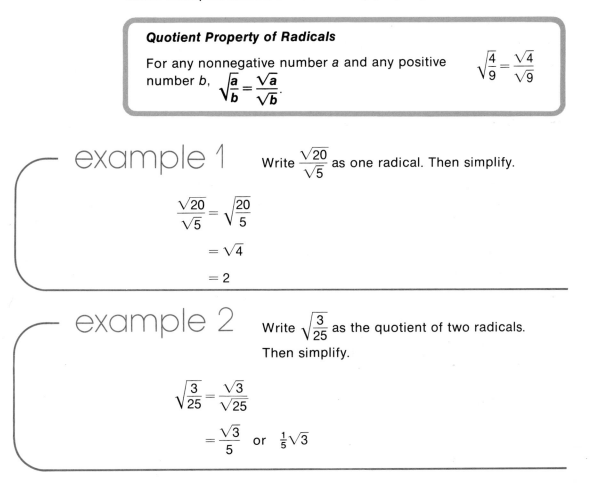

example 1    Write $\dfrac{\sqrt{20}}{\sqrt{5}}$ as one radical. Then simplify.

$$\frac{\sqrt{20}}{\sqrt{5}} = \sqrt{\frac{20}{5}}$$

$$= \sqrt{4}$$

$$= 2$$

example 2    Write $\sqrt{\dfrac{3}{25}}$ as the quotient of two radicals. Then simplify.

$$\sqrt{\frac{3}{25}} = \frac{\sqrt{3}}{\sqrt{25}}$$

$$= \frac{\sqrt{3}}{5} \text{ or } \tfrac{1}{5}\sqrt{3}$$

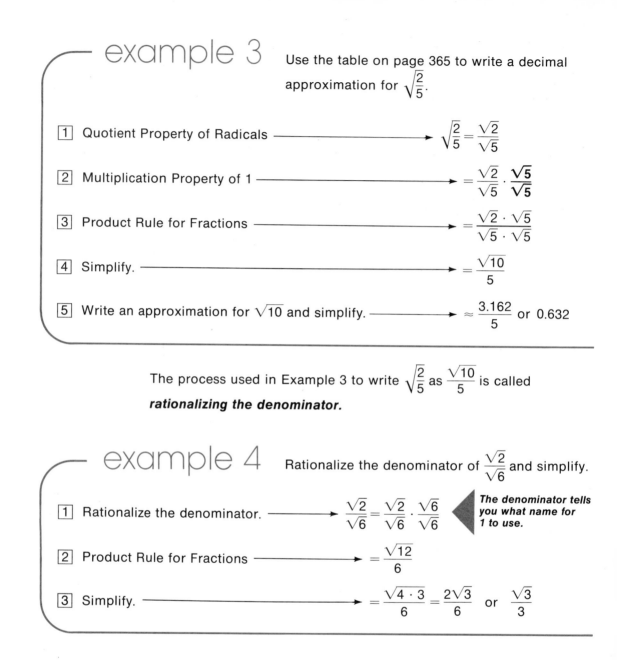

example 3   Use the table on page 365 to write a decimal approximation for $\sqrt{\frac{2}{5}}$.

☐1 Quotient Property of Radicals ⟶ $\sqrt{\frac{2}{5}} = \frac{\sqrt{2}}{\sqrt{5}}$

☐2 Multiplication Property of 1 ⟶ $= \frac{\sqrt{2}}{\sqrt{5}} \cdot \frac{\sqrt{5}}{\sqrt{5}}$

☐3 Product Rule for Fractions ⟶ $= \frac{\sqrt{2} \cdot \sqrt{5}}{\sqrt{5} \cdot \sqrt{5}}$

☐4 Simplify. ⟶ $= \frac{\sqrt{10}}{5}$

☐5 Write an approximation for $\sqrt{10}$ and simplify. ⟶ $\approx \frac{3.162}{5}$ or 0.632

The process used in Example 3 to write $\sqrt{\frac{2}{5}}$ as $\frac{\sqrt{10}}{5}$ is called **rationalizing the denominator.**

example 4   Rationalize the denominator of $\frac{\sqrt{2}}{\sqrt{6}}$ and simplify.

☐1 Rationalize the denominator. ⟶ $\frac{\sqrt{2}}{\sqrt{6}} = \frac{\sqrt{2}}{\sqrt{6}} \cdot \frac{\sqrt{6}}{\sqrt{6}}$ ◀ **The denominator tells you what name for 1 to use.**

☐2 Product Rule for Fractions ⟶ $= \frac{\sqrt{12}}{6}$

☐3 Simplify. ⟶ $= \frac{\sqrt{4 \cdot 3}}{6} = \frac{2\sqrt{3}}{6}$ or $\frac{\sqrt{3}}{3}$

## ORAL EXERCISES 14.6

*Express each quotient as one radical. Simplify where necessary.* (Example 1)

1. $\frac{\sqrt{32}}{\sqrt{8}}$      2. $\frac{\sqrt{27}}{\sqrt{3}}$      3. $\frac{\sqrt{50}}{\sqrt{2}}$      4. $\frac{\sqrt{32}}{\sqrt{2}}$      5. $\frac{\sqrt{60}}{\sqrt{6}}$

*Express each radical as a quotient of two radicals. (Example 2)*

6. $\sqrt{\dfrac{2}{7}}$
7. $\sqrt{\dfrac{3}{10}}$
8. $\sqrt{\dfrac{5}{17}}$
9. $\sqrt{\dfrac{3}{19}}$
10. $\sqrt{\dfrac{19}{29}}$

*Rationalize the denominator. (Example 4)*

11. $\dfrac{\sqrt{3}}{\sqrt{7}}$
12. $\dfrac{\sqrt{2}}{\sqrt{11}}$
13. $\dfrac{\sqrt{5}}{\sqrt{3}}$
14. $\dfrac{\sqrt{15}}{\sqrt{2}}$
15. $\dfrac{\sqrt{3}}{\sqrt{64}}$

## WRITTEN EXERCISES 14.6

**A**  **Goal:** To apply the Quotient Property of Radicals

**Sample Problems: a.** $\dfrac{\sqrt{3}}{\sqrt{10}} = \sqrt{\dfrac{?}{?}}$   **b.** $\sqrt{\dfrac{5}{6}} = \dfrac{?}{?}$   **c.** $\dfrac{2}{\sqrt{5}} = \dfrac{?}{5}$

**Answers: a.** $\sqrt{\dfrac{3}{10}}$   **b.** $\dfrac{\sqrt{5}}{\sqrt{6}}$   **c.** $\dfrac{2\sqrt{5}}{5}$

*Write each quotient as one radical. Then simplify. (Example 1)*

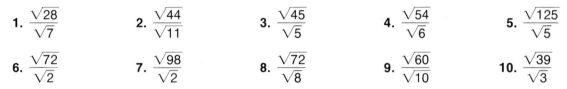

1. $\dfrac{\sqrt{28}}{\sqrt{7}}$
2. $\dfrac{\sqrt{44}}{\sqrt{11}}$
3. $\dfrac{\sqrt{45}}{\sqrt{5}}$
4. $\dfrac{\sqrt{54}}{\sqrt{6}}$
5. $\dfrac{\sqrt{125}}{\sqrt{5}}$

6. $\dfrac{\sqrt{72}}{\sqrt{2}}$
7. $\dfrac{\sqrt{98}}{\sqrt{2}}$
8. $\dfrac{\sqrt{72}}{\sqrt{8}}$
9. $\dfrac{\sqrt{60}}{\sqrt{10}}$
10. $\dfrac{\sqrt{39}}{\sqrt{3}}$

*Write each radical as a quotient of two radicals. Then simplify. (Example 2)*

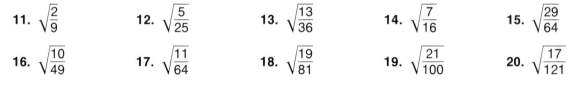

11. $\sqrt{\dfrac{2}{9}}$
12. $\sqrt{\dfrac{5}{25}}$
13. $\sqrt{\dfrac{13}{36}}$
14. $\sqrt{\dfrac{7}{16}}$
15. $\sqrt{\dfrac{29}{64}}$

16. $\sqrt{\dfrac{10}{49}}$
17. $\sqrt{\dfrac{11}{64}}$
18. $\sqrt{\dfrac{19}{81}}$
19. $\sqrt{\dfrac{21}{100}}$
20. $\sqrt{\dfrac{17}{121}}$

*Use the table on page 365 and write an approximation for each radical to three decimal places. (Example 3)*

21. $\sqrt{\dfrac{3}{4}}$
22. $\sqrt{\dfrac{5}{9}}$
23. $\sqrt{\dfrac{2}{7}}$
24. $\sqrt{\dfrac{3}{5}}$
25. $\sqrt{\dfrac{1}{15}}$
26. $\sqrt{\dfrac{1}{21}}$

*Rationalize the denominator. Then simplify. (Example 4)*

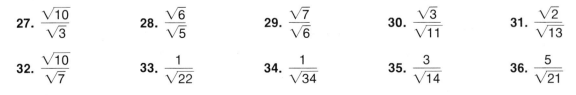

27. $\dfrac{\sqrt{10}}{\sqrt{3}}$
28. $\dfrac{\sqrt{6}}{\sqrt{5}}$
29. $\dfrac{\sqrt{7}}{\sqrt{6}}$
30. $\dfrac{\sqrt{3}}{\sqrt{11}}$
31. $\dfrac{\sqrt{2}}{\sqrt{13}}$

32. $\dfrac{\sqrt{10}}{\sqrt{7}}$
33. $\dfrac{1}{\sqrt{22}}$
34. $\dfrac{1}{\sqrt{34}}$
35. $\dfrac{3}{\sqrt{14}}$
36. $\dfrac{5}{\sqrt{21}}$

# Electrician

Construction electricians install electrical service equipment and wiring in homes, factories, businesses, schools, hospitals, and other buildings. They must be able to read blueprints or plans that show the type and location of wiring, outlets, and all other parts of the electrical system being installed. There are more than 240,000 construction electricians in the country.

Electricians can prepare for their trade in several ways, but participation in a four-year apprenticeship program is recommended. The program requires training on the job and related classroom instruction. A high school education is necessary in order to enter an apprenticeship program. Courses in mathematics and physics are recommended.

The watt, volt, and ampere are units of electrical measure in the metric system that are common terms to the electrician. These terms are related by the formula,

$$\text{watts} = (\text{volts})(\text{amperes}).$$

In planning the wiring for a home, an electrician follows these two basic conditions.

1. At least 3 watts of electrical power per square foot, or about 32.3 watts per square meter of floor area

2. 1 circuit for each 46 square meters of floor area

**EXAMPLE:** Find (1) the total number of watts and (2) the number of circuits required for a house with a floor area of 225.63 square meters.

**SOLUTION:** (1) (32.3)(area) = number of watts
(32.3)(225.63) $\approx$ 7300 watts

(2) area ÷ 46 = number of circuits
225.63 ÷ 46 $\approx$ 4.90 circuits, or 5 circuits

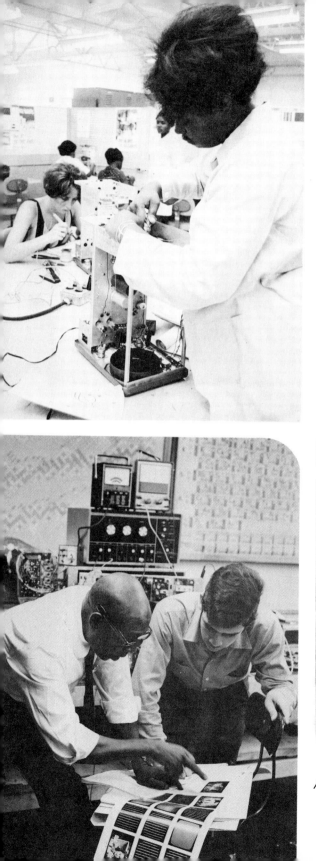

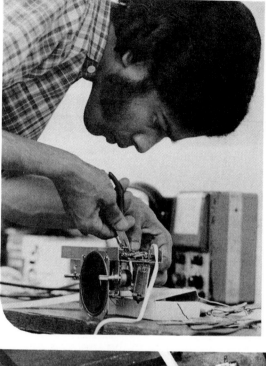

Apprentice electricians learn by doing.

371

## CHAPTER SUMMARY

| | |
|---|---|
| **IMPORTANT TERMS** | Square root *(p. 352)*      Irrational number *(p. 355)*<br>Radical *(p. 352)*      Real numbers *(p. 356)*<br>Radicand *(p. 352)*      Real-number line *(p. 356)*<br>Perfect square *(p. 352)*      Like radicals *(p. 361)*<br>Nonrepeating decimal *(p. 355)*      Rationalizing the denominator *(p. 368)* |

**IMPORTANT IDEAS**

**1.** Every positive number has both a positive and a negative square root.

**2.** For any number $a$, $(\sqrt{a})^2 = a$ and $(-\sqrt{a})^2 = a$.

**3.** Any whole number that is not a perfect square has an irrational square root.

**4.** Every point on the number line has a real number for a coordinate.

**5.** *Product Property of Radicals:* For any nonnegative numbers $a$ and $b$, $\sqrt{a} \cdot \sqrt{b} = \sqrt{ab}$.

**6.** A radical is in simplest form if the radicand has no perfect square factor other than 1.

**7.** *Quotient Property of Radicals:* For any nonnegative number $a$ and any positive number $b$, $\sqrt{\dfrac{a}{b}} = \dfrac{\sqrt{a}}{\sqrt{b}}$.

## CHAPTER REVIEW

### SECTION 14.1

*Simplify.*

**1.** $-\sqrt{25}$      **2.** $\sqrt{81}$      **3.** $\sqrt{\dfrac{9}{25}}$      **4.** $-\sqrt{\dfrac{16}{49}}$

**5.** $\sqrt{\dfrac{1}{9}}$      **6.** $\sqrt{\dfrac{1}{16}}$      **7.** $-\sqrt{0.16}$      **8.** $-\sqrt{0.81}$

### SECTION 14.2

*Write the square of each number.*

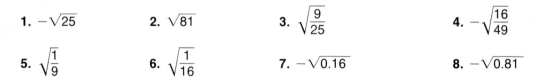

**9.** $\sqrt{17}$      **10.** $\sqrt{200}$      **11.** $-\sqrt{\dfrac{5}{8}}$

**12.** $-\sqrt{\dfrac{3}{4}}$      **13.** $\sqrt{1078}$      **14.** $-\sqrt{53\dfrac{1}{2}}$

Write _Rational_ or _Irrational_ to describe each number.

**15.** $\sqrt{14}$      **16.** $-\sqrt{\dfrac{1}{16}}$      **17.** $-\sqrt{\dfrac{1}{9}}$      **18.** $-\sqrt{18}$

**19.** $-2\dfrac{7}{8}$      **20.** $\dfrac{13}{16}$      **21.** $0.535353\cdots$      **22.** $2.41424344\cdots$

### SECTION 14.3

_Simplify each product._

**23.** $\sqrt{3} \cdot \sqrt{13}$                        **24.** $\sqrt{5} \cdot \sqrt{17}$

**25.** $\sqrt{64} \cdot \sqrt{11}$                  **26.** $\sqrt{81} \cdot \sqrt{23}$

**27.** $\sqrt{79} \cdot \sqrt{79}$                  **28.** $\sqrt{93} \cdot \sqrt{93}$

_Simplify each radical._

**29.** $\sqrt{25 \cdot 3}$      **30.** $\sqrt{36 \cdot 5}$      **31.** $\sqrt{50}$      **32.** $\sqrt{75}$

**33.** $\sqrt{63}$      **34.** $\sqrt{52}$      **35.** $\sqrt{108}$      **36.** $\sqrt{117}$

### SECTION 14.4

_Add or subtract. Simplify where necessary._

**37.** $7\sqrt{5} + 8\sqrt{5}$              **38.** $15\sqrt{11} + 14\sqrt{11}$

**39.** $18\sqrt{3} - \sqrt{3}$              **40.** $7\sqrt{10} - 13\sqrt{10}$

**41.** $3\sqrt{6} - 5\sqrt{6} - 10\sqrt{6}$      **42.** $5\sqrt{15} - \sqrt{15} - 3\sqrt{15}$

**43.** $\sqrt{24} - 5\sqrt{6}$              **44.** $-\sqrt{2} + \sqrt{18}$

### SECTION 14.5

_Multiply. Simplify where necessary._

**45.** $7(-8\sqrt{5})$             **46.** $-11(6\sqrt{10})$

**47.** $-\dfrac{1}{3}(-12\sqrt{6})$         **48.** $-\dfrac{3}{4}(-24\sqrt{2})$

**49.** $(-12\sqrt{5})(4\sqrt{3})$       **50.** $(6\sqrt{7})(-9\sqrt{7})$

**51.** $(\sqrt{27})(2\sqrt{5})$         **52.** $(\sqrt{44})(3\sqrt{2})$

**SECTION 14.6**

*Write each quotient as one radical and simplify.*

53. $\dfrac{\sqrt{52}}{\sqrt{13}}$ 54. $\dfrac{\sqrt{117}}{\sqrt{13}}$ 55. $\dfrac{\sqrt{128}}{\sqrt{8}}$ 56. $\dfrac{\sqrt{350}}{\sqrt{14}}$

*Write each radical as a quotient of two radicals and simplify.*

57. $\sqrt{\dfrac{7}{36}}$ 58. $\sqrt{\dfrac{13}{49}}$ 59. $\sqrt{\dfrac{10}{81}}$ 60. $\sqrt{\dfrac{23}{144}}$

*Rationalize the denominator of each fraction and simplify.*

61. $\dfrac{\sqrt{5}}{\sqrt{13}}$ 62. $\dfrac{\sqrt{6}}{\sqrt{7}}$ 63. $\dfrac{\sqrt{10}}{\sqrt{11}}$

64. $\dfrac{\sqrt{15}}{\sqrt{2}}$ 65. $\dfrac{4\sqrt{2}}{\sqrt{6}}$ 66. $\dfrac{3\sqrt{6}}{\sqrt{3}}$

# 15

# Relations and Functions

# 15.1 Graphs in a Plane

There are two intersecting number lines called **axes** in the figure at the right.
The horizontal number line is the **X axis**.
The vertical number line is the **Y axis**.

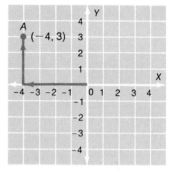

**P-1** How many units is point A to the left of the Y axis?

**P-2** How many units is point A above the X axis?

The numbers −4 and 3 are the **coordinates** of point A. They are also called the *x value* and *y value* of the point. The dot at A is the **graph** of (−4, 3).

**P-3** What is the x value in each pair of numbers below?   the y value?

**a.** (0, 3)      **b.** (6, −2)      **c.** (7, 0)      **d.** (−5, 8)      **e.** (0, 0)

The point with coordinates (0, 0) is called the **origin**.

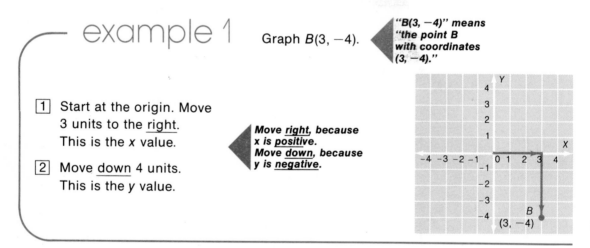

example 1        Graph B(3, −4).        "B(3, −4)" means "the point B with coordinates (3, −4)."

1 Start at the origin. Move 3 units to the <u>right</u>. This is the x value.

*Move <u>right</u>, because x is <u>positive</u>. Move <u>down</u>, because y is <u>negative</u>.*

2 Move <u>down</u> 4 units. This is the y value.

**P-4** Why is (−4, 3) not the same as (3, −4)?

The order of the coordinates −4 and 3 is important. That is why number pairs such as (−4, 3) and (3, −4) are called **ordered pairs**.

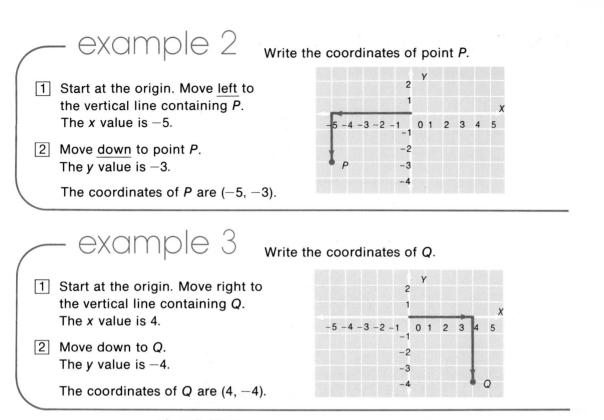

## example 2 — Write the coordinates of point P.

1 Start at the origin. Move <u>left</u> to the vertical line containing P. The x value is −5.

2 Move <u>down</u> to point P. The y value is −3.

The coordinates of P are (−5, −3).

## example 3 — Write the coordinates of Q.

1 Start at the origin. Move <u>right</u> to the vertical line containing Q. The x value is 4.

2 Move down to Q. The y value is −4.

The coordinates of Q are (4, −4).

## ORAL EXERCISES 15.1

*Tell the steps needed to graph each point.* (Example 1)

**EXAMPLE:** (4, 7)  **ANSWER:** 4 units right; 7 units up

**1.** (3, −6)  **2.** (4, 8)  **3.** (−1, −7)  **4.** (−12, 6)  **5.** (8, −9)

**6.** (15, 10)  **7.** (−12, −20)  **8.** (100, −5)  **9.** (−25, 50)  **10.** (0, −8)

**11.** (−15, 0)  **12,** (−8, 0)  **13.** (0, 30)  **14.** (−18, −18)  **15.** (32, −32)

*Tell the coordinates of each point.* (Example 2, Example 3)

**16.** A  **17.** B  **18.** C  **19.** D

**20.** E  **21.** F  **22.** G  **23.** H

**24.** I  **25.** J  **26.** K  **27.** L

**28.** M  **29.** N  **30.** P  **31.** Q

## WRITTEN EXERCISES 15.1

**A**

**Goal:** To write the coordinates of a point
**Sample Problem:** Write the coordinates of *R*.
**Answer:** (−4, 2)

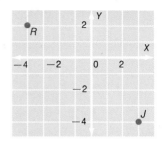

**Goal:** To graph a point
**Sample Problem:** Graph *J*(3, −4).
**Answer:** See the figure at the right.

*Write the two steps needed to graph each point.* (Example 1)

**EXAMPLE:** (−3, 6)     **ANSWER:** 3 units left; 6 units up

**1.** (4, 13)
**2.** (16, 6)
**3.** (−5, −12)
**4.** (−14, −15)

**5.** (15, −3)
**6.** (7, −12)
**7.** (−30, 10)
**8.** (−9, 24)

**9.** (−14, 0)
**10.** (23, 0)
**11.** (0, 11)
**12.** (0, −19)

*In Exercises 13–24, graph the odd-numbered exercises in one coordinate plane and the even-numbered exercises in another coordinate plane. Write the letter for each point near its dot.* (Example 1)

**13.** *A*(4, 2)
**14.** *B*(3, 5)
**15.** *C*(−3, −5)
**16.** *D*(−2, −4)

**17.** *E*(4, −5)
**18.** *F*(6, −3)
**19.** *G*(−5, 4)
**20.** *H*(−2, 6)

**21.** *I*(6, 0)
**22.** *J*(−4, 0)
**23.** *K*(0, −5)
**24.** *L*(0, 6)

*Write the coordinates of each point shown below.* (Example 2, Example 3)

**25.** *R*
**26.** *S*
**27.** *F*
**28.** *P*

**29.** *K*
**30.** *W*
**31.** *T*
**32.** *Q*

**33.** *B*
**34.** *V*
**35.** *N*
**36.** *A*

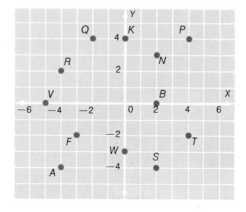

# 15.2 Relations and Graphs

**P-1**  **What are the coordinates of the points in Figure 1?**

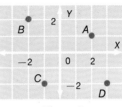

The coordinates of *A*, *B*, *C*, and *D* form set R, called a <u>relation</u>.

R = {(2, 1), (−2, 2), (−1, −2), (3, −2)}

**Figure 1**

> A ***relation*** is a set of ordered pairs.

The plane determined by the *X* axis and *Y* axis is called a ***coordinate plane***. Its four regions are called ***quadrants*** I, II, III, and IV.

**P-2**  **In which quadrant of Figure 2 is point *R*?  *K*?  *W*?  *T*?**

**P-3**  **What is an estimate for the coordinates of each point?**

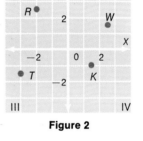

**Figure 2**

The relation described by these coordinates is shown in <u>roster form</u>.

{(2½, 1½), (−2, 2½), (−3, −1½), (1½, −1)}

A relation can also be described by a <u>word rule</u>.

## example 1

Write the missing *y* values of relation S described by the word rule. Then graph S.

"Each *y* value is 1 less than half each *x* value."

**Roster form** ➤ S = {(−2, ?), (0, ?), (2, ?), (3, ?)}

**Solution:**

| x | Multiply by $\frac{1}{2}$ | Subtract 1 | Ordered Pair |
|---|---|---|---|
| −2 | −1 | −2 | (−2, −2) |
| 0 | 0 | −1 | (0, −1) |
| 2 | 1 | 0 | (2, 0) |
| 3 | $\frac{3}{2}$ | $\frac{1}{2}$ | (3, $\frac{1}{2}$) |

Relations are often written in table form as shown below.

| x | 1 | 2 | 3 | 0 | −1 | −2 | −3 |
|---|---|---|---|---|---|---|---|
| y | −2 | −4 | −6 | 0 | 2 | 4 | 6 |

**P-4**  **What word rule describes the relation in this table?**

## example 2

Complete the table. Then draw a graph.

"Multiply each x value by $\frac{1}{3}$ and add −2."

**Solution:**

| x | y |
|---|---|
| −9 | ? |
| −6 | ? |
| −3 | ? |
| 0 | ? |
| 3 | ? |
| 6 | ? |
| 9 | ? |

| x | y |
|---|---|
| −9 | −5 |
| −6 | −4 |
| −3 | −3 |
| 0 | −2 |
| 3 | −1 |
| 6 | 0 |
| 9 | 1 |

## ORAL EXERCISES 15.2

*Tell the missing y values.* (Example 1, Example 2)

**1.** "Add 2 to each x value."

| x | y |
|---|---|
| −5 | ? |
| −1 | ? |
| 0 | ? |
| 4 | ? |

**2.** "Add −1 to each x value."

| x | y |
|---|---|
| −3 | ? |
| −1 | ? |
| 0 | ? |
| 3 | ? |

**3.** "Multiply each x value by 2 and add 5."

| x | y |
|---|---|
| −3 | ? |
| −1 | ? |
| 0 | ? |
| $1\frac{1}{2}$ | ? |

**4.** "Take the opposite of each x value and subtract 3."

| x | y |
|---|---|
| −5 | ? |
| −2 | ? |
| 0 | ? |
| 3 | ? |

*Tell a word rule for each relation.* (P-4)

**5.** {(2, 4), (3, 6), (0, 0), (−3, −6)}

**6.** {($1\frac{1}{2}$, $-1\frac{1}{2}$), (0, 0), (1.6, −1.6), (−10, 10)}

# WRITTEN EXERCISES 15.2

**Goal:** To describe a relation in four ways: **a.** graph;
**b.** roster; **c.** word rule; **d.** table

**Sample Problem:** Describe the relation graphed
at the right in roster form, by
a word rule, and by a table.

**Answer:** $\{(0, 1), (3, 7), (-2, -3)\}$
Multiply each $x$ value by 2 and add 1.

| x | 0 | 3 | -2 |
|---|---|---|----|
| y | 1 | 7 | -3 |

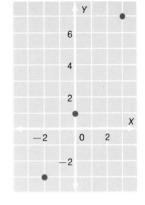

*Graph each relation in a separate coordinate plane.* (Example 1, Example 2)

**1.** $\{(-3, 2), (4, -2), (0, 3), (2, 5)\}$

**2.** $\{(5, 2), (0, -4), (-2, 4), (3, 0)\}$

**3.** $\{(2, -2), (-4, -5), (0, -3), (4, -1)\}$

**4.** $\{(-2, 5), (0, 1), (3, -5), (1, -1)\}$

**5.** $\{(2\frac{1}{2}, 3), (-4, -1\frac{1}{2}), (0, -3\frac{1}{2}), (4\frac{1}{2}, 2\frac{1}{2})\}$

**6.** $\{(-4\frac{1}{2}, 0), (1\frac{1}{2}, 3), (3\frac{1}{2}, -5), (-1\frac{1}{2}, -2\frac{1}{2})\}$

*Write each relation in roster form for these x values: $0, 1\frac{1}{2}, 3, -4$.*
(Example 1, Example 2)

**7.** Multiply each $x$ value by $-2$.

**8.** Multiply each $x$ value by $-3$.

**9.** Multiply each $x$ value by 2; add $-2$.

**10.** Multiply each $x$ value by $-2$; add 1.

**11.** Multiply each $x$ value by $\frac{1}{2}$; add $-1\frac{1}{2}$.

**12.** Multiply each $x$ value by $-\frac{1}{2}$; add $2\frac{1}{2}$.

*Determine a word rule for each relation. Then write the missing numerals.*
(P-4, Example 2)

**13.**

| x | 5 | 1 | -3 | 0 | 3 | -4 |
|---|---|---|----|---|---|----|
| y | 3 | -1 | -5 | ? | ? | ? |

**14.**

| x | 3 | -2 | 0 | 4 | -3 | -1 |
|---|---|----|---|---|----|----|
| y | 6 | 1 | 3 | ? | ? | ? |

**15.**

| x | $-1\frac{1}{2}$ | 0 | 3 | -5 | $\frac{3}{4}$ | -1.7 |
|---|---|---|---|----|---|------|
| y | $1\frac{1}{2}$ | 0 | -3 | ? | ? | ? |

**16.**

| x | 6 | -4 | 0 | -3.6 | $3\frac{1}{2}$ | 4.5 |
|---|---|----|---|------|---|-----|
| y | -6 | 4 | 0 | ? | ? | ? |

*Each open phrase is the rule for a relation. Write the missing numerals.*

**17.**

| x | $3x - 2$ |
|---|----------|
| -3 | ? |
| -1 | ? |
| 0 | ? |
| 5 | ? |

**18.**

| x | $2x + 5$ |
|---|----------|
| -5 | ? |
| -2 | ? |
| 3 | ? |
| 12 | ? |

**19.**

| x | $-x + 3$ |
|---|----------|
| -5 | ? |
| 0 | ? |
| 12 | ? |
| $-3\frac{1}{2}$ | ? |

**20.**

| x | $-2x - 1$ |
|---|-----------|
| 6 | ? |
| 4 | ? |
| $-\frac{1}{2}$ | ? |
| -5 | ? |

# 15.3 Functions

**P-1**  **What are the x values of set A?  of set B?**

$$A = \{(2, 3), (1, 5), (2, 4)\} \qquad\qquad B = \{(4, 1), (5, 6), (7, 2)\}$$

In set A, (2, 3) and (2, 4) have the same x value. All the x values in set B are different. Set B is a special relation called a <u>function</u>.

> A **function** is a relation in which no two ordered pairs have the same x value.

**P-2**  **Which of these sets are functions?**

**a.** $\{(\frac{1}{2}, \frac{3}{4}), (0, -\frac{1}{2}), (-\frac{1}{2}, \frac{1}{2})\}$

**b.** $\{(0, 1), (1, 0), (-1, 0), (0, -1)\}$

**c.** $\{(5.1, 1.1), (3.4, 2.1), (-1.7, 4.3)\}$

Functions can be described by graphs, tables, and word rules.

| Word Rule | Formula |
|---|---|
| "Subtract 3 from each x value." | $y = x - 3$ |
| "Add 5 to twice each x value." | $y = 2x + 5$ |
| "Take the absolute value of each x value and subtract 1." | $y = |x| - 1$ |

*Often the rules are given as formulas.*

## example 1

Compute the y values in the table by using the formula $y = |x| - 1$ for these x values: $\{2, 1, 0, -1, -2\}$.

| x | y |
|---|---|
| 2 | ? |
| 1 | ? |
| 0 | ? |
| -1 | ? |
| -2 | ? |

$y = |x| - 1$
$y = |2| - 1 = 1$
$y = |1| - 1 = 0$
$y = |0| - 1 = -1$
$y = |-1| - 1 = 0$
$y = |-2| - 1 = 1$

| x | y |
|---|---|
| 2 | 1 |
| 1 | 0 |
| 0 | -1 |
| -1 | 0 |
| -2 | 1 |

The *x* values form set D below called the <u>domain</u>. The corresponding *y* values form set R called the <u>range</u>.

$$D = \{2, 1, 0, -1, -2\} \qquad R = \{1, 0, -1\}$$

> The **domain** of a function is the set of *x* values of its ordered pairs. The **range** of a function is the set of *y* values of its ordered pairs.

**P-3** **What is the domain of the function below?  What is the range?**

$$\{(\tfrac{1}{2}, 3), (5, \tfrac{2}{3}), (-7, 0)\}$$

example 2   List the elements of the range of the function described by $y = 3x + 1$. The domain is $\{-1, 0, \tfrac{1}{3}, 2\}$.

| x | 3x  + 1 | | | y |
|---|---|---|---|---|
| −1 | 3(−1) + 1 = −3 + 1 | or | −2 | |
| 0 | 3 (0)  + 1 = 0 + 1 | or | 1 | |
| $\frac{1}{3}$ | 3 ($\frac{1}{3}$) + 1 = 1 + 1 | or | 2 | |
| 2 | 3 (2)  + 1 = 6 + 1 | or | 7 | |

The range is $\{-2, 1, 2, 7\}$.

## ORAL EXERCISES 15.3

*Say <u>Yes</u> or <u>No</u> to tell if each set is a function.* (P-2)

**1.** $\{(3, 1), (5, -2)\}$

**2.** $\{(4, 0), (0, 2), (0, -1)\}$

**3.** $\{(\tfrac{1}{2}, 2), (\tfrac{1}{2}, -2), (\tfrac{1}{2}, 1)\}$

**4.** $\{(-3, 1), (-2, -1), (-1, 1)\}$

**5.** $\{(0.1, 2), (0.2, 3), (0.3, 4)\}$

**6.** $\{(1, 1), (-1, 1), (-1, -1), (1, -1)\}$

*Tell the elements of each domain. Then tell the elements of the range.* (P-3)

**7.** $\{(1, 4), (-3, 5), (-1, 4)\}$

**8.** $\{(3.4, 5), (1.3, 2), (-2, 2.5)\}$

**9.** $\{(\tfrac{1}{2}, 3), (-\tfrac{1}{4}, 2), (7, \tfrac{3}{4})\}$

**10.** $\{(2, -\tfrac{1}{2}), (3, \tfrac{1}{2}), (0, 5)\}$

**11.**

| x | 0 | −1 | 3 | 5 |
|---|---|---|---|---|
| y | 5 | 6 | −2 | −1 |

**12.**

| x | 5.2 | 0.5 | −1.3 | 0.8 |
|---|---|---|---|---|
| y | −1.2 | 1.7 | 4.2 | −1.2 |

Each formula describes a function. Tell the elements of the range of each function. The domain is $\{-1, 0, 1, 2\}$. (Example 2)

**13.** $y = 5x$          **14.** $y = x + 3$          **15.** $y = -2x$          **16.** $y = -x + 1$

**17.** $y = 3x - 1$      **18.** $y = -x - 2$      **19.** $y = x$          **20.** $y = \frac{1}{2}x + \frac{1}{2}$

## WRITTEN EXERCISES 15.3

**A**     **Goal:** To identify a function and write the domain and range
**Sample Problem:** Write Yes or No to show if the relation below is a function:

$$\{(2, 8), (4, -5), (\tfrac{6}{3}, 7)\}$$

**Answer:** No

Write Yes or No to show whether each relation is a function. (P-2)

**1.** $\{(5, 9), (23, 3), (8, 2)\}$          **2.** $\{(3, 16), (0, 10), (5, 25)\}$

**3.** $\{(1, 0), (0, -1), (-1, 0), (0, 1)\}$     **4.** $\{(2, -2), (-2, 2), (1, -1), (-1, 1)\}$

**5.** $\{(\tfrac{1}{2}, 1), (-\tfrac{1}{2}, \tfrac{1}{2}), (0.5, 1)\}$       **6.** $\{(\tfrac{1}{4}, 0), (\tfrac{2}{8}, -1), (-1, 0)\}$

Use the given formula to compute the unknown y values. (Example 1)

**7.** $y = 4x + 1$         $\{(0, 1), (-1, ?), (2, ?), (-3, ?)\}$

**8.** $y = 2x + 5$         $\{(1, 7), (0, ?), (-1, ?), (-2, ?)\}$

**9.** $y = -2x + 3$       $\{(0, ?), (2, ?), (-2, ?), (3, ?)\}$

**10.** $y = -x + 5$        $\{(3, ?), (0, ?), (-1, ?), (-3, ?)\}$

**11.** $y = -x - 2$        $\{(-5, ?), (2, ?), (0, ?), (\tfrac{1}{2}, ?)\}$

**12.** $y = -3x - 2$      $\{(-1, ?), (0, ?), (-\tfrac{1}{2}, ?), (\tfrac{1}{3}, ?)\}$

Write the domain, D, and the range, R, of each function in roster form. (P-3)

**EXAMPLE:** $\{(2, 1), (-3, 1), (0, -1), (-1, -2)\}$

**ANSWER:** $D = \{2, -3, 0, -1\}$; $R = \{-1, 1, -2\}$

**13.** $\{(5, 0), (3, -2), (8, 3)\}$        **14.** $\{(-2, 1), (4, -2), (5, -6)\}$

**15.** $\{(-1, 8), (5, 2), (0, 2), (2, -3)\}$    **16.** $\{(7, 0), (-5, 2), (-1, 3), (0, 2)\}$

**17.** $\{(3, 0), (0, 3), (-3, 0), (4, -3)\}$    **18.** $\{(2, 2), (0, 2), (-2, 2), (1, -2)\}$

**19.**

| x | 1 | -2 | -3 | -4 |
|---|---|----|----|----|
| y | 2 | 3  | 4  | 0  |

**20.**

| x | -1 | 1  | 2  | 0 |
|---|----|----|----|---|
| y | 3  | -2 | -6 | 5 |

# 15.4 Graphs of Functions

**P-1**  **What is the domain of the function in Figure 1?  the range?**

$$y = -\tfrac{1}{2}x + 3$$

| x | y |
|----|---|
| −4 | 5 |
| −2 | 4 |
| 0 | 3 |
| 2 | 2 |
| 4 | 1 |

◀ **This function is a _finite set_.**

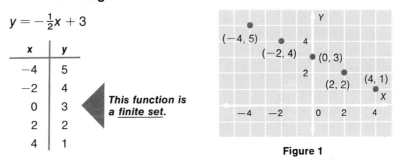

**Figure 1**

**P-2**  **What geometric figure is suggested by the graph?**

The graph of Figure 1 is repeated in Figure 2, and a line is drawn containing the points.

The entire line of Figure 2 is also the graph of a function. The domain is {real numbers}, and the range is {real numbers}. This function is an _infinite set_.

**Figure 2**

---

## example 1

Graph the function defined by $y = -x + 2$.
The domain is {real numbers}.

| Select some numbers of the domain. | → | Compute the y values. | → | Graph the ordered pairs. | → | Draw the line. |
|---|---|---|---|---|---|---|

**Choose x values small in absolute value.** ▶

| x | y |
|----|---|
| −3 | ? |
| −1 | ? |
| 0 | ? |
| 3 | ? |

$y = -x + 2$
$y = -(-3) + 2 = 5$
$y = -(-1) + 2 = 3$
$y = -0 + 2 = 2$
$y = -3 + 2 = -1$

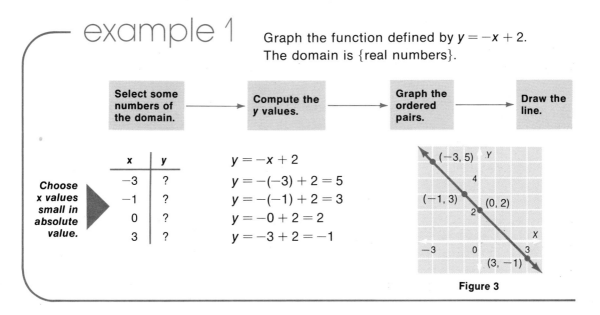

**Figure 3**

**P-3**   What are the missing numerals below from the graph of Figure 3 on page 385?

   **a.** $(4, ?)$      **b.** $(-2, ?)$      **c.** $(?, 1)$      **d.** $(?, -3)$

**P-4**   How can you tell whether an ordered pair belongs to a function?

The functions of Figures 1, 2, and 3 are called <u>linear functions</u>.

> A **linear function** is a function in which the points of its graph lie in a straight line.
>
> Rule:
> $$y = ax + b$$

**P-5**   What are the values of *a* and *b* in each formula?

   **a.** $y = 2x - 3$      **b.** $y = -x + \frac{1}{2}$      **c.** $y = \frac{3}{2}x - 1.7$

## ORAL EXERCISES 15.4

*Tell the y value for each given x value in each formula.* (Step 2 of Example 1)

**1.** $y = x + 4$
   $x = -6$

**2.** $y = 2x - 5$
   $x = 2$

**3.** $y = -4x + 1$
   $x = \frac{1}{2}$

**4.** $y = 2 - x$
   $x = -3$

**5.** $y = \frac{1}{2}x + 3$
   $x = -4$

**6.** $y = -2x + 25$
   $x = 0$

**7.** $y = x + \frac{1}{2}$
   $x = \frac{1}{2}$

**8.** $y = \frac{3}{4}x + \frac{1}{4}$
   $x = 1$

*Tell the missing numerals.* (Step 2 of Example 1)

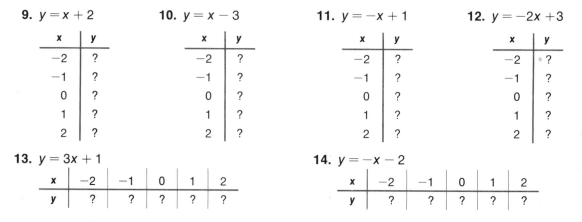

**9.** $y = x + 2$

| x | y |
|---|---|
| -2 | ? |
| -1 | ? |
| 0 | ? |
| 1 | ? |
| 2 | ? |

**10.** $y = x - 3$

| x | y |
|---|---|
| -2 | ? |
| -1 | ? |
| 0 | ? |
| 1 | ? |
| 2 | ? |

**11.** $y = -x + 1$

| x | y |
|---|---|
| -2 | ? |
| -1 | ? |
| 0 | ? |
| 1 | ? |
| 2 | ? |

**12.** $y = -2x + 3$

| x | y |
|---|---|
| -2 | ? |
| -1 | ? |
| 0 | ? |
| 1 | ? |
| 2 | ? |

**13.** $y = 3x + 1$

| x | -2 | -1 | 0 | 1 | 2 |
|---|---|---|---|---|---|
| y | ? | ? | ? | ? | ? |

**14.** $y = -x - 2$

| x | -2 | -1 | 0 | 1 | 2 |
|---|---|---|---|---|---|
| y | ? | ? | ? | ? | ? |

# WRITTEN EXERCISES 15.4

**A**

**Goal:** To graph a linear function

**Sample Problem:** Graph $y = -x + 2$. The domain is {real numbers}.

**Answer:** See Figure 3.

*Copy each table and write the missing numerals. (Step 2 of Example 1)*

**1.** $y = x + 2$

| x | y |
|---|---|
| −4 | ? |
| −2 | ? |
| 0 | ? |
| 2 | ? |

**2.** $y = x - 2$

| x | y |
|---|---|
| −3 | ? |
| −1 | ? |
| 2 | ? |
| 4 | ? |

**3.** $y = -x - 3$

| x | y |
|---|---|
| −4 | ? |
| −2 | ? |
| 0 | ? |
| 2 | ? |

**4.** $y = -x + 1$

| x | y |
|---|---|
| −3 | ? |
| −1 | ? |
| 2 | ? |
| 4 | ? |

**5.** $y = 2x - 3$

| x | y |
|---|---|
| −1 | ? |
| 0 | ? |
| 2 | ? |
| 4 | ? |

**6.** $y = -2x + 1$

| x | y |
|---|---|
| −2 | ? |
| 0 | ? |
| 2 | ? |
| 3 | ? |

**7.** $y = \frac{1}{2}x - 1$

| x | y |
|---|---|
| −4 | ? |
| −2 | ? |
| 0 | ? |
| 2 | ? |

**8.** $y = -\frac{1}{2}x + 3$

| x | y |
|---|---|
| −4 | ? |
| −2 | ? |
| 0 | ? |
| 2 | ? |

*Graph each function. Use the ordered pairs in Exercises 1–8. Then draw a line containing the points. (Steps 3 and 4 of Example 1)*

**9.** $y = x + 2$      **10.** $y = x - 2$      **11.** $y = -x - 3$      **12.** $y = -x + 1$

**13.** $y = 2x - 3$      **14.** $y = -2x + 1$      **15.** $y = \frac{1}{2}x - 1$      **16.** $y = -\frac{1}{2}x + 3$

*Graph each function with {real numbers} as the domain. Use at least four ordered pairs. (Example 1)*

**17.** $y = -x + 4$      **18.** $y = -x - 1$      **19.** $y = 2x - 1$      **20.** $y = 3x + 1$

**21.** $y = -\frac{1}{2}x + 2$      **22.** $y = \frac{1}{2}x - 3$      **23.** $y = \frac{3}{2}x - 1$      **24.** $y = -\frac{3}{2}x + 2$

**C**

*Graph each relation. Use at least four ordered pairs. Write <u>Linear</u> or <u>Not Linear</u> to describe the relation.*

**25.** $y = x \cdot x$                **26.** $y = x + 3 - x$                **27.** $y = |x + 1|$

**28.** $y = |x| + 1$                **29.** $x = y - 1$                **30.** $x = 0 \cdot y + 2$

# 15.5 The Intercepts

**P-1**    **What are the coordinates of point _A_ in Figure 1?**

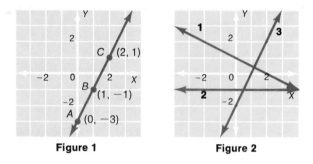

Figure 1            Figure 2

Since _A_ is on the _Y_ axis, its _x_ value is 0. Its _y_ value, −3, is called the _Y_ intercept of the line.

> The **Y intercept** of a line is the _y_ value of its point on the _Y_ axis.

**P-2**    **What is the Y intercept of each line in Figure 2 above?**

Any linear function can be described by $y = ax + b$. This is called the **intercept form** because _b_ is the _Y_ intercept.

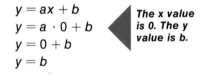

$$y = ax + b$$
$$y = a \cdot 0 + b$$
$$y = 0 + b$$
$$y = b$$

_The x value is 0. The y value is b._

**P-3**    **What is each Y intercept below?**

**a.** $y = \frac{1}{2}x + 4$    **b.** $y = -x + \frac{13}{4}$    **c.** $y = 5x - 10$

**P-4**    **What is the Y intercept of the line in Figure 3?**

The _x_ value, −3, of point _A_ is the _X_ intercept of the line. Note that the corresponding _y_ value is 0.

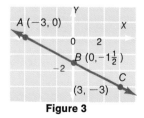

Figure 3

> The **X intercept** of a line is the x value of its point
> on the X axis.

P-5    **What is the X intercept of each line in Figure 2?**

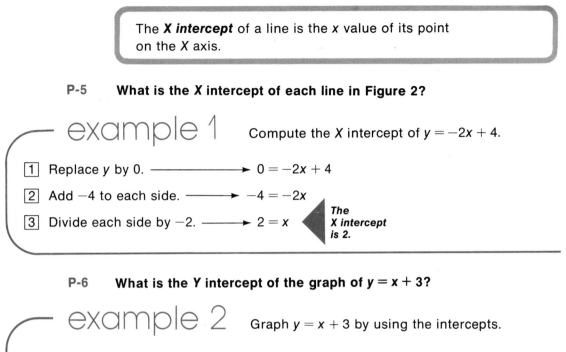

example 1    Compute the X intercept of $y = -2x + 4$.

1  Replace y by 0. ⟶ $0 = -2x + 4$

2  Add −4 to each side. ⟶ $-4 = -2x$

3  Divide each side by −2. ⟶ $2 = x$    **The X intercept is 2.**

P-6    **What is the Y intercept of the graph of $y = x + 3$?**

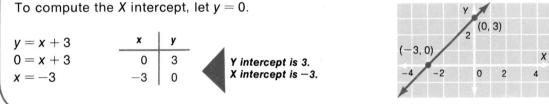

example 2    Graph $y = x + 3$ by using the intercepts.

To compute the X intercept, let $y = 0$.

$y = x + 3$
$0 = x + 3$
$x = -3$

| x | y |
|---|---|
| 0 | 3 |
| −3 | 0 |

**Y intercept is 3.**
**X intercept is −3.**

## ORAL EXERCISES 15.5

*Tell the Y intercept.* (P-3)

**1.** $y = x - 2$      **2.** $y = 2x + 3$      **3.** $y = -x + 10$

**4.** $y = -\frac{1}{2}x - 6$      **5.** $y = 4x - \frac{1}{2}$      **6.** $y = 2 + x$

**7.** $y = 0.5x + 0.7$      **8.** $y = -5x - 1.8$      **9.** $y = -0.7x - 8.4$

*Tell the X intercept.* (Example 1)

**10.** $y = x - 1$      **11.** $y = x + 1$      **12.** $y = x - 5$

**13.** $y = x + 4$      **14.** $y = 2x - 4$      **15.** $y = 3x + 6$

**16.** $y = 2x - 1$      **17.** $y = 2x + 1$      **18.** $y = 4x + 2$

## WRITTEN EXERCISES 15.5

**A**   **Goal:** To graph a linear function using the $X$ and $Y$ intercepts
**Sample Problem:** Graph $y = x + 3$.
**Answer:** See Example 2.

*Write the Y intercept. (P-3)*

1. $y = x + 5$

2. $y = x - 3$

3. $y = -3x - 4$

4. $y = 2x + 3$

5. $y = \frac{5}{2}x - x$

6. $y = \frac{7}{4}x - 2x$

7. $y = \frac{3}{2}x - \frac{1}{2}$

8. $y = \frac{1}{4}x - \frac{3}{4}$

9. $y = 1.3x - 2.1$

10. $y = -1.9x + 1.2$

11. $y = 0.5x + 6.9$

12. $y = -4.7x - 2.5$

*Compute the X intercept. (Example 1)*

13. $y = x - 3$

14. $y = x - 2$

15. $y = x + 10$

16. $y = x + 15$

17. $y = -x - 2$

18. $y = -x - 4$

19. $y = 3x - 1$

20. $y = 4x - 3$

21. $y = 2x + 5$

22. $y = 3x - 7$

23. $y = 6x + 14$

24. $y = 8x - 33$

*Graph each function. Use the two intercepts and one other point. (Example 2)*

25. $y = x - 3$

26. $y = -x + 2$

27. $y = x + \frac{5}{2}$

28. $y = x - \frac{7}{2}$

29. $y = 2x - 4$

30. $y = 2x + 2$

31. $y = \frac{1}{2}x - 2$

32. $y = -\frac{1}{2}x + 1$

33. $y = -\frac{3}{2}x + 3$

34. $y = \frac{3}{4}x - 3$

35. $y = 3x - 6$

36. $y = \frac{3}{5}x + 3$

**B**   *Compute the X and Y intercepts of the function defined by each equation.*

**EXAMPLE:** $2x + y = 4$     **SOLUTION:**

| X intercept | Y intercept |
|---|---|
| Let $y = 0$. | Let $x = 0$. |
| $2x + 0 = 4$ | $2 \cdot 0 + y = 4$ |
| $2x = 4$ | $0 + y = 4$ |
| $x = 2$ | $y = 4$ |

37. $x - y = 2$

38. $x + y = -3$

39. $x - 2y = 8$

40. $x + 3y = 6$

41. $2x - y = -5$

42. $3x - y = 4$

43. $4x + y = -9$

44. $4x - y = -9$

45. $x - 3y = -6$

# 15.6 Intersection of Two Functions

## example 1

Graph these linear functions. Write the ordered pair that is common to the two functions.

**a.** $y = -x + 1$      **b.** $y = x + 3$

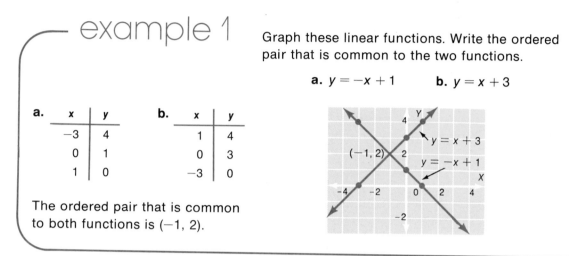

**a.**

| x | y |
|---|---|
| −3 | 4 |
| 0 | 1 |
| 1 | 0 |

**b.**

| x | y |
|---|---|
| 1 | 4 |
| 0 | 3 |
| −3 | 0 |

The ordered pair that is common to both functions is (−1, 2).

The set $\{(-1, 2)\}$ is called the <u>intersection</u> of the two functions.

> The **intersection** of two functions is the set of ordered pairs common to both functions.

## example 2

Graph the following functions. Write their intersection.

**a.** $y = \frac{1}{2}x + 2$      **b.** $y = \frac{1}{2}x - 1$

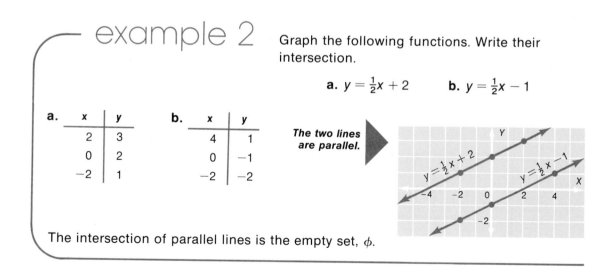

**a.**

| x | y |
|---|---|
| 2 | 3 |
| 0 | 2 |
| −2 | 1 |

**b.**

| x | y |
|---|---|
| 4 | 1 |
| 0 | −1 |
| −2 | −2 |

The two lines are parallel.

The intersection of parallel lines is the empty set, $\phi$.

You can tell when the graphs of two functions are parallel. Examine their rules as given in the form $y = ax + b$. If the values of $a$ are equal but the values of $b$ are unequal, the graphs are parallel lines.

## ORAL EXERCISES 15.6

Say <u>Yes</u> or <u>No</u> to tell whether each given set is the intersection of the two given functions.

**1.** $\{(-1, 3)\}$:   $y = x + 4$
                 $y = -x + 2$

**2.** $\{(2, 3)\}$:   $y = 2x - 1$
               $y = x + 4$

**3.** $\{(0, -1)\}$:   $y = \frac{1}{2}x - 1$
                $y = -\frac{1}{2}x + 1$

**4.** $\phi$:   $y = -x + 3$
       $y = -x - 2$

**5.** $\{(-1, 3)\}$:   $y = x + 4$
                $y = -2x + 1$

**6.** $\{(\frac{1}{2}, -2)\}$:   $y = 2x - 3$
               $y = -4x + 4$

## WRITTEN EXERCISES 15.6

**A**

**Goal:** To find the intersection of two functions from their graphs

**Sample Problem:** Graph $y = -x + 1$ and $y = x + 3$. Write their intersection.

**Answer:** See Example 1.

Complete each table. Graph the two functions and write their intersection. (Example 1, Example 2)

**1.** $y = x - 2$      $y = -x + 1$

| x | y |
|---|---|
| -2 | ? |
| 0 | ? |
| 4 | ? |

| x | y |
|---|---|
| -3 | ? |
| 0 | ? |
| 4 | ? |

**2.** $y = -x + 3$      $y = x + 1$

| x | y |
|---|---|
| -2 | ? |
| 0 | ? |
| 4 | ? |

| x | y |
|---|---|
| -4 | ? |
| -2 | ? |
| 3 | ? |

**3.** $y = 2x - 1$      $y = x + 1$

| x | y |
|---|---|
| -2 | ? |
| 0 | ? |
| 2 | ? |

| x | y |
|---|---|
| -4 | ? |
| -2 | ? |
| 3 | ? |

**4.** $y = x - 1$      $y = -2x + 2$

| x | y |
|---|---|
| -2 | ? |
| 0 | ? |
| 2 | ? |

| x | y |
|---|---|
| -3 | ? |
| -1 | ? |
| 2 | ? |

**5.** $y = -3x - 1$      $y = -2x + 1$

| x | y |
|---|---|
| -2 | ? |
| 0 | ? |
| 2 | ? |

| x | y |
|---|---|
| -1 | ? |
| 1 | ? |
| 3 | ? |

**6.** $y = 3x - 3$      $y = -x + 1$

| x | y |
|---|---|
| -1 | ? |
| 1 | ? |
| 3 | ? |

| x | y |
|---|---|
| -3 | ? |
| -1 | ? |
| 3 | ? |

**7.** $y = \frac{1}{2}x - 2$      $y = \frac{1}{2}x + 1$

| x | y |
|---|---|
| -4 | ? |
| -2 | ? |
| 0 | ? |

| x | y |
|---|---|
| -2 | ? |
| 0 | ? |
| 4 | ? |

**8.** $y = -x + 3$      $y = -x - 2$

| x | y |
|---|---|
| -2 | ? |
| 0 | ? |
| 4 | ? |

| x | y |
|---|---|
| -4 | ? |
| -2 | ? |
| 2 | ? |

## CHAPTER SUMMARY

| IMPORTANT TERMS | | | |
|---|---|---|---|
| | Axes *(p. 376)* | Ordered pair *(p. 376)* | Domain; Range *(p. 383)* |
| | X axis *(p. 376)* | Relation *(p. 379)* | Linear function *(p. 386)* |
| | Y axis *(p. 376)* | Coordinate | Y intercept *(p. 388)* |
| | Coordinates *(p. 376)* | plane *(p. 379)* | Intercept form *(p. 388)* |
| | Graph *(p. 376)* | Quadrants *(p. 379)* | X intercept *(p. 389)* |
| | Origin *(p. 376)* | Function *(p. 382)* | Intersection *(p. 391)* |

**IMPORTANT IDEAS**

1. A point in the coordinate plane is represented by an ordered pair of numbers.

2. Elements of a set can be ordered pairs of numbers.

3. Relations and functions can be described
   a. by a graph in a coordinate plane,
   b. in roster form,
   c. by a word rule,
   d. by a table of ordered pairs, or
   e. by a formula.

4. The intercept form of the rule for any linear function is $y = ax + b$.

5. The Y intercept has a corresponding x value of 0. The X intercept has a corresponding y value of 0.

6. The Y intercept of a linear function is the value of b in the rule $y = ax + b$.

7. The intersection of two functions whose graphs are parallel lines is the empty set.

8. If two rules of the form $y = ax + b$ have a values that are equal but b values that are unequal, the graphs of the two functions are parallel.

## CHAPTER REVIEW

**SECTION 15.1**

*Write the coordinates of each point shown at the right.*

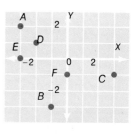

**1.** A        **2.** B        **3.** C        **4.** D        **5.** E        **6.** F

*Graph the following points.*

**7.** $A(-2, -3)$        **8.** $B(2, -2)$        **9.** $C(2, 4)$

**10.** $D(-3, 1)$        **11.** $E(0, 2)$        **12.** $F(3, 0)$

## SECTION 15.2

Graph each relation in a separate coordinate plane.

**13.** $\{(2, 3), (-4, 2), (0, -3), (-2, -2)\}$  **14.** $\{(-1, -3), (2, 4), (3, -3), (-4, 0)\}$

**15.** $\{(2\frac{1}{2}, 1\frac{1}{2}), (-3, 2\frac{1}{2}), (-3\frac{1}{2}, -4), (-\frac{1}{2}, 0)\}$  **16.** $\{(-3, 2\frac{1}{2}), (0, -1\frac{1}{2}), (3\frac{1}{2}, -2\frac{1}{2}), (\frac{1}{2}, 3)\}$

Write each relation in roster form for these x values: 0, -1, 2, -2.

**17.** Subtract 5 from each x value.  **18.** Multiply each x value by -3; add 1.

**19.** Add -3 to each x value.  **20.** Divide each x value by 2; subtract 3.

## SECTION 15.3

Write <u>Yes</u> or <u>No</u> to show whether each relation is a function.

**21.** $\{(5, -1), (0, 2), (3, 2)\}$  **22.** $\{(-1, 2), (0, 5), (\frac{1}{2}, 2)\}$

Write the domain, D, and the range, R, in roster form.

**23.** $\{(7, -2), (4, 0), (-6, 1)\}$  **24.** $\{(3, -1), (0, 0), (5, 2)\}$

**25.** $\{(-\frac{1}{2}, 1), (3, -4), (0, 1)\}$  **26.** $\{(4, 2), (0, -3), (5, -3)\}$

## SECTION 15.4

Graph each function with {real numbers} as the domain.

**27.** $y = -x - 2$  **28.** $y = \frac{1}{2}x + 3$  **29.** $y = -\frac{1}{2}x - 2$  **30.** $y = -2x + 1$

## SECTION 15.5

Write the Y intercept.

**31.** $y = 5x - 6$  **32.** $y = -\frac{3}{2}x + \frac{1}{4}$  **33.** $y = 15 - 2x$  **34.** $y = 3.8 - 1.5x$

Compute the X intercept.

**35.** $y = x - 12$  **36.** $y = -x + 7$  **37.** $y = -x - 6$  **38.** $y = 3x + 2$

## SECTION 15.6

Graph the two functions, and write their intersection.

**39.** $y = 2x - 1$   $y = x - 3$  **40.** $y = -x + 1$   $y = -3x - 3$

# 16

# Equations with
# Two Variables

# 16.1 Graphical Method

An equation like $x + y - 2 = 0$ is a *linear equation* in two variables.

> The **standard form** of a linear equation is $Ax + By + C = 0$ in which $A$, $B$, and $C$ represent integers. ($A$ and $B$ not both 0)

**P-1** **What are the values of $A$, $B$, and $C$ in $x + y - 2 = 0$?**

> The **truth set of a linear equation** in two variables is the set of ordered pairs that make the equation true.

Solution set is another name for truth set.

**P-2** **What is the intercept form of $x - y + 2 = 0$? of $x + 3y - 2 = 0$?**

example 1    Graph the truth sets of these equations in the same coordinate plane. Write their intersection.

$$\begin{cases} \textbf{1.}\ x - y + 2 = 0 \\ \textbf{2.}\ x + 3y - 2 = 0 \end{cases}$$

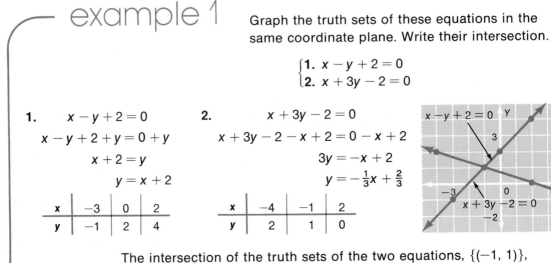

**1.**
$$x - y + 2 = 0$$
$$x - y + 2 + y = 0 + y$$
$$x + 2 = y$$
$$y = x + 2$$

| x | −3 | 0 | 2 |
|---|----|---|---|
| y | −1 | 2 | 4 |

**2.**
$$x + 3y - 2 = 0$$
$$x + 3y - 2 - x + 2 = 0 - x + 2$$
$$3y = -x + 2$$
$$y = -\tfrac{1}{3}x + \tfrac{2}{3}$$

| x | −4 | −1 | 2 |
|---|----|----|---|
| y | 2  | 1  | 0 |

The intersection of the truth sets of the two equations, $\{(-1, 1)\}$, is the truth set of the <u>system of equations</u>.

> Two equations in the same two variables form a **system of equations**.
>
> $$\begin{cases} x - 2y + 3 = 0 \\ 3x + 4y - 1 = 0 \end{cases}$$

## ORAL EXERCISES 16.1

*Say Yes or No to tell whether each equation is in standard form.*

**1.** $8x - 3y + 7 = 0$

**2.** $y = 3x + 7$

**3.** $x - y = 3$

**4.** $-2x + y - 1 = 0$

**5.** $2x + 3y = 0$

**6.** $x + 6 = 0$

*Tell the intercept form of each equation.* (P-2)

**7.** $-x + y + 1 = 0$

**8.** $x - y + 3 = 0$

**9.** $y - 2x = 5$

**10.** $y - 6 = -x$

**11.** $4x + 2y = -6$

**12.** $4x = 3 - y$

*Say Yes or No to tell whether the truth set of each system of equations is shown.* (Example 1)

**13.** $\{(1, 1)\}$;  $\begin{cases} x + y - 2 = 0 \\ 2x - y - 1 = 0 \end{cases}$

**14.** $\{(5, -7)\}$;  $\begin{cases} x + 2y - 3 = 0 \\ x + y + 2 = 0 \end{cases}$

## WRITTEN EXERCISES 16.1

**A**

**Goal:** To solve a system of equations by the graphical method

**Sample Problem:** Graph $\begin{cases} \textbf{1.} \ x - y + 2 = 0 \\ \textbf{2.} \ x + 3y - 2 = 0 \end{cases}$ and write the truth set.

**Answer:** See Example 1.

*Graph the two equations of each system in the same coordinate plane. Write the truth set of the system.* (Example 1)

**1.** $\begin{cases} x + y - 2 = 0 \\ 2x - y - 1 = 0 \end{cases}$

**2.** $\begin{cases} 2x - y + 1 = 0 \\ x - 2y - 1 = 0 \end{cases}$

**3.** $\begin{cases} x - 2y + 2 = 0 \\ x - y + 3 = 0 \end{cases}$

**4.** $\begin{cases} x + y - 2 = 0 \\ x - 3y - 6 = 0 \end{cases}$

**5.** $\begin{cases} x - 2y + 2 = 0 \\ x + y + 2 = 0 \end{cases}$

**6.** $\begin{cases} x + 4y + 4 = 0 \\ 2x - y - 1 = 0 \end{cases}$

**7.** $\begin{cases} 2x - y = 0 \\ x + 3y = 0 \end{cases}$

**8.** $\begin{cases} x + y = 0 \\ 2x - 3y = 0 \end{cases}$

**9.** $\begin{cases} 2x + 3y - 3 = 0 \\ x - 2y + 2 = 0 \end{cases}$

**10.** $\begin{cases} x - 3y + 1 = 0 \\ x - y - 1 = 0 \end{cases}$

**11.** $\begin{cases} 2x - y + 2 = 0 \\ x - 2y - 2 = 0 \end{cases}$

**12.** $\begin{cases} x + 3y - 4 = 0 \\ x - 2y + 6 = 0 \end{cases}$

**B**

**13.** $\begin{cases} x + 2y + 1 = 0 \\ x - 2y + 3 = 0 \end{cases}$

**14.** $\begin{cases} 4x + 3y - 3 = 0 \\ 2x - 3y - 6 = 0 \end{cases}$

**15.** $\begin{cases} 4x + y + 11 = 0 \\ 2x - 3y + 2 = 0 \end{cases}$

# 16.2 Substitution Method

example 1    Solve: $\begin{cases} \textbf{1. } 2x + y - 1 = 0 \\ \textbf{2. } 3x + y + 2 = 0 \end{cases}$

[1] Write an equation equivalent to either **1** or **2** with only a variable on one side.

> **1.** $2x + y - 1 = 0$
>
> $y = -2x + 1$

[2] Substitute $(-2x + 1)$ for $y$ in equation **2**. Solve for $x$.

> **2.** $\qquad 3x + y + 2 = 0$
>
> $3x + (\textbf{-2x + 1}) + 2 = 0$
>
> $3x - 2x + 1 + 2 = 0$
>
> $x + 3 = 0$
>
> $x = -3$

[3] Substitute $-3$ for $x$ in one of the equations. Solve for $y$.

> **1.** $\qquad 2x + y - 1 = 0$
>
> $2(\textbf{-3}) + y - 1 = 0$
>
> $-6 + y - 1 = 0$
>
> $y - 7 = 0$
>
> $y = 7$

[4] Check by substituting $-3$ for $x$ and $7$ for $y$ in both equations.

> **Check:** **1.** $\quad 2x + y - 1 = 0$     **2.** $\quad 3x + y + 2 = 0$
>
> $\qquad 2(\textbf{-3}) + 7 - 1 \qquad\qquad\qquad 3(\textbf{-3}) + 7 + 2$
>
> $\qquad -6 + 7 - 1 \qquad\qquad\qquad\quad -9 + 7 + 2$
>
> $\qquad\qquad 0 \qquad\qquad\qquad\qquad\qquad\quad 0$

The truth set is $\{(-3, 7)\}$.

Example 1 shows the **substitution method** of solving linear equations. In $2x + y - 1$ the number 2 is the **coefficient** of $2x$. The coefficient of $y$ is 1 since $2x + y - 1$ can be written as $2x + 1y - 1$. In this method try to solve first for a variable that has 1 or $-1$ as its coefficient.

# example 2

Solve: $\begin{cases} \textbf{1. } 2x - 2y + 1 = 0 \\ \textbf{2. } -x + 2y - 3 = 0 \end{cases}$

☐1 Write an equation equivalent to either **1** or **2** with only a variable on one side.

$$\textbf{2.} \quad -x + 2y - 3 = 0$$
$$-x + 2y - 3 + x = 0 + x$$
$$2y - 3 = x$$

◀ *x is chosen in **2** because its coefficient is −1.*

☐2 Substitute $(2y - 3)$ for *x* in equation **1**.

$$\textbf{1.} \quad 2x - 2y + 1 = 0$$
$$2(\textbf{2y} - \textbf{3}) - 2y + 1 = 0$$
$$4y - 6 - 2y + 1 = 0$$
$$2y - 5 = 0$$
$$2y = 5$$
$$y = \tfrac{5}{2}$$

☐3 Substitute $\tfrac{5}{2}$ for *y* in either equation.

$$\textbf{1.} \quad 2x - 2\textbf{y} + 1 = 0$$
$$2x - 2(\tfrac{5}{2}) + 1 = 0$$
$$2x - 5 + 1 = 0$$
$$2x - 4 = 0$$
$$2x = 4$$
$$x = 2$$

☐4 Check by substituting 2 for *x* and $\tfrac{5}{2}$ for *y* in both equations to determine whether $\{(2, \tfrac{5}{2})\}$ is the truth set.

---

### Steps for the Substitution Method

☐1 Write an equation that is equivalent to one of the equations with only a variable on one side.

☐2 Substitute the phrase that equals that variable in the other equation. Solve the resulting equation.

☐3 Substitute the value of the variable in step ☐2 in either equation. Solve the resulting equation.

☐4 Check by substituting both values in both equations.

## ORAL EXERCISES 16.2

*Tell an equivalent equation with only a variable on one side.* (Step 1 of Examples 1 and 2)

1. $x + y - 10 = 0$

2. $x - 3y + 4 = 0$

3. $-3x - y + 1 = 0$

4. $4x + y - 5 = 0$

5. $2y - x = 7$

6. $x + y = -9$

7. $3x - 9 - y = 0$

8. $4x + 2y = 6$

9. $x - 2y + 4 = 0$

*Tell the next step in solving each equation.* (Step 2 of Examples 1 and 2)

**EXAMPLE:** $2x - 3(x - 1) + 3 = 0$     **ANSWER:** $2x - 3x + 3 + 3 = 0$

10. $3x - 5(x + 2) - 3 = 0$

11. $-2(y - 3) + 3y - 1 = 0$

12. $3(2y - 2) - 4y + 5 = 0$

13. $-x + 2(-2x - 3) + 4 = 0$

14. $-3x - (4x - 2) - 6 = 0$

15. $2(\frac{1}{2}y - 1) + y - 5 = 0$

## WRITTEN EXERCISES 16.2

**A**

**Goal:** To solve a system of equations by the substitution method

**Sample Problem:** Solve: $\begin{cases} \text{1. } 2x + 3y - 1 = 0 \\ \text{2. } x - 2y + 3 = 0 \end{cases}$

**Answer:** $\{(-1, 1)\}$

*Solve each system of equations by the substitution method. Check.* (Example 1, Example 2)

1. $\begin{cases} 2x + y - 1 = 0 \\ 5x + 2y - 4 = 0 \end{cases}$

2. $\begin{cases} -x + y + 3 = 0 \\ 3x - 2y - 5 = 0 \end{cases}$

3. $\begin{cases} x - 3y - 1 = 0 \\ -2x + 4y - 2 = 0 \end{cases}$

4. $\begin{cases} x + 2y - 3 = 0 \\ -2x - y - 3 = 0 \end{cases}$

5. $\begin{cases} x + 3y + 2 = 0 \\ -x - y + 4 = 0 \end{cases}$

6. $\begin{cases} 3x + y - 5 = 0 \\ -4x - 2y + 2 = 0 \end{cases}$

7. $\begin{cases} 2x - y = 4 \\ 2x - \frac{1}{2}y = -5 \end{cases}$

8. $\begin{cases} -x + 4y = 2 \\ -\frac{1}{2}x - 2y = 5 \end{cases}$

9. $\begin{cases} 4x - y - 3 = 0 \\ 6x - 2y - 3 = 0 \end{cases}$

10. $\begin{cases} -2x + y - 5 = 0 \\ -4x + 3y + 10 = 0 \end{cases}$

11. $\begin{cases} x - y - 4 = 0 \\ 2x - 3y + 2 = 0 \end{cases}$

12. $\begin{cases} x - y - 3 = 0 \\ 5x + y + 15 = 0 \end{cases}$

**B**

13. $\begin{cases} 2x + 2y - 4 = 0 \\ 2x - 2y + 5 = 0 \end{cases}$

14. $\begin{cases} -3x + 3y - 6 = 0 \\ x - 4y + 8 = 0 \end{cases}$

15. $\begin{cases} 2x - 3y + 6 = 0 \\ 4x - 3y + 3 = 0 \end{cases}$

# 16.3 Addition Method

P-1 **What is the truth set of the system below based on its graph?**

$$\begin{cases} 1.\ x + 2y - 1 = 0 \\ 2.\ x - y + 2 = 0 \end{cases}$$

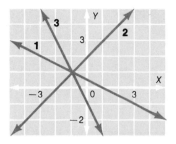

P-2 **How is equation 3 formed from equations 1 and 2?**

$$3.\ (x + 2y - 1) + (x - y + 2) = 0 + 0$$
$$2x + y + 1 = 0$$

◄ *Equation 3 also contains (−1, 1) in its truth set.*

The following examples are solved by the **addition method**.

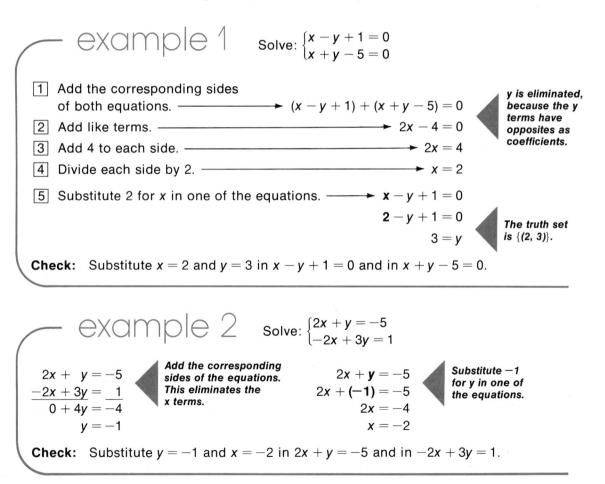

## example 1

Solve: $\begin{cases} x - y + 1 = 0 \\ x + y - 5 = 0 \end{cases}$

1. Add the corresponding sides of both equations. ⟶ $(x - y + 1) + (x + y - 5) = 0$
2. Add like terms. ⟶ $2x - 4 = 0$
3. Add 4 to each side. ⟶ $2x = 4$
4. Divide each side by 2. ⟶ $x = 2$
5. Substitute 2 for x in one of the equations. ⟶ $x - y + 1 = 0$
$$2 - y + 1 = 0$$
$$3 = y$$

◄ *y is eliminated, because the y terms have opposites as coefficients.*

◄ *The truth set is {(2, 3)}.*

**Check:** Substitute $x = 2$ and $y = 3$ in $x - y + 1 = 0$ and in $x + y - 5 = 0$.

## example 2

Solve: $\begin{cases} 2x + y = -5 \\ -2x + 3y = 1 \end{cases}$

$$\begin{array}{r} 2x + \ y = -5 \\ -2x + 3y = \ \ 1 \\ \hline 0 + 4y = -4 \\ y = -1 \end{array}$$

◄ *Add the corresponding sides of the equations. This eliminates the x terms.*

$$2x + y = -5$$
$$2x + (-1) = -5$$
$$2x = -4$$
$$x = -2$$

◄ *Substitute −1 for y in one of the equations.*

**Check:** Substitute $y = -1$ and $x = -2$ in $2x + y = -5$ and in $-2x + 3y = 1$.

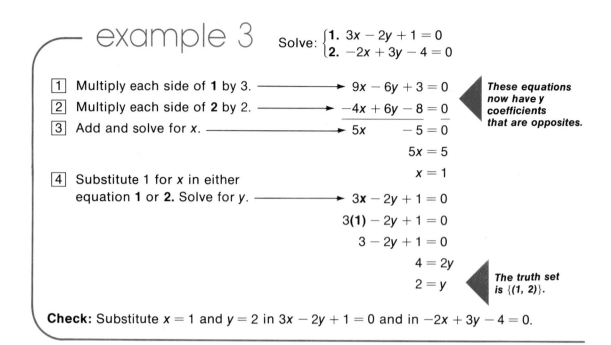

example 3   Solve: $\begin{cases} \textbf{1. } 3x - 2y + 1 = 0 \\ \textbf{2. } -2x + 3y - 4 = 0 \end{cases}$

1. Multiply each side of **1** by 3. ⟶ $9x - 6y + 3 = 0$

2. Multiply each side of **2** by 2. ⟶ $-4x + 6y - 8 = 0$

3. Add and solve for $x$. ⟶ $5x \qquad\quad - 5 = 0$

These equations now have $y$ coefficients that are opposites.

$$5x = 5$$
$$x = 1$$

4. Substitute 1 for $x$ in either equation **1** or **2**. Solve for $y$. ⟶ $3x - 2y + 1 = 0$

$$3(1) - 2y + 1 = 0$$
$$3 - 2y + 1 = 0$$
$$4 = 2y$$
$$2 = y$$

The truth set is $\{(1, 2)\}$.

**Check:** Substitute $x = 1$ and $y = 2$ in $3x - 2y + 1 = 0$ and in $-2x + 3y - 4 = 0$.

---

### Steps for the Addition Method

1. Check for opposite coefficients of one variable. If necessary, multiply each side of either or both equations by numbers that will make opposite coefficients for one variable.

2. Add the corresponding sides to eliminate one of the variables.

3. Solve for the remaining variable.

4. Substitute the value from step 3 in one of the equations. Solve for the other variable.

5. Check by substituting both values in both equations.

## ORAL EXERCISES 16.3

*Tell what equation results if you add corresponding sides of the two equations in each system.* (Step 1 of Examples 1 and 2)

1. $\begin{cases} x + 2y - 3 = 0 \\ -x + y + 1 = 0 \end{cases}$

2. $\begin{cases} 2x - 3y + 2 = 0 \\ x + 3y - 4 = 0 \end{cases}$

3. $\begin{cases} 4x - 5y = -2 \\ x + 5y = 8 \end{cases}$

4. $\begin{cases} -2x + 3y = 7 \\ 2x - 5y = -3 \end{cases}$

5. $\begin{cases} 10x - 3y = 0 \\ -7x + 3y = -5 \end{cases}$

6. $\begin{cases} -3x - y + 8 = 0 \\ 3x - 2y - 7 = 0 \end{cases}$

*Tell what number to multiply each side of each equation by in order to eliminate x by addition. (Steps 1 and 2 of Example 3)*

**EXAMPLE:** $\begin{cases} \textbf{1.} \ 2x - y - 1 = 0 \\ \textbf{2.} \ 3x + 2y + 1 = 0 \end{cases}$    **ANSWER:** Multiply **1** by −3 and **2** by 2, or multiply **1** by 3 and **2** by −2.

**7.** $\begin{cases} x + y - 2 = 0 \\ -2x + 3y + 1 = 0 \end{cases}$

**8.** $\begin{cases} 3x - y + 5 = 0 \\ x + 2y - 1 = 0 \end{cases}$

**9.** $\begin{cases} -3x + 2y - 5 = 0 \\ x - y + 3 = 0 \end{cases}$

**10.** $\begin{cases} 2x - y + 2 = 0 \\ -3x + y - 1 = 0 \end{cases}$

**11.** $\begin{cases} 2x - y + 3 = 0 \\ 5x + 2y - 1 = 0 \end{cases}$

**12.** $\begin{cases} 4x - y - 2 = 0 \\ -3x + 2y - 1 = 0 \end{cases}$

*Tell the truth set of each system. (Example 1, Example 2, Example 3)*

**13.** $\begin{cases} x + y = 2 \\ x - y = -6 \end{cases}$

**14.** $\begin{cases} -2x + y = 1 \\ 2x + y = 3 \end{cases}$

**15.** $\begin{cases} 3x - y = 5 \\ -3x - y = 1 \end{cases}$

## WRITTEN EXERCISES 16.3

**A**

**Goal:** To solve a system of equations by the addition method.

**Sample Problem:** Solve: $\begin{cases} \textbf{1.} \ 3x + 4y - 10 = 0 \\ \textbf{2.} \ 2x - y + 8 = 0 \end{cases}$

**Answer:** $\{(-2, 4)\}$

*Solve each system by the addition method. Check. (Examples 1, 2, and 3)*

**1.** $\begin{cases} x + y - 1 = 0 \\ x - y + 3 = 0 \end{cases}$

**2.** $\begin{cases} -2x + y - 2 = 0 \\ 2x + y + 4 = 0 \end{cases}$

**3.** $\begin{cases} 3x - 2y + 3 = 0 \\ -3x + y - 1 = 0 \end{cases}$

**4.** $\begin{cases} x - 5y - 2 = 0 \\ 2x + 5y - 4 = 0 \end{cases}$

**5.** $\begin{cases} 2x - y + 1 = 0 \\ -2x + 2y - 2 = 0 \end{cases}$

**6.** $\begin{cases} 3x + 2y - 5 = 0 \\ -3x - y + 4 = 0 \end{cases}$

**7.** $\begin{cases} -3x + 7y + 1 = 0 \\ 2x - 7y - 3 = 0 \end{cases}$

**8.** $\begin{cases} x - 4y - 5 = 0 \\ -2x + 4y + 2 = 0 \end{cases}$

**9.** $\begin{cases} x - 3y = 1 \\ -x + y = -5 \end{cases}$

**10.** $\begin{cases} -4x - y = 3 \\ 2x + y = 3 \end{cases}$

**11.** $\begin{cases} 2x - 3y = 0 \\ -x + 3y = 0 \end{cases}$

**12.** $\begin{cases} 4x - 2y = 0 \\ -4x + 3y = 0 \end{cases}$

**13.** $\begin{cases} 2x - 3y = -5 \\ 3x + 3y = -5 \end{cases}$

**14.** $\begin{cases} 3x - 2y - 2 = 0 \\ x + 2y - 2 = 0 \end{cases}$

**15.** $\begin{cases} x + y = 3 \\ 2x + y = -1 \end{cases}$

**16.** $\begin{cases} x - 3y = 1 \\ 2x - 3y = -4 \end{cases}$

**17.** $\begin{cases} 2x + 3y = -3 \\ -x - 2y = 2 \end{cases}$

**18.** $\begin{cases} -4x + y = 2 \\ 3x - 2y = 1 \end{cases}$

**B**

**19.** $\begin{cases} 2x - y = -1 \\ -3x + 4y = -1 \end{cases}$

**20.** $\begin{cases} x - 2y = 1 \\ 5x - 3y = -2 \end{cases}$

**21.** $\begin{cases} 4x - y = 1 \\ 2x + 2y = 3 \end{cases}$

# 16.4 Number Problems

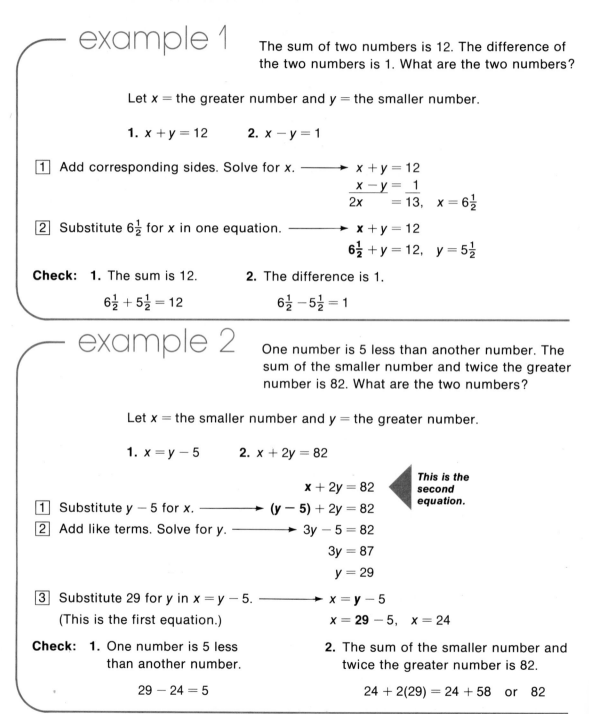

## example 1

The sum of two numbers is 12. The difference of the two numbers is 1. What are the two numbers?

Let $x$ = the greater number and $y$ = the smaller number.

**1.** $x + y = 12$ **2.** $x - y = 1$

1 Add corresponding sides. Solve for $x$. ⟶
$$\begin{array}{r} x + y = 12 \\ x - y = \underline{\phantom{0}1} \\ 2x = 13, \quad x = 6\frac{1}{2} \end{array}$$

2 Substitute $6\frac{1}{2}$ for $x$ in one equation. ⟶
$$x + y = 12$$
$$6\frac{1}{2} + y = 12, \quad y = 5\frac{1}{2}$$

**Check:** **1.** The sum is 12. **2.** The difference is 1.
$$6\frac{1}{2} + 5\frac{1}{2} = 12 \qquad\qquad 6\frac{1}{2} - 5\frac{1}{2} = 1$$

## example 2

One number is 5 less than another number. The sum of the smaller number and twice the greater number is 82. What are the two numbers?

Let $x$ = the smaller number and $y$ = the greater number.

**1.** $x = y - 5$ **2.** $x + 2y = 82$

$$x + 2y = 82$$

◀ This is the second equation.

1 Substitute $y - 5$ for $x$. ⟶ $(y - 5) + 2y = 82$

2 Add like terms. Solve for $y$. ⟶ $3y - 5 = 82$
$$3y = 87$$
$$y = 29$$

3 Substitute 29 for $y$ in $x = y - 5$. ⟶ $x = y - 5$
(This is the first equation.) $\qquad x = 29 - 5, \quad x = 24$

**Check:** **1.** One number is 5 less than another number.
$$29 - 24 = 5$$

**2.** The sum of the smaller number and twice the greater number is 82.
$$24 + 2(29) = 24 + 58 \quad \text{or} \quad 82$$

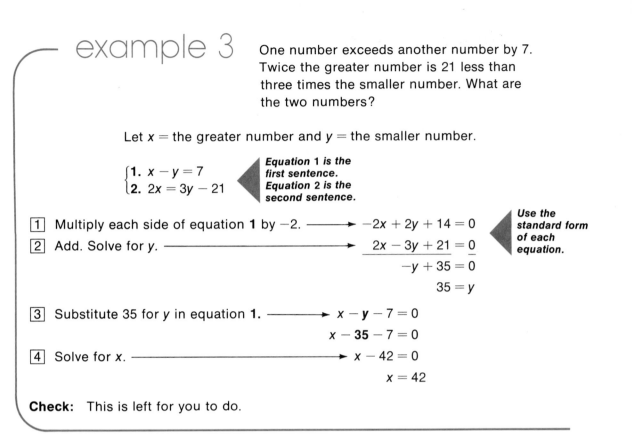

example 3
One number exceeds another number by 7. Twice the greater number is 21 less than three times the smaller number. What are the two numbers?

Let $x$ = the greater number and $y$ = the smaller number.

$$\begin{cases} \textbf{1.} \ x - y = 7 \\ \textbf{2.} \ 2x = 3y - 21 \end{cases}$$

**Equation 1 is the first sentence.**
**Equation 2 is the second sentence.**

boxed 1 Multiply each side of equation **1** by $-2$. ⟶ $-2x + 2y + 14 = 0$

**Use the standard form of each equation.**

boxed 2 Add. Solve for $y$. ⟶ $\underline{2x - 3y + 21 = 0}$
$$-y + 35 = 0$$
$$35 = y$$

boxed 3 Substitute 35 for $y$ in equation **1**. ⟶ $x - \textbf{y} - 7 = 0$
$$x - \textbf{35} - 7 = 0$$

boxed 4 Solve for $x$. ⟶ $x - 42 = 0$
$$x = 42$$

**Check:** This is left for you to do.

## ORAL EXERCISES 16.4

*Tell an equation that describes each sentence. Let x equal the smaller number and y the greater number.* (Examples 1, 2, and 3)

**1.** One number is 12 greater than the other.

**2.** One number is 5 less than the other.

**3.** One number is 3 times as great as the other.

**4.** The sum of the two numbers is 15.

**5.** The difference of the two numbers is $-3$.

**6.** One number is 3 more than twice the other number.

**7.** One number is one third as great as the other number.

**8.** One number exceeds the other number by 5.

**9.** One number is 16 more than the other number.

**10.** The greater number is 10 less than 5 times the smaller number.

11. Twice the smaller number is 2 more than the greater number.

12. Three times the sum of the two numbers is 52.

13. One number diminished by the other number equals −25.

14. Three times one number equals five times the other number.

15. The opposite of the smaller number is 12 more than the greater number.

## WRITTEN EXERCISES 16.4

**A**  **Goal:** To solve a word problem about numbers using a system of equations in two variables

**Sample Problem:** The sum of two numbers is −5. Twice the greater number equals ten more than three times the smaller number.

**Answer:** The two numbers are −1 and −4.

*In each problem, (a) select two variables for the unknown numbers, (b) write two equations, and (c) solve to find the unknown numbers. (Example 1, Example 2, Example 3)*

1. The sum of two numbers is 31. The difference of the two numbers is 3.

2. The sum of two numbers is 25. The difference of the two numbers is 4.

3. The sum of two numbers is 5. The difference of the two numbers is −2.

4. The sum of two numbers is −6. The difference of the two numbers is 11.

5. One number is 13 more than another number. The sum of the numbers is 38.

6. One number is 15 less than another number. The sum of the numbers is 24.

7. One number exceeds another number by 8. Twice the smaller number is 4 more than the greater number.

8. One number less another number equals 18. Twice the smaller number is one less than the greater number.

9. The sum of two numbers is −20. Three times the greater number equals twice the smaller number.

10. The sum of two numbers is −44. Four times the greater number is 8 less than three times the smaller number.

11. Twice the smaller of two numbers is 18 less than the greater number. Three times the greater number exceeds the smaller number by 34.

12. One number is 15 more than another number. Five times the smaller number is 20 less than the greater number.

# 16.5 Problems Involving Money

example 1

A woman bought 8 blouses for $84. One kind cost $8 each and another kind cost $12 each. How many blouses of each kind did she buy?

Let $x$ = the number of blouses costing $8 each, and $y$ = the number of blouses costing $12 each.

**1.** $x + y = 8$    **2.** $8x + 12y = 84$    ◄ $x + y$ = total number of blouses. $8x + 12y$ = total cost of blouses.

1. Write $x + y = 8$ in intercept form. ⟶ $y = -x + 8$
2. Substitute $-x + 8$ for $y$ in **2.** ⟶ $8x + 12(-x + 8) = 84$
3. Distributive Property ⟶ $8x - 12x + 96 = 84$
4. Add like terms. ⟶ $-4x + 96 = 84$
5. Solve for $x$. ⟶ $-4x = -12, \quad x = 3$

6. Substitute 3 for $x$ in $x + y = 8$. ⟶ $3 + y = 8$
7. Solve for $y$. ⟶ $y = 5$

◄ **She bought 3 blouses for $8 and 5 blouses for $12.**

example 2

Hank sold 54 tickets for the school play for $35.00. Student tickets cost $0.50 and adult tickets cost $0.90. How many tickets of each kind did he sell?

Let $x$ = the number of student tickets, and $y$ = the number of adult tickets.

**1.** $x + y = 54$    **2.** $50x + 90y = 3500$    ◄ $x + y$ = number of tickets sold. $50x + 90y$ = value of the tickets in cents.

$$50x + 90y = 3500$$
$$50x + 90(54 - x) = 3500$$
$$50x + 4860 - 90x = 3500$$
$$-40x = -1360$$
$$x = 34$$

◄ **Substitute 54 − x for y in 2.**

$$x + y = 54$$
$$34 + y = 54$$
$$y = 20$$

◄ **He sold 34 student and 20 adult tickets.**

## example 3

One kind of candy sells for $1.60 per kilogram, and another kind sells for $1.20 per kilogram. A grocer mixes the two kinds of candy to get a mixture of 32 kilograms to sell for $1.35 per kilogram. How many kilograms of each kind of candy are in the mixture?

| | Number of Kilograms | Cost per Kilogram (in cents) | Total Cost (in cents) |
|---|---|---|---|
| Less Expensive Candy | $x$ | 120 | $120x$ |
| More Expensive Candy | $y$ | 160 | $160y$ |
| Mixture | 32 | 135 | $32(135)$ |

$$\begin{cases} \textbf{1. } x + y = 32 \\ \textbf{2. } 120x + 160y = 4320 \end{cases}$$
or
$$\begin{cases} \textbf{1. } y = 32 - x \\ \textbf{2. } 120x + 160y = 4320 \end{cases}$$

◄ **Replace y in 2 with 32 − x.**

$$120x + 160(\mathbf{32 - x}) = 4320$$
$$120x + 5120 - 160x = 4320$$
$$-40x = -800$$
$$x = 20$$

$$y = 32 - \mathbf{x}$$
$$y = 32 - \mathbf{20}$$
$$y = 12$$

◄ **He uses 20 kg @ $1.20 and 12 kg @ $1.60.**

Although no check is shown for Examples 1, 2, or 3, it is important to do a check as the last step.

## ORAL EXERCISES 16.5

*Tell two equations that describe each problem.* (Example 1, Example 2, Example 3)

**1.** Jean has a collection of 21 coins worth $2.30 consisting of $x$ dimes and $y$ nickels.

**2.** Mrs. King bought three dozen doughnuts for $5.04. She bought $x$ doughnuts at 15 cents each and $y$ doughnuts at 12 cents each.

**3.** A club of 48 members has $x$ senior members and $y$ junior members. The receipts from dues are $216 with $5 from each senior member and $2 from each junior member.

**4.** Nan and Jan walked a total of 28 miles for the March of Dimes and earned $5.00. Nan walked $x$ miles for 15 cents a mile, and Jan walked $y$ miles for 20 cents a mile.

## WRITTEN EXERCISES 16.5

**A**

**Goal:** To solve a word problem about money using a system of equations in two variables

**Sample Problem:** Hector pays $4 for stamps. The number of eight-cent stamps equals five times the number of ten-cent stamps. How many of each kind does he buy?

**Answer:** He buys 40 eight-cent stamps and 8 ten-cent stamps.

*In each problem, (a) select two variables for the unknown numbers, (b) write two equations, and (c) solve. (Example 1, Example 2, Example 3)*

1. Jerry has nickels and dimes in his bank worth $1.85. There are a total of 27 coins. How many of each kind are there?

2. A candy machine contains dimes and quarters worth $29.45. There are 215 coins in all. How many of each kind are there?

3. Susie sold 29 boxes of Girl Scout cookies worth $68. One kind sold for $2.00 a box, and the other kind for $2.50. How many boxes of each kind did she sell?

4. Randy sold 27 magazine subscriptions for $192. The magazine *Now* sold for $6.00, and the magazine *World* sold for $8.50. How many subscriptions did he sell for each magazine?

5. Mrs. Flores purchased hamburgers and hot dogs for a school committee meeting at a cost of $19.65. There were four more hot dogs than hamburgers. The hot dogs cost $0.65 each, and the hamburgers cost $0.90 each. How many hot dogs and hamburgers did she buy?

6. Mr. Wood bought popcorn and ice cream bars for his Little League team costing $9.50. He bought twice as many ice cream bars as boxes of popcorn. The ice cream bars cost $0.30 each and the popcorn cost $0.35 per box. How many ice cream bars and how many boxes of popcorn did he buy?

7. White tickets (singles) to the Senior Class dance cost $0.75, and red tickets (couples) cost $1.25. A total of 260 tickets, worth $290, were sold. How many white tickets and how many red tickets were sold?

8. The Parent Music Club served 700 persons at their Mexican dinner. Dinners cost $2.50 for adults and $1.50 for children. A total of $1530 was earned. How many adults and how many children were served?

**B**

9. A bank contains nickels, dimes, and quarters worth $4.90. There are four more nickels than dimes and 34 coins in all. How many of each kind of coin are there?

## 16.6 Miscellaneous Problems

### example 1

The perimeter of a rectangle is 40 centimeters. The length is 6 centimeters more than the width. Find the length, $y$, and the width, $x$.

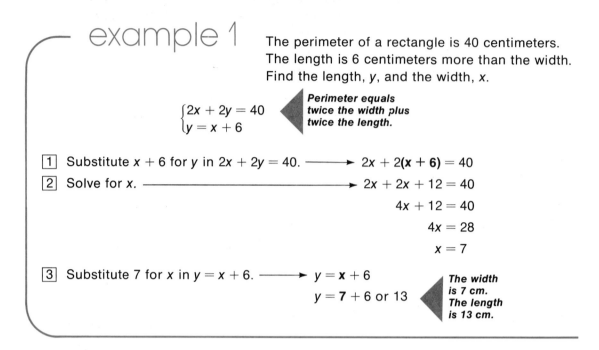

$$\begin{cases} 2x + 2y = 40 \\ y = x + 6 \end{cases}$$

***Perimeter equals twice the width plus twice the length.***

[1] Substitute $x + 6$ for $y$ in $2x + 2y = 40$. ⟶ $2x + 2(\mathbf{x + 6}) = 40$

[2] Solve for $x$. ⟶ $2x + 2x + 12 = 40$

$$4x + 12 = 40$$
$$4x = 28$$
$$x = 7$$

[3] Substitute 7 for $x$ in $y = x + 6$. ⟶ $y = \mathbf{x} + 6$

$y = \mathbf{7} + 6$ or 13

***The width is 7 cm. The length is 13 cm.***

### example 2

The sum of the ages of a father and his son is 56. The father's age is three times the age of his son. Find $y$, the age of the father, and $x$, the age of the son.

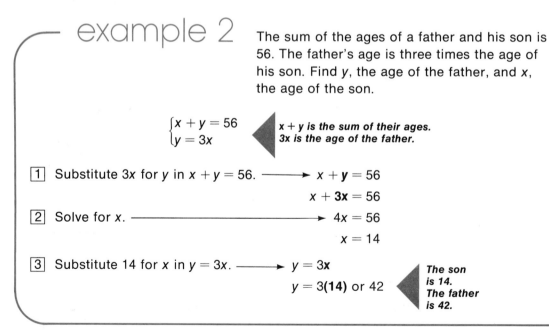

$$\begin{cases} x + y = 56 \\ y = 3x \end{cases}$$

***$x + y$ is the sum of their ages. $3x$ is the age of the father.***

[1] Substitute $3x$ for $y$ in $x + y = 56$. ⟶ $x + \mathbf{y} = 56$

$$x + \mathbf{3x} = 56$$

[2] Solve for $x$. ⟶ $4x = 56$

$$x = 14$$

[3] Substitute 14 for $x$ in $y = 3x$. ⟶ $y = 3\mathbf{x}$

$y = 3(\mathbf{14})$ or 42

***The son is 14. The father is 42.***

**P-1** **How can Examples 1 and 2 be checked?**

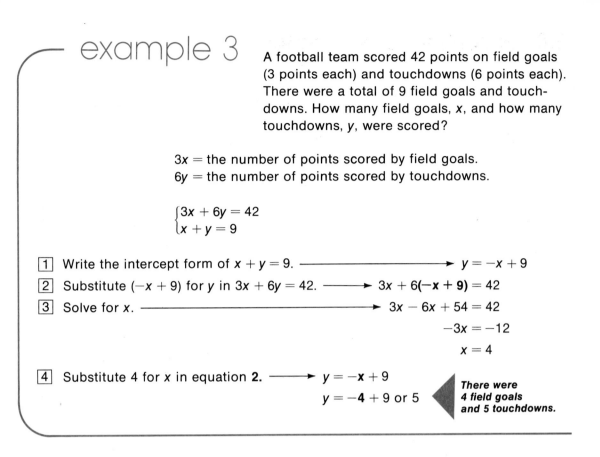

## example 3

A football team scored 42 points on field goals (3 points each) and touchdowns (6 points each). There were a total of 9 field goals and touchdowns. How many field goals, $x$, and how many touchdowns, $y$, were scored?

$3x$ = the number of points scored by field goals.
$6y$ = the number of points scored by touchdowns.

$$\begin{cases} 3x + 6y = 42 \\ x + y = 9 \end{cases}$$

1. Write the intercept form of $x + y = 9$. ⟶ $y = -x + 9$
2. Substitute $(-x + 9)$ for $y$ in $3x + 6y = 42$. ⟶ $3x + 6(-x + 9) = 42$
3. Solve for $x$. ⟶ $3x - 6x + 54 = 42$
   $$-3x = -12$$
   $$x = 4$$
4. Substitute 4 for $x$ in equation 2. ⟶ $y = -x + 9$
   $$y = -4 + 9 \text{ or } 5$$

◀ **There were 4 field goals and 5 touchdowns.**

## ORAL EXERCISES 16.6

*Tell an equation if the perimeter of each figure is 25 centimeters.* (Example 1)

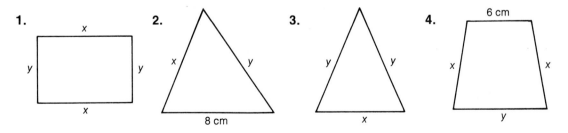

1.
2.
3.
4.

*Tell an equation that describes each problem.*

5. The distance from Dallas to Atlanta is $x$ km and from Atlanta to Miami $y$ km. The first distance is 200 km more than the second.

6. A man spent $x$ hours at his office and $y$ hours playing golf. The total length of time spent was $11\frac{1}{2}$ hours.

*Equations with Two Variables* / **411**

7. A scout troop hiked $x$ kilometers on Saturday and $y$ kilometers on Sunday. The total distance hiked was 37 kilometers.

8. Mrs. Scott's age is $x$ years and her daughter's age is $y$ years. The daughter is 26 years younger than her mother.

9. A tennis coach buys $x$ cans of Brand $A$ tennis balls and $y$ cans of Brand $B$. She buys a total of 81 tennis balls (3 balls per can).

10. The ones digit of a number is $x$. The tens digit is 7, and the hundreds digit is $y$. The sum of the digits is 19.

11. On an exam, $x$ students scored 92 points, and $y$ students scored 85 points. The total number of points scored was 1225 points.

12. Mr. Tanner bought a used car that had been driven $x$ kilometers. He has driven it $y$ kilometers. The car's odometer now shows 38,000 kilometers.

13. The ones digit of a number is $x$. The tens digit is $y$. The sum of the digits is 16.

14. Three heads of lettuce at $x$ cents each and five heads of cabbage at $y$ cents each cost $2.20.

## WRITTEN EXERCISES 16.6

**A**  **Goal:** To solve a word problem using a system of equations in two variables

**Sample Problem:** Marita scored 76 points on an algebra test. Each problem in Part A had a value of 5 points, and each problem in Part B had a value of 2 points. She had 20 correct answers. How many problems in each part did she answer correctly?

**Answer:** She had 12 correct answers in Part A and 8 correct answers in Part B.

*In each problem, (a) select two variables for the unknown numbers, (b) write two equations, and (c) solve. (Example 1, Example 2)*

1. The width $x$ of a rectangle is 5 millimeters less than the length $y$. The perimeter is 54 millimeters. Solve for $x$ and $y$.

2. The sum of the length $x$ and width $y$ of a rectangle is 21 centimeters. The length is 7 centimeters more than the width. Solve for $x$ and $y$.

3. Two sides of a triangle have equal lengths as in Figure 1. The length of the third side is 3 meters more than the length of each of the other sides. The perimeter is 18 meters. Find the lengths of the sides.

Figure 1

**4.** The perimeter of the triangle in Figure 2 is 40 decimeters. The length *x* of the longest side is 5 decimeters more than the length *y* of the shortest side. Solve for *x* and *y*.

**5.** The difference of the ages of Jody and her younger brother is 6 years. Jody's age is two years more than twice her brother's age. Find the age of each.

**6.** A stick 50 centimeters long is broken into two parts as shown in Figure 3. One part is 8 centimeters longer than the other. Find the lengths of the two pieces.

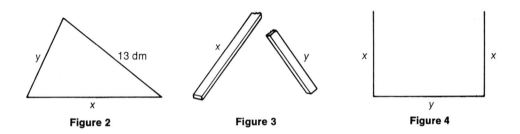

| Figure 2 | Figure 3 | Figure 4 |

**7.** A piece of wire 53 centimeters long is bent as shown in Figure 4. The length *x* is 5 centimeters less than the length *y*. Solve for *x* and *y*.

**8.** Mrs. Johnson's age is twice that of her son. The sum of their ages is 60. Find the age of Mrs. Johnson and her son.

**9.** The airline distance from Dallas to Houston is 850 kilometers less than the distance from Houston to Mexico City. The sum of the two distances is 1550 kilometers. Find each unknown distance.

**10.** The road distance from Los Angeles to Oklahoma City is 1400 kilometers less than the distance from Oklahoma City to St. Louis. The distance from Los Angeles to St. Louis is 3000 kilometers. Find each unknown distance.

**B**

**11.** The sum of the digits of a two-digit number is 17. The tens digit is one less than the ones digit. Find the number.

**12.** The sum of the digits of a two-digit number is 7. The difference of the digits is also 7 (tens digit less the ones digit). Find the number.

# Photographer

Photography has been a popular activity for almost 150 years. There are many kinds of jobs for persons interested in photography.

Commercial photography
Darkroom work
Industrial photography
Lighting

News photography
Photo-finishing
Portrait photography
Scientific photography

Making good pictures takes a knowledge of how light behaves. It also requires some knowledge of mathematics and chemistry. The photographer controls (1) the length of time film is exposed to light, and (2) the amount of light that hits the film. The photographer controls the length of time light is allowed to hit the film by adjusting the speed of the shutter. The shutter is a device that opens and closes in fractions of a second. Shutter speeds as marked on adjustable cameras in fractions of seconds are shown.

$$\frac{1}{2}, \frac{1}{4}, \frac{1}{8}, \frac{1}{15}, \frac{1}{30}, \frac{1}{60}, \frac{1}{125}, \frac{1}{250}, \frac{1}{500}, \frac{1}{1000}$$

Light enters a camera through a small hole called the aperture. The photographer controls the size of the aperture by rotating a ring with numerals on it. These numerals name "f" stops. Starting with the largest aperture on a camera (the smallest f number), each f stop after that allows one-half as much light into the camera as the previous opening.

**EXAMPLE:** Find the ratio of the aperture at f 11 to the aperture at f 2.8.

**SOLUTION:** The difference between f 11 and f 2.8 is four f stops. Use $\frac{1}{2}$ as a factor four times.

$$f 8 \quad f 5.6 \quad f 4 \quad f 2.8$$

f 11 is $\frac{1}{2} \times \frac{1}{2} \times \frac{1}{2} \times \frac{1}{2}$ or $\frac{1}{16}$, the size of f 2.8.

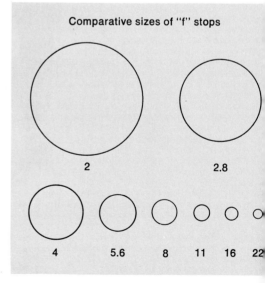

Comparative sizes of "f" stops

2    2.8

4    5.6    8    11    16    22

414

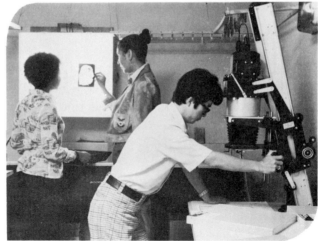

# CHAPTER SUMMARY

| | |
|---|---|
| **IMPORTANT TERMS** | Linear equation *(p. 396)*      System of equations *(p. 396)* |

**IMPORTANT TERMS**

Linear equation *(p. 396)*

Standard form *(p. 396)*

Truth set of
  a linear equation *(p. 396)*

System of equations *(p. 396)*

Substitution method *(p. 398)*

Coefficient *(p. 398)*

Addition method *(p. 401)*

**IMPORTANT IDEAS**

*1. Steps for the Substitution Method:*

  *a.* Write an equation that is equivalent to one of the equations with only a variable on one side.

  *b.* Substitute the phrase that equals that variable in the other equation. Solve the resulting equation.

  *c.* Substitute the value of the variable in step *b* in either equation. Solve the resulting equation.

  *d.* Check by substituting both values in both equations.

*2. Steps for the Addition Method:*

  *a.* Check for opposite coefficients of one variable. If necessary, multiply each side of either or both equations by numbers that will make opposite coefficients for one variable.

  *b.* Add the corresponding sides to eliminate one of the variables.

  *c.* Solve for the remaining variable.

  *d.* Substitute the value from step *c* in one of the equations. Solve for the other variable.

  *e.* Check by substituting both values in both equations.

## CHAPTER REVIEW

### SECTION 16.1

*Graph the two equations of each system in the same coordinate plane. Write the truth set of the system.*

**1.** $\begin{cases} x - y + 1 = 0 \\ x + 2y + 4 = 0 \end{cases}$

**2.** $\begin{cases} x - 2y + 3 = 0 \\ x - y + 2 = 0 \end{cases}$

**3.** $\begin{cases} x + y - 1 = 0 \\ 2x - y + 1 = 0 \end{cases}$

**4.** $\begin{cases} 3x + y - 2 = 0 \\ 6x + y + 4 = 0 \end{cases}$

### SECTION 16.2

*Solve each system of equations by the substitution method. Check.*

**5.** $\begin{cases} 2x + y + 3 = 0 \\ 3x - 2y + 1 = 0 \end{cases}$

**6.** $\begin{cases} 2x - 4y - 3 = 0 \\ -x + 3y + 1 = 0 \end{cases}$

**7.** $\begin{cases} x - 2y + 2 = 0 \\ 2x - 3y - 2 = 0 \end{cases}$

**8.** $\begin{cases} 2x + y - 5 = 0 \\ 8x - y - 45 = 0 \end{cases}$

### SECTION 16.3

*Solve each system of equations by the addition method. Check.*

**9.** $\begin{cases} x - 3y + 2 = 0 \\ 2x + 3y + 4 = 0 \end{cases}$

**10.** $\begin{cases} 4x - y - 3 = 0 \\ -4x + 3y + 5 = 0 \end{cases}$

**11.** $\begin{cases} 2x + y + 2 = 0 \\ 2x + 3y - 6 = 0 \end{cases}$

**12.** $\begin{cases} 2x + y - 1 = 0 \\ 4x - 2y - 6 = 0 \end{cases}$

### SECTION 16.4

*In each problem, (a) select two variables for the unknown numbers, (b) write two equations, and (c) solve to find the numbers.*

**13.** The sum of two numbers is 32. The difference of the two numbers is 7. Find the unknown numbers.

**14.** The sum of two numbers is 11. The difference of the two numbers is 35. Find the unknown numbers.

**15.** One number is 22 more than another number. The sum of the numbers is 52. Find the unknown numbers.

**16.** One number is 29 less than another number. The sum of the numbers is −17. Find the unknown numbers.

### SECTION 16.5

*In each problem, (a) select two variables for the unknown numbers, (b) write two equations, and (c) solve to find the numbers.*

**17.** Les and Fran sold 30 glasses of cold drinks at their stand. Iced tea sold for 15 cents a glass and lemonade for 20 cents a glass. They took in $5.10. How many glasses of each drink were sold?

**18.** The freshman class sold 205 tickets to their dance. Tickets cost 75 cents for freshmen and 90 cents for other students. They took in $165. How many tickets of each type did they sell?

**19.** Sazuko has 15 nickels and dimes in a coin bank. The coins are worth $1.20. How many of each kind of coin does she have?

**20.** Abel buys eight-cent and ten-cent stamps at the post office for his sister. He buys 32 stamps, and they cost $2.98. How many of each kind of stamp does he buy?

**SECTION 16.6**

*In each problem, (a) select two variables for the unknown numbers, (b) write two equations, and (c) solve.*

**21.** The width of a rectangle is 10 centimeters less than twice the length. The perimeter is 28 centimeters. Find the length and width.

**22.** The difference of the length and width of a rectangle is 3 decimeters. Four times the width equals three times the length. Find the length and width.

**23.** Pat's teacher is 29 years older than Pat. The sum of their ages is 61. Find the ages of Pat and her teacher.

**24.** Karl and his father get on the scales together. Their combined weight is 230 pounds. Karl weighs 110 pounds less than his father. Find the weights of Karl and his father.

# 17
# More
# Algebraic Fractions

# 17.1  Simplest Names

Fractions such as $-\dfrac{a}{b}$, $\dfrac{-a}{b}$, and $\dfrac{a}{-b}$ are equivalent. Of these, $-\dfrac{a}{b}$ is the simplest name.

**P-1**  **What is the simplest name for $\dfrac{3}{-x}$?**

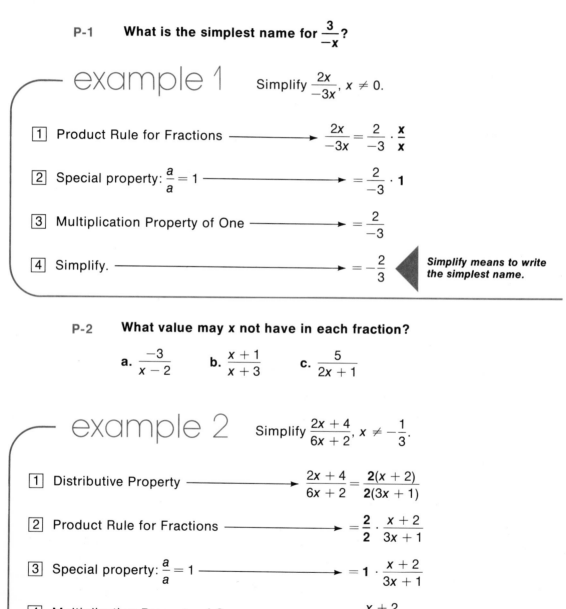

example 1   Simplify $\dfrac{2x}{-3x}$, $x \neq 0$.

1  Product Rule for Fractions  ⟶  $\dfrac{2x}{-3x} = \dfrac{2}{-3} \cdot \dfrac{x}{x}$

2  Special property: $\dfrac{a}{a} = 1$  ⟶  $= \dfrac{2}{-3} \cdot 1$

3  Multiplication Property of One  ⟶  $= \dfrac{2}{-3}$

4  Simplify.  ⟶  $= -\dfrac{2}{3}$   ◀  *Simplify means to write the simplest name.*

**P-2**  **What value may x not have in each fraction?**

a. $\dfrac{-3}{x - 2}$     b. $\dfrac{x + 1}{x + 3}$     c. $\dfrac{5}{2x + 1}$

example 2   Simplify $\dfrac{2x + 4}{6x + 2}$, $x \neq -\dfrac{1}{3}$.

1  Distributive Property  ⟶  $\dfrac{2x + 4}{6x + 2} = \dfrac{2(x + 2)}{2(3x + 1)}$

2  Product Rule for Fractions  ⟶  $= \dfrac{2}{2} \cdot \dfrac{x + 2}{3x + 1}$

3  Special property: $\dfrac{a}{a} = 1$  ⟶  $= 1 \cdot \dfrac{x + 2}{3x + 1}$

4  Multiplication Property of One  ⟶  $= \dfrac{x + 2}{3x + 1}$

Here is a shorter way to show the work for Example 2.

$$\frac{2x + 4}{6x + 2} = \frac{\overset{1}{\cancel{2}}(x + 2)}{\underset{1}{\cancel{2}}(3x + 1)}$$

◀ **Note how the name for 1 is taken out.**

$$= \frac{x + 2}{3x + 1}$$

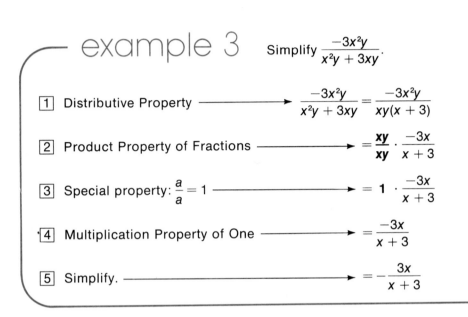

example 3    Simplify $\dfrac{-3x^2y}{x^2y + 3xy}$.

1. Distributive Property ⟶ $\dfrac{-3x^2y}{x^2y + 3xy} = \dfrac{-3x^2y}{xy(x + 3)}$

2. Product Property of Fractions ⟶ $= \dfrac{xy}{xy} \cdot \dfrac{-3x}{x + 3}$

3. Special property: $\dfrac{a}{a} = 1$ ⟶ $= 1 \cdot \dfrac{-3x}{x + 3}$

4. Multiplication Property of One ⟶ $= \dfrac{-3x}{x + 3}$

5. Simplify. ⟶ $= -\dfrac{3x}{x + 3}$

P-3    **What is the simplest name for each fraction?**

a. $\dfrac{2(x - 3)}{5(x - 3)}$    b. $\dfrac{x(x + 4)}{3(x + 4)}$    c. $\dfrac{-2x(3x - 1)}{4x(3x - 1)}$

## ORAL EXERCISES 17.1

*Tell a name for 1 that can be used to simplify each fraction. (Examples 1, 2, 3)*

1. $\dfrac{2 \cdot 3}{3 \cdot 5}$

2. $\dfrac{(5)(-2)}{(2)(3)}$

3. $\dfrac{2(-3)(5)}{3(7)(5)}$

4. $\dfrac{-5x}{5y}, y \neq 0$

5. $\dfrac{2(-a)(3)}{3(a)(5)}, a \neq 0$

6. $\dfrac{2(x + 2)}{5(x + 2)}, x \neq -2$

7. $\dfrac{-x(y + 1)}{(y + 3)x}, y \neq -3, x \neq 0$

8. $\dfrac{25a}{-35ab}, a \neq 0, b \neq 0$

9. $\dfrac{12a^2b}{16ab}, a \neq 0, b \neq 0$

*Simplify. Assume no divisor is zero. (Example 1, Example 2, Example 3)*

**10.** $\dfrac{2a}{5a}$

**11.** $\dfrac{-2x}{4y}$

**12.** $\dfrac{4t}{8t}$

**13.** $\dfrac{10x}{15x^2}$

**14.** $\dfrac{12n}{-18n}$

**15.** $\dfrac{2xy}{3x^2y}$

**16.** $\dfrac{-12y}{24y^2}$

**17.** $\dfrac{3x}{3x+3}$

**18.** $\dfrac{-8rt^2}{12r^2t}$

**19.** $\dfrac{2x+2}{2x-2}$

**20.** $\dfrac{3x+3y}{5x+5y}$

**21.** $\dfrac{3x}{3x-6}$

## WRITTEN EXERCISES 17.1

**A**

**Goal:** To simplify an algebraic fraction

**Sample Problem:** Simplify $\dfrac{2x+6}{4x+18}$.

**Answer:** $\dfrac{x+3}{2x+9}$

*Write the missing numerals. Assume no divisor is zero. (Steps 1 and 2 of Example 1, Example 2 and Example 3)*

**1.** $\dfrac{-4}{12} = \dfrac{4}{4} \cdot -\dfrac{?}{?}$

**2.** $\dfrac{6}{-15} = \dfrac{3}{3} \cdot -\dfrac{?}{?}$

**3.** $\dfrac{-15a}{10} = \dfrac{-3a}{2} \cdot \dfrac{?}{?}$

**4.** $\dfrac{-6x}{8x} = -\dfrac{3}{4} \cdot \dfrac{?}{?}$

**5.** $\dfrac{10y}{-15y} = -\dfrac{2}{3} \cdot \dfrac{?}{?}$

**6.** $\dfrac{-25a}{10} = \dfrac{?}{?} \cdot -\dfrac{5a}{2}$

**7.** $\dfrac{12}{-20t} = \dfrac{?}{?} \cdot -\dfrac{3}{5t}$

**8.** $\dfrac{2x^2y}{3xy^2} = \dfrac{xy}{xy} \cdot \dfrac{?}{?}$

**9.** $\dfrac{18y}{24y^2} = \dfrac{6y}{6y} \cdot \dfrac{?}{?}$

**10.** $\dfrac{2x+4}{6y} = \dfrac{2}{2} \cdot \dfrac{?}{?}$

**11.** $\dfrac{3x+6}{5x+10} = \dfrac{3}{5} \cdot \dfrac{?}{?}$

**12.** $\dfrac{2x+10}{3x+15} = \dfrac{2}{3} \cdot \dfrac{?}{?}$

*Simplify. Assume no divisor is zero. (Example 1, Example 2, Example 3)*

**13.** $\dfrac{-5x}{5y}$

**14.** $\dfrac{3m}{-3n}$

**15.** $\dfrac{4rs}{8st}$

**16.** $\dfrac{5pq}{15qr}$

**17.** $\dfrac{5x^2}{-3xy}$

**18.** $\dfrac{-7ab}{12b^2}$

**19.** $-\dfrac{12a^2b}{28ab}$

**20.** $-\dfrac{18xy^2}{24x^2y^2}$

**21.** $\dfrac{-3(x+7)}{6x(x+7)}$

**22.** $\dfrac{5x(2x-1)}{-10(2x-1)}$

**23.** $\dfrac{4y+8}{7y+14}$

**24.** $\dfrac{2x+4}{5x+10}$

**25.** $-\dfrac{5x-5}{10x+10}$

**26.** $-\dfrac{4x+4y}{8x-8y}$

**27.** $\dfrac{ax+2a}{bx+2b}$

**28.** $\dfrac{3x-12}{xy-4y}$

# 17.2 Special Fractions

You are familiar with the Property of the Opposite of a Sum.

$$-(a + b) = (-a) + (-b)$$

**P-1**  **What phrases do you get by applying this property below?**

**a.** $-(x + 2)$    **b.** $-(-5 + n)$    **c.** $-(k + -3)$

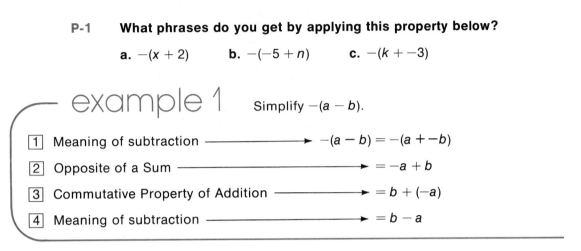

example 1  Simplify $-(a - b)$.

| 1 | Meaning of subtraction | $-(a - b) = -(a + -b)$ |
| 2 | Opposite of a Sum | $= -a + b$ |
| 3 | Commutative Property of Addition | $= b + (-a)$ |
| 4 | Meaning of subtraction | $= b - a$ |

The simplest name is $b - a$ rather than $-a + b$, because $b - a$ contains fewer symbols.

Example 1 suggests the following property.

> **Property of the Opposite of a Difference**      $-(t - 4) = 4 - t$
>
> For any numbers $a$ and $b$,                        $-(5 - y) = y - 5$
> $-(a - b) = b - a$.

This property shows that $a - b$ and $b - a$ are opposites.

$$-(a - b) = b - a \qquad -(b - a) = a - b$$

**P-2**  **What is the opposite of each phrase below?**

**a.** $m - \dfrac{3}{4}$    **b.** $r - 1.8$    **c.** $-p - 10$

**P-3**  **What is the value of each phrase below?**

**a.** $\dfrac{-t}{-t}, t \neq 0$    **b.** $\dfrac{x + 5}{x + 5}, x \neq -5$    **c.** $\dfrac{2q - 1}{2q - 1}, q \neq \dfrac{1}{2}$    ◀ **Use** $\dfrac{a}{a} = 1$.

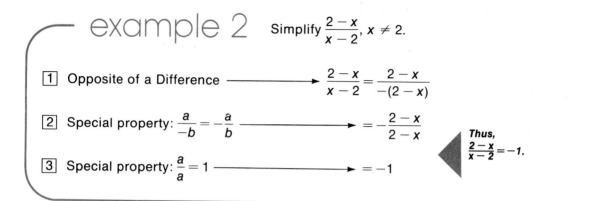

example 2   Simplify $\dfrac{2-x}{x-2}$, $x \neq 2$.

1  Opposite of a Difference  $\longrightarrow$  $\dfrac{2-x}{x-2} = \dfrac{2-x}{-(2-x)}$

2  Special property: $\dfrac{a}{-b} = -\dfrac{a}{b}$  $\longrightarrow$  $= -\dfrac{2-x}{2-x}$

3  Special property: $\dfrac{a}{a} = 1$  $\longrightarrow$  $= -1$

Thus,
$\dfrac{2-x}{x-2} = -1$.

Example 2 suggests the following property.

**Property of the Quotient of Opposites**

For any numbers $a$ and $b$, $a \neq b$,

$$\dfrac{a-b}{b-a} = -1.$$

$\dfrac{r-6}{6-r} = -1$

$\dfrac{2p-3q}{3q-2p} = -1$

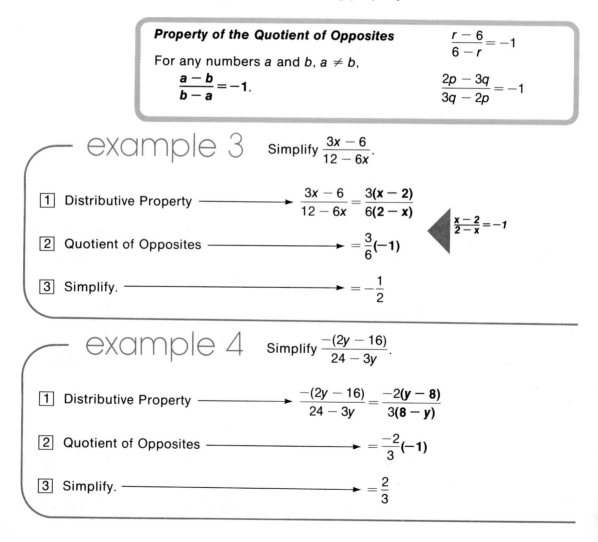

example 3   Simplify $\dfrac{3x-6}{12-6x}$.

1  Distributive Property  $\longrightarrow$  $\dfrac{3x-6}{12-6x} = \dfrac{3(x-2)}{6(2-x)}$

2  Quotient of Opposites  $\longrightarrow$  $= \dfrac{3}{6}(-1)$

3  Simplify.  $\longrightarrow$  $= -\dfrac{1}{2}$

$\dfrac{x-2}{2-x} = -1$

example 4   Simplify $\dfrac{-(2y-16)}{24-3y}$.

1  Distributive Property  $\longrightarrow$  $\dfrac{-(2y-16)}{24-3y} = \dfrac{-2(y-8)}{3(8-y)}$

2  Quotient of Opposites  $\longrightarrow$  $= \dfrac{-2}{3}(-1)$

3  Simplify.  $\longrightarrow$  $= \dfrac{2}{3}$

## ORAL EXERCISES 17.2

*Simplify. Assume no divisor is zero.* (P-2, P-3, Example 1, Example 2, Example 3, Example 4)

**1.** $-(n-7)$

**2.** $-(t-0.5)$

**3.** $-(s-r)$

**4.** $-(-k-3)$

**5.** $-(3y-\frac{1}{2})$

**6.** $-(4m-3p)$

**7.** $\dfrac{r}{r}$

**8.** $\dfrac{a+3}{a+3}$

**9.** $\dfrac{x-15}{x-15}$

**10.** $\dfrac{2t-5}{2t-5}$

**11.** $\dfrac{k-8}{8-k}$

**12.** $\dfrac{n-6}{6-n}$

**13.** $\dfrac{2(3-y)}{8(y-3)}$

**14.** $\dfrac{8(r-x)}{12(x-r)}$

**15.** $-\dfrac{k-9}{9-k}$

**16.** $\dfrac{-5(2p-5)}{15(5-2p)}$

## WRITTEN EXERCISES 17.2

**A**

**Goal:** To simplify a fraction using the Property of the Quotient of Opposites

**Sample Problem:** Simplify $\dfrac{3(x-5)}{9(5-x)}$.  **Answer:** $-\dfrac{1}{3}$

*Simplify. Assume no divisor is zero.* (P-2, P-3, Example 1, Example 2, Example 3, Example 4)

**1.** $-(r-18)$

**2.** $-(m-25)$

**3.** $-(1.9-y)$

**4.** $-(0.8-t)$

**5.** $-(2a-6)$

**6.** $-(5k-12)$

**7.** $-(3x-2y)$

**8.** $-(4t-3s)$

**9.** $\dfrac{3n}{3n}$

**10.** $\dfrac{8q}{8q}$

**11.** $\dfrac{b-19}{b-19}$

**12.** $\dfrac{2x+1}{2x+1}$

**13.** $\dfrac{x-13}{13-x}$

**14.** $\dfrac{r-25}{25-r}$

**15.** $-\dfrac{t-8}{8-t}$

**16.** $-\dfrac{3-k}{k-3}$

**17.** $\dfrac{2(8-y)}{3(y-8)}$

**18.** $\dfrac{3(t-12)}{5(12-t)}$

**19.** $\dfrac{-2(3x-5)}{4(5-3x)}$

**20.** $\dfrac{6(1-2x)}{-8(2x-1)}$

**21.** $\dfrac{2x-4}{8-4x}$

**22.** $\dfrac{3x-9}{18-6x}$

**23.** $-\dfrac{4-4r}{6r-6}$

**24.** $-\dfrac{8x-24}{12-4x}$

**B**

**25.** $\dfrac{2ax-6a}{9a-3ax}$

**26.** $\dfrac{4ry-4r}{8r-8ry}$

**27.** $\dfrac{x^2-4x}{8x-2x^2}$

**28.** $\dfrac{3t^2-6t}{8t-4t^2}$

**29.** $-\dfrac{y^2-y^3}{2y^2-2y}$

**30.** $-\dfrac{2a-2a^2}{a^2+a^3}$

**31.** $\dfrac{5a^2-ab}{3a^2+6ab}$

**32.** $\dfrac{3a^2+3ab}{3ab+3b^2}$

# 17.3 Products of Fractional Numbers

**P-1**    **What is the simplest name for each product?**

**a.** $\dfrac{x}{4} \cdot \dfrac{3}{y}$     **b.** $\dfrac{2}{t} \cdot \dfrac{-t}{4}$     **c.** $\dfrac{2r}{-3} \cdot \dfrac{-4}{r}$

**Product Rule:**
$\dfrac{a}{b} \cdot \dfrac{c}{d} = \dfrac{ac}{bd}$, $b \ne 0$, $d \ne 0$.

The Product Rule for Fractions can be applied to fractions with
<u>binomial</u> (having two terms) numerators and denominators.

## example 1    Multiply and simplify: $\dfrac{3}{x-2} \cdot \dfrac{x-2}{5}$

1️⃣ Product Rule for Fractions ⟶ $\dfrac{3}{x-2} \cdot \dfrac{x-2}{5} = \dfrac{3(x-2)}{(x-2)5}$

2️⃣ Commutative Property of Multiplication ⟶ $= \dfrac{3(x-2)}{5(x-2)}$

3️⃣ Product Rule for Fractions ⟶ $= \dfrac{3}{5} \cdot \dfrac{x-2}{x-2}$    $\dfrac{x-2}{x-2} = 1$

4️⃣ Multiplication Property of One ⟶ $= \dfrac{3}{5}$

---

**P-2**    **What is the simplest name for each product below?**

**a.** $\dfrac{x+3}{x} \cdot \dfrac{2}{x+3}$     **b.** $\dfrac{3}{x-5} \cdot \dfrac{x-5}{x+1}$     **c.** $\dfrac{x-5}{x+2} \cdot \dfrac{x-6}{x-5}$

## example 2    Multiply and simplify: $\dfrac{4x}{x+5} \cdot \dfrac{x+5}{6x}$

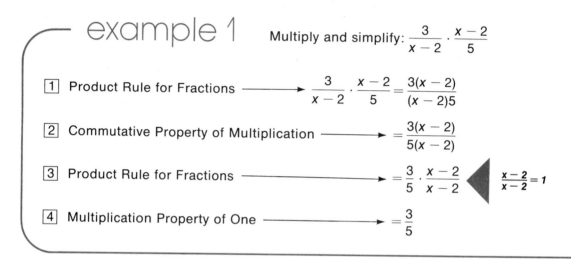

$$\dfrac{4x}{x+5} \cdot \dfrac{x+5}{6x} = \dfrac{4x(x+5)}{(x+5)6x}$$

$$= \dfrac{\overset{2}{\cancel{4}}\overset{1}{\cancel{x}}(\cancel{x+5})}{(\cancel{x+5})\underset{3}{\cancel{6}}\underset{1}{\cancel{x}}}$$

$$= \dfrac{2}{3}$$

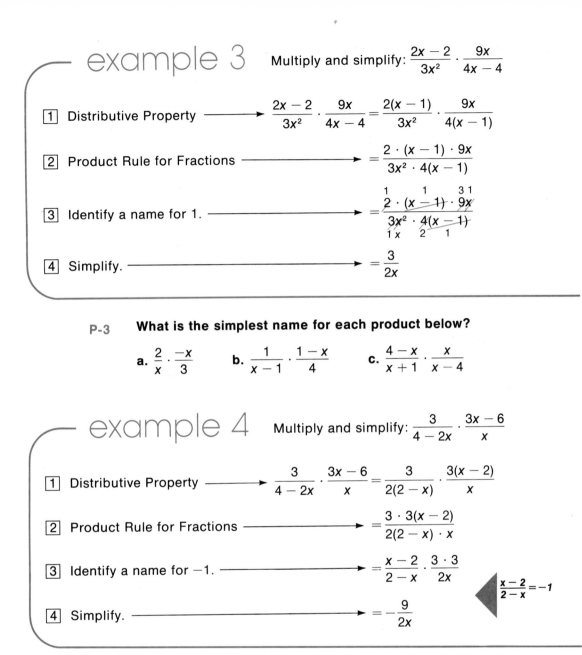

example 3

Multiply and simplify: $\dfrac{2x-2}{3x^2} \cdot \dfrac{9x}{4x-4}$

1 Distributive Property $\longrightarrow \dfrac{2x-2}{3x^2} \cdot \dfrac{9x}{4x-4} = \dfrac{2(x-1)}{3x^2} \cdot \dfrac{9x}{4(x-1)}$

2 Product Rule for Fractions $\longrightarrow = \dfrac{2 \cdot (x-1) \cdot 9x}{3x^2 \cdot 4(x-1)}$

3 Identify a name for 1. $\longrightarrow = \dfrac{\overset{1}{2} \cdot \overset{1}{(x-1)} \cdot \overset{3}{\cancel{9}}\overset{1}{\cancel{x}}}{\underset{1 \, x}{3\cancel{x}^2} \cdot \underset{2}{4}\underset{1}{(x-1)}}$

4 Simplify. $\longrightarrow = \dfrac{3}{2x}$

P-3   **What is the simplest name for each product below?**

a. $\dfrac{2}{x} \cdot \dfrac{-x}{3}$   b. $\dfrac{1}{x-1} \cdot \dfrac{1-x}{4}$   c. $\dfrac{4-x}{x+1} \cdot \dfrac{x}{x-4}$

example 4

Multiply and simplify: $\dfrac{3}{4-2x} \cdot \dfrac{3x-6}{x}$

1 Distributive Property $\longrightarrow \dfrac{3}{4-2x} \cdot \dfrac{3x-6}{x} = \dfrac{3}{2(2-x)} \cdot \dfrac{3(x-2)}{x}$

2 Product Rule for Fractions $\longrightarrow = \dfrac{3 \cdot 3(x-2)}{2(2-x) \cdot x}$

3 Identify a name for $-1$. $\longrightarrow = \dfrac{x-2}{2-x} \cdot \dfrac{3 \cdot 3}{2x}$

$\blacktriangleleft \quad \dfrac{x-2}{2-x}=-1$

4 Simplify. $\longrightarrow = -\dfrac{9}{2x}$

## ORAL EXERCISES 17.3

*Simplify. Assume no divisor is zero. (P-1, Example 1, Example 2, Example 3, Example 4)*

1. $\dfrac{2}{7} \cdot \dfrac{-3}{11}$    2. $\dfrac{-1}{5} \cdot \dfrac{2}{-7}$    3. $\dfrac{a}{5} \cdot \dfrac{-3}{x}$    4. $\dfrac{2x}{5} \cdot \dfrac{-3}{10}$

*Tell the simplest name. Assume no divisor is zero.* (P-1, Example 1, Example 2, Example 3, Example 4)

**5.** $\dfrac{-2}{y} \cdot \dfrac{5}{-x}$

**6.** $-\dfrac{2}{3} \cdot \dfrac{-x}{y}$

**7.** $\dfrac{-3a}{2y} \cdot \dfrac{-5y}{a}$

**8.** $\dfrac{5x}{2a} \cdot \dfrac{-7a}{-3y}$

**9.** $\dfrac{-a}{-b} \cdot \dfrac{-x}{-y}$

**10.** $\dfrac{2ac}{3d} \cdot \dfrac{-5d}{c}$

**11.** $\dfrac{x-2}{5} \cdot \dfrac{3}{x-2}$

**12.** $\dfrac{x}{x+3} \cdot \dfrac{x+3}{-4}$

**13.** $\dfrac{x-1}{8} \cdot \dfrac{5}{1-x}$

**14.** $\dfrac{-4}{x-5} \cdot \dfrac{5-x}{3}$

**15.** $\dfrac{x-2}{5-x} \cdot \dfrac{x-5}{2-x}$

**16.** $\dfrac{2x}{x+4} \cdot \dfrac{x+4}{4x}$

# WRITTEN EXERCISES 17.3

**A**

**Goal:** To multiply with algebraic fractions

**Sample Problem:** Multiply and simplify: $\dfrac{6}{x-2y} \cdot \dfrac{2y-x}{-12}$

**Answer:** $\dfrac{1}{2}$

*Multiply and simplify. Assume no divisor is zero.* (P-1, Example 1, Example 2, Example 3, Example 4)

**1.** $\dfrac{-2}{5} \cdot \dfrac{-3}{11}$

**2.** $\dfrac{5}{-8} \cdot \dfrac{-3}{7}$

**3.** $\dfrac{-y}{5} \cdot \dfrac{2}{t}$

**4.** $\dfrac{a}{6} \cdot \dfrac{-3}{x}$

**5.** $\dfrac{2}{-y} \cdot \dfrac{-5y}{3}$

**6.** $\dfrac{-3x}{7} \cdot \dfrac{5}{2x}$

**7.** $-\dfrac{3}{y} \cdot -\dfrac{y}{2}$

**8.** $-\dfrac{2a}{3} \cdot -\dfrac{5}{a}$

**9.** $\dfrac{3}{y+5} \cdot \dfrac{y+5}{12}$

**10.** $\dfrac{n-7}{8} \cdot \dfrac{6}{n-7}$

**11.** $\dfrac{2x+3}{3x} \cdot \dfrac{-x}{2x+3}$

**12.** $\dfrac{3x+1}{-2x} \cdot \dfrac{x}{3x+1}$

**13.** $\dfrac{x-4}{4x} \cdot \dfrac{2}{4-x}$

**14.** $\dfrac{5}{x-3} \cdot \dfrac{3-x}{10x}$

**15.** $\dfrac{3x-2}{-5x} \cdot \dfrac{5}{2-3x}$

**16.** $\dfrac{3}{2x-1} \cdot \dfrac{1-2x}{3x}$

**17.** $\dfrac{4}{2x+2} \cdot \dfrac{x+1}{2x}$

**18.** $\dfrac{3x-3}{3x} \cdot \dfrac{2}{x-1}$

**B**

**19.** $\dfrac{x-2}{6x} \cdot \dfrac{4}{4-2x}$

**20.** $\dfrac{6}{3-3x} \cdot \dfrac{x-1}{4}$

**21.** $\dfrac{-3x}{2x-2} \cdot \dfrac{1-x}{4x^2}$

**22.** $\dfrac{3x-6}{-8x^2} \cdot \dfrac{6x}{2-x}$

**23.** $\dfrac{2x+8}{4x-4} \cdot \dfrac{2-2x}{3x+12}$

**24.** $\dfrac{5x+10}{3x-6} \cdot \dfrac{4-4x}{2x+4}$

# 17.4 Sums and Differences

**Sum and Difference Rules for Fractions**

For any numbers $a$, $b$, and $c$, with $c \neq 0$:

1. $\dfrac{a}{c} + \dfrac{b}{c} = \dfrac{a+b}{c}$

2. $\dfrac{a}{c} - \dfrac{b}{c} = \dfrac{a-b}{c}$

$\dfrac{3}{x} + \dfrac{5}{x} = \dfrac{8}{x}$

$\dfrac{2x}{y} - \dfrac{3}{y} = \dfrac{2x-3}{y}$

**P-1** **What is the simplest name for each of these?**

a. $\dfrac{5}{n} + \dfrac{7}{n}$     b. $\dfrac{3a}{5} - \dfrac{a}{5}$     c. $\dfrac{r}{2x} + \dfrac{7}{2x}$

## example 1

Add and simplify: $\dfrac{5}{8x} + \dfrac{-3}{8x}$

1 Sum Rule for Fractions ⟶ $\dfrac{5}{8x} + \dfrac{-3}{8x} = \dfrac{5+(-3)}{8x}$

2 Add. ⟶ $= \dfrac{2}{8x}$

3 Simplify. ⟶ $= \dfrac{1}{4x}$

## example 2

Subtract and simplify: $\dfrac{3x}{x+2} - \dfrac{-x}{x+2}$

1 Difference Rule for Fractions ⟶ $\dfrac{3x}{x+2} - \dfrac{-x}{x+2} = \dfrac{3x-(-x)}{x+2}$

2 Meaning of subtraction ⟶ $= \dfrac{3x+x}{x+2}$

3 Simplify. ⟶ $= \dfrac{4x}{x+2}$

**P-2** **What is the simplest name for each of these?**

a. $\dfrac{3x}{x-1} + \dfrac{2x}{x-1}$     b. $\dfrac{5y}{y+5} + \dfrac{5}{y+5}$     c. $\dfrac{-2}{t+3} - \dfrac{1}{t+3}$

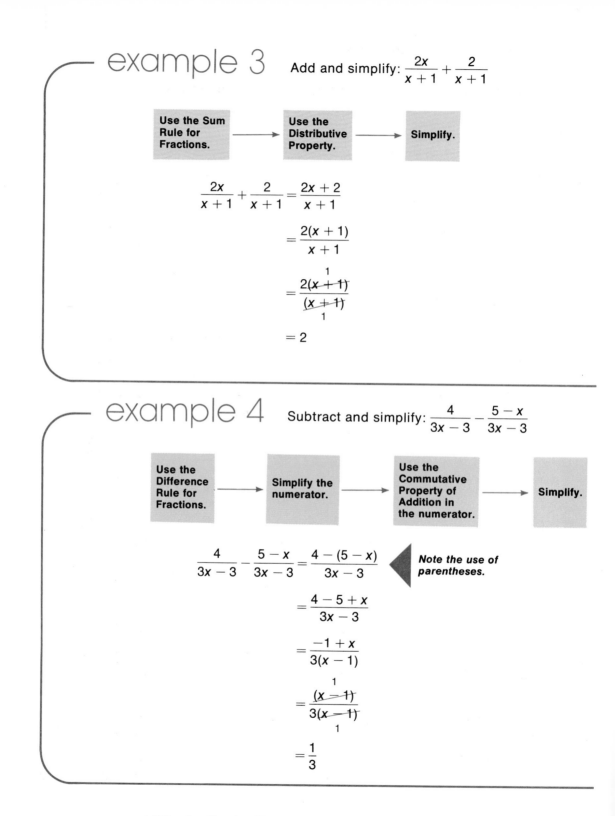

example 3   Add and simplify: $\dfrac{2x}{x+1} + \dfrac{2}{x+1}$

| Use the Sum Rule for Fractions. | → | Use the Distributive Property. | → | Simplify. |

$$\frac{2x}{x+1} + \frac{2}{x+1} = \frac{2x+2}{x+1}$$

$$= \frac{2(x+1)}{x+1}$$

$$= \frac{2\overset{1}{\cancel{(x+1)}}}{\underset{1}{\cancel{(x+1)}}}$$

$$= 2$$

example 4   Subtract and simplify: $\dfrac{4}{3x-3} - \dfrac{5-x}{3x-3}$

| Use the Difference Rule for Fractions. | → | Simplify the numerator. | → | Use the Commutative Property of Addition in the numerator. | → | Simplify. |

$$\frac{4}{3x-3} - \frac{5-x}{3x-3} = \frac{4-(5-x)}{3x-3}$$  ◀ **Note the use of parentheses.**

$$= \frac{4-5+x}{3x-3}$$

$$= \frac{-1+x}{3(x-1)}$$

$$= \frac{\overset{1}{\cancel{(x-1)}}}{3\underset{1}{\cancel{(x-1)}}}$$

$$= \frac{1}{3}$$

## ORAL EXERCISES 17.4

*Tell the simplest name. Assume no divisor is zero.* (Example 1, Example 2, Example 3, Example 4)

1. $\dfrac{3}{y} + \dfrac{4}{y}$

2. $\dfrac{5}{t} - \dfrac{2}{t}$

3. $\dfrac{a}{x} + \dfrac{2a}{x}$

4. $\dfrac{5r}{3x} - \dfrac{r}{3x}$

5. $\dfrac{1}{y} - \dfrac{5}{y}$

6. $\dfrac{3}{x-3} + \dfrac{7}{x-3}$

7. $\dfrac{3y}{x-2} - \dfrac{y}{x-2}$

8. $\dfrac{2}{x} - \dfrac{-5}{x}$

9. $\dfrac{x}{3t} + \dfrac{2x}{3t}$

10. $\dfrac{-3m}{2n} - \dfrac{m}{2n}$

11. $\dfrac{2t}{x+4} + \dfrac{3}{x+4}$

12. $\dfrac{3r}{x+1} - \dfrac{-r}{x+1}$

## WRITTEN EXERCISES 17.4

Ⓐ

**Goal:** To add or subtract with algebraic fractions that have like denominators

**Sample Problem:** Subtract and simplify: $\dfrac{5x-1}{2x-1} - \dfrac{3x}{2x-1}$    **Answer:** 1

*Add or subtract as indicated. Then simplify. Assume no divisor is zero.*
(Example 1, Example 2, Example 3, Example 4)

1. $\dfrac{-12}{5x} + \dfrac{9}{5x}$

2. $\dfrac{13}{7t} + \dfrac{-9}{7t}$

3. $\dfrac{11}{12m} - \dfrac{5}{12m}$

4. $\dfrac{13}{8r} - \dfrac{7}{8r}$

5. $\dfrac{5s}{9t} + \dfrac{s}{9t}$

6. $\dfrac{a}{12b} + \dfrac{7a}{12b}$

7. $\dfrac{11x}{15y} - \dfrac{-x}{15y}$

8. $\dfrac{7m}{15n} - \dfrac{-2m}{15n}$

9. $\dfrac{5x}{x+7} + \dfrac{x}{x+7}$

10. $\dfrac{7x}{2x-1} + \dfrac{x}{2x-1}$

11. $\dfrac{3p}{q+6} - \dfrac{2p}{q+6}$

12. $\dfrac{8t}{w+6} - \dfrac{3t}{w+6}$

13. $\dfrac{2x-3}{x-8} + \dfrac{-2}{x-8}$

14. $\dfrac{-x}{3x+1} + \dfrac{3x-5}{3x+1}$

15. $\dfrac{5y-3}{y-3} - \dfrac{4y}{y-3}$

16. $\dfrac{7n+1}{3n+1} - \dfrac{4n}{3n+1}$

17. $\dfrac{1-x}{2x-1} - \dfrac{x}{2x-1}$

18. $\dfrac{2-n}{3n-2} - \dfrac{2n}{3n-2}$

19. $\dfrac{2x+1}{x+2} - \dfrac{x-3}{x+2}$

20. $\dfrac{4y-1}{y+4} - \dfrac{3y-2}{y+4}$

Ⓑ

21. $\dfrac{3x+5}{2x+1} + \dfrac{x-3}{2x+1}$

22. $\dfrac{x-4}{x-3} + \dfrac{2x-5}{x-3}$

23. $\dfrac{5x+1}{4x+4} - \dfrac{3x-1}{4x+4}$

24. $\dfrac{3x-1}{12x-6} - \dfrac{3-5x}{12x-6}$

25. $\dfrac{x^2+x}{2x+6} + \dfrac{2x}{2x+6}$

26. $\dfrac{x^2-x}{6x^2-9x} + \dfrac{x^2-2x}{6x^2-9x}$

# 17.5 Quotients of Fractional Numbers

> **Quotient Rule for Fractions**
>
> For any numbers $a$, $b$, $c$, and $d$, with $b \neq 0$, $c \neq 0$, and $d \neq 0$,
>
> $$\frac{a}{b} \div \frac{c}{d} = \frac{a}{b} \cdot \frac{d}{c}.$$
>
> $$\frac{2}{3} \div \left(-\frac{5}{7}\right) = \frac{2}{3} \cdot \left(-\frac{7}{5}\right)$$
> $$= -\frac{14}{15}$$

**P-1**  What is the simplest name for each quotient?

**a.** $\left(-\dfrac{1}{2}\right) \div \left(-\dfrac{2}{3}\right)$  **b.** $\dfrac{5}{x} \div \left(-\dfrac{7}{x}\right)$  **c.** $\dfrac{2r}{s} \div \dfrac{2}{3}$

## example 1

Divide and simplify: $\dfrac{2}{x-1} \div \dfrac{-3}{x-1}$

1️⃣ Quotient Rule for Fractions ⟶ $\dfrac{2}{x-1} \div \dfrac{-3}{x-1} = \dfrac{2}{x-1} \cdot \dfrac{x-1}{-3}$

2️⃣ Product Rule for Fractions ⟶ $= \dfrac{2(x-1)}{-3(x-1)}$ ◀ $\dfrac{x-1}{x-1} = 1$

3️⃣ Simplify. ⟶ $= -\dfrac{2}{3}$

## example 2

Simplify $\dfrac{\frac{2}{3}}{\frac{1}{3} - \frac{x}{5}}$. ◀ Fractions with fractional numerators or denominators are **complex fractions**.

1️⃣ Multiply by 1 in the form $\dfrac{15}{15}$. ⟶ $\dfrac{\frac{2}{3}}{\frac{1}{3} - \frac{x}{5}} = \dfrac{15}{15} \cdot \dfrac{\frac{2}{3}}{\frac{1}{3} - \frac{x}{5}}$ ◀ $\dfrac{15}{15}$ is chosen because 15 is the LCM of all the denominators.

2️⃣ Product Rule for Fractions ⟶ $= \dfrac{15\left(\frac{2}{3}\right)}{15\left(\frac{1}{3} - \frac{x}{5}\right)}$

$\boxed{3}$ Distributive Property $\longrightarrow$ $= \dfrac{\dfrac{15}{1}\left(\dfrac{2}{3}\right)}{\dfrac{15}{1}\left(\dfrac{1}{3}\right) - \dfrac{15}{1}\left(\dfrac{x}{5}\right)}$ ◀ **Write 15 as $\dfrac{15}{1}$.**

$\boxed{4}$ Simplify. $\longrightarrow$ $= \dfrac{10}{5 - 3x}$

**P-2** **What name for 1 would be used to simplify each complex fraction?**

**a.** $\dfrac{\dfrac{x}{3} + \dfrac{1}{2}}{\dfrac{x}{6}}$   **b.** $\dfrac{\dfrac{x}{4}}{3x - \dfrac{1}{6}}$   **c.** $\dfrac{\dfrac{1}{x} - \dfrac{3}{2x}}{\dfrac{1}{2}}$

example 3   Simplify $\dfrac{\dfrac{2}{3} + \dfrac{5}{n}}{\dfrac{1}{2}}$.

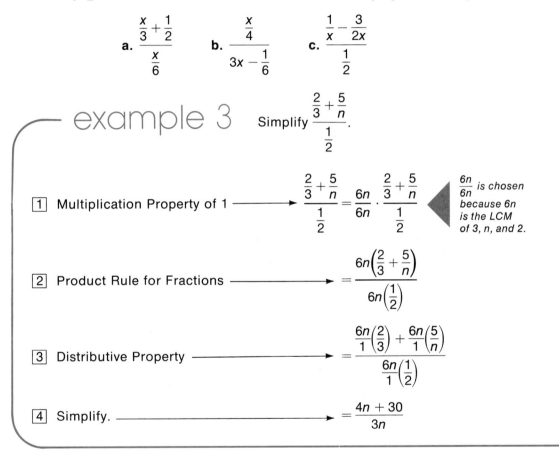

$\boxed{1}$ Multiplication Property of 1 $\longrightarrow$ $\dfrac{\dfrac{2}{3} + \dfrac{5}{n}}{\dfrac{1}{2}} = \dfrac{6n}{6n} \cdot \dfrac{\dfrac{2}{3} + \dfrac{5}{n}}{\dfrac{1}{2}}$ ◀ $\dfrac{6n}{6n}$ *is chosen because 6n is the LCM of 3, n, and 2.*

$\boxed{2}$ Product Rule for Fractions $\longrightarrow$ $= \dfrac{6n\left(\dfrac{2}{3} + \dfrac{5}{n}\right)}{6n\left(\dfrac{1}{2}\right)}$

$\boxed{3}$ Distributive Property $\longrightarrow$ $= \dfrac{\dfrac{6n}{1}\left(\dfrac{2}{3}\right) + \dfrac{6n}{1}\left(\dfrac{5}{n}\right)}{\dfrac{6n}{1}\left(\dfrac{1}{2}\right)}$

$\boxed{4}$ Simplify. $\longrightarrow$ $= \dfrac{4n + 30}{3n}$

## ORAL EXERCISES 17.5

*Tell a product for each quotient. (P-1, Example 1, Example 2, Example 3)*

**1.** $\left(-\dfrac{1}{4}\right) \div \dfrac{3}{4}$   **2.** $\dfrac{x}{3} \div \dfrac{5}{x}$   **3.** $\left(-\dfrac{r}{6}\right) \div \left(-\dfrac{s}{2}\right)$   **4.** $\dfrac{10}{x} \div \dfrac{3}{x+2}$

**5.** $\dfrac{5t}{t-3} \div \dfrac{t+2}{4}$    **6.** $\dfrac{x+8}{y} \div \dfrac{x+4}{2y}$    **7.** $\dfrac{\dfrac{x}{2}}{\dfrac{x-3}{5}}$    **8.** $\dfrac{\dfrac{y+6}{y}}{\dfrac{5}{y-1}}$

*Tell the least common multiple of the numbers in each set.* (Examples 2, 3)

**9.** {2, 5}    **10.** {4, 7}    **11.** {2, 8}    **12.** {4, 6}

**13.** {3, 4, 6}    **14.** {2, 10, x}    **15.** {6, 8, y}    **16.** {5, 10, 2x, x}

## WRITTEN EXERCISES 17.5

**A**    **Goal:** To divide with algebraic fractions and to simplify complex fractions

**Sample Problem:** Simplify $\dfrac{\dfrac{3x}{7}}{\dfrac{5}{7}+\dfrac{x}{7}}$.    **Answer:** $\dfrac{3x}{5+x}$

*Write each quotient as a product. Then simplify.* (P-1, Example 1)

**1.** $\dfrac{3}{5} \div \left(-\dfrac{7}{8}\right)$    **2.** $-\dfrac{4}{7} \div \dfrac{3}{5}$    **3.** $\dfrac{a}{3} \div \dfrac{2a}{9}$    **4.** $\dfrac{5}{x} \div \dfrac{10}{7x}$

**5.** $\left(-\dfrac{a}{5}\right) \div \left(-\dfrac{2a}{3}\right)$    **6.** $\left(-\dfrac{2x}{3}\right) \div \left(-\dfrac{x}{9}\right)$    **7.** $\dfrac{5}{x-2} \div \dfrac{3}{x-2}$

**8.** $\dfrac{a+3}{2} \div \dfrac{a+3}{5}$    **9.** $\dfrac{y+3}{2y} \div \dfrac{y+3}{y}$    **10.** $\dfrac{3x}{2x-1} \div \dfrac{4x}{2x-1}$

*Simplify.* (Example 2, Example 3)

**11.** $\dfrac{\dfrac{x}{5}}{\dfrac{2x}{5}}$    **12.** $\dfrac{\dfrac{a}{7}}{\dfrac{2a}{7}}$    **13.** $\dfrac{\dfrac{2n}{5}}{\dfrac{3}{5}+\dfrac{n}{5}}$    **14.** $\dfrac{\dfrac{5}{4}}{\dfrac{r}{4}+\dfrac{3}{4}}$

**15.** $\dfrac{\dfrac{5}{2}+\dfrac{x}{3}}{\dfrac{2}{3}}$    **16.** $\dfrac{\dfrac{1}{4}+\dfrac{y}{8}}{\dfrac{3}{4}}$    **17.** $\dfrac{\dfrac{3}{x}+\dfrac{1}{2}}{\dfrac{1}{3x}}$    **18.** $\dfrac{\dfrac{2}{a}+\dfrac{2}{3}}{\dfrac{5}{6a}}$

**B**    **19.** $\dfrac{\dfrac{3}{4y}-\dfrac{1}{2y}}{\dfrac{1}{6y}+\dfrac{2}{3}}$    **20.** $\dfrac{\dfrac{1}{8t}+\dfrac{5}{6}}{\dfrac{5}{2}-\dfrac{1}{4t}}$    **21.** $\dfrac{\dfrac{a}{2}-\dfrac{3}{-8}}{-\dfrac{5}{4}+\dfrac{a}{12}}$    **22.** $\dfrac{\dfrac{y}{9}+\dfrac{4}{3}}{\dfrac{-5}{3}-\dfrac{5y}{6}}$

# CHAPTER SUMMARY

**IMPORTANT IDEAS**

1. *Property of the Opposite of a Difference:* For any numbers $a$ and $b$, $-(a - b) = b - a$.

2. *Property of the Quotient of Opposites:* For any numbers $a$ and $b$, with $a \neq b$, $\dfrac{a - b}{b - a} = -1$.

3. *Product Rule for Fractions:* For any numbers $a$, $b$, $c$, and $d$, with $b \neq 0$ and $d \neq 0$, $\dfrac{a}{b} \cdot \dfrac{c}{d} = \dfrac{ac}{bd}$.

4. *Sum and Difference Rules for Fractions:* For any numbers $a$, $b$, and $c$, with $c \neq 0$, $\dfrac{a}{c} + \dfrac{b}{c} = \dfrac{a + b}{c}$ and $\dfrac{a}{c} - \dfrac{b}{c} = \dfrac{a - b}{c}$.

5. *Quotient Rule for Fractions:* For any numbers $a$, $b$, $c$, and $d$, with $b \neq 0$, $c \neq 0$, and $d \neq 0$, $\dfrac{a}{b} \div \dfrac{c}{d} = \dfrac{a}{b} \cdot \dfrac{d}{c}$.

# CHAPTER REVIEW

### SECTION 17.1

*Simplify. Assume no divisor is zero.*

1. $\dfrac{12r}{-12s}$

2. $\dfrac{-8mn}{12np}$

3. $\dfrac{4x(x + 5)}{6y(x + 5)}$

4. $\dfrac{5s(2s + 1)}{15t(2s + 1)}$

5. $-\dfrac{3x - 12}{4x - 16}$

6. $-\dfrac{a(2xa + 3a)}{6x + 9}$

### SECTION 17.2

*Simplify. Assume no divisor is zero.*

7. $\dfrac{r - 6}{6 - r}$

8. $\dfrac{3 - 2t}{2t - 3}$

9. $\dfrac{5(2 - 3x)}{-6(3x - 2)}$

10. $\dfrac{-x(4x - 1)}{4(1 - 4x)}$

11. $\dfrac{8 - 4y}{5y - 10}$

12. $\dfrac{4x - 6}{3x - 2x^2}$

**SECTION 17.3**

*Multiply and simplify. Assume that no divisor is zero.*

13. $\dfrac{4r}{3s} \cdot \dfrac{9s^2}{-10r}$

14. $\dfrac{6k}{-5n} \cdot \dfrac{5n}{8k^2}$

15. $\dfrac{3t}{2t-3} \cdot \dfrac{2t-3}{-4t}$

16. $\dfrac{4r-1}{2s} \cdot \dfrac{-12s}{3(4r-1)}$

17. $\dfrac{y-5}{5} \cdot \dfrac{15}{7(5-y)}$

18. $\dfrac{6m}{(5m-1)} \cdot \dfrac{(1-5m)}{-30}$

**SECTION 17.4**

*Add or subtract as indicated. Then simplify. Assume that no divisor is zero.*

19. $\dfrac{-7}{8x} + \dfrac{5}{8x}$

20. $\dfrac{19}{12t} + \dfrac{-10}{12t}$

21. $\dfrac{3q+4}{q+2} + \dfrac{q+1}{q+2}$

22. $\dfrac{b-6}{2b-3} + \dfrac{4b}{2b-3}$

23. $\dfrac{3m+1}{m+3} - \dfrac{3-2m}{m+3}$

24. $\dfrac{2k+5}{k-6} - \dfrac{k-2}{k-6}$

**SECTION 17.5**

*Write each quotient as a product. Then simplify.*

25. $-\dfrac{2a}{3} \div \dfrac{10a}{9}$

26. $\dfrac{5}{8x} \div \left(-\dfrac{25}{2x}\right)$

27. $\dfrac{4x-3}{3y} \div \dfrac{4x-3}{6}$

28. $\dfrac{4x^2}{3x+1} \div \dfrac{12x}{3x+1}$

*Simplify.*

29. $\dfrac{\dfrac{3}{x} + \dfrac{2}{3}}{\dfrac{1}{2x} - \dfrac{5}{6}}$

30. $\dfrac{\dfrac{2}{5} - \dfrac{3}{2y}}{\dfrac{7}{2} + \dfrac{2}{5y}}$

# 18

## Polynomials

# 18.1 Simplest Names

The following are examples of *monomials.*

**a.** $2x^3$     **b.** $-x$     **c.** $\frac{1}{2}x$     **d.** $-3.5$

You have worked with *binomials* such as the ones below.

**a.** $x - 3$     **b.** $2x + 5$     **c.** $3x^2 - x$     ◀ A **binomial** is the sum or difference of *two* monomials.

Monomials and binomials belong to a larger class of numerals or phrases called <u>polynomials</u>.

> A *polynomial* is a monomial or the sum or difference of two or more monomials.     $-2x^2$; $5x + 7$    $x^2 - 3x + 5$

**P-1**    **Which numerals or phrases below are polynomials?**   **binomials?**

**a.** $x^2 + 5x$     **b.** $-4x^5$          **c.** $-x^2 + 4x - 6$

**d.** $-19$        **e.** $x^3 - x^2 + x - 3$     **f.** $-5x + 1$

## example 1

Simplify $x - 3x^2 + 5x - 3 + 5x^2$.

1️⃣ Add like terms.  ⟶  $x - 3x^2 + 5x - 3 + 5x^2 = 6x + 2x^2 - 3$
2️⃣ Arrange terms in order with the largest exponent first.  ⟶  $= 2x^2 + 6x - 3$

It is often helpful to first group like terms.

## example 2

Simplify $4x + x^3 + 12 - 2x^2 - 3x^3 + 2x^2 - x - 17$.

1️⃣ Group like terms.  ⟶  $(4x - x) + (x^3 - 3x^3) + (12 - 17) + (-2x^2 + 2x^2)$
2️⃣ Add like terms.  ⟶  $3x - 2x^3 - 5 + 0$
3️⃣ Arrange terms in order.  ⟶  $-2x^3 + 3x - 5$

## ORAL EXERCISES 18.1

*Simplify.* (Example 1, Example 2)

**1.** $3x - 5x + 2$

**2.** $2x^2 - 4 + 7$

**3.** $x^2 - x - 2x + 6$

**4.** $4x^2 + x - 5x - 3$

**5.** $x - 2x^2 + 7$

**6.** $2x + x^2 - 3x + 5$

**7.** $\frac{1}{2}x^2 + 2\frac{1}{2}x^2 - \frac{3}{4}$

**8.** $1.2x^2 + 1.8x^2 - x + 6$

**9.** $-3x + x^2 + x + 2x^2 - 3$

**10.** $5x + 8 - 2x^4 + 5x - 3x^2$


## WRITTEN EXERCISES 18.1

**A**

**Goal:** To simplify a polynomial

**Sample Problem:** Simplify $x^2 + 5x - 2x^2 + 6 - 8x - 3x^3$.

**Answer:** $-3x^3 - x^2 - 3x + 6$

*Simplify.* (Example 1, Example 2)

**1.** $-3x + 7x - 2$

**2.** $5x - 8x + 7$

**3.** $3x^2 - x^2 + x + 9$

**4.** $8x^2 - x^2 - 3x - 5$

**5.** $-5x^2 - x - x + 2 - 9$

**6.** $-x^2 + 3x + 4x - 11 + 8$

**7.** $10x^3 - x^2 + 3x^2 - x + 1$

**8.** $19x^3 + 4x^2 - 5x^2 + 4x - 6$

**9.** $3x - 10 + 4x^2 - 12x + 1$

**10.** $9 - 12x + x^2 - x - 5$

**11.** $12 - x + 4x^3 - 3x + 3$

**12.** $-2x^2 - 8 + 4x^3 - x^2 + 7$

**13.** $x^4 - 6x^2 - 10 + 2x^3 + 6x^2 - 1$

**14.** $-5x^2 - 11 + 8x - x^3 - 6 - 8x$

**15.** $-\frac{1}{2}x^2 + \frac{3}{4}x^3 - \frac{5}{2} + \frac{3}{2}x^2 + \frac{3}{2}$

**16.** $-\frac{5}{4}x + \frac{7}{2} - \frac{3}{4}x^2 + \frac{1}{4}x - \frac{5}{2}$

**17.** $2.7 - 1.3x^2 - 1.9 + 1.8x - 3.4x^2$

**18.** $-5.1x + 4.8 - 2.7x^2 - 0.8x - 3.7$

**19.** $23x^4 - 16x + 13x^2 - x^4 + 9x - 2x^2 + 24$

**20.** $12x - 5x^3 + 19x^5 - 15 + x - 2x^3 + 21$

**B**

**21.** $(2x^2 - 5x) + (8x - 3)$

**22.** $(-3x^3 + 9) + (x^3 - 4)$

**23.** $(12x - 2) - (5x - 3)$

**24.** $(-4x + 1) - (6x - 3)$

**25.** $(x^2 - 3x + 4) - (7 - 3x^2 - x)$

**26.** $(5x - 3x^2 + 9) - (x^2 - x + 5)$

# 18.2 Evaluating Polynomials

P-1   **What is the value of each monomial if x equals −2?**

**a.** $-5x$     **b.** $3x^2$     **c.** $-x^2$     **d.** $(-x)^2$

> *Raise to a power before performing any other operation.*

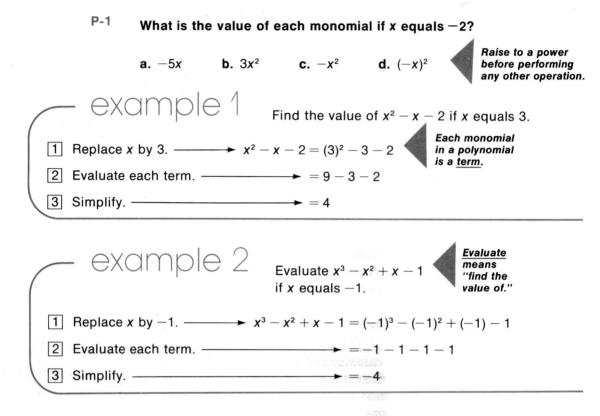

## example 1

Find the value of $x^2 - x - 2$ if $x$ equals 3.

> *Each monomial in a polynomial is a **term**.*

1. Replace $x$ by 3.  ⟶  $x^2 - x - 2 = (3)^2 - 3 - 2$
2. Evaluate each term.  ⟶  $= 9 - 3 - 2$
3. Simplify.  ⟶  $= 4$

## example 2

Evaluate $x^3 - x^2 + x - 1$ if $x$ equals $-1$.

> *Evaluate means "find the value of."*

1. Replace $x$ by $-1$.  ⟶  $x^3 - x^2 + x - 1 = (-1)^3 - (-1)^2 + (-1) - 1$
2. Evaluate each term.  ⟶  $= -1 - 1 - 1 - 1$
3. Simplify.  ⟶  $= -4$

It is often helpful to first simplify a polynomial.

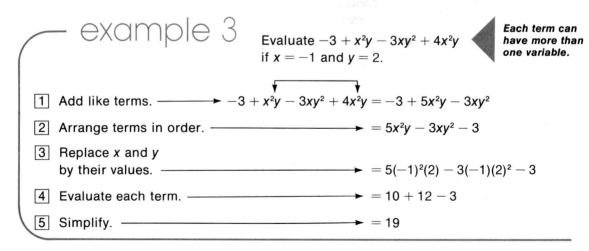

## example 3

Evaluate $-3 + x^2y - 3xy^2 + 4x^2y$ if $x = -1$ and $y = 2$.

> *Each term can have more than one variable.*

1. Add like terms.  ⟶  $-3 + x^2y - 3xy^2 + 4x^2y = -3 + 5x^2y - 3xy^2$
2. Arrange terms in order.  ⟶  $= 5x^2y - 3xy^2 - 3$
3. Replace $x$ and $y$ by their values.  ⟶  $= 5(-1)^2(2) - 3(-1)(2)^2 - 3$
4. Evaluate each term.  ⟶  $= 10 + 12 - 3$
5. Simplify.  ⟶  $= 19$

## ORAL EXERCISES 18.2

*Tell the value of each polynomial if $x = -2$, $y = 1$, and $z = 3$. (Example 1, Example 2, Example 3)*

1. $x^2$

2. $-y^3$

3. $x^2 + y^2$

4. $x^2 - y^2$

5. $x + y - z$

6. $y^2 + z - 5$

7. $y^2z - yz$

8. $y^5 - 1$

9. $-3x^2 + 5x - 2$

10. $-y^3 + y^2 - y + 1$

11. $x^3 - x^2 + x - 1$

12. $-x^3 - x^2 - x - 1$

## WRITTEN EXERCISES 18.2

**A** **Goal:** To evaluate a polynomial
**Sample Problem:** $-2x^2 + 3xy - y^2$ if $x = 1$ and $y = -2$
**Answer:** $-12$

*Evaluate each polynomial. (Example 1, Example 2, Example 3)*

1. $x^2 - 2x + 3$ if $x = -2$

2. $-2x^2 + x - 1$ if $x = -2$

3. $3x^2 - 5x - 2$ if $x = 3$

4. $2x^2 + 3x - 10$ if $x = 1$

5. $-4x^2 + x - 2$ if $x = -3$

6. $-5x^2 + 2x - 3$ if $x = -3$

7. $x^3 + 2x^2 - x - 3$ if $x = 1$

8. $x^3 - x^2 + 3x - 5$ if $x = 1$

9. $-x^3 + x^2 + 3x - 4$ if $x = -1$

10. $-x^3 + 2x^2 - 5x + 3$ if $x = -1$

11. $x^4 - 5x^2 + 2$ if $x = 2$

12. $x^4 - 3x^2 - 3$ if $x = 2$

13. $-x^5 + x^3 - x$ if $x = -2$

14. $x^5 - x^3 + x + 3$ if $x = -2$

15. $x^2y - 2xy^2 + 5$ if $x = -2$ and $y = 3$

16. $2x^2y - xy + y^2$ if $x = -1$ and $y = -2$

17. $-x^2y + 3xy^2 - 5x + 4y - 2$ if $x = 1$ and $y = -1$

18. $3y^3x^2 - 2y^2x + yx - 5$ if $x = -2$ and $y = 1$

19. $x^3y^2z - x^2yz^2 + xyz^3$ if $x = 1$, $y = -1$, and $z = 1$

20. $-p^3qr + 2p^2q^2r^2 - pq^3r^3$ if $p = -1$, $q = 1$, $r = -1$

**B**

21. $x^2 - 3x + \frac{1}{4}$ if $x = \frac{1}{4}$

22. $-x^2 + 2x - \frac{5}{2}$ if $x = -\frac{1}{2}$

23. $x^3 - x^2 + x - \frac{1}{2}$ if $x = \frac{1}{2}$

24. $-x^3 + x^2 - 2x + \frac{1}{3}$ if $x = -\frac{2}{3}$

25. $x^3 - x^2 + x - 1.2$ if $x = 0.4$

26. $-2x^3 + x^2 - x + 0.8$ if $x = -0.3$

27. $x^3 - x^2 - x + 2.4$ if $x = 0.2$

28. $-x^3 + 2x^2 - x - 0.4$ if $x = -0.1$

# 18.3 Addition of Polynomials

P-1 **What is the simplest name of each polynomial?**

    **a.** $5x^2 + (-x^2)$      **b.** $-2xy^2 + 5xy^2$      **c.** $5x^3y - x^3y + (-6x^3y)$

Here are the steps for adding two or more polynomials.

| Write as a sum of monomials. | → | Add like terms. | → | Arrange the terms in order and simplify. |

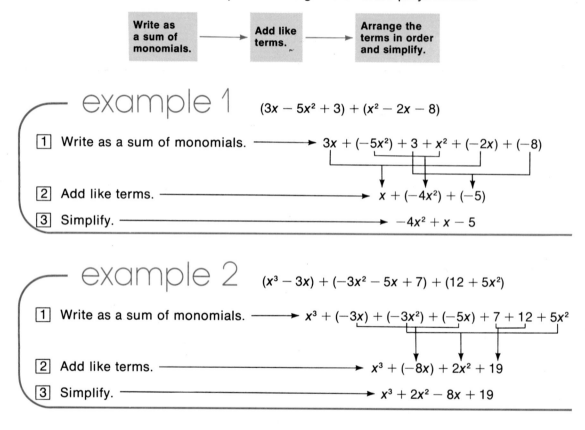

example 1     $(3x - 5x^2 + 3) + (x^2 - 2x - 8)$

1. Write as a sum of monomials.   ⟶   $3x + (-5x^2) + 3 + x^2 + (-2x) + (-8)$

2. Add like terms.   ⟶   $x + (-4x^2) + (-5)$

3. Simplify.   ⟶   $-4x^2 + x - 5$

example 2     $(x^3 - 3x) + (-3x^2 - 5x + 7) + (12 + 5x^2)$

1. Write as a sum of monomials.   ⟶   $x^3 + (-3x) + (-3x^2) + (-5x) + 7 + 12 + 5x^2$

2. Add like terms.   ⟶   $x^3 + (-8x) + 2x^2 + 19$

3. Simplify.   ⟶   $x^3 + 2x^2 - 8x + 19$

It is often helpful to arrange polynomials vertically for adding.

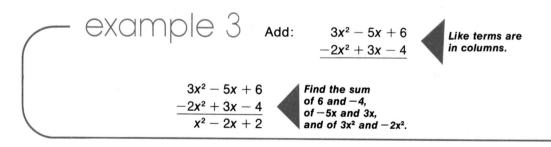

example 3    Add:   
$$\begin{array}{r} 3x^2 - 5x + 6 \\ -2x^2 + 3x - 4 \end{array}$$
◀ **Like terms are in columns.**

$$\begin{array}{r} 3x^2 - 5x + 6 \\ -2x^2 + 3x - 4 \\ \hline x^2 - 2x + 2 \end{array}$$
◀ **Find the sum of 6 and −4, of −5x and 3x, and of 3x² and −2x².**

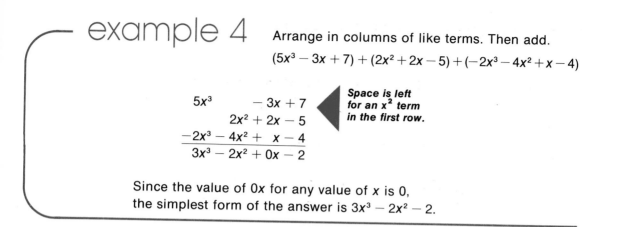

example 4  Arrange in columns of like terms. Then add.

$$(5x^3 - 3x + 7) + (2x^2 + 2x - 5) + (-2x^3 - 4x^2 + x - 4)$$

$$
\begin{array}{r}
5x^3 \quad\quad - 3x + 7 \\
2x^2 + 2x - 5 \\
-2x^3 - 4x^2 + \ x - 4 \\
\hline
3x^3 - 2x^2 + 0x - 2
\end{array}
$$

**Space is left for an $x^2$ term in the first row.**

Since the value of $0x$ for any value of $x$ is 0,
the simplest form of the answer is $3x^3 - 2x^2 - 2$.

## ORAL EXERCISES 18.3

*Add.* (Example 1, Example 2, Example 3, Example 4)

**1.** $3x - 2$
$4x + 5$

**2.** $-5x^2 + 1$
$4x^2 - 3$

**3.** $2x^2 - x$
$x^2 + 5x$

**4.** $x^2 - 3x + 2$
$2x^2 + 5x - 6$

**5.** $4x^2 \quad\quad + 3$
$x^2 - 3x + 4$

**6.** $-5x^2 + 4x - 7$
$-2x^2 \quad\quad + 3$

**7.** $-x^2 - 3x + 1$
$2x^2 + \ x - 2$
$x^2 - 2x + 6$

**8.** $2x^2 \quad\quad - 1$
$3x + 5$
$-5x^2 - 2x$

**9.** $3x^2y \quad\quad + 4xy^2 - y^3$
$-4x^2y + 6xy \quad\quad + 2y^3$
$- 3xy + 2xy^2 - 3y^3$

**10.** $(x - 3) + (2x + 1)$

**11.** $(-3x^2 + 5) + (x^2 - 3)$

**12.** $(2x^2 - x) + (4x - 5)$

**13.** $(x^2 - 3x) + (4x - 2) + (3x^2 - 5)$

**14.** $(3x^3 + x - 5) + (x^2 - 5x + 3)$

**15.** $(2x^2y + xy - 5) + (3x^2y - 2xy + 7)$

## WRITTEN EXERCISES 18.3

Ⓐ

**Goal:** To add polynomials
**Sample Problem:** Add: $(x^2y + 3xy - xy^2) + (2x^2y - xy - 4xy^2)$
**Answer:** $3x^2y + 2xy - 5xy^2$

*Add.* (Example 1, Example 2, Example 3, Example 4)

**1.** $(3x + 7) + (-5x - 2)$

**2.** $(-8x + 3) + (4x - 6)$

**3.** $(-x^2 + 8) + (3x^2 - 11)$

**4.** $(7x^2 - 10) + (-x^2 + 8)$

Add. (Example 1, Example 2, Example 3, Example 4)

**5.** $(5x^2 - x - 2) + (2x^2 - 2x + 7)$

**6.** $(-2x^2 + 3x - 4) + (5x^2 - x + 3)$

**7.** $(x^2 - 3x + 1) + (2x^2 + x - 3) + (3x^2 - x + 5)$

**8.** $(4x^2 - 5x + 2) + (x^2 - x - 3) + (-3x^2 + 2x - 5)$

**9.** $(4.3x^3 - 1.7x + 2.5) + (3.9x^3 - 5.6x^2 - 4.8)$

**10.** $(1.8x^4 - 3.7x^2 + 2.9) + (2.5x^3 - 1.7x^2 + 4.2x)$

**11.** $\begin{aligned} 5x^2 - 2x + 3 \\ -2x^2 + 6x - 5 \end{aligned}$

**12.** $\begin{aligned} 4x^2 - \phantom{0}x + 5 \\ -x^2 + 6x - 3 \end{aligned}$

**13.** $\begin{aligned} 2x^3 \phantom{000} - 5x + 16 \\ -3x^2 + 7x - \phantom{0}9 \end{aligned}$

**14.** $\begin{aligned} -4x^3 + 3x^2 \phantom{000} - 8 \\ 5x^3 \phantom{000} - 3x + 7 \end{aligned}$

**15.** $\begin{aligned} x^2 - 5x + 3 \\ 2x^2 + \phantom{0}x - 7 \\ -x^2 - 4x + 9 \end{aligned}$

**16.** $\begin{aligned} -6x^2 + 4x - 8 \\ 3x^2 - 5x + 6 \\ x^2 + 7x - 9 \end{aligned}$

**17.** $\begin{aligned} 5x^2y - 4xy^2 + 2xy - 5 \\ -3x^2y + \phantom{0}xy^2 - 5xy + 1 \end{aligned}$

**18.** $\begin{aligned} -12x^2y + 4xy^2 - \phantom{0}y^3 \\ 5x^2y - 2xy^2 + 6y^3 \end{aligned}$

*Arrange in columns of like terms. Then add.* (Example 4)

**19.** $(3x^3 - 2x + 10) + (-2x^3 + 4x - 6)$

**20.** $(3x^2 - 17) + (5x^3 - x^2 + 9x)$

**21.** $(5x - 3x^3 + 9) + (x^2 + x^3 - 6x + 3)$

**22.** $(4x^4 - x^3 + 2x - 7) + (3x - 2x^2 + 5x^3 - x^4)$

**23.** $(13 - 2x^3) + (x^2 - 5x + 6) + (-3 + 4x^3 - x^2 + 2x)$

**24.** $(10x - 3x^2 + x^3) + (4x^2 - 5 - 6x) + (9 - 5x + 4x^3)$

**B**

**25.** $(2x^3y^2 - 4xy^3 + 5xy + 6x^2y^2) + (5x^2y - x^2y^2 + 2xy^3 - 6)$

**26.** $(-xy^2 + 5xy - x^2y + x^3y^2) + (4x^2y - xy + 5y - 6x^3y^2)$

**27.** $(1.2xy - 3.4xy^2 + 1.5x^2 - 5.8y) + (1.9xy^2 - 6.3x + 5.3xy^2 - 2.1xy)$

**28.** $(4.3xy^3 + 1.9x^3y^2 - 0.8xy - 1.9) + (6.3x^2y^2 - 2.9xy^3 + 3.1xy - 7.2x)$

**29.** $(12xy^2z - 5x^2yz^3) + (-5xyz^2 + 14x^2yz^3) + (-3xy^2z + 7xyz + 19xz)$

# 18.4 Subtraction of Polynomials

To subtract polynomials, subtract like monomials.

## example 1

Subtract:

$$5x^2 + 2x - 3$$
$$(-)\ 2x^2 + 3x + 7$$

> **Remember!**
> To subtract a number, add its opposite.

$$
\begin{array}{r}
5x^2 + 2x - 3 \\
(-)\ 2x^2 + 3x + 7
\end{array}
\longrightarrow
\begin{array}{r}
5x^2 + 2x - 3 \\
-2x^2 - 3x - 7 \\
\hline
3x^2 - x - 10
\end{array}
$$

## example 2

Subtract:

$$-2x^3 \qquad + 4x - 1$$
$$(-)\quad x^3 + 4x^2 - 2x + 5$$

$$
\begin{array}{r}
-2x^3 \quad + 4x - 1 \\
(-)\quad x^3 + 4x^2 - 2x + 5
\end{array}
\longrightarrow
\begin{array}{r}
-2x^3 \quad + 4x - 1 \\
-x^3 - 4x^2 + 2x - 5 \\
\hline
-3x^3 - 4x^2 + 6x - 6
\end{array}
$$

**P-1** **How would you write each polynomial without parentheses?**

**a.** $-(2x - 5)$  **b.** $-(-2x^2 + 8x + 7)$  **c.** $-(-2x^2 + 5x - 2)$

You can also subtract polynomials horizontally.

## example 3  $(x^2 - 3x + 5) - (-2x^2 + 5x - 2)$

1. Property of the Opposite of a Sum $\longrightarrow$ $x^2 - 3x + 5 + 2x^2 - 5x + 2$

2. Add like terms. $\longrightarrow$ $3x^2 - 8x + 7$

## example 4  $(5x - 3x^3 + 17) - (15 - x^2 + 8x)$

1. Property of the Opposite of a Sum $\longrightarrow$ $5x - 3x^3 + 17 - 15 + x^2 - 8x$

2. Add like terms. $\longrightarrow$ $-3x - 3x^3 + 2 + x^2$

3. Arrange in order. $\longrightarrow$ $-3x^3 + x^2 - 3x + 2$

## ORAL EXERCISES 18.4

*Subtract.* (Example 1, Example 2, Example 3, Example 4)

1.  $12x - 3$
    $(-)\ \underline{8x + 4}$

2.  $4x^2 + 7$
    $(-)\ \underline{x^2 - 1}$

3.  $-x^2 + 2x - 3$
    $(-)\ \underline{4x^2 + 6x - 5}$

4.  $3x^2 \qquad - 8$
    $(-)\ \underline{5x^2 + 2x + 3}$

5.  $(5x - 2) - (3x - 7)$

6.  $(-4x^2 + 3x) - (2x - 5x^2)$

7.  $(3x^2 + 2x - 5) - (x^2 + x - 3)$

8.  $(10x^2 - 3x + 2) - (5x^2 + 2x - 8)$

## WRITTEN EXERCISES 18.4

**A**

**Goal:** To subtract polynomials
**Sample Problem:** Subtract: $(6x^2 + 10x - 3) - (-2x^2 - 5)$
**Answer:** $8x^2 + 10x + 2$

*Subtract.* (Example 1, Example 2)

1.  $12x - 3$
    $(-)\ \underline{8x + 2}$

2.  $8x + 6$
    $(-)\ \underline{3x + 9}$

3.  $5x^2 + 2x$
    $(-)\ \underline{6x^2 - 5x}$

4.  $9x^3 - 4x$
    $(-)\ \underline{3x^3 + 3x}$

5.  $12x^2 - 2x + 3$
    $(-)\ \underline{4x^2 + 3x - 7}$

6.  $-10x^2 + 5x + 6$
    $(-)\ \underline{-8x^2 + 2x + 7}$

7.  $1.3x^2 \qquad + 2.7$
    $(-)\ \underline{4.8x^2 - 3.7x - 1.9}$

8.  $4.1x^2 \qquad - 3.2$
    $(-)\ \underline{5.9x^2 + 2.6x - 1.9}$

*Subtract.* (Example 3, Example 4)

9.  $(3x^2 - 2x + 5) - (x^2 + 5x - 6)$

10. $(-6x^2 + 4x - 1) - (2x^2 + 3x - 7)$

11. $(-15x^3 - 2x + 6) - (-12x^3 + 3x^2 - 5x)$

12. $(13x^3 - 5x^2 + 8) - (9x^3 - 4x^2 - 5)$

13. $(2.4x - 0.9x^2 + 1.9) - (2.5 + 5.1x - 3.7x^2)$

14. $(12.3 + 0.5x - 6.1x^2) - (3.6x - 4.8x^2 + 8.7)$

15. $(2x - 5x^3 + 7) - (15 + 2x^2 - 3x^3)$

16. $(12 + 3x^2 - x^3) - (-7x - x^2 + 19)$

17. $(5x - 3x^4 + 2x^2 - 6) - (3x^3 - 6x + 15 - x^4)$

18. $(-6x^3 + 18 - 7x - x^4) - (2x^2 - 6x + 13 - 3x^4)$

19. $(2x^2y^2 - 5xy^3 - 6xy + 1) - (5xy + 7xy^2 - x^2y^2 - 8)$

20. $(-xy^3 + 4x^2y - 7x^2y^2 + 6) - (2x^2y - 5x^3y + 3 - xy^2)$

# 18.5  Multiplication of Polynomials

P-1  **What is the simplest name of each product below?**

a. $(-2x)(3)$    b. $(-5x)(-3x)$    c. $(4x^2)(-xy)$

Example 1 reviews multiplication of binomials.

## example 1  $(2x + 3)(x - 5)$

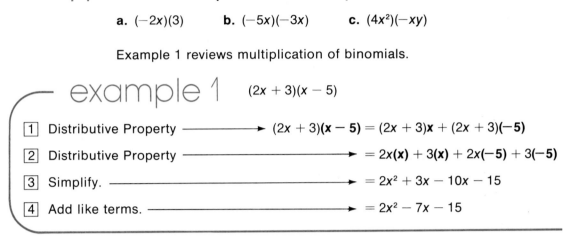

1 Distributive Property ⟶ $(2x + 3)(x - 5) = (2x + 3)x + (2x + 3)(-5)$

2 Distributive Property ⟶ $= 2x(x) + 3(x) + 2x(-5) + 3(-5)$

3 Simplify. ⟶ $= 2x^2 + 3x - 10x - 15$

4 Add like terms. ⟶ $= 2x^2 - 7x - 15$

Example 2 reviews the shorter method.

## example 2  $(3x - 2)(x + 4)$

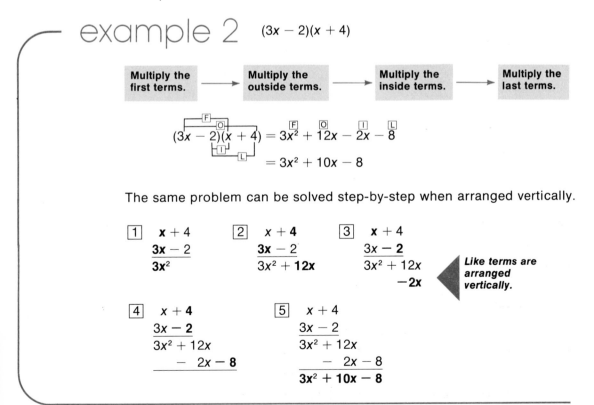

| Multiply the first terms. | Multiply the outside terms. | Multiply the inside terms. | Multiply the last terms. |

$$(3x - 2)(x + 4) = 3x^2 + 12x - 2x - 8$$

$$= 3x^2 + 10x - 8$$

The same problem can be solved step-by-step when arranged vertically.

1  $x + 4$
   $3x - 2$
   $\overline{3x^2}$

2  $x + 4$
   $3x - 2$
   $\overline{3x^2 + 12x}$

3  $x + 4$
   $3x - 2$
   $\overline{3x^2 + 12x}$
   $\phantom{3x^2 + 12x} - 2x$

*Like terms are arranged vertically.*

4  $x + 4$
   $3x - 2$
   $\overline{3x^2 + 12x}$
   $\phantom{3x^2} - 2x - 8$

5  $x + 4$
   $3x - 2$
   $\overline{3x^2 + 12x}$
   $\underline{\phantom{3x^2} - 2x - 8}$
   $3x^2 + 10x - 8$

To multiply any two polynomials, multiply each term of one polynomial by each term of the other. Then add like terms.

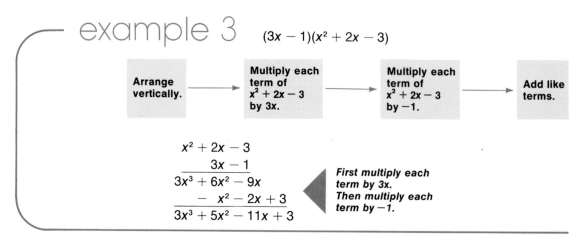

example 3  $(3x - 1)(x^2 + 2x - 3)$

| Arrange vertically. | Multiply each term of $x^2 + 2x - 3$ by $3x$. | Multiply each term of $x^2 + 2x - 3$ by $-1$. | Add like terms. |

$$x^2 + 2x - 3$$
$$\underline{3x - 1}$$
$$3x^3 + 6x^2 - 9x$$
$$\underline{\phantom{3x^3} - x^2 - 2x + 3}$$
$$3x^3 + 5x^2 - 11x + 3$$

First multiply each term by $3x$.
Then multiply each term by $-1$.

example 4  $(2x - 3)(2x + 3 - x^3)$

$$-x^3 \qquad + 2x + 3$$
$$2x - 3$$
$$-2x^4 \qquad + 4x^2 + 6x$$
$$\underline{\phantom{-2x^4} 3x^3 \qquad - 6x - 9}$$
$$-2x^4 + 3x^3 + 4x^2 \qquad - 9$$

Arrange terms in order. Leave space for missing terms.

## ORAL EXERCISES 18.5

*Multiply.* (Example 1, Example 2)

**1.** $(x + 3)(x + 2)$      **2.** $(x + 4)(x - 1)$      **3.** $(x - 2)(x + 5)$

**4.** $(x + 5)(x + 5)$      **5.** $(2x + 1)(x - 3)$      **6.** $(3x - 1)(x + 3)$

**7.** $(x - 3)(x - 3)$      **8.** $(4x - 1)(x + 3)$      **9.** $(2x + 1)(3x - 2)$

*Tell the terms missing from each row.* (Example 2, Example 3, Example 4)

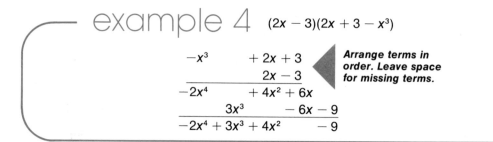

**10.** $3x - 5$
$\underline{2x + 7}$
$6x^2 - 10x$
$\underline{\phantom{6x^2 - 10x} 21x - 35}$
[      ]

**11.** $2x^2 - 3x$
$\underline{2x + 4}$
$4x^3 - 6x^2$
[      ]
$4x^3 + 2x^2 - 12x$

**12.** $5x^2 - 2$
    $3x + 4$

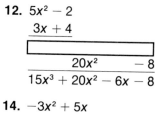

      $20x^2 \quad\quad - 8$
$15x^3 + 20x^2 - 6x - 8$

**13.** $2x^2 - 3x + 4$
        $2x - 3$
   $4x^3 - 6x^2 + 8x$

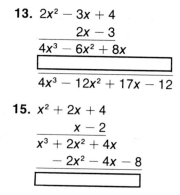

  $4x^3 - 12x^2 + 17x - 12$

**14.** $-3x^2 + 5x$
    $2x - 3$
  $-6x^3 + 10x^2$

  $-6x^3 + 19x^2 - 15x$

**15.** $x^2 + 2x + 4$
      $x - 2$
$x^3 + 2x^2 + 4x$
   $- 2x^2 - 4x - 8$

## WRITTEN EXERCISES 18.5

**A**

**Goal:** To multiply polynomials
**Sample Problem:** Multiply: $(x + 1)(x^2 - x + 1)$
**Answer:** $x^3 + 1$

*Multiply.* (Example 1, Example 2, Example 3, Example 4)

**1.** $(x - 2)(x + 5)$      **2.** $(x + 7)(x - 3)$      **3.** $(x - 8)(x - 9)$

**4.** $(x - 6)(x - 7)$      **5.** $(3x - 2)(x + 3)$      **6.** $(2x - 5)(x + 4)$

**7.** $(4x - 5)(4x - 5)$      **8.** $(6x + 7)(6x + 7)$      **9.** $(3x - 7)(3x + 7)$

**10.** $(2x + 5)(2x - 5)$      **11.** $(2x^2 + 3)(x - 1)$      **12.** $(x^2 - 3)(x^2 + 4)$

**13.** $2x^2 - x + 3$
      $x - 5$

**14.** $-3x^2 + x - 2$
       $x + 4$

**15.** $x^2 - 3x + 5$
      $x + 8$

**16.** $2x^2 + 4x - 3$
      $x - 6$

**17.** $x^2 - 2x + 5$
      $x + 3$

**18.** $x^3 - x + 3$
      $x - 5$

**19.** $-3x^3 + 2x - 1$
       $x + 2$

**20.** $x^2 + 5x - 3$
      $x + 2$

**21.** $-2x^2 + 3x - 2$
      $x^2 + 3$

**22.** $4x^2 - x + 3$
      $x^2 - 4$

**23.** $x^4 - x^2 + 1$
      $x - 1$

**24.** $x^5 - x^3 + x$
      $x + 2$

**B**

**25.** $x^2 + 2x - 3$
    $x^2 - x + 2$

**26.** $2x^2 - x + 1$
    $x^2 + 2x - 3$

**27.** $-3x^3 + 3x - 1$
      $x^2 + 3$

**28.** $x^3 + 2x^2 - 5$
      $x^2 + x$

**29.** $3x - 2x^3 + 5$
    $2 - x^2 + 3x$

**30.** $3 - x^4 + 5x$
    $x^2 - 2 + x^3$

# 18.6 Division of Polynomials

**P-1** **What is the product of $(2x + 1)(x - 2)$?**

Two division problems can be written from this one multiplication problem.

**1**

$$(2x^2 - 3x - 2) \div (x - 2) = 2x + 1$$

**2**

$$(2x^2 - 3x - 2) \div (2x + 1) = x - 2$$

**P-2** **What monomial represents each quotient below?**

a. $\dfrac{2x^2}{x}$    b. $\dfrac{-6x^2}{2x}$    c. $\dfrac{10x^3}{-5x}$    d. $\dfrac{-5x^2}{-x^2}$

## example 1    $(3x^2 - 7x - 6) \div (x - 3)$

1 Find $\dfrac{3x^2}{x}$ to get the first term of the quotient. ⟶

$$x - 3 \overline{)\, 3x^2 - 7x - 6}^{\,3x}$$

2 Multiply $(x - 3)$ by $3x$. Subtract the product from the dividend. ⟶

$$\begin{array}{r} 3x \phantom{xxxxxxx} \\ x - 3 \overline{)\, 3x^2 - 7x - 6} \\ \underline{3x^2 - 9x \phantom{xx}} \\ 2x - 6 \end{array}$$

3 Find $\dfrac{2x}{x}$ to get the second term of the quotient. ⟶

$$\begin{array}{r} 3x + 2 \phantom{xxx} \\ x - 3 \overline{)\, 3x^2 - 7x - 6} \\ \underline{3x^2 - 9x \phantom{xx}} \\ 2x - 6 \end{array}$$

4 Multiply $(x - 3)$ by $2$. Subtract the product from $2x - 6$. ⟶

$$\begin{array}{r} 3x + 2 \phantom{xxx} \\ x - 3 \overline{)\, 3x^2 - 7x - 6} \\ \underline{3x^2 - 9x \phantom{xx}} \\ 2x - 6 \\ \underline{2x - 6} \\ 0 \end{array}$$

## ORAL EXERCISES 18.6

*Tell each quotient.* (P-2)

1. $\dfrac{-5x}{x}$    2. $\dfrac{3x^2}{-x}$    3. $\dfrac{-4x^2}{-4x}$    4. $\dfrac{10x^3}{5x}$    5. $\dfrac{-2x^3}{x^2}$    6. $\dfrac{-15x^3}{-5x^2}$

*Subtract.*

7. $x^2 - 3x + 2$
$\underline{x^2 - \phantom{3}x\phantom{ + 2}}$

8. $-x^2 \phantom{+ 2x} - 5$
$\underline{-x^2 + 2x + 3}$

9. $6x^2 - x - 3$
$\underline{6x^2 \phantom{- x} + 5}$

*Tell each quotient.* (Example 1)

10.
$$\begin{array}{r} 2x \phantom{aaaaaaaaa} \\ x + 4 \overline{)\, 2x^2 + 5x - 12} \\ \underline{2x^2 + 8x \phantom{aaaaa}} \\ -3x - 12 \end{array}$$

11.
$$\begin{array}{r} x \phantom{aaaaaaaaa} \\ x - 9 \overline{)\, x^2 - 18x + 81} \\ \underline{x^2 - \phantom{1}9x \phantom{aaaaa}} \\ -9x + 81 \end{array}$$

## WRITTEN EXERCISES 18.6

**A**

**Goal:** To divide polynomials
**Sample Problem:** Divide: $3x + 1 \overline{)\, 3x^2 - 14x - 5}$    **Answer:** $x - 5$

*Divide.* (Example 1)

1. $x - 4 \overline{)\, 2x^2 - 5x - 12}$

2. $x + 3 \overline{)\, 3x^2 + 5x - 12}$

3. $3x - 2 \overline{)\, -6x^2 + 19x - 10}$

4. $3x - 6 \overline{)\, -12x^2 + 27x - 6}$

5. $x - 7 \overline{)\, x^2 - 14x + 49}$

6. $x + 12 \overline{)\, x^2 + 24x + 144}$

7. $x + 3 \overline{)\, x^3 + x^2 - 3x + 9}$

8. $x - 4 \overline{)\, 2x^3 - 3x^2 - 21x + 4}$

9. $2x - 2 \overline{)\, 2x^3 - 10x^2 + 20x - 12}$

10. $3x + 5 \overline{)\, 3x^3 - 4x^2 - 3x + 20}$

**B**

**EXAMPLE:** $x + 1 \overline{)\, x^3 - 2x^2 + 3}$     **SOLUTION:**
$$\begin{array}{r} x^2 - 3x + 3 \phantom{aa} \\ x + 1 \overline{)\, x^3 - 2x^2 \phantom{aaaa} + 3} \\ \underline{x^3 + \phantom{1}x^2 \phantom{aaaaaaaa}} \\ -3x^2 \phantom{aaaa} + 3 \\ \underline{-3x^2 - 3x \phantom{aaa}} \\ 3x + 3 \\ \underline{3x + 3} \\ 0 \end{array}$$

**Leave space for an *x* term.**

11. $x - 1 \overline{)\, x^3 - 6x^2 + 5}$

12. $2x - 6 \overline{)\, 2x^3 - 32x + 42}$

# Data Processing

Many different occupations are related to the use of electronic computers including computer programmers, systems analysts, and computer operating personnel. This latter group includes console operators, keypunch operators, data typists, high-speed printer operators, card-to-tape operators, and tape-to-card operators. A college degree is important for persons who expect to be systems analysts and top notch programmers. Computer operators usually need at least a high school education and must have on-the-job experience. About three-fourths of a million people are employed as systems analysts, programmers, or computer operating personnel.

High speed digital computers perform mathematical operations on numbers expressed in the *binary numeration system*. The binary system of numeration only uses the digits 0 and 1. The base for numbers in binary form is 2. The expanded notation for numbers in decimal form shows the meaning of the binary system.

**Decimal Form    Expanded Notation**

$$20583 = 2 \cdot 10^4 + 0 \cdot 10^3 + 5 \cdot 10^2 + 8 \cdot 10^1 + 3 \cdot 10^0$$

**Binary Form    Expanded Notation**

$$100111_{two} = 1 \cdot 2^5 + 0 \cdot 2^4 + 0 \cdot 2^3 + 1 \cdot 2^2 + 1 \cdot 2^1 + 1 \cdot 2^0$$
$$= 32 + 0 + 0 + 4 + 2 + 1$$
$$= 39_{ten}$$

Some computers use the *octal* (base 8) *numeration system*.

**Octal digits:** 0, 1, 2, 3, 4, 5, 6, 7

$$273_{eight} = 2 \cdot 8^2 + 7 \cdot 8^1 + 3 \cdot 8^0$$
$$= 128 + 56 + 3$$
$$= 187_{ten}$$

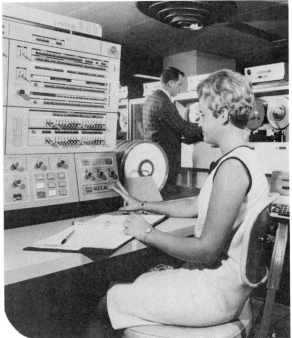

# CHAPTER SUMMARY

| | | | |
|---|---|---|---|
| **IMPORTANT TERMS** | Monomial *(p. 438)* <br> Binomial *(p. 438)* <br> Polynomial *(p. 438)* | Term *(p. 440)* <br> Evaluate *(p. 440)* | |

**IMPORTANT IDEAS**

*1.* To simplify a polynomial:
   *a.* Add like terms.
   *b.* Arrange terms in order with the largest exponent first, the next larger exponent second, and so on.

*2.* In evaluating a phrase, raise a number to a power before performing any other operation.

*3.* Steps in adding two polynomials:
   *a.* Write as a sum of monomials.
   *b.* Add like terms.
   *c.* Arrange the terms in order and simplify.

*4.* To subtract polynomials, subtract like monomials.

*5.* To multiply any two polynomials, multiply each term of one polynomial by each term of the other. Then add like terms.

*6.* In dividing polynomials, the terms of each polynomial must be arranged in order by their exponents.

# CHAPTER REVIEW

### SECTION 18.1

*Simplify.*

**1.** $5x - 2x^2 + 3 + x^2$

**2.** $18x^2 + 11x - x^2 - 7$

**3.** $4x^2 - 2x^3 + 5 - x^2 + 3x^3$

**4.** $12x - 3x^2 + 6 - x - 2x^3 + x^2$

**5.** $7.3x - 12.6 + 1.9x^2 - 3.7x - 2.3x^2$

**6.** $2.9x^3 - 4.7 + 3.2x - 3.4x^3 - 1.9x$

### SECTION 18.2

*Evaluate each polynomial.*

**7.** $-2x^2 + 5x - 3$ if $x = -4$

**8.** $3x^2 - 2x + 1$ if $x = -3$

**9.** $-x^3 + 2x^2 - x - 3$ if $x = -1$

**10.** $-x^5 + 3x^3 - x + 2$ if $x = -1$

**11.** $-2x^2y^2 - xy^2 + 3xy - 2$ if $x = -2$ and $y = 1$

**12.** $-x^3y + 2x^2y^2 - 3xy^3 + 1$ if $x = 3$ and $y = -2$

## SECTION 18.3

*Add and simplify.*

**13.** $(4x - 7) + (-x + 3)$

**14.** $(-6x + 5) + (2x - 8)$

**15.** $(3x^2 - 2x + 3) + (-x^2 + 3x - 5) + (-4x^2 + 5x - 2)$

**16.** $(-5x^2 + 4x - 1) + (3x^2 - 8x + 5) + (x^2 - x - 2)$

**17.** $\begin{aligned}-2x^3 +\ x^2 -\ 5x + 7\\5x^3 - 2x^2 + 11x - 3\end{aligned}$

**18.** $\begin{aligned}8x^3 - 5x^2 + 2x - 3\\-x^3 + 6x^2 - 3x + 5\end{aligned}$

**19.** $\begin{aligned}-x^4 \qquad\ + 2x^2 - 3x\\2x^3 -\ x^2 + 7x - 3\\5x^4 +\ x^3 \qquad\ -\ x - 9\end{aligned}$

**20.** $\begin{aligned}5x^4 - 3x^3 \qquad\ + 7x - 10\\4x^3 -\ x^2 - 2x +\ 8\\-3x^4 - 2x^3 + 3x^2 -\ x\end{aligned}$

## SECTION 18.4

*Subtract and simplify.*

**21.** $(4x^2 - 3x + 9) - (-x^2 + 2x - 6)$

**22.** $(-3x^2 + 7x - 5) - (4x^2 - x + 10)$

**23.** $(2.5x - 1.8 + 3.7x^2 - 0.9x^3) - (-2.7 + 1.9x^2 - 5.3x + 1.2x^3)$

**24.** $(5.1x^2 - 1.8x^4 + 3.7x - 1.5) - (5.3x + 0.6x^4 - 2.1x^3 - 2.3x^2)$

**25.** $\begin{aligned}19x^4 \qquad\ - 12x^2 + 20x\\(-)\ \underline{-x^4 + 24x^3 \qquad\ +\ 3x - 19}\end{aligned}$

**26.** $\begin{aligned}-2x^3 + 5x^2 \qquad\ - 35\\(-)\ \underline{9x^3 -\ x^2 - 27x + 18}\end{aligned}$

## SECTION 18.5

*Multiply and simplify.*

**27.** $\begin{aligned}2x^2 - 3x + 5\\\underline{2x - 3}\end{aligned}$

**28.** $\begin{aligned}-3x^2 + 4x - 6\\\underline{5x - 2}\end{aligned}$

**29.** $\begin{aligned}-3x^3 - x^2 + 3\\\underline{x^2 + 2}\end{aligned}$

**30.** $\begin{aligned}5x^3 - 3x + 7\\\underline{x^2 - 3}\end{aligned}$

**31.** $\begin{aligned}4x^2 - x + 2\\\underline{x^2 + 3}\end{aligned}$

**32.** $\begin{aligned}x^2 - 2x + 3\\\underline{-2x^2 + 5}\end{aligned}$

## SECTION 18.6

*Divide.*

**33.** $4x - 3\overline{)20x^2 - 7x - 6}$

**34.** $3x - 7\overline{)6x^2 - 23x + 21}$

**35.** $x + 3\overline{)-3x^3 - 8x^2 + 5x + 6}$

**36.** $2x + 1\overline{)8x^3 - 2x^2 + 3x + 3}$

# REVIEW EXERCISES FOR CHAPTERS 13-18

*Solve and check each equation. Show all steps. (Section 13.1)*

**1.** $x - 27 = 19$

**2.** $x + 23 = 42$

*Solve and check each equation. Show all steps. (Section 13.2)*

**3.** $8x - 13 - 7x = -17$

**4.** $-12x + 5 + 13x = 13 - 29$

*Solve and check each equation. Show all steps. (Section 13.3)*

**5.** $3x - 7 = 4x + 8$

**6.** $12x - 3 = 11x - 19$

*Solve and check each equation. Show all steps. (Section 13.4)*

**7.** $\frac{8}{3}x = -48$

**8.** $-\frac{7}{4}x = 21$

*Solve and check each equation. Show all steps. (Section 13.5)*

**9.** $6x + 9 = -15$

**10.** $8x - 7 = -55$

*Solve and check each equation. Show all steps. (Section 13.6)*

**11.** $12x - 21 = 5x + 7$

**12.** $14 - 5x = 3x + 54$

*Write the truth number or numbers of each equation. (Section 13.7)*

**13.** $(x - 8)(x + 11) = 0$

**14.** $(x + \frac{1}{2})(x - 12) = 0$

*Simplify. (Section 14.1)*

**15.** $-\sqrt{16}$

**16.** $\sqrt{100}$

**17.** $\sqrt{\dfrac{1}{64}}$

**18.** $-\sqrt{\dfrac{9}{16}}$

*Write Rational or Irrational to describe each number. (Section 14.2)*

**19.** $\sqrt{24}$

**20.** $-\sqrt{25}$

**21.** $-2\frac{7}{8}$

**22.** $\sqrt{\dfrac{5}{4}}$

*Simplify each radical. (Section 14.3)*

**23.** $\sqrt{16 \cdot 5}$

**24.** $\sqrt{49 \cdot 7}$

**25.** $\sqrt{54}$

**26.** $\sqrt{90}$

*Add or subtract. Simplify where necessary. (Section 14.4)*

**27.** $12\sqrt{3} + 9\sqrt{3}$

**28.** $15\sqrt{10} + \sqrt{10}$

**29.** $-14\sqrt{15} - \sqrt{15}$

**30.** $12\sqrt{7} - 23\sqrt{7}$

*Multiply. Simplify where necessary. (Section 14.5)*

**31.** $(-3\sqrt{15})(-7\sqrt{3})$

**32.** $(4\sqrt{7})(-5\sqrt{6})$

*Write each quotient as one radical. Then simplify. (Section 14.6)*

**33.** $\dfrac{\sqrt{12}}{\sqrt{3}}$

**34.** $\dfrac{\sqrt{27}}{\sqrt{3}}$

**35.** $\dfrac{\sqrt{128}}{\sqrt{8}}$

**36.** $\dfrac{\sqrt{175}}{\sqrt{7}}$

*Graph the following points. (Section 15.1)*

**37.** $A(5, -3)$

**38.** $B(-4, 2)$

**39.** $C(0, -3)$

**40.** $D(-4, 0)$

*Determine a word rule for each relation. Then write the missing numerals. (Section 15.2)*

**41.**

| x | 2 | 5 | 0 | -3 | -8 |
|---|---|---|---|----|----|
| y | 10 | 13 | 8 | ? | ? |

**42.**

| x | 10 | 6 | -3 | 0 | 12 |
|---|----|---|----|---|----|
| y | 4 | 0 | -9 | ? | ? |

*Write the domain, D, and the range, R, in roster form. (Section 15.3)*

**43.** $\{(-1, 2), (0, -5), (\tfrac{1}{2}, 3), (-10, 1)\}$

**44.** $\{(4.2, -4), (1.7, 2.5), (0, -3.8), (5.3, 0)\}$

*Graph each function with {real numbers} as the domain. (Section 15.4)*

**45.** $y = x + 2$

**46.** $y = -x + 3$

**47.** $y = -\tfrac{1}{2}x - 3$

**48.** $y = \tfrac{1}{2}x - 1$

*Write the Y intercept. (Section 15.5)*

**49.** $y = -x + 7$

**50.** $y = \tfrac{1}{2}x - 2$

**51.** $y = \tfrac{5}{2}x - \tfrac{3}{2}$

**52.** $y = 0.7x + 1.8$

*Compute the X intercept. (Section 15.5)*

**53.** $y = x + 5$

**54.** $y = -x + 3$

**55.** $y = 2x - 7$

**56.** $y = 4x + 2$

*Graph the two functions and write their intersection. (Section 15.6)*

**57.** $y = 2x + 1 \qquad y = -x - 2$

**58.** $y = \tfrac{1}{2}x - 1 \qquad y = -x + 2$

*Graph the two equations of each system in the same coordinate plane. Write the truth set of the system. (Section 16.1)*

**59.** $\begin{cases} x - y + 3 = 0 \\ x + 2y - 3 = 0 \end{cases}$

**60.** $\begin{cases} x + y - 2 = 0 \\ x - 3y + 2 = 0 \end{cases}$

*Solve each system by the substitution method. Check. (Section 16.2)*

**61.** $\begin{cases} 2x - 3y + 4 = 0 \\ x + 2y - 5 = 0 \end{cases}$

**62.** $\begin{cases} 4x - y + 2 = 0 \\ 2x + y - 5 = 0 \end{cases}$

*Solve each system by the addition method. Check. (Section 16.3)*

**63.** $\begin{cases} 5x - 2y - 1 = 0 \\ -3x + 2y - 5 = 0 \end{cases}$

**64.** $\begin{cases} -4x + 3y - 2 = 0 \\ x - 3y + 14 = 0 \end{cases}$

*In each problem, (a) select two variables for the unknown numbers, (b) write two equations, and (c) solve. (Section 16.4)*

**65.** One number exceeds another number by 12. The sum of the two numbers is 6. Find the numbers.

**66.** The sum of two numbers is 7. Twice the greater number increased by three times the smaller number equals 9. Find the unknown numbers.

*In each problem, (a) select two variables for the unknown numbers, (b) write two equations, and (c) solve. (Section 16.5)*

**67.** Terry Jones bought 12 hamburgers and 9 milk shakes for $13.20. Each hamburger cost twice as much as each milk shake. Find the price of each hamburger and each milk shake in cents.

**68.** The chess club sold 25 boxes of cookies and 40 boxes of candy for a total of $91.25. The candy sold for 25 cents more per box than the cookies. Find the price of a box of cookies and a box of candy in cents.

*In each problem, (a) select two variables for the unknown numbers, (b) write two equations, and (c) solve. (Section 16.6)*

**69.** The road distance from Chicago to Kansas City is 227 kilometers less than the distance from Kansas City to Denver. The total distance from Chicago to Denver through Kansas City is 1945 kilometers. Find each unknown distance.

**70.** The length of a rectangle is 3 centimeters less than twice the width. The perimeter is 27 centimeters. Find the length and width.

*Simplify. Assume that no divisor is zero. (Section 17.1)*

**71.** $\dfrac{-12x}{14x^2}$

**72.** $\dfrac{10x^2y}{-15xy}$

**73.** $\dfrac{3y - 6}{4y - 8}$

**74.** $\dfrac{6x^2 - 10x}{6x^2y + 12xy}$

*Simplify. Assume that no divisor is zero. (Section 17.2)*

**75.** $\dfrac{2x - 5}{5 - 2x}$

**76.** $-\dfrac{r - 3t}{3t - r}$

**77.** $\dfrac{6x - 2}{3 - 9x}$

**78.** $-\dfrac{2t^2 - 6t}{15t - 5t^2}$

*Multiply and simplify. Assume that no divisor is zero.* (Section 17.3)

**79.** $\dfrac{3}{-t} \cdot \dfrac{-2t}{7}$

**80.** $-\dfrac{2a}{3} \cdot -\dfrac{5}{6a}$

*Add or subtract as indicated. Then simplify.* (Section 17.4)

**81.** $\dfrac{12s}{7t} - \dfrac{-s}{7t}$

**82.** $\dfrac{13a}{12b} - \dfrac{5a}{12b}$

*Write each quotient as a product. Then simplify.* (Section 17.5)

**83.** $\dfrac{10a}{9} \div \left(-\dfrac{4a}{3}\right)$

**84.** $\left(-\dfrac{6x}{11}\right) \div \left(-\dfrac{9x}{22}\right)$

*Simplify.* (Section 18:1)

**85.** $2x^3 - x^2 - 5x^2 + 4$

**86.** $5x^4 - 2x^3 + 4x^3 - 7x + 3$

*Evaluate each polynomial.* (Section 18.2)

**87.** $x^3 - 2x^2 + x - 5$ if $x = -1$

**88.** $x^3 - x^2 + x - 1$ if $x = -2$

*Add.* (Section 18.3)

**89.** $(x^2 - 5x + 3) + (-3x^2 - x - 10)$

**90.** $(4x^2 + 3x - 8) + (x^2 - 7x - 3)$

*Subtract.* (Section 18.4)

**91.** $(-4x^4 - 2x^2 + 5x + 1) - (x^4 - 5x^3 - 3x^2 + 6)$

**92.** $(3x^3 - x^2 + 3x - 8) - (-x^3 + 4x^2 - x + 10)$

*Multiply.* (Section 18.5)

**93.** $(3x^2 - 5x + 2)(2x - 3)$

**94.** $(4x^2 + x - 5)(3x + 2)$

*Divide.* (Section 18.6)

**95.** $2x - 3\overline{)10x^2 - 11x - 6}$

**96.** $4x - 5\overline{)8x^2 + 2x - 15}$

# ANSWERS TO PIVOTAL QUESTIONS

## CHAPTER 1

**1.1** (page 2)    **P-1**   5 units     **P-2**   **a.** 150 millimeters    **b.** 35 millimeters

**1.2** (page 5)    **P-1**   A decimeter     **P-2**   10

**1.3** (page 8)    **P-1**   20 units     **P-2**   $4 \cdot 5$     **P-3**   $n$     **P-4**   $n + n + n + n$; $4n$     **P-5**   **a.** and **d.**     **P-6**   2.8     **P-7**   13;   30     **P-8**   46;   36     **P-9**   **a.** 19   **b.** 8   **c.** 11     **P-10**   **b.** and **c.**

**1.4** (page 11)    **P-1**   100

**1.5** (page 14)    **P-1**   **a.**;   **b.**;   **c.**     **P-2**   8     **P-3**   $2l + 2w$

## CHAPTER 2

**2.1** (page 20)    **P-1**   Adding 0 to a number does not change its value.    **P-2**   **a.** 0;   **b.** 0;   **c.** 225     **P-3**   The product of 0 and a number is 0.     **P-4**   **a.** 0;   **b.** Any number;   **c.** Any number    **P-5**   The product of 1 and a number is the number.    **P-6**   **a.** 15;   **b.** 1;   **c.** $16\frac{1}{2}$     **P-7**   **a.** and **c.**

**2.2** (page 22)    **P-1**   $2 + 2 + 2$     **P-2**   **a.** and **c.**     **P-3**   $4 \cdot 5$     **P-4**   60     **P-5**   $3 \cdot 4$     **P-6**   60     **P-7**   **a.**     **P-8**   **a.** $5y$;   **b.** $48m$;   **c.** $36t$     **P-9**   **a.** $5 \cdot x \cdot x$;   **b.** $x \cdot x \cdot y$;   **c.** $a \cdot b \cdot b \cdot b$;   **d.** $7 \cdot m \cdot m \cdot m \cdot n \cdot n$     **P-10**   **a.** Commutative Property of Multiplication;   **b.** Associative Property of Multiplication;   **c.** Commutative and Associative Properties of Multiplication

**2.3** (page 26)    **P-1**   48;   48     **P-2**   $4 \cdot 12$;   $4 \cdot 7$;   $4 \cdot 5$

**2.4** (page 28)    **P-1**   12     **P-2**   **a.** $2x - 2y$;   **b.** $3a - 12$;   **c.** $24t - 28$; $6r^2 - 10r$     **P-3**   **a.** $5(a + b)$;   **b.** $10(r - s)$;   **c.** $6(a - 1)$    **P-4**   **a.** $4(t - 1)$;   **b.** $12(m + 1)$;   **c.** $8(q + 1)$;   **d.** $j(17 - 1)$    **P-5**   **a.** $m(m + 7)$;   **b.** $t(t - 12)$;   **c.** $r(r - 4)$

**2.5** (page 31)    **P-1**   **a.** $\frac{1}{2}$;   **b.** 0.8;   **c.** 1;   **d.** 12     **P-2**   **a.** and **d.**

**2.6** (page 33)    **P-1**   Start at 0 and move 2 units to the right.     **P-2**   $8 + 5$     **P-3**   16     **P-4**   $3 + 8$     **P-5**   16     **P-6**   $3x^2$ and $4x^2$    **P-7**   $21ab$     **P-8**   **a.** Commutative Property of Addition;   **b.** Associative Property of Addition;   **c.** Both Properties

## CHAPTER 3

**3.1** (page 42)    **P-1**   6, 7, 8, 9     **P-2**   **a.** 1;   **b.** 0     **P-3**   1, 2, 3, 4, 6, 8, 12, 24     **P-4**   1, 2, 3, 4, 6, 9, 12, 18, 36     **P-5**   $3 \cdot 5$    **P-6**   **a.**;   **c.**;   **d.**

**3.2** (page 45)    **P-1**  The set of whole numbers consists of 0 and the set of counting numbers.    **P-2**  **b.** and **c.**    **P-3**  $5 + 3 = 8$;  No;  No; $5 + 6 + 7 = 18$;  Yes;  Yes    **P-4**  **a.**;  **d.**    **P-5**  **a.**, **c.**, **d.**; **a.**, **d.**

**3.3** (page 48)    **P-1**  Each set contains only 1 and the number itself.
**P-2**  **a.** 2;  **b.** 2, 3;  **c.** 2, 4;  **d.** 3, 5;  **e.** 2, 5, 10, 25
**P-3**  $3 \cdot 17$

**3.4** (page 51)    **P-1**  2

**3.5** (page 54)    **P-1**  10, 20, 30, $\cdots$    **P-2**  10    **P-3**  12;  12    **P-4**  72
**P-5**  **a.** 60;  **b.** 36;  **c.** 210

## CHAPTER 4

**4.1** (page 60)    **P-1**  0    **P-2**  **a.** 10;  **b.** 0;  **c.** 1;  **d.** 1    **P-3**  **a.** $6 \cdot 2$;
**b.** $\frac{120}{10}$;    **P-4**  **a.** $\frac{35}{48}$;  **b.** $\frac{2}{15}$;  **c.** 7    **P-5**  **a.** 3;  **b.** 2;
**c.** 1;  **d.** 5    **P-6**  **a.**;  **d.**    **P-7**  **a.** and **d.** are equivalent;
**b.** and **e.** are equivalent.

**4.2** (page 64)    **P-1**  **a.** $\frac{2}{5}$;  **b.** 3;  **c.** $\frac{1}{3}$;  **d.** $\frac{5}{12}$    **P-2**  **a.** 0;  **b.** 0;  **c.** 5
**P-3**  0;  0    **P-4**  $\dfrac{x^2 y}{x^2 y}$

**4.4** (page 70)    **P-1**  **a.** 1;  **b.** 1;  **c.** 1    **P-2**  **a.** $\frac{16}{5}$;  **b.** $\frac{1}{12}$;  **c.** $\frac{y}{x}$;  **d.** $\frac{1}{7n}$
**P-3**  **a.** and **b.** have the same answer;    **c.** and **d.** have the same answer.

**4.5** (page 73)    **P-1**  **a.** $\frac{10}{13}$;  **b.** $\frac{13}{x}$;  **c.** $\frac{r+s}{t}$    **P-2**  $8m$    **P-3**  **a.** $\frac{8}{15}$;
**b.** $\frac{4}{5x}$;  **c.** $\frac{p-q}{x}$    **P-4**  $8x$

**4.6** (page 76)    **P-1**  $\frac{4}{4}$;  $\frac{3}{3}$    **P-2**  $42x$    **P-3**  5 and $6x$ have no common factors.

## CHAPTER 5

**5.1** (page 86)    **P-1**  **a.** {0, 1, 2, 3, 4};  **b.** {4, 8, 12, 16, $\cdots$}    **P-2**  Note: Many answers are possible. Only one is given for each set.
**a.** {whole numbers less than 3};  **b.** {counting-number multiples of 2}    **P-3**  None    **P-4**  Note: Many answers are possible. Only two are given for each number.  **a.** $\frac{5}{1}$, $\frac{10}{2}$;  **b.** $\frac{25}{8}$, $\frac{50}{16}$;
**c.** $\frac{27}{100}$, $\frac{54}{200}$;  **d.** $\frac{256}{100}$, $\frac{128}{50}$

**5.2** (page 89)    **P-1**  **a.** $\neq$;  **b.** $=$    **P-2**  **a.** $(3 \cdot 2 + 3)5 = 45$;  **b.** $\frac{1}{2}(\frac{1}{5} + \frac{3}{10}) \neq \frac{2}{5}$
**P-3**  **a.**;  **b.**

**5.3** (page 91)    **P-1**  2    **P-2**  6, 7, 8, and any other numbers less than 9.
**P-3**  5, 6, 8, and all other numbers except 7.    **P-4**  5, 7, 9, 11

**5.4** (page 94)    **P-1**  3.14    **P-2**  {0, 1, $1\frac{3}{4}$, $\pi$, 4.42}    **P-3**  3    **P-4**  4

**P-5** Note: Many answers are possible. Only one is given for each graph.　**a.** $x < 3$;　**b.** $x > 1.5$

**5.5** (page 97)　**P-1** **d.**　**P-2** **a.** The sentence is true because "$15 - 8 = 7$" is true;　**c.** The sentence is true because "$24 < 33 - 8$" is true;　**d.** The sentence is true because both clauses are true.

**5.6** (page 101)　**P-1** True;　False　**P-2** **b.**

**5.7** (page 105)　**P-1** $x$ is less than 5 or $x$ is equal to 5.　**P-2** $\{4, 5, 6, \cdots\}$;　$\{4, 5, 6, \cdots\}$　**P-3** **a.** $x \geq 2$　**b.** $x > 2$　**P-4** **a.** $x < 7$;　**b.** $x \leq 7$

## CHAPTER 6

**6.1** (page 110)　**P-1** **a.** 10;　**b.** $5\frac{1}{2}$;　**c.** $n$　**P-2** **a.**;　**b.**;　**c.**

**6.2** (page 113)　**P-1** **a.** 13;　**b.** 9.7;　**c.** $3\frac{1}{2}$;　**d.** $n$;　**e.** 5　**P-2** **a.** 12;　**b.** $3\frac{1}{2}$;　**c.** 7.3　**P-3** **a.**;　**b.**;　**c.**

**6.3** (page 116)　**P-1** **a.** 2;　**b.** 3;　**c.** $x$;　**d.** $y$　**P-2** **a.**;　**b.**;　**c.**

**6.4** (page 119)　**P-1** **a.** 36;　**b.** 25;　**c.** $n$　**P-2** **a.**;　**b.**;　**c.**
**P-3** **a.** $t + 26 - 26 = 42 - 26$;　**b.** $s - 19 + 19 = 47 + 19$;　**c.** $\frac{39k}{39} = \frac{136}{39}$;　**d.** $116\left(\frac{a}{116}\right) = 116(23)$

**6.5** (page 122)　**P-1** Divide by 2.　**P-2** Add 3;　Divide by 5.　**P-3** Divide by 3.　**P-4** Add 10;　Divide by 4.　**P-5** Addition　**P-6** Subtraction

**6.6** (page 126)　**P-1** **a.** $5x + 5$;　**b.** $6a + 4$;　**c.** $6x - 5$　**P-2** **a.** $2x + 10$;　**b.** $3a - 21$;　**c.** $12t + 28$;　**d.** $10k - 45$　**P-3** $6a + 14$

## CHAPTER 7

**7.1** (page 140)　**P-1** 7 to 2　**P-2** $7 : 2$　**P-3** $3 : 5$　**P-4** $3 : 8$　**P-5** $5 : 2$　**P-6** $14 : 5$　**P-7** 0

**7.2** (page 144)　**P-1** $\frac{2}{5} = \frac{4}{10}$　**P-2** $2 \cdot 6 = 12$;　$3 \cdot 4 = 12$;　$3 \cdot 6 = 18$;　$4 \cdot 5 = 20$

**7.3** (page 148)　**P-1** $17 : 100$ or $\frac{17}{100}$　**P-2** **a.** 5%,　**b.** 75%,　**c.** 125%,　**d.** $3\frac{1}{2}$%　**P-3** 2;　Right　**P-4** 2;　Left

**7.4** (page 152)　**P-1** 2　**P-2** 50　**P-3** 20

**7.5** (page 156)　**P-1** $\frac{25}{100} = \frac{x}{60}$　**P-2** 0.25　**P-3** Multiply 75 by 0.12.　**P-4** 0.427　**P-5** 0.04　**P-6** $0.06a$;　$0.075a$

**7.6** (page 160)　**P-1** Principal;　Interest　**P-2** $30　**P-3** $(d)(0.065)(\frac{1}{2})$ or $0.0325d$　**P-4** $0.01r$　**P-5** $(75)(0.01r)(4)$ or $3r$

**7.7** (page 164)  **P-1** Ad 1: $50;   Ad 2: $10.10;   Ad 3: $21.33   **P-2** $40;
$29.90   **P-3** $51.09   **P-4** $(0.01p)(25)$;   $25 - 0.25p$

## CHAPTER 8

**8.1** (page 172)  **P-1** $n + 5$   **P-2** Note: Many answers are possible. Not all are
given.   **a.** The sum of $x$ and 3, $x$ plus 3, $x$ increased by 3;
**b.** $t$ less 5, 5 less than $t$;   **c.** The product of 3 and $y$, $y$ multiplied
by 3, 3 times $y$;   **d.** The quotient of $r$ and 12, $r$ divided by 12
**P-3** Length;   Subtraction   **P-4** "Less" is used in place of
"less than."   **P-5** $6 - l$   **P-6** The cost of the trip by auto;
Multiplication, Addition

**8.3** (page 180)  **P-1** 12 cm;   20 cm;   11.5 cm

**8.4** (page 184)  **P-1** $2.28;   $6c$   **P-2** $18.00

**8.5** (page 189)  **P-1** $n + 1$   **P-2** $n + 6$;   $x + 6$   **P-3** $n + 2$;   $n + 4$

**8.6** (page 192)  **P-1** 12 cm³   **P-2** 10 cm   **P-3** 1000 cm³

**8.7** (page 196)  **P-1** 4 grams

## CHAPTER 9

**9.1** (page 206)  **P-1** ⁻5;   ⁻6   **P-2** ⁻25;   100   **P-3** **a.** Set of negative
integers;   **b.** Set of positive integers;   **c.** Set of integers

**9.2** (page 210)  **P-1** 0, $1\frac{1}{2}$, 2.4, 3, $4\frac{1}{3}$   **P-2** $\frac{0}{1}$, $\frac{3}{2}$, $\frac{24}{10}$, $\frac{3}{1}$, $\frac{13}{3}$ Note: Other
answers are possible.   **P-3** Halfway between the points with
coordinates ⁻1 and ⁻2   **P-4** It is located two thirds of a unit to
the left of the point with coordinate ⁻3;   It is located two thirds of a
unit to the left of the point with coordinate 0.   **P-5** $4\frac{1}{3}$;   ⁻2.6;
⁻3   **P-6** $\frac{4}{1}$, $\frac{8}{2}$, $\frac{12}{3}$;   $-(\frac{10}{1})$, $-(\frac{20}{2})$, $-(\frac{30}{3})$;   $\frac{0}{1}$, $\frac{0}{2}$, $\frac{0}{3}$;   Note:
Many answers are possible. Only three are given for each.

**9.3** (page 214)  **P-1** **a.** Five tenths, 0.5;   **b.** Seventy-five hundredths, 0.75;
**c.** Negative one and two tenths, ⁻1.2;   **d.** Negative three tenths,
⁻0.3;   **e.** Four and six tenths, 4.6   **P-2** 2.17181
**P-3** ⁻1.812   **P-4** ⁻1.812

**9.4** (page 218)  **P-1** 3 units;   3 units   **P-2** $2\frac{1}{2}$;   ⁻$4\frac{1}{3}$   **P-3** 0
**P-4** **a.** Negative ten;   **b.** The opposite of ten;   **c.** The opposite of
negative ten;   **d.** The opposite of one half;   **e.** Negative one half;
**f.** The opposite of negative one half   **P-5** 10   **P-6** The
opposite of $3\frac{1}{2}$

**9.5** (page 222)  **P-1** $7 > ⁻3$   **P-2** 3;   ⁻7   **P-3** It is the reverse of the
order of ⁻3 and 7.   **P-4** **a.** $⁻5 < 7$;   $7 > ⁻5$   **b.** $2 < 3$;   $3 > 2$
**c.** $⁻3 \leq 7$;   $7 \geq ⁻3$   **d.** $⁻4 \geq ⁻10$;   $⁻10 \leq ⁻4$

**9.6** (page 225)  **P-1** **a.** {1};   **b.** {0, 1, 2, 3};   **c.** {0, 1, 2, 3}   **P-2** ⁻5, ⁻6,

$^-7$, $^-4\frac{3}{4}$, $^-4\frac{3}{5}$  Note: Many answers are possible. Only five are given.
**P-3**  $^-3\frac{1}{2}$

**9.7** (page 228)  **P-1**  $^-4$;  3;  0  **P-2**  3 units;  4 units  **P-3**  2.3;  $3\frac{1}{2}$
**P-4**  **a.** 5.2;  **b.** $4\frac{1}{2}$;  **c.** 7;  **d.** $^-60$

## CHAPTER 10

**10.1** (page 234)  **P-1**  **B**  **P-2**  2;  Forward  **P-3**  **U**  **P-4**  3;  Backward  **P-5**  Two spaces backward  **P-6**  Seven spaces
forward  **P-7**  On **J** (7 spaces backward from **Q**)  **P-8**  **J**

**10.2** (page 238)  **P-1**  $^-5$;  7  **P-2**  Move 4 units right;  Move 8 units left.

**10.3** (page 241)  **P-1**  **a.** 15;  **b.** $^-17$;  **c.** 4;  **d.** $^-4.6$;  **e.** $^-400$  **P-2**  The
sum is a positive number;  The sum is a negative number.
**P-3**  **a.** 5;  **b.** 7;  **c.** 4;  **d.** 6.1;  **e.** $^-3$;  **f.** $^-6$;  **g.** $^-2\frac{1}{4}$;
**h.** $^-4.1$  **P-4**  Answers in Group I are positive numbers. Answers
in Group II are negative numbers.  **P-5**  **a.** $^-21$;  **b.** 56;
**c.** $^-5\frac{1}{2}$;  **d.** $^-13.8$;  **e.** 0.19;  **f.** $\frac{7}{13}$

**10.4** (page 245)  **P-1**  **a.** $^-45$;  **b.** $^-3\frac{1}{2}$;  **c.** $^-13.9$  **P-2**  **a.** $5\frac{3}{4}$;  **b.** 0;
**c.** $^-0.47$;  **d.** 600  **P-3**  **a.** 0;  **b.** 0;  **c.** 0  **P-4**  $^-2$;  $^-2$
**P-5**  4;  4

**10.5** (page 248)  **P-1**  Add ($^-4$) to the sum of ($^-2$) and 3;  Add 3 to the sum of ($^-2$)
and ($^-4$);  Add ($^-2$) to the sum of 3 and ($^-4$).  **P-2**  2.7
**P-3**  $x + (^-2.1)$  **P-4**  The opposite of $a$

**10.6** (page 251)  **P-1**  $^-5$;  $^-8$

**10.7** (page 254)  **P-1**  **d.** and **f.**;  **a.**, **b.**, **c.**, **e.**

## CHAPTER 11

**11.1** (page 266)  **P-1**  Each answer is 2 less than the one before it.  **P-2**  $^-2$, $^-4$,
$^-6$  **P-3**  **a.** $^-8$;  **b.** $^-10$;  **c.** $^-12$  **P-4**  The answers decrease by the amount of the first factor in columns **a** and **b**. The
answers decrease by 5 in column **c**.  **P-5**  Column **a**: $^-3$, $^-6$, $^-9$;
Column **b**: $^-6$, $^-12$, $^-18$;  Column **c**: $^-5$, $^-10$, $^-15$  **P-6**  **a.** $^-40$;
**b.** $^-36$;  **c.** $^-6$;  **d.** $^-4.6$  **P-7**  **a.** 0;  **b.** 0;  **c.** 0;  **d.** 0
**P-8**  **a.** 0;  **b.** 0;  **c.** 0

**11.2** (page 270)  **P-1**  Each answer is 3 more than the one above it.  **P-2**  3
**P-3**  3, 6, 9, 12  **P-4**  **a.** 15;  **b.** 18;  **c.** 21  **P-5**  One
factor remains the same. In columns **a** and **b** the other factor decreases by 1 at each step. In column **c** the other factor decreases by
0.5 at each step.  **P-6**  The answers increase by a constant
amount at each step.  **P-7**  Column **a**: 4, 8, 12;  Column **b**:
5, 10, 15;  Column **c**: 5, 10, 15  **P-8**  **a.** 56;  **b.** 6;  **c.** 12.3;
**d.** 4.2

**11.3** (page 273)  **P-1**  **a.** $^-2.7$;  **b.** 0;  **c.** $^-(\frac{3}{4})$  **P-2**  **a.** $^-63$;  **b.** $^-63$;  **c.** 40;
**d.** 40  **P-3**  **b.** and **c.**  **P-4**  $^-24$;  $^-24$  **P-5**  60

**P-6**  **a.** Negative;  **b.** Positive;  **c.** Negative

**11.4** (page 277)   **P-1**  a., d., f.;  b., c., e.   **P-2**  ⁻2   **P-3**  ⁻5x   **P-4**  x
**P-5**  24x²

**11.5** (page 281)   **P-1**  **a.**  ⁻3;  **b.**  0.3;  **c.**  4;  **d.**  ⁻150;  **e.**  ⁻($\frac{3}{4}$);  **f.**  2$\frac{1}{2}$
**P-2**  **a.**  $-mn$;  **b.**  $st$;  **c.**  3x;  **d.**  ⁻8n   **P-3**  $-tk$;
$-rst$;   $rs$

**11.6** (page 284)   **P-1**  5x   **P-2**  10, $-a$, ⁻5b²   **P-3**  **a.**  ⁻2x² and 3x²;  **b.**  ⁻3ax²
and $-ax^2$, 5a²x and ⁻3a²x   **P-4**  3   **P-5**  ⁻1
**P-6**  2x² and $-x^2$;   ⁻1.2x and ⁻0.5x

**11.7** (page 287)   **P-1**  3   **P-2**  x²;  y²   **P-3**  xy;  xy   **P-4**  2xy
**P-5**  ⁻2xy   **P-6**  y²   **P-7**  4x²;  9

## CHAPTER 12

**12.1** (page 294)   **P-1**  **a.**  4;  **b.**  0;  **c.**  5.5   **P-2**  3;  3   **P-3**  ⁻5;  16;
⁻3.1;   4.5;   ⁻23;   19;  0   **P-4**  ⁻12   **P-5**  **a.**  ⁻6;
**b.**  ⁻18;  **c.**  7;  **d.**  $r - s$;  **e.**  $r + s$   **P-6**  "a minus the opposite of b"

**12.2** (page 297)   **P-1**  The opposite of 10 equals negative 10.   **P-2**  **a.**  $-7$;
**b.**  $-30$;  **c.**  $-1.2$   **P-3**  $27 + (-45)$;   $(-45) + (-31)$

**12.3** (page 301)   **P-1**  $5x + (-2x)$   **P-2**  3x   **P-3**  Subtraction is not a commutative operation.   **P-4**  Subtraction is not an associative opera-
tion.   **P-5**  $(-3x) + (-7)$

**12.4** (page 304)   **P-1**  **a.**  $3x - 2y - 5$;  **b.**  $8n + y - 9$   **P-2**  **a.**  $4t - w + 9$;
**b.**  $-3m - 16 + 4n$   **P-3**  15;   15   **P-4**  $6r^2 - 15r$

**12.5** (page 308)   **P-1**  **a.**  1;  **b.**  1;  **c.**  1;  **d.**  1   **P-2**  **a.**  {1};  **b.**  {−1};
**c.**  { }   **P-3**  1;   −1   **P-4**  **a.**  $\frac{1}{5}$;  **b.**  $\frac{2}{1}$;  **c.**  $\frac{4}{5}$;  **d.**  $\frac{8}{7}$
**P-5**  **a.**  1;  **b.**  1;  **c.**  1   **P-6**  $-\frac{4}{3}$;   $-\frac{1}{10}$;   $-\frac{2}{3}$
**P-7**  $\left(-\frac{13}{16}\right)\left(-\frac{16}{13}\right) = 1$

**12.6** (page 311)   **P-1**  **a.**  −2;  **b.**  1;  **c.**  $\frac{3}{5}$   **P-2**  2;  2   **P-3**  $-\frac{1}{3}$
**P-4**  $-\frac{1}{6}$   **P-5**  **a.**  −9;  **b.**  −9;  **c.**  9

**12.7** (page 314)   **P-1**  **a.**  1;  **b.**  1;  **c.**  1;  **d.**  1   **P-2**  **a.**  1;  **b.**  1
**P-3**  **a.**  $\frac{3}{-4}$, $-\frac{3}{4}$;  **b.**  $\frac{-5}{12}$, $-\frac{5}{12}$;  **c.**  $-\frac{2}{-(x-3)}$, $-\frac{-2}{x-3}$
**P-4**  **a.**  $-\frac{5}{13}$;  **b.**  $-\frac{5}{13}$;  **c.**  $\frac{5}{13}$;  **d.**  $\frac{m}{n}$   **P-5**  $-\frac{t}{7}$

**12.8** (page 317)   **P-1**  $-\frac{3}{8}$   **P-2**  $-\frac{3}{10}$

## CHAPTER 13

**13.1** (page 330)   **P-1**  $\frac{1}{4}$   **P-2**  4.7

**13.2** (page 332)   **P-1**  14;   $x + 19$   **P-2**  $-6x - 15$

**13.3** (page 334)   **P-1**  Add 3x to each side.   **P-2**  $12 - x = 27$
**P-3**  $2x - 7$;   $3x - 8$

**13.4** (page 336)   **P-1**  $2(\frac{1}{2}x) = 2(-3)$     **P-2**  $\dfrac{-4x}{-4} = \dfrac{28}{-4}$     **P-3**  $12\left(\dfrac{x}{12}\right) = 12(-9)$
**P-4**  $\dfrac{-4x}{-4} = \dfrac{15}{-4}$

**13.5** (page 339)   **P-1**  $3x + 11 - 11 = 5 - 11$     **P-2**  Subtraction Property of Equality

**13.6** (page 343)   **P-1**  $5x + 7 - 2x = 2x - 8 - 2x$     **P-2**  $-12x - 6 + 5x$
**P-3**  $2n - 3$;    $12 - 3n$

**13.7** (page 346)   **P-1**  0;   0     **P-2**  $2x - 5 = 0$ *or* $4x + 1 = 0$     **P-3**  $2x(x - 3)$

## CHAPTER 14

**14.1** (page 352)   **P-1**  **a.** 9;   **b.** 9     **P-2**  **a.** 4, $-4$;   **b.** $\frac{2}{3}, -\frac{2}{3}$;   **c.** 0.6, $-0.6$
**P-3**  0, 0     **P-4**  1     **P-5**  25, 36, and 121

**14.2** (page 355)   **P-1**  **a.** 64;   **b.** 49;   **c.** 5;   **d.** 5     **P-2**  **b., c.;**   **a., d.**
**P-3**  **a.** Rational;   **b.** Rational;   **c.** Irrational;   **d.** Rational;
**e.** Irrational;   **f.** Rational

**14.3** (page 358)   **P-1**  **a.** $\sqrt{3} \cdot \sqrt{11}$;   **b.** $\sqrt{5} \cdot \sqrt{13}$;   **c.** $\sqrt{29} \cdot \sqrt{31}$
**P-2**  **a.** $\sqrt{40}, 2\sqrt{10}$;   **b.** $\sqrt{42}, \sqrt{42}$;   **c.** $\sqrt{72}, 6\sqrt{2}$     **P-3**  $\sqrt{15}$
and $\sqrt{34}$     **P-4**  4     **P-5**  16

**14.4** (page 361)   **P-1**  **a.** and **d.**;   **b., e.,** and **f.**;   **c.** and **g.**     **P-2**  $7\sqrt{2}$
**P-3**  4     **P-4**  9;   4

**14.5** (page 364)   **P-1**  $\sqrt{60}$     **P-2**  4;   9     **P-3**  **a.** $12\sqrt{35}$;   **b.** $20\sqrt{21}$;
**c.** $2\sqrt{6}$     **P-4**  3.873     **P-5**  361     **P-6**  19;   26

**14.6** (page 367)   **P-1**  **a.** $\frac{4}{9}$;   **b.** $\frac{9}{16}$;   **c.** $\frac{25}{49}$     **P-2**  **a.** $\frac{2}{3}$;   **b.** $\frac{3}{4}$;   **c.** $\frac{5}{7}$

## CHAPTER 15

**15.1** (page 376)   **P-1**  4     **P-2**  3     **P-3**  0, 6, 7, $-5$, 0;   3, $-2$, 0, 8, 0
**P-4**  The $x$ and $y$ values are reversed in the second ordered pair.

**15.2** (page 379)   **P-1**  $A$ (2, 1);   $B$ ($-2$, 2);   $C$ ($-1$, $-2$);   $D$ (3, $-2$)     **P-2**  II;
IV;   I;   III     **P-3**  $R(-2, 2\frac{1}{2})$;   $K(1\frac{1}{2}, -1)$;   $W(2\frac{1}{2}, 1\frac{1}{2})$;
$T(-3, -1\frac{1}{2})$     **P-4**  Each $y$ value is the opposite of twice each
$x$ value.

**15.3** (page 382)   **P-1**  2, 1, 2;   4, 5, 7     **P-2**  **a.** and **c.**     **P-3**  $D = \{\frac{1}{2}, 5, -7\}$;
$R = \{3, \frac{2}{3}, 0\}$

**15.4** (page 385)   **P-1**  $D = \{-4, -2, 0, 2, 4\}$;   $R = \{5, 4, 3, 2, 1\}$     **P-2**  A
straight line     **P-3**  **a.** $-2$;   **b.** 4;   **c.** 1;   **d.** 5     **P-4**  Substitute the values of $x$ and $y$ in the equation for the function. If the
equation obtained is true, the pair belongs to the function.
**P-5**  **a.** $a = 2; b = -3$;   **b.** $a = -1; b = \frac{1}{2}$;   **c.** $a = \frac{3}{2}; b = -1.7$

**15.5** (page 388)   **P-1**  (0, $-3$)     **P-2**  **1.** 1;   **2.** $-1$;   **3.** $-2$     **P-3**  **a.** 4;

**b.** $\frac{13}{4}$;   **c.** $-10$    **P-4**   $-1\frac{1}{2}$    **P-5**   **1.** 2;    **2.** None;    **3.** 1
**P-6**   3

## CHAPTER 16

**16.1** (page 396)   **P-1**   1;   1;   $-2$     **P-2**   $y = x + 2$;   $y = -\frac{1}{3}x + \frac{2}{3}$

**16.3** (page 401)   **P-1**   $\{(-1,\ 1)\}$     **P-2**   Each side of equation **1** is added to the corresponding side of equation **2**.

**16.6** (page 410)   **P-1**   Substitute the values of $x$ and $y$ for the words in each problem. If the conditions are met, the answers are correct.

## CHAPTER 17

**17.1** (page 420)   **P-1**   $-\dfrac{3}{x}$     **P-2**   **a.** $x \neq 2$;   **b.** $x \neq -3$;   **c.** $x \neq -\dfrac{1}{2}$

**P-3**   **a.** $\dfrac{2}{5}$;   **b.** $\dfrac{x}{3}$;   **c.** $-\dfrac{1}{2}$

**17.2** (page 423)   **P-1**   **a.** $(-x) + (-2)$;   **b.** $5 + (-n)$;   **c.** $(-k) + 3$
**P-2**   **a.** $\frac{3}{4} - m$;   **b.** $1.8 - r$;   **c.** $p + 10$     **P-3**   **a.** 1;   **b.** 1;
**c.** 1

**17.3** (page 426)   **P-1**   **a.** $\dfrac{3x}{4y}$;   **b.** $-\dfrac{1}{2}$;   **c.** $\dfrac{8}{3}$    **P-2**   **a.** $\dfrac{2}{x}$;   **b.** $\dfrac{3}{x+1}$;   **c.** $\dfrac{x-6}{x+2}$

**P-3**   **a.** $-\dfrac{2}{3}$;   **b.** $-\dfrac{1}{4}$;   **c.** $-\dfrac{x}{x+1}$

**17.4** (page 429)   **P-1**   **a.** $\dfrac{12}{n}$;   **b.** $\dfrac{2a}{5}$;   **c.** $\dfrac{r+7}{2x}$    **P-2**   **a.** $\dfrac{5x}{x-1}$;   **b.** $\dfrac{5y+5}{y+5}$;

**c.** $-\dfrac{3}{t+3}$

**17.5** (page 432)   **P-1**   **a.** $\dfrac{3}{4}$;   **b.** $-\dfrac{5}{7}$;   **c.** $\dfrac{3r}{s}$    **P-2**   **a.** $\dfrac{6}{6}$;   **b.** $\dfrac{12}{12}$;   **c.** $\dfrac{2x}{2x}$

## CHAPTER 18

**18.1** (page 438)   **P-1**   **a., b., c., d., e., f.**;   **a., f.**

**18.2** (page 440)   **P-1**   **a.** 10;   **b.** 12;   **c.** $-4$;   **d.** 4

**18.3** (page 442)   **P-1**   **a.** $4x^2$;   **b.** $3xy^2$;   **c.** $-2x^3y$

**18.4** (page 445)   **P-1**   **a.** $-2x + 5$;   **b.** $2x^2 - 8x - 7$;   **c.** $2x^2 - 5x + 2$

**18.5** (page 447)   **P-1**   **a.** $-6x$;   **b.** $15x^2$;   **c.** $-4x^3y$

**18.6** (page 450)   **P-1**   $2x^2 - 3x - 2$     **P-2**   **a.** $2x$;   **b.** $-3x$;   **c.** $-2x^2$;   **d.** 5

# INDEX

# Answers to Odd-Numbered Exercises

CHAPTER 1  METRIC UNITS AND FORMULAS

PAGE 3  ORAL EXERCISES 1.1
1.  6 centimeters   3.  11 centimeters   5.  14 millimeters   7.  180 millimeters

PAGE 4  WRITTEN EXERCISES 1.1
1.  4 centimeters   3.  3 centimeters   5.  34 millimeters   7.  6 centimeters
9.  140 millimeters   11.  96 millimeters

PAGE 6  ORAL EXERCISES 1.2
1.  multiply   3.  1000   5.  120 millimeters   7.  25 millimeters   9.  230 mm
11.  15 meters   13.  6000 meters   15.  145,000 m   17.  3500 cm   19.  7.5 cm
21.  500,000 cm   23.  8300 cm

PAGE 7  WRITTEN EXERCISES 1.2
1.  Divide by 10.   3.  Divide by 100,000.   5.  5200   7.  340   9.  1.8   11.  0.173
13.  34   15.  1.35   17.  17.8   19.  8.3   21.  58   23.  3.7   25.  0.53   27.  75,000
29.  3800   31.  1.4   33.  136

PAGE 10  ORAL EXERCISES 1.3
1.  3   3.  19   5.  3   7.  26   9.  2   11.  4   13.  8   15.  4   17.  23

PAGE 10  WRITTEN EXERCISES 1.3
1.  17   3.  2   5.  31   7.  11   9.  27   11.  63   13.  23   15.  50   17.  5
19.  8   21.  4   23.  4   25.  7 and 7; Yes   27.  10 and 25; No   29.  20 and 20; Yes

PAGE 13  ORAL EXERCISES 1.4
1.  10,000   3.  1,000,000   5.  30,000   7.  3500   9.  8,000,000   11.  7500   13.  8
15.  23

PAGE 13  WRITTEN EXERCISES 1.4
1.  5300   3.  4,000,000   5.  370,000   7.  180   9.  34   11.  6.2   13.  2.58
15.  523   17.  7,642,000,000   19.  1390   21.  72,080   23.  .0947   25.  .48
27.  0.0957   29.  172.83

PAGE 15  ORAL EXERCISES 1.5
1.  30 cm   3.  28 dm   5.  8 cm   7.  15 $m^2$   9.  21 $cm^2$   11.  15 $km^2$   13.  81
15.  .25   17.  18   19.  18.9   21.  64 $cm^2$   23.  .25 $m^2$   25.  225 $mm^2$   27.  17 cm
29.  37 km   31.  12.56 cm   33.  3.14 m

PAGE 16  WRITTEN EXERCISES 1.5
1.  97 dm   3.  270 km   5.  16.2 dm   7.  532 $m^2$   9.  57.27 $dm^2$   11.  576 $km^2$
13.  7.29 $m^2$   15.  54 $km^2$   17.  3.84 $m^2$   19.  14.444 cm   21.  219.8 mm
23.  452.16 $dm^2$   25.  19.625 $m^2$   27.  10.6 cm   29.  40.506 cm

PAGE 17   CHAPTER REVIEW

1. 4 cm   3. 6.5 cm   5. 340   7. 7.2   9. 130   11. 23   13. 18   15. 16
17. 12   19. 56   21. 2   23. 5   25. 31   27. 9   29. 104   31. 5300   33. 4.35
35. 2,830,000   37. 50.2 cm   39. 40.6944 cm$^2$   41. 1.286144 km$^2$

CHAPTER 2   PROPERTIES OF NUMBERS

PAGE 21   ORAL EXERCISES 2.1

1. True   3. False   5. False   7. True   9. False   11. $\frac{5}{6}$   13. 0   15. 1

PAGE 21   WRITTEN EXERCISES 2.1

1. False   3. True   5. True   7. False   9. False   11. True   13. 0   15. 23
17. 0   19. 13   21. 0   23. 1   25. 6   27. 4

PAGE 24   ORAL EXERCISES 2.2

1. Commutative Property of Multiplication   3. Associative Property of Multiplication
5. Both Propoerties   7. Associative Property of Multiplication   9. Associative
Property of Multiplication   11. 50y   13. 28k   15. 7m   17. 18xy   19. $6x^2y$
21. 8rst

PAGE 25   WRITTEN EXERCISES 2.2

1. 35x   3. 4a   5. 1.5x   7. 5.6s   9. 8.4n   11. 8w   13. .06r   15. 63ab
17. $39x^2$   19. $36mn^2$   21. $2x^2y$   23. $2np^2$   25. $2x^3y$   27. $9x^3y$   29. $12gk^2t^3$
31. $6r^2s^2t^3$   33. $3x^3y^2$; 24   35. $x^3y^4$; 8   37. $6x^2y^3$; 24   39. 12   41. 75

PAGE 27   ORAL EXERCISES 2.3

1. Product   3. Product   5. Sum   7. $2 \cdot 10 + 2 \cdot 3 = 20 + 6$   9. $3 \cdot 5 + 3 \cdot \frac{1}{3}$
$= 15 + 1$   11. $10 \cdot \frac{1}{2} + 5 \cdot \frac{1}{2} = 5 + \frac{5}{2}$   13. $5 \cdot m + 5 \cdot n = 5m + 5n$
15. $x \cdot x + x \cdot 3 = x^2 + 3x$   17. $3a \cdot b + 3a \cdot 2 = 3ab + 6a$

PAGE 27   WRITTEN EXERCISES 2.3

1. 4r + 4t   3. 15m + 15n   5. rx + 2x   7. 12a + at   9. 2x + 24   11. 2n + 32
13. $s^2 + 13s$   15. $2a^2 + 5a$   17. $12r^2 + 15r$   19. $2x^2 + 2xy$   21. 48a + 36b
23. $12t^2 + 14st$   25. $4p^2q + 6pq^2$   27. 2a + 3   29. $36a^2x + 27abx^2$
31. $12a^2 + 36a + 28$   33. $10x^4 + 50x^2 + 35x$   35. $12m^3n + 48m^2n^2 + 36mn$

PAGE 29   ORAL EXERCISES 2.4

1. 3(p + q)   3. 12(m − n)   5. 4(r − s)   7. 4(a + 3)   9. $\frac{1}{2}(c + d)$
11. r(x + y)   13. 2(r + 1)   15. 19(t + 1)   17. n(n + 2)   19. t(t − 10)
21. w(5 + w)   23. 3(x + 2)   25. 2(m + 5)   27. 6(b − 2)   29. y(ry + 12)
31. $r(h^2 + k^2)$

PAGE 30   WRITTEN EXERCISES 2.4

1. 7(k + n)   3. 19(p − q)   5. (h + 7)5   7. $(x - n)\frac{1}{2}$   9. (p + 5)d

2   CHAPTER 2

11. $r(x + y)$   13. $2(r + 1)$   15. $19(t + 1)$   17. $n(n + 2)$   19. $t(t - 10)$
21. $w(5 + w)$   23. $3(x + 2)$   25. $2(m + 5)$   27. $6(b - 2)$   29. $y(ry + 12)$
31. $r(h^2 + k^2)$

PAGE 30   WRITTEN EXERCISES 2.4
1. $7(k + n)$   3. $19(p - q)$   5. $(h + 7)5$   7. $(x - n)\frac{1}{2}$   9. $(p + 5)d$
11. $15(x + 1)$   13. $10(r - 1)$   15. $\frac{1}{2}(q + a)$   17. $12(y - 5)$   19. $q(a + b)$
21. $(n - t)a$   23. $7(n + 1)$   25. $19(q - 1)$   27 $y(y + 5)$   29. $k(k - \frac{1}{4})$
31. $t(13 + t)$   33. $2(n + 2)$   35. $7(y - 2)$   37. $3(y + 5)$   39. $3(g + 7)$
41. $3(m^2 - m + 2)$   43. $(a + b + c)n$   45. $x(x^2 + x - 1)$   47. $9(1 - 5x + 3y)$
49. $7(6a - 3b - 5c)$

PAGE 32   ORAL EXERCISES 2.5
1. Yes   3. Yes   5. No   7. $5rs$ and $rs$; $3a^2b$ and $6.2a^2b$; $12r$ and $9r$   9. $5t$
11. $2xy$   13. $4.6rt^2$   15. $31ab^2c$

PAGE 32   WRITTEN EXERCISES 2.5
1. G   3. F   5. M   7. B, I   9. D   11. $16a$   13. $7s$   15. $13ab$   17. $5a^2$
19. $4y$   21. $3.9x$   23. $6.8rt$   25. $mn$   27. $3x^2$   29. $\frac{3}{2}ab$   31. $15ab^2c$
33. $2.4r^2t$   35. $16.02m^5n^2$

PAGE 35   ORAL EXERCISES 2.6
1. Associative Property of Addition   3. Both Properties   5. Both Properties
7. $15n$   9. $12a$   11. $6x + 15$   13. $3s^2 + 14s + 3$   15. $4t^2 + 15t + 5$

PAGE 35   WRITTEN EXERCISES 2.6
1. $33m$   3. $25x$   5. $11.6k$   7. $2.7r^2$   9. $6x^2 + 15x + 7$   11. $n^3 + 3n^2 + 3n + 6$
13. $1.3p + 2.8r + 0.9pr$   15. $10.00r^2 + 1.03r + 5.23$   17. Both Properties
19. Associative Property of Addition   21. Both Properties

PAGE 38   CHAPTER REVIEW
1. 0   3. 1   5. 0   7. 1   9. 0   11. $50x$   13. $36ab$   15. $84r^2s$   17. $3.2p^3q^2$
19. $12a^4b^2$   21. $9a + 63$   23. $19p + 19q$   25. $14x + 35$   27. $24y^2 + 12ty$
29. $4f + 9$   31. $16(c + d)$   33. $(k - 7)9.3$   35. $(x + 19)k$   37. $20(t - 1)$
39. $(4.2 + r)r$   41. $37r$   43. $4.2n$   45. $42ab^2$   47. $4.7m^2n^2$   49. $xy^2$   51. $80q$
53. $6t^2 + 12t + 3$   55. $1\frac{1}{4}p + 5\frac{1}{2}r + \frac{3}{4}pr$   57. $2.7rs^2 + 3.8rs + 5.3r^2s$
59. $5x^2 + 7x + 32$   61. $8x^2 + 13x + 18$

CHAPTER 3   BASIC NUMBER CONCEPTS

PAGE 43   ORAL EXERCISES 3.1
1. 35 is divisible by 7.   3. 10 is divisible by 10.   5. 30 is divisible by 5.
7. 18 is divisible by 1.   9. 2 is a factor of 10.   11. 7 is a factor of 35.

13. 1 is a factor of 19. 15. 17 is a factor of 34. 17. 28 is a multiple of 4.
19. 36 is a multiple of 9. 21. 27 is a multiple of 27. 23. 45 is a multiple of 5.
25. False 27. True 29. False 31. True 33. False 35. True

PAGE 44 WRITTEN EXERCISES 3.1
1. $\{1, 2, 4\}$ 3. $\{1, 5\}$ 5. $\{1, 2, 4, 8\}$ 7. $\{1, 2, 5, 10\}$ 9. $\{1, 2, 3, 4, 6, 12\}$
11. $\{1, 11\}$ 13. $\{1, 3, 5, 15\}$ 15. $\{1, 2, 3, 6, 9, 18\}$ 17. $\{1, 23\}$
19. $\{1, 5, 25\}$ 21. $\{1, 2, 4, 7, 14, 28\}$ 23. $\{1, 2, 3, 4, 6, 8, 12, 16, 24, 48\}$
25. $2 \cdot 3$ 27. $3 \cdot 5$ 29. $3 \cdot 3$ 31. $3 \cdot 7$ 33. $2 \cdot 6, 3 \cdot 4$ 35. $2 \cdot 9, 3 \cdot 6$
37. $3 \cdot 9$ 39. $2 \cdot 15, 3 \cdot 10, 5 \cdot 6$ 41. $3 \cdot 11$ 43. True 45. False
47. True 49. False 51. True 53. False 55. $8 \cdot 7 + 2$ 57. $17 \cdot 12 + 4$
59. $16 \cdot 19 + 0$ 61. $32 \cdot 18 + 5$

PAGE 46 ORAL EXERCISES 3.2
1. True; 958 ends in 8. 3. True; 706 ends in 6. 5. False; 1023 does not end in
0, 2, 4, 6, or 8. 7. False; 8 + 5 = 13, not divisible by 3. 9. False; 1 + 2 + 7
= 10, not divisible by 3. 11. True; 2 + 7 + 6 = 15, divisible by 3. 13. True;
8 + 2 + 1 + 7 = 18, divisible by 3. 15. True; 16 is divisible by 4. 17. False;
74 is not divisible by 4. 19. True; 12 is divisible by 4. 21. True; 835 ends in 5.
23. False; 538 does not end in 0 or 5.

PAGE 47 WRITTEN EXERCISES 3.2
1. True; 546 ends in 6. 3. False; 811 does not end in 0, 2, 4, 6, or 8. 5. True;
1048 ends in 8. 7. False; 15,207 does not end in 0, 2, 4, 6, or 8. 9. True; 8 + 1 + 3
= 12, divisible by 3. 11. False; 8 + 2 = 10, not divisible by 3. 13. False;
3 + 0 + 3 + 7 = 13, not divisible by 3. 15. False; digit sum 22, is not divisible by 3.
17. True; 24 is divisible by 4. 19. False; 38 is not divisible by 4. 21. True; 28 is
divisible by 4. 23. True; 32 is divisible by 4. 25. False; 56 does not end in 0 or 5.
27. True; 85 ends in 5. 29. True; 120 ends in 0. 31. True; 180 ends in 0.
33. False; 105 ends in 5 but not 0. 35. True; 18,000 ends in 0. 37. True; digit sum,
9, is divisible by 9. 39. True; digit sum, 27, is divisible by 9. 41. False; digit
sum, 30, is not divisible by 9. 43. False; digit sum, 21, is divisible by 3 but not 9.

PAGE 49 ORAL EXERCISES 3.3
1. 2 3. 49 = 7 · 7 and is therefore a composite. 5. $2 \cdot 5$ 7. $3 \cdot 7$ 9. $5 \cdot 7$
11. $2^2 \cdot 3 \cdot 5$ 13. $2^3 \cdot 3^2 \cdot 5$ 11 15. $5^2 \cdot 11 \cdot 17^3$ 17. $2^3 \cdot 3^4 \cdot 7^5$

PAGE 50 WRITTEN EXERCISES 3.3
1. Note: In Exercise 1 follow the method in Example 1. The prime numbers greater than
50 and less than 75 are 53, 59, 61, 67, 71, and 73. 3. $2 \cdot 13$ 5. $2 \cdot 19$
7. $5 \cdot 11$ 9. $3 \cdot 23$ 11. $5 \cdot 13$ 13. $7 \cdot 11$ 15. $7 \cdot 17$ 17. $11 \cdot 41$
19. $3 \cdot 67$ 21. $2 \cdot 3^2 \cdot 5$ 23. $2 \cdot 3 \cdot 5^2 \cdot 7^2$ 25. $2 \cdot 3^3 \cdot 5 \cdot 7^2$
27. $2 \cdot 3^2 \cdot 5 \cdot 7^3 \cdot 13$ 29. $2^2 \cdot 3^2 \cdot 5^2 \cdot 7 \cdot 11^2 \cdot 17^2$ 31. $3 + 5$ 33. $5 + 7$
35. $3 + 17$ 37. $5 + 23$ 39. $5 + 43$ 41. $3 + 67$

PAGE 52    ORAL EXERCISES 3.4

1.  2    3.  2, 3, 5, 7, 11, 13, 17, 19, 23    5.  $5 \cdot 7 \cdot 13$    7.  $2 \cdot 3 \cdot 5^2$
9.  $2^2 \cdot 3 \cdot 41$    11.  $2 \cdot 3^2 \cdot 11$    13.  $3^2 \cdot 29$    15.  $2 \cdot 3^2 \cdot 5^2$    17.  $2 \cdot 3$
19.  $3^2$    21.  $2^4$    23.  $2 \cdot 7$    25.  $2 \cdot 11$    27.  $2 \cdot 13$    29.  $2^2 \cdot 5 \cdot 11$

PAGE 53    WRITTEN EXERCISES 3.4

1.  $2 \cdot 3^2$    3.  $3^3$    5.  $2^3 \cdot 5$    7.  $2^2 \cdot 11$    9.  $2 \cdot 5^2$    11.  $2 \cdot 3^3$
13.  $2^2 \cdot 3 \cdot 5$    15.  $2^6$    17.  $2 \cdot 3 \cdot 13$    19.  $2^3 \cdot 11$    21.  $5 \cdot 23$    23.  $2^3 \cdot 31$
25.  $2^2 \cdot 3^4$    27.  $3^2 \cdot 5^2$    29.  $2^2 \cdot 3 \cdot 5 \cdot 7$    31.  $2 \cdot 13 \cdot 19$    33.  $3 \cdot 7 \cdot 19$
35.  $2^9$    37.  $11 \cdot 13 \cdot 17$    39.  $3^2 \cdot 5^2 \cdot 7 \cdot 23$    41.  $3^3 \cdot 5 \cdot 11^2$    43.  9
45.  5    47.  8    49.  25    51.  18    53.  Yes    55.  Yes    57.  No    59.  No    61.  Yes

PAGE 55    ORAL EXERCISES 3.5

1.  6    3.  14    5.  21    7.  33    9.  20    11.  42    13.  12    15.  15    17.  24
19.  18    21.  $2^2 \cdot 3 \cdot 5$    23.  $11 \cdot 13 \cdot 17$    25.  $2^3 \cdot 3^2 \cdot 5^3$

PAGE 56    WRITTEN EXERCISES 3.5

1.  $2^2 \cdot 3 \cdot 7$    3.  $2^3 \cdot 3' \cdot 5$    5.  $2 \cdot 3^2 \cdot 7^2 \cdot 13$    7.  $2^3 \cdot 11 \cdot 13$
9.  $2^2 \cdot 3 \cdot 5$    11.  $7 \cdot 11 \cdot 29$    13.  $3^5 \cdot 5^3 \cdot 17^2 \cdot 23$    15.  $2 \cdot 3 \cdot 5 \cdot 7 \cdot 11^2$
$\cdot 13 \cdot 17 \cdot 19 \cdot 23^2$    17.  $2^3 \cdot 3^2 \cdot 5^2 \cdot 11 \cdot 13$    19.  12    21.  140    23.  270
25.  120    27.  840    29.  240    31.  252    33.  168    35.  675    37.  $ab^2c^4$    39.  $k^3ng^4$

PAGE 57    CHAPTER REVIEW

1.  $\{1, 17\}$    3.  $\{1, 2, 5, 10, 25, 50\}$    5.  True    7.  False    9.  True    11.  True;
digit sum, 18, is divisible by 3.    13.  False; 02 is not divisible by 4.    15.  True;
digit sum, 18, is divisible by 9.    17.  False; 73,195 ends in 5 but not 0.    19.  False;
26,703 does not end in 0, 2, 4, 6, or 8.    21.  False; 78,920 ends in 0, but digit sum,
26, is not divisible by 3 or 9.    23.  $2^3 \cdot 3 \cdot 5^2 \cdot 7^2 \cdot 19$    25.  $2^3 \cdot 3^4 \cdot 5^4$
27.  $2^2 \cdot 3$    29.  $2^2 \cdot 7$    31.  $2^2 \cdot 17$    33.  $2^2 \cdot 23$    35.  $2 \cdot 3^3 \cdot 5^2 \cdot 11 \cdot 13^2$
37.  $2^3 \cdot 3^4 \cdot 5^2 \cdot 7 \cdot 11$    39.  40    41.  36    43.  385    45.  120    47.  525
49.  360

CHAPTER 4    FRACTIONS

PAGE 62    ORAL EXERCISES 4.1

1.  $\frac{3}{5}$    3.  $\frac{2}{5}$    5.  $\frac{5}{7}$    7.  $\frac{5}{6}$    9.  $\frac{1}{12}$    11.  $\frac{3}{4}$    13.  $\frac{3}{11}$    15.  $\frac{1}{6}$    17.  $\frac{1}{4}$    19.  $\frac{2}{5}$
21.  $\frac{2}{5}$    23.  $\frac{1}{3}$    25.  $\frac{3}{2}$    27.  $\frac{1}{4}$    29.  $\frac{1}{3}$    31.  $\frac{1}{9}$    33.  $\frac{4}{21}$    35.  $\frac{2}{5}$

PAGE 63    WRITTEN EXERCISES 4.1

1.  $\frac{13}{17}$    3.  $\frac{5}{11}$    5.  $\frac{10}{21}$    7.  $\frac{20}{77}$    9.  $\frac{3}{4}$    11.  $\frac{15}{8}$    13.  $\frac{1}{2}$    15.  $\frac{1}{3}$    17.  $\frac{3}{4}$    19.  $\frac{5}{8}$
21.  $\frac{2}{3}$    23.  $\frac{3}{5}$    25.  $\frac{7}{8}$    27.  $\frac{3}{16}$    29.  $\frac{7}{16}$    31.  $\frac{11}{16}$    33.  $\frac{5}{7}$    35.  $\frac{5}{9}$    37.  $\frac{3}{4}$

39. $\frac{2}{3}$  41. $\frac{8}{3}$  43. $\frac{4}{3}$  45. $\frac{16}{7}$  47. $\frac{7}{3}$  49. 9  51. 20  53. $2 \cdot 3 \cdot 3 \cdot 2$

PAGE 65  ORAL EXERCISES 4.2

1. 0  3. 0  5. 5  7. $\frac{2}{3}$  9. $\frac{r}{s}$  11. $\frac{bc}{5a}$  13. $\frac{q}{2p}$  15. $\frac{1}{3}$  17. $\frac{2}{3}$  19. $\frac{1}{a}$
21. $\frac{3}{7}$

PAGE 66  WRITTEN EXERCISES 4.2

1. $\frac{5}{11}$  3. $\frac{3}{x}$  5. 1  7. $\frac{3}{2p}$  9. $\frac{1}{15x}$  11. $\frac{3z}{50xy}$  13. $\frac{3}{4}$  15. $\frac{1}{5}$  17. $\frac{1}{n}$
19. $\frac{2}{3y}$  21. $\frac{2m}{3p}$  23. $\frac{5r}{8b}$  25. $\frac{5x^2y^3}{6r^2s^2t}$  27. $\frac{3g}{2f}$  29. $\frac{3}{2x^2yz}$  31. 5b  33. 6y
35. 10ab

PAGE 68  ORAL EXERCISES 4.3

1. $\frac{1}{14}$  3. $\frac{1}{30}$  5. $\frac{8}{3}$  7. $\frac{6}{xy}$  9. $\frac{6r}{st}$  11. $\frac{2x}{3}$  13. 1  15. 2  17. 2x  19. $\frac{3}{5}$
21. $\frac{1}{5}$  23. $\frac{3a}{5}$

PAGE 69  WRITTEN EXERCISES 4.3

1. $\frac{1}{36}$  3. $\frac{4a}{7b}$  5. $\frac{7}{2}$  7. $\frac{10}{3}$  9. $\frac{3x}{4}$  11. $\frac{2r}{3}$  13. $\frac{5}{3}$  15. $\frac{7}{9}$  17. $\frac{1}{2}$  19. $\frac{3}{7}$
21. $\frac{3s}{2t}$  23. $\frac{1}{2}$  25. $\frac{3}{7}$  27. $\frac{3}{10}$  29. $\frac{2}{15t}$  31. $\frac{c}{2ab}$  33. $\frac{a}{b}$  35. $\frac{21}{b}$  37. 2st
39. $\frac{1}{8}$  41. $\frac{8y}{15z}$  43. $\frac{3b^2}{10c}$

PAGE 71  ORAL EXERCISES 4.4

1. $\frac{3}{4} \cdot \frac{3}{5}$  3. $\frac{7}{8} \cdot \frac{3}{4}$  5. $\frac{5}{12} \cdot \frac{7}{2}$  7. $\frac{4}{3} \cdot \frac{2}{3}$  9. $\frac{3}{8} \cdot \frac{1}{4}$  11. $\frac{y}{3} \cdot \frac{8}{1}$  13. $\frac{3}{8} \cdot \frac{1}{y}$
15. $\frac{r}{s} \cdot \frac{t}{1}$  17. $\frac{2}{3}$  19. $\frac{1}{3}$  21. $\frac{2}{15}$  23. $\frac{3}{2}$  25. $\frac{3a}{2b}$  27. $\frac{x}{3}$  29. $\frac{5}{4}$  31. $\frac{x}{y}$
33. $\frac{1}{11}$

PAGE 72  WRITTEN EXERCISES 4.4

1. $\frac{3}{10}$  3. $\frac{2}{5}$  5. $\frac{1}{6}$  7. $\frac{1}{4}$  9. $\frac{1}{2}$  11. $\frac{2a}{3}$  13. $\frac{2r}{3q}$  15. $\frac{5}{3}$  17. $\frac{5}{7}$  19. $\frac{2}{3}$
21. $\frac{2b^2}{c}$  23. $\frac{s}{t}$  25. $\frac{6p}{q^2}$  27. $\frac{s}{t^2}$  29. $\frac{27kp}{20dt}$  31. $\frac{1}{2}$  33. $\frac{3}{5c}$  35. $\frac{wx^3}{y^2}$

PAGE 74  ORAL EXERCISES 4.5

1. $\frac{2}{3}$  3. $\frac{5}{x}$  5. $\frac{5}{8}$  7. $\frac{4t}{13}$  9. $\frac{2}{3c}$  11. $\frac{2a}{b}$  13. $\frac{1}{x}$  15. $\frac{3y}{8}$  17. $\frac{r}{3w}$  19. $\frac{3}{4}$
21. $\frac{17p}{10}$  23. $\frac{6k}{11}$

PAGE 75  WRITTEN EXERCISES 4.5

1. $\frac{8}{11}$  3. $\frac{19}{y}$  5. $\frac{2r}{9}$  7. $\frac{13}{16}$  9. $\frac{5}{3x}$  11. $\frac{8h}{11}$  13. $\frac{8w}{13}$  15. $\frac{k+7}{9}$  17. $\frac{a}{n}$
19. $\frac{7}{8}$  21. $\frac{4x}{5}$  23. $\frac{1}{6x}$  25. $\frac{3r}{4s}$  27. $\frac{2k}{3m}$  29. $\frac{3a}{p}$  31. $\frac{14}{19}$  33. $\frac{25}{y}$  35. $\frac{22x}{7}$

37. $\dfrac{3}{2s}$   39. $\dfrac{8a}{9b}$

1. 8   3. 30   5. 15   7. 26   9. 12   11. 90   13. 12   15. $\dfrac{2}{2}$   17. $\dfrac{4}{4}$
19. $\dfrac{5}{5}$   21. $\dfrac{4}{4}$   23. $\dfrac{3}{3}$   25. $\dfrac{5}{6}$   27. $\dfrac{x}{8}$   29. $\dfrac{7}{3x}$

1. $\dfrac{2}{3} + \dfrac{4}{5} = \dfrac{2}{3} \cdot \dfrac{5}{5} + \dfrac{4}{5} \cdot \dfrac{3}{3}$   3. $\dfrac{1}{6} + \dfrac{1}{4} = \dfrac{1}{6} \cdot \dfrac{2}{2} + \dfrac{1}{4} \cdot \dfrac{3}{3}$   5. $\dfrac{a}{4} + \dfrac{3a}{10} = \dfrac{a}{4} \cdot \dfrac{5}{5} + \dfrac{3a}{10} \cdot \dfrac{2}{2}$

$\quad\quad = \dfrac{10}{15} + \dfrac{12}{15}$   $\quad\quad\quad = \dfrac{2}{12} + \dfrac{3}{12}$   $\quad\quad\quad = \dfrac{5a}{20} + \dfrac{6a}{20}$

$\quad\quad = \dfrac{22}{15}$   $\quad\quad\quad = \dfrac{5}{12}$   $\quad\quad\quad = \dfrac{11a}{20}$

7. $\dfrac{5}{8}$   9. $\dfrac{3}{10}$   11. $\dfrac{5}{2n}$   13. $\dfrac{7}{5x}$   15. $\dfrac{8}{3s}$   17. $\dfrac{5}{9x}$   19. $\dfrac{8x}{15}$   21. $\dfrac{13d}{10}$   23. $\dfrac{7w}{24}$
25. $\dfrac{7k}{20}$   27. $\dfrac{11}{6r}$   29. $\dfrac{7}{15q}$   31. $\dfrac{15r}{8}$   33. $\dfrac{17n}{12}$   35. $\dfrac{1}{x}$

1. $\dfrac{6}{5}$   3. $\dfrac{4}{7}$   5. $\dfrac{7}{9}$   7. $\dfrac{5}{4s}$   9. $\dfrac{1}{5x}$   11. $\dfrac{7a}{12b}$   13. $\dfrac{7}{15}$   15. $9r$   17. $\dfrac{10m}{9a}$
19. $\dfrac{5}{b}$   21. $\dfrac{1}{4}$   23. $\dfrac{3}{20b}$   25. $\dfrac{2a^2c}{15}$   27. $t$   29. $\dfrac{15}{17}$   31. $\dfrac{9x}{11}$   33. $\dfrac{9r}{16}$   35. $\dfrac{3}{4y}$
37. $\dfrac{x}{2}$   39. $\dfrac{11y}{12}$   41. $\dfrac{11}{3t}$   43. $\dfrac{1}{15n}$

CHAPTER 5   OPEN SENTENCES AND GRAPHS

Note: For Exercises 1-7, many answers are possible. Only one is given for each set.

1. {counting numbers less than 4}   3. {even numbers between 1 and 11}   5. {counting numbers less than 1}   7. {whole-number multiples of 3 greater than 11}   9. {6, 7}
11. Empty set   13. {11, 13, 17, 19, 23, 29}   15. {1, 4, 5}   17. {1, $2\frac{3}{4}$, 4.6}
19. $\dfrac{0}{1}, \dfrac{0}{2}$   21. $\dfrac{1000}{1}, \dfrac{2000}{2}$   23. $\dfrac{31}{8}, \dfrac{62}{16}$   25. $\dfrac{52}{10}, \dfrac{26}{5}$   27. $\dfrac{37}{3}, \dfrac{74}{6}$   29. $\dfrac{13}{100}, \dfrac{26}{200}$

Note: For Exercises 1-11, many answers are possible. Only one is given for each set.
1. {add counting numbers}   3. {whole numbers}   5. {rational numbers of arithmetic halfway between 7 and 8}   7. {whole number multiples of 4 between 15 and 29}
9. {prime numbers less than 12}   11. {counting-number powers of 10 less than $10^4$}
13. {13, 14, 15, 16, 17, 18, 19}   15. { }   17. {2, 3, 5}   19. {1, 2, 3, 4, 6, 12}
21. {11, 22, 33, $\cdots$}   23. {1, 3}   25. $\left\{\dfrac{1}{2}, \dfrac{5}{2}, \dfrac{9}{2}\right\}$   27. $\left\{\dfrac{3}{4}, \dfrac{7}{3}, \dfrac{15}{4}\right\}$

29.   31.   33.

35. $\frac{15}{1}, \frac{30}{2}$    37. $\frac{100}{1}, \frac{200}{2}$    39. $\frac{16}{5}, \frac{32}{10}$    41. $\frac{23}{10}, \frac{230}{100}$    43. $\frac{203}{100}, \frac{406}{200}$    45. $\frac{381}{100}, \frac{762}{200}$

47. $\left\{0, 2, \frac{24}{8}, 4, \frac{35}{7}\right\}$    49. $\left\{2, \frac{24}{8}, \frac{35}{7}\right\}$

PAGE 90  ORAL EXERCISES 5.2

1. True    3. False    5. True    7. True    9. True    11. False    13. $5.9 < 7.3$;
$5.9 \neq 7.3$    15. $\frac{24}{53} < \frac{24}{37}$; $\frac{24}{37} \neq \frac{24}{53}$    17. $17.3 < 18.6$; $18.6 > 17.3$    19. $\frac{1}{3} + \frac{1}{2} > \frac{2}{5}$;
$\frac{2}{5} < \frac{1}{3} + \frac{1}{2}$

PAGE 90  WRITTEN EXERCISES 5.2

1. $2 \cdot (3 + 5) > 15$    3. $15 + (8 \div 2) \neq 11\frac{1}{2}$    5. $(8 - 3) \cdot (2 + 5) > 30$
7. $\frac{1}{2} \cdot (\frac{1}{3} + \frac{2}{3}) < \frac{5}{6}$    9. $(5 + 3) \cdot (5 + 4) = 72$    11. $(8.2 - 1.2) \div 2 < 5$    13. $=$
15. $<$    17. $>$    19. $<$    21. $>$    23. $=$    25. $<$    27. $=$    29. $=$

PAGE 92  ORAL EXERCISES 5.3

1. 1, 6, 11    3. 0, 2, 4    5. 9, 8, 7    7. 4, 6, 8    9. 6, $6\frac{1}{2}$, 7    11. 8    13. 4
15. 7    17. 15    19. $\{5\}$    21. $\{0, 1\}$    23. $\{\}$    25. $\{0, 1, 2, 3, 4, 5\}$
27. $\{\}$    29. $\{\}$

PAGE 93  WRITTEN EXERCISES 5.3

1. $\{8\}$    3. $\{18\}$    5. $\{8\}$    7. $\{13\}$    9. $\{7\}$    11. $\{\}$    13. $\{6\}$    15. $\{3\}$
17. $\{\}$    19. $\{4\}$    21. $\{4, 5\}$    23. $\{3\}$    25. $\{0\}$    27. $\{\}$    29. $\{5\}$
31. $\{0, 1, 2, 3, 4, 5\}$    33. $\{0, 1, 2, 3, 5\}$    35. $\{0, 1, 2, 3, 4, 5\}$    37. $\{\}$
39. $\{0, 1, 2\}$

PAGE 95  ORAL EXERCISES 5.4

1. No    3. Yes    5. No    7. No    9. $x > 1$    11. $x < x + 1$    13. $x > 3$
15. $x < 4\frac{3}{4}$    17. $x < \pi$

PAGE 96  WRITTEN EXERCISES 5.4

1.    3.    5.    7.

9.    11.    13.

15.    17. $x > 2$    19. $x < 6$    21. $x < 2$    23. $x \neq 1$

25. $x > 3$    27. $x \neq 5$    29.    31.    33.

35.

PAGE 99  ORAL EXERCISES 5.5

1. True    3. False    5. True    7. $\{2\}, \{4\}, \{2, 4\}$    9. $\{0, 1, 2, 3, 4\}, \{0, 1, 2\}$,
$\{0, 1, 2, 3, 4\}$    11. $\{5\}, \{0, 1, 2, 3, 4\}, \{0, 1, 2, 3, 4, 5\}$    13. Yes    15. Yes
17. $\{2, 4\}$    19. $\{0, 1, 2, 3, 4\}$
8  CHAPTER 5

PAGE 100   WRITTEN EXERCISES 5.5

1. True   3. True   5. False   7. True   Note: For Exercises 9-19, only the truth set of the compound sentences are given.   9. {0, 1, 2, 3, 4}   11. {0, 1, 2, 3}
13. {0, 1, 9}   15. {9, 10, 11, 12, ···}   17. {0, 1, 2, 3, 4, 5, ···}
19. {0, 1, 2, 3, 4, 5, ···}

21.   23.   25.

27.   29.   31.

33.   35.   37.

PAGE 102   ORAL EXERCISES 5.6

1. False   3. True   5. False   7. {2}, {0, 1, 2, 3, 4}, {2}   9. {0, 1, 2, 3}, {0, 1}, {0, 1}   11. {0, 1, 2, 3, 4}, {6, 7, 8, ···}, { }   13. No   15. No
17. {2, 3}   19. { }

PAGE 103   WRITTEN EXERCISES 5.6

1. True   3. False   5. False   7. True   Note: For Exercises 9-13, only the truth sets of the compound sentences are given.   9. {1, 2, 3, 4}   11. {0, 1, 2, 3}
13. {5}   Note: For Exercises 15-31, only the graphs of the truth sets of the compound sentences are given.   15.   17.

19.   21.   23.

25.   27.   29.

31.   33. x > 1 and x < 4   35. x < 5 and x ≠ 2   37. x < 2 or x > 4   39. x = 0 or x = 4   41. x < 2 or x > 4   43. x > 1 and x < 5

PAGE 106   ORAL EXERCISES 5.7

1. True   3. True   5. True   7. {0, 1, 2, 3}   9. {2, 3, 4, 5}   11. {0}
13. {0, 1, 2, 3, 4, 5}   15. {0, 1}   17. {0, 1, 2, 3, 4}   19. x ≥ 1
21. x ≤ 4   23. x > 4

PAGE 106   WRITTEN EXERCISES 5.7

1. {0, 2, 4, 6}   3. { }   5. {0, 2, 4, 6, 8, 10}   7. {2, 4, 6, 8, 10}
9. {0, 2, 4, 6}   11. {6, 8, 10}   13.   15.

17.   19.   21. Graph contains no points.
23. Graph contains no points.

1. $\{24, 25, 26, 27\}$   3. $\{2, 3, 5, 7, 11\}$   Note:  For Exercises 5-9, many answers are possible.  Only two are given for each number.   5. $\frac{12}{1}, \frac{24}{2}$   7. $\frac{5}{2}, \frac{10}{4}$   9. $\frac{23}{10}$, $\frac{230}{100}$   11. $18 - (5 + 7) < 10$   13. $(8 + 2) \cdot 5 > 45$   15. $(3 + 2) \cdot (4 - 1) = 15$

17. $\{7\}$   19. $\{63\}$   21. $\{0, 1, 2, 3, 5\}$   23. $\{0, 1, 2\}$   25. [number line 0 1 2 3 4 5]

27. [number line 6 7]   29. [number line 0 7.4]   31. [number line 0 3]

33. $\{0, 1, 2, 3, 4, 5, 6\}$   35. [number line 0 7.3]

37. [number line 0 $3\frac{1}{2}$ $5\frac{1}{2}$]   39. $\{0, 1, 2, 3, 4\}$   41. [number line $3\frac{1}{2}$ $5\frac{1}{4}$]   43. [number line 0 3]

45. $\{10, 11, 12, 13, 14, 15\}$   47. $\{13, 14, 15, \ldots\}$   49. [number line 5]

51. [number line 0 $6\frac{1}{2}$]   Note:  For Ex. 33-43 above, answers are given only for compound sentences.

## CHAPTER 6   SOLVING EQUATIONS

### PAGE 111   ORAL EXERCISES 6.1

1. x   3. b   5. n   7. k   9. 12   11. 112   13. $x + 5 - 5 = 19 - 5$
15. $n + 92 - 92 = 105 - 92$   17. $t + 1.8 - 1.8 = 2.3 - 1.8$   19. $b + \frac{1}{2} - \frac{1}{2} = 19 - \frac{1}{2}$
21. $x + 12.5 - 12.5 = 21.3 - 12.5$

### PAGE 112   WRITTEN EXERCISES 6.1

1. $n = 7$   3. $y = 17$   5. $t = 24$   7. $a = 17$   9. $q = 27$   11. $x = 4.2$
13. $n = 2.4$   15. $b = 2.3$   17. $s = 0.24$   19. $q = 4.16$   21. $x = 2\frac{1}{4}$   23. $t = 3\frac{1}{2}$
25. x: unknown number; $x + 29 = 105$; $x = 76$   27. x: unknown number; $x + 18.7 = 34.3$; $x = 15.6$   29. t   31. x   33. 12   35. 17   37. $3\frac{1}{2}$   39. 1.4

### PAGE 114   ORAL EXERCISES 6.2

1. r   3. x   5. n   7. b   9. $3\frac{1}{4}$   11. $a - 12 + 12 = 5 + 12$   13. $t - 83 + 83 = 47 + 83$   15. $b - 5.6 + 5.6 = 12.9 + 5.6$   17. $n - 1\frac{7}{8} + 1\frac{7}{8} = 4\frac{1}{4} + 1\frac{7}{8}$   19. $y + 87 - 87 = 193 - 87$   21. $t + 15.9 - 15.9 = 28.3 - 15.9$   23. $q - \frac{3}{4} + \frac{3}{4} = 6\frac{1}{2} + \frac{3}{4}$

### PAGE 115   WRITTEN EXERCISES 6.2

1. $x = 58$   3. $t = 101$   5. $n = 203$   7. $a = 392$   9. $m = 338$   11. $s = 10.1$
13. $w = 1.13$   15. $g = 48.0$   17. $r = 24.37$   19. $b = 8$   21. $n = 14\frac{1}{2}$   23. $x = 748$
25. x: unknown number; $x - 78 = 97$; $x = 175$   27. x: unknown number; $x - 29.7 = 35.8$; $x = 65.5$   29. x: unknown number; $x + 2\frac{3}{4} = 12\frac{1}{4}$; $x = 9\frac{1}{2}$   31. 8   33. 17
35. x   37. a

### PAGE 117   ORAL EXERCISES 6.3

1. x   3. t   5. k   7. 35   9. x   11. $\frac{9x}{9} = \frac{72}{9}$   13. $\frac{53t}{53} = \frac{87}{53}$   15. $\frac{0.7w}{0.7} = \frac{21}{0.7}$
17. $\frac{108b}{108} = \frac{226}{108}$   19. Yes   21. No   23. No

PAGE 118   WRITTEN EXERCISES 6.3

1. $x = 9$   3. $n = 5$   5. $y = 32$   7. $q = 5\frac{1}{2}$   9. $r = 14.0$   11. $k = 41.0$
13. $x = 20.0$   15. $t = 120$   17. $x = 24$   19. $x = 136$   21. $y = 14.5$   23. $p = 1.8$
25. x: unknown number; $23x = 207$; $x = 9$   27. x: unknown number; $56x = 604.8$; $x = 10.8$

PAGE 120   ORAL EXERCISES 6.4

1. a   3. s   5. b   7. $16p$   9. $15(\frac{x}{15}) = 15(13)$   11. $1.8(\frac{y}{1.8}) = 1.8(12)$
13. $3\frac{1}{2}(\frac{t}{3\frac{1}{2}}) = 3\frac{1}{2}(8)$   15. $19(\frac{5r}{19}) = 19(12)$   17. $x + 102 - 102 = 193 - 102$
19. $\frac{83t}{83} = \frac{317}{83}$   21. $w + 5\frac{3}{4} - 5\frac{3}{4} = 13\frac{1}{4} - 5\frac{3}{4}$   23. $61(\frac{s}{61}) = 61(28)$

PAGE 121   WRITTEN EXERCISES 6.4

1. $t = 136$   3. $x = 276$   5. $a = 126$   7. $x = 283.5$ or $283\frac{1}{2}$   9. x: unknown number;
$\frac{x}{28} = 17$; $x = 476$   11. x: unknown number; $\frac{x}{6} = 16$; $x = 96$   13. $x - 140 + 140 =$
$68 + 140$   15. $\frac{16s}{16} = \frac{112}{16}$   17. $y + 74 - 74 = 78 - 74$   19. $34(\frac{n}{34}) = 34(18)$
21. $x = 40$   23. $x = 11\frac{3}{8}$   25. $b = 12\frac{1}{2}$   27. $r = 168$

PAGE 124   ORAL EXERCISES 6.5

1. $x + 56 - 56 = 91 - 56$   3. $x - 12.7 + 12.7 = 8.9 + 12.7$   5. $\frac{12x}{12} = \frac{256}{12}$
7. $19(\frac{x}{19}) = 19(56)$   9. $21 + x - 21 = 92 - 21$   11. $9y + 3 - 3 = 16 - 3$
13. $11w + 8 - 8 = 25 - 8$   15. $13x - 6.9 + 6.9 = 47.1 + 6.9$   17. $5p + 6\frac{1}{4} - 6\frac{1}{4} =$
$12\frac{3}{4} - 6\frac{1}{4}$   19. $22.3y - 19.5 + 19.5 = 3.6 + 19.5$   21. $\frac{q}{12} + 7 - 7 = 19 - 7$
23. No   25. Yes

PAGE 125   WRITTEN EXERCISES 6.5

1. $x = 14$   3. $x = 56$   5. $x = 28$   7. $x = 165$   9. $x = 8$   11. $x = 14$
13. $x = 8.5$   15. $x = 105$   17. $x = 216$   19. $x = 97.6$   21. $x = 12$   23. $x = 9$
25. $x = 3.9$   27. x: unknown number; $2x - 17 = 67$; $x = 42$   29. x: unknown number;
$\frac{x}{8} + 13\frac{1}{2} = 19$; $x = 44$   31. $x = 16$   33. $x = 20$   35. $x = 16$

PAGE 128   ORAL EXERCISES 6.6

1. $20r + 3$   3. $3b + 6$   5. $4s + 12$   7. $4n$   9. $7k - 10$   11. $7m + 14$
13. $8t + 12$   15. $36w + 15$   17. $\frac{3}{4}s - 2$   19. $5x + 35 = 14$   21. $2x - 6 + x = 9$
23. $20x - 4 - 3x = 19$   25. $7x + 3x - 15 = 42$   27. $2x + 2 + 3x + 15 = 17$

PAGE 128   WRITTEN EXERCISES 6.6

1. $x = 7$   3. $x = 9$   5. $x = 27$   7. $x = 5$   9. $x = 13$   11. $x = 4\frac{1}{2}$   13. $x = 7$
15. $x = 54$   17. $x = 9$   19. $x = 3\frac{1}{4}$   21. $x = 7$   23. $x = \frac{143}{16}$ or $8\frac{15}{16}$   25. $51.6 =$
$4s$; $s = 12.9$ cm   27. $23.8 = x + x + 3 + 2x$; $x = 5.2$ cm; $x + 3 = 8.2$ cm; $2x = 10.4$cm
29. $90 = 2(2x + 3) + 2x$; $2x + 3 = 31$ mm; $x = 14$ mm

PAGE 132   CHAPTER REVIEW

1. $r = 45$   3. $y = 12.8$   5. $x = 10\frac{3}{4}$   7. x: unknown number; $x + 96 = 123$; $x = 27$

9.  a = 82   11.  k = 96.4   13.  m = $61\frac{3}{8}$   15.  x: unknown number; x - 14.9 = 297; x = 44.6   17.  x = 9   19.  a = 430   21.  t = 56   23.  x: unknown number; 29x = 406; x = 14   25.  x = 133   27.  r = 305.1   29.  t = 225   31.  x: unknown number; $\frac{x}{37}$ = 52; x = 1924   33.  x = 19   35.  w = 40   37.  a = 518   39.  x: unknown number; $\frac{x}{29}$ - 15 = 13; x = 812   41.  x = 7   43.  r = $\frac{21}{4}$ or $5\frac{1}{4}$   45.  b = 15.6 or $15\frac{3}{5}$   47.  81 = x + 3x + 2x + 3; x = 13 cm; 3x = 39 cm; 2x + 3 = 29 cm

## PAGE 135  REVIEW EXERCISES FOR CHAPTERS 1-6

1.  53 mm   3.  4800   5.  2.83   7.  4   9.  22   11.  2830   13.  90 $mm^2$   15.  0
17.  18   19.  48t   21.  132rs   23.  27r + 36   25.  $12p^2$ + 10p   27.  12(r + s)
29.  3t(t - 2)   31.  27t   33.  6.4n   35.  101r   37.  $\{1, 2, 11, 22\}$
39.  $\{1, 3, 5, 9, 15, 45\}$   41.  $\{1, 47\}$   43.  False   45.  False; 527 does not end in 0 or 5.   47.  2 · 43   49.  5 · 17   51.  $2^3 \cdot 3^2 \cdot 5 \cdot 7$   53.  2 · 17
55.  $2 \cdot 3^2 \cdot 5$   57.  $2^3 \cdot 3^2 \cdot 5 \cdot 7$   59.  60   61.  60   63.  $\frac{2}{9}$   65.  $\frac{3}{11}$
67.  $\frac{5}{13}$   69.  $\frac{2a}{5b^2}$   71.  $\frac{2}{3}$   73.  $\frac{3b}{8a}$   75.  $\frac{2}{5}$   77.  $\frac{3m}{n}$   79.  $\frac{4t}{11}$   81.  $\frac{2r}{3w}$
83.  $\frac{11}{12}$   85.  $\frac{4}{3x}$   87.  2, 3, 7   89. 

91. 

93.  4 · 3 + 11 · 3 = (4 + 11)3

95.  $\{0, 1, 2, 3\}$   97. 

99. 

101. 

103. 

105.  $\{21, 23, 25, 27, 29,$ 31, 33, 35, 37, 39, 41, 43, 45$\}$   107.  $\{23, 25, 27, 29, \cdots\}$   109.  x = 1.83
111.  x = 10.32   113.  x = 180   115.  x = 391   117.  x = 13   119.  x:  unknown number; 3x + 13.8 = 27.9; x = 4.7   121.  x = $17\frac{1}{2}$   123.  28 = x + 2x + 2x + 3; x = 5 cm; 2x = 10 cm; 2x + 3 = 13 cm

PAGE 142  ORAL EXERCISES 7.1

1.  3 to 5    3.  2 to 9    5.  x to y    7.  $\frac{3}{4}$    9.  $\frac{1}{10}$    11.  $\frac{4}{3}$ or 4 : 3    13.  $\frac{17}{23}$ or

17 : 23    15.  $\frac{11}{6}$ or 11 : 6    17.  $\frac{3}{5}$    19.  $\frac{2}{5}$

PAGE 143  WRITTEN EXERCISES 7.1

1.  $\frac{5}{9}$    3.  $\frac{7}{12}$    5.  $\frac{15}{2}$    7.  $\frac{1}{100}$    9.  $\frac{4}{5}$    11.  $\frac{4}{7}$    13.  $\frac{5}{1}$    15.  $\frac{x}{5}$    17.  $\frac{b}{a}$    19.  $\frac{5}{6}$

21.  $\frac{2m}{5n}$    23.  $\frac{2x}{5y}$    25.  $\frac{11}{24}$ or 11 : 24    27.  $\frac{1}{8}$ or 1 : 8    29.  $\frac{24}{49}$ or 24 : 49

31.  $\frac{4}{5}$ or 4 : 5

PAGE 146  ORAL EXERCISES 7.2

1.  True    3.  True    5.  True    7.  False    9.  False    11.  False    13.  3    15.  1

17.  1    19.  20    21.  5    23.  8    25.  $\frac{3}{x} = \frac{100}{500}$    27.  $\frac{1}{w} = \frac{150}{3600}$

PAGE 147  WRITTEN EXERCISES 7.2

1.  True    3.  False    5.  True    7.  False    9.  False    11.  False    13.  5    15.  18

17.  18    19.  $3\frac{1}{2}$    21.  $19\frac{1}{2}$    23.  20    25.  $\frac{3}{x} = \frac{1}{5}$; 15 yd.    27.  $\frac{12}{x} = \frac{10}{25}$; 30 hits

29.  $\frac{16}{40} = \frac{8}{x}$; 20 hr.    31.  $\frac{3}{2} = \frac{1200}{x}$; 800 girls

PAGE 150  ORAL EXERCISES 7.3

1.  8%    3.  56%    5.  137%    7.  x%    9.  $37\frac{1}{2}$%    11.  1.8%    13.  43%    15.  5%

17.  270%    19.  75%    21.  80%    23.  100%    25.  $\frac{1}{10}$    27.  $\frac{7}{20}$    29.  $\frac{1}{3}$    31.  0.39

33.  0.276    35.  0.0018    37.  0.4; $\frac{2}{5}$    39.  70%; 0.7

PAGE 151  WRITTEN EXERCISES 7.3

1.  19%    3.  256%    5.  $62\frac{1}{2}$%    7.  8.3%    9.  306.1%    11.  $120\frac{1}{2}$%    13.  25%    15.  98%

17.  8%    19.  250%    21.  60%    23.  28.3%    25.  $\frac{1}{4} = \frac{x}{100}$; 25%    27.  $\frac{3}{10} = \frac{x}{100}$; 30%

29.  $\frac{12}{10} = \frac{x}{100}$; 120%    31.  $\frac{25}{20} = \frac{x}{100}$; 125%    33.  $\frac{13}{25} = \frac{x}{100}$; 52%    35.  $\frac{5}{6} = \frac{x}{100}$; $83\frac{1}{3}$%

37.  $\frac{4}{10} = \frac{x}{100}$; 40%    39.  $\frac{36}{10} = \frac{x}{100}$; 360%    41.  $\frac{37}{100} = \frac{x}{100}$; 37%    43.  17%; $\frac{17}{100}$

45.  0.22; $\frac{11}{50}$    47.  95%; 0.95    49.  $\frac{3}{20}$    51.  $\frac{9}{20}$    53.  $\frac{2}{3}$

PAGE 154  ORAL EXERCISES 7.4

1.  $\frac{x}{36} = \frac{25}{100}$    3.  $\frac{17}{82} = \frac{y}{100}$    5.  $\frac{10}{a} = \frac{15}{100}$    7.  $\frac{t}{100} = \frac{92}{15}$    9.  $\frac{25}{100} = \frac{144}{t}$    11.  75%

13.  15

PAGE 154  WRITTEN EXERCISES 7.4

1.  $\frac{25}{100} = \frac{x}{28}$; 7    3.  $\frac{r}{100} = \frac{69}{92}$; 75    5.  $\frac{15}{a} = \frac{20}{100}$; 75    7.  $\frac{x}{100} = \frac{150}{100}$; 150    9.  $\frac{12}{100} =$

$\frac{n}{13}$; 1.56   11. $\frac{x}{100} = \frac{15}{40}$; 37.5   13. $\frac{14}{t} = \frac{12\frac{1}{2}}{100}$; 112   15. $\frac{66\frac{2}{3}}{100} = \frac{y}{126}$; 84

17. $\frac{8}{1000} = \frac{20}{m}$; 2500   19. $\frac{84}{n} = \frac{83\frac{1}{3}}{100}$; 100.8   21. $37\frac{1}{2}\%$   23. 48   25. 110

27. $\frac{x}{12} = \frac{25}{100}$; 3   29. $\frac{192}{x} = \frac{20}{100}$; $960   31. $\frac{20}{400} = \frac{x}{100}$; 5%

### PAGE 158   ORAL EXERCISES 7.5

1. (0.14)(25); 3.5   3. (1.2)(83); 99.6   5. (0.01x)(10); 0.1x   7. (0.12)r; 0.12r
9. (0.1)a; 0.1a   11. (0.01r)(15.8); 0.158r   13. 0.15x   15. 0.28c   17. 0.05d
19. 0.63b   21. 0.7g   23. 26x   25. 65x

### PAGE 159   WRITTEN EXERCISES 7.5

1. 1.25   3. 7   5. 27   7. 114.75   9. 0.096   11. 13.23   13. 4.03   15. 1.53
17. 0.12x   19. 0.53f   21. 25x   23. 30p   25. 0.1p   27. 2.25v   29. 0.007w
31. 2.25x   33. 12   35. 112   37. 0.5   39. 37.5   41. $\frac{93}{248} = \frac{x}{100}$; $37\frac{1}{2}\%$

### PAGE 162   ORAL EXERCISES 7.6

1. $5   3. $7   5. $12   7. $5.50   9. $0.80   11. $50   13. $3   15. 0.08t
17. 0.05x   19. 0.055x

### PAGE 163   WRITTEN EXERCISES 7.6

1. $40   3. $22.50   5. $8.50   7. $11.20   9. $29   11. $15   13. $80   15. $39
17. 0.05x   19. 0.08r   21. 0.025n   23. 0.0025t   25. x   27. $0.83\frac{1}{3}r$   29. 6%
31. $800

### PAGE 166   ORAL EXERCISES 7.7

1. $27   3. $70   5. $55 - n   7. $6   9. $8   11. $60   13. $45   15. $12
17. $25 - $3.75 or $21.25   19. 1.5r; 150 - 1.5r   21. $\frac{15}{300} = \frac{5}{100}$   23. $\frac{15}{85} = \frac{r}{100}$

### PAGE 167   WRITTEN EXERCISES 7.7

1. $85   3. $30   5. $195 - x   7. $15 + n   9. 0.85x   11. $259 - n
13. $6000; $24,000   15. $16; $32   17. $48.75; $276.25   19. $35.95; $323.55
21. (0.01x)(50) = 13; 26%   23. (0.15)(x) = 48; $320

### PAGE 169   CHAPTER REVIEW

1. 1 : 8 or $\frac{1}{8}$   3. 1 : 2 or $\frac{1}{2}$   5. False   7. False   9. x = 4   11. x = $1\frac{3}{13}$
13. $\frac{15}{x} = \frac{2}{8}$; x = 60   15. 83%   17. 18%   19. 60%   21. 290%   23. 37.5%
25. $\frac{33}{100} = \frac{x}{28}$; 9.24   27. $\frac{3}{y} = \frac{15}{100}$; 20   29. $\frac{23}{276} = \frac{r}{100}$; $8\frac{1}{3}\%$   31. 24   33. 0.336
35. 0.12x   37. 2.25r   39. 0.04x   41. 15 - 0.15t

CHAPTER 8 WORD PROBLEMS

PAGE 173 ORAL EXERCISES 8.1

1. Subtraction   3. Multiplication   5. Division   7. Addition   9. Multiplication
11. 3(12) or 36 months   13. 10(7) or 70 days   15. $\frac{56}{7}$ or 8 weeks   17. $\frac{1900}{100}$ or
19 $cm^2$   19. f: number of fish; f + 6   21. m: number of meters; $\frac{m}{1000}$
23. c: number of centimeters; 10c   25. c: number of centimeters; 2c + 3
27. s: number of scuba divers; s - 15   29. c: number of children; 782 - c

PAGE 174 WRITTEN EXERCISES 8.1

1. h: number of hours; h + 12   3. d: number of dollars; 5d   5. m: number of mice;
m - 15   7. n: number of months; n - 120   9. p: number of planes; 25 - p
11. p: number of packages; 17.2p   13. p: number of players; p - 27   15. d: number of doctors; 2d + 7   17. s: number of square meters; 16s - 8   19. m: number of
meters; $\frac{m}{100}$ - 15   21. (0.05)(1200) or \$60.00   23. 0.08d   25. (16.9)(100) or 1690 cm
27. 100x   29. $\frac{279}{10}$ or 27.9 cm   31. $\frac{m}{10}$   33. $\frac{48}{12}$ or 4 yrs.   35. $\frac{m}{12}$ 37. (0.20)(90)
or \$18   39. 0.15d

PAGE 177 ORAL EXERCISES 8.2

1. x + 7 = 15   3. t + 7 = 18   5. y + 2y = 30   7. 26 - q = 3q   9. 15 = t - 9
11. n - 5   13. 2d   15. 3p   17. x + 12

PAGE 178 WRITTEN EXERCISES 8.2

1. x + 4 = 63   3. 59 - 8 - n   5. 2q + 5 = 28   7. t - 7 = 23   9. 5w + 8 = 42
11. $\frac{n}{5}$ - 8 = 50   13. v: votes Bob received; v + 30: votes Nancy received;
v + v + 30 = 150; v = 60 votes; v + 30 = 90 votes (Nancy)   15. k: km on Fri.;
km on Sat.; k + k - 54 = 970; k = 512 (Fri.); k - 54 = 458 km (Sat.)   17. c: cm of
rain; c + 1.8: cm of snow; c + c + 1.8 = 156.6; c = 77.4 cm of rain; c + 1.8 = 79.2 cm
of snow   19. x: number of adults; $\frac{1}{4}$x - 15: number of children; $\frac{1}{4}$x - 15 = 88;
x = 412 adults

PAGE 182 ORAL EXERCISES 8.3

1. 32 units   3. 54 units   5. 7x - 2 units   7. 2(x + 8) + 2x = 48   9. 2(3x - 5)
+ 2x = 52   11. 2(5x) + 2x = 90   13. x + 2x + 2x + 3 = 88   15. 2x - 1 + x + 3x = 72
17. 5w + 2   19. 4w - 3   21. 19 - w

PAGE 183 WRITTEN EXERCISES 8.3

1. x: width; x + 6: length; 2x + 2(x + 6) = 44: x = 8 units (width); x + 6 = 14 units
(length)   3. x: length of each of 2 sides; x + 3: length of third side:
x + x + x + 3 = 60; x = 19 units; x + 3 = 22 units   5. x: length; x - 12: width;
2x + 2(x - 12) = 58; x = 20$\frac{1}{2}$ meters (length); x - 12 = 8$\frac{1}{2}$ meters (width)
7. x: width; 3x - 2.7: length; 2x + 2(3x - 2.7) = 48.2; x = 6.7 meters (width);
3x - 2.7 = 17.4 meters (length)   9. x: length; x - 15.9: width; 2x + 2(x - 15.9) =

65.4; x = 24.3 units (length); x - 15.9 = 8.4 units (width)   11.   s:  side of square;
4s = 96; 24 units = length of one side of triangle; x:  length of third side;
3x:  length of second side; 24 + x + 3x = 96; x = 18 units (third side); 3x = 54 units
(second side)

PAGE 186   ORAL EXERCISES 8.4
1.   126t   3.   5x   5.   25q   7.   100d   9.   0.06y   11.   5x   13.   x + 2; 25(x + 2)
15.   5x + 10(3x) + 25(x + 2) = 410   17.   2x + 200; 0.065(2x + 200)   19.   16x
21.   800 cents

PAGE 187   WRITTEN EXERCISES 8.4
1.   x:  pairs of socks; 150x:  cost of socks in cents; 3(750) = 2250 = cost of shirts
in cents; 150x + 2250 = 3450; x = 8 pairs of socks   3.   x:  cases of tuna; x + 6:
cases of tuna; x + 6:  cases of coffee; 1480x:  cost of tuna; 2300(x + 6): cost of
coffee; x = 10(tuna); x + 6 = 16(coffee)   5.   x:  nickels; 2x - 3:  quarters; 5x:
values of nickels; 25(2x - 3):  value of quarters; 5x + 25(2x - 3) = 640; x = 13;
2x - 3 = 23   7.   x:  dollars; x + 7:  quarters; 2x - 2:  dimes; 100x:  value of dollars;
25(x + 7):  value of quarters; 10(2x - 2):  values of dimes; 100x + 25(x + 7) +
10(2x - 2) = 4070; x = 27; x + 7 = 34; 2x - 2 = 52   9.   x:  amount invested at 4%;
2x + 50:  amount invested at 6%; 0.04x:  interest on 4% investment; 0.06(2x + 50):
interest on 6% investment; 0.04x + 0.06(2x + 50) = 59.00; x = $350; 2x + 50 = $750

PAGE 190   ORAL EXERCISES 8.5
1.   16, 17, 18, 19   3.   30, 32, 34, 36   5.   w, w + 2, w + 4   7.   2k + 1   9.   2k + 3
11.   No   13.   No   15.   Yes   17.   Yes   19.   No

PAGE 191   WRITTEN EXERCISES 8.5
1.   x:  lesser number; x + 1:  greater number; x + x + 1 = 35; x = 17; x + 1 = 18
3.   x:  lesser number; x + 2:  greater number; x + x + 2 = 98; x = 48; x + 2 = 50
5.   x:  lesser odd number; x + 2:  greater odd number; x + x + 2 = 72; x = 35; x + 2 = 37
7.   x:  least number; x + 1:  next greater number; x + x + 1 + x + 2 = 168; x:  42;
x + 1:  43; x + 2 = 44   9.   x:  width; x + 2:  length; 2x + 2(x + 2) = 148;  x = 36 cm
(width); x + 2 = 38 cm (length)   11.   x:  least number; x + 2:  next greater number;
x + 4:  greatest number; 2x + 3(x + 4) = 122; x = 22; x + 2 = 24; x + 4 = 26
13.   x:  least number; x + 1:  next greater number; x + 2:  greatest number;  x + x
+ 1 + x + 2 = 40; x = $\frac{37}{3}$, which is not a whole number.

PAGE 194   ORAL EXERCISES 8.6
1.   $\frac{x}{1000} = \frac{2.3}{1}$   3.   $\frac{178}{1000} = \frac{x}{1}$   5.   $\frac{x}{1000} = \frac{19}{1}$   7.   $\frac{x}{1,000,000} = \frac{13}{1}$   9.   2000   11.   3
13.   8000   15.   2.4   17.   2300   19.   8.4

PAGE 195   WRITTEN EXERCISES 8.6
1.   $\frac{x}{1000} = \frac{36}{1}$; x = 36,000 dm$^3$   3.   $\frac{y}{1} = \frac{6000}{1000}$; r = 6 dm$^3$   5.   $\frac{2,500,000}{1,000,000} = \frac{w}{1}$; w = 2.5 m$^3$

7. $\frac{x}{1000} = \frac{2.6}{1}$; x = 2600 g   9. $\frac{6800}{1000} = \frac{y}{1}$; y = 6.8 g   11. $\frac{x}{1000} = \frac{20.8}{1}$; x = 20.800 mℓ

13. $\frac{84.6}{1000} = \frac{n}{1}$; n = 0.0846 kℓ   15. $\frac{0.03}{1} = \frac{r}{1000}$; r = 30 ℓ   17. $\frac{14.8}{1000} = \frac{x}{1}$; 0.0148 dm$^3$

19. $\frac{0.00904}{1} = \frac{x}{1,000,000}$; x = 9040 mm$^3$   21. 1000   23. 1000   25. 1000   27. 1000

29. 1000   31. 1,000,000   33. 1000   35. 1000   37. 1000

## PAGE 197   ORAL EXERCISES 8.7

1. 200 mℓ of orange juice; 600 mℓ of water   3. 100 g of salt; 300 g of water

5. 100 m$^3$ of oxygen; 400 m$^3$ of nitrogen   7. 6   9. 0.15y   11. 200   13. 2; 48

15. 54; 546   17. 25; 15

## PAGE 198   WRITTEN EXERCISES 8.7

1. 7.2 kg   3. 75 kg   5. 100 + x   7. w - 500   9. x: grams of oil soap;

4x: grams of glycerin; 8x = grams of water; x + 4x + 8x = 520; 40 g (oil soap);

160 g (glycerin); 320 g (water)   11. x: milliliters of solution; 0.08x = 152;

x = 1900 milliliters of solution   13. 2x: amount of Bran X; 5x: amount of Brand Y;

11x: amount of Brand Z; 2x + 5x + 11x = 54; 6 kg (Brand X); 15 kg (Brand Y);

33 kg (Brand Z)

15.

| Per Cent Solution | Number of Milliliters | Amount of Pure Acid |
|---|---|---|
| 5% | x | 0.05x |
| 10% | 360 - x | 0.10(360 - x) |
| $8\frac{1}{3}$% | 360 | 30 |

Equation:   0.05x + 0.10(360 - x) = 30

x = 120 mℓ of 5% solution

360 - x = 240 mℓ of 10% solution

## PAGE 202   CHAPTER REVIEW

1. n: number of stamps; n + 23   3. n: number of games; n - 12   5. 27 = 19 + n

7. 18 + 3q = 51   9. $\frac{x}{10}$ + 7 = 28   11. x: Saints' runs; x + 3: Braves' runs;

x + x + 3 = 21; x = 9 runs (Saints'); x + 3 = 12 runs (Braves')   13. x: width;

3x + 5: length; 2x + 2(3x + 5) = 122; x - 14 cm (width); 3x + 5 = 47 cm (length)

15. x: quarters; x + 12: dimes; 2x - 8: nickels; 25x: value of quarters;

10(x + 12): values of dimes; 5(2x - 8): value of nickels; 25x + 10(x + 12) + 5(2x - 8)

= 1700; x = 36 (quarters); x + 12 = 48 (dimes); 2x - 8 = 64 (nickels)

17. x: lesser number; x + 2: greater number; x + x + 2 = 108; x = 53; x + 2 = 55

19. $\frac{6.8}{1} = \frac{x}{1000}$; x = 6800 cm$^3$   21. $\frac{0.023}{1} = \frac{x}{1,000,000}$; x = 23,000 cm$^3$

23. $\frac{2560}{1000} = \frac{x}{1}$; x = 2.56 kℓ   25. 12x: grams of carbon; 22x: grams of hydrogen; 11x:

grams of oxygen; 12x + 22x + 11x = 180; 12x = 48 g (carbon)

CHAPTER 9  RATIONAL NUMBERS

PAGE 207  ORAL EXERCISES 9.1
1. Negative ten    3. Negative forty-seven    5. Negative seventy-seven    7. Negative
three hundred    9.  5, 4, 3, 2, 1, 0, ⁻1, ⁻2, ⁻3    11.  ⁻10, ⁻9, ⁻8, ⁻7, ⁻6, ⁻5, ⁻4,
⁻3, ⁻2    13.  ⁻8, ⁻6, ⁻4, ⁻2, 0, 2, 4, 6, 8, 10    15.  ⁻3, ⁻6, ⁻9, ⁻12, ⁻15    17.  True
19.  False    21.  True    23.  True    25.  2    27.  35    29.  ⁻5

PAGE 208  WRITTEN EXERCISES 9.1
1. $\{2, 4, 6, 8, \cdots\}$    3. $\{0, 1, 2, 3, \cdots\}$    5. $\{⁻4, ⁻5, ⁻6, ⁻7, \cdots\}$
7. $\{⁻4, ⁻3, ⁻2, ⁻1, 0, 1, 2\}$    9. $\{$negative integers$\}$    11. $\{$odd integers$\}$
13. $\{$integers $\geq$ -4$\}$    15. $\{$integers $\leq$ -2$\}$    17.  ⁻10, ⁻3, 0, 1, 7    19.  ⁻9, ⁻8, ⁻1,
5, 12    21.  ⁻31, ⁻23, ⁻19, ⁻11, ⁻5    23.  ⁻99, ⁻56, ⁻42, 0, 1, 72    25.  ⁻101, ⁻88
⁻29, ⁻26, 19    27.  ⁻2536, ⁻1024, ⁻117, 28, 33    29.  Same graph as P-3a., p. 207
31.  Same graph as Example for Ex. 9-16, p. 209    33.  Same graph as Sample Problem,
p. 208    35.  Graph of the 4 coordinates with the word "etc." over the arrow at the
right    37.  Graph of only the 4 coordinates

PAGE 211 ORAL EXERCISES 9.2
1. Negative three-fourths    3. Negative six and three-tenths    5. Negative nine-tenths
7. Negative fifteen and seven-eighths    9. True    11. True    13. False    15. False
17. False    19. $\frac{2}{5}$    21. 3    23. $\frac{1}{3}$    25. $⁻(\frac{7}{16})$    27. $⁻2\frac{3}{4}$    29. ⁻1.31    31. 0

PAGE 212  WRITTEN EXERCISES 9.2
1. R    3. $\{⁻10, ⁻(\frac{8}{2}), 0, 3, \frac{15}{3}\}$    5. $\{0, 3, \frac{15}{3}\}$    7. $\{0, 3, \frac{15}{3}\}$    9. $\{\frac{5}{8}, 3, \frac{13}{4}, \frac{15}{3}\}$
11. Points at ⁻3, $⁻2\frac{1}{2}$, $⁻(\frac{1}{2})$, 0, 3    13. Points at ⁻3.6, ⁻1.3, $⁻(\frac{3}{4})$, $\frac{3}{4}$    15. Points
in order given with word "etc." over arrows at right and at left.    17. $\frac{1}{4}$    19. $⁻3\frac{1}{2}$
21. $⁻(\frac{33}{8})$    23. ⁻0.61    25. 0    Note: Many answers are possible for Ex. 27-33. Only
one is given for each Exercise.    27. $⁻3\frac{1}{2}$    29. $⁻(\frac{3}{8})$    31. $⁻3\frac{3}{16}$    33. $⁻(\frac{1}{32})$
35. $⁻(\frac{11}{4})$, $⁻(\frac{4}{11})$, $\frac{4}{11}$, $\frac{11}{4}$    37. $⁻(\frac{6}{7})$, $⁻(\frac{5}{6})$, $⁻(\frac{5}{7})$, $\frac{5}{7}$, $\frac{5}{6}$, $\frac{6}{7}$    39. ⁻1.2, $⁻(\frac{4}{5})$, 1.2, $\frac{7}{5}$
41. $⁻4\frac{2}{3}$, ⁻4.6, $⁻(\frac{14}{5})$, $5\frac{1}{3}$

PAGE 216  ORAL EXERCISES 9.3
1. 1    3. 0    5. ⁻3    7. 1.126    9. 10    11. $2\frac{1}{8}$    13. 2.1503    15. 0.153
17. ⁻2.5    19. True    21. True    23. False    25. True    27. True    29. True
31. False    33. True

PAGE 216  WRITTEN EXERCISES 9.3
1. ⁻3.5    3. 2.75    5. 0.1875    7. ⁻0.777 $\cdots$    9. ⁻1.7272 $\cdots$    11. 16.000 $\cdots$
13. 0.000 $\cdots$    15. 0.875000 $\cdots$    17. False    19. True    21. True

23. $5 > {}^-5$; ${}^-5 < 5$   25. $0 > {}^-3$; ${}^-3 < 0$   27. ${}^-3\frac{1}{4} > {}^-4\frac{1}{4}$; ${}^-4\frac{1}{4} < {}^-3\frac{1}{4}$

29. ${}^-9.6 > {}^-10.2$; ${}^-10.2 < 9.6$   31. ${}^-(\frac{1}{2}) > {}^-1$; ${}^-1 < {}^-(\frac{1}{2})$   33. $2.131 > 2.13$;

$2.13 < 2.131$   35. ${}^-0.003 > {}^-0.06$; ${}^-0.06 < {}^-0.003$   37. ${}^-0.18 > {}^-0.181818 \cdots$;

${}^-0.181818 \cdots < {}^-0.18$   39. ${}^-(\frac{7}{6}) > {}^-(\frac{7}{4})$; ${}^-(\frac{7}{4}) < {}^-(\frac{7}{6})$   41. ${}^-1\frac{7}{8}$, $1\frac{1}{4}$, ${}^-0.6$, ${}^-(\frac{1}{2})$

43. ${}^-(\frac{23}{7})$, ${}^-(\frac{19}{8})$, ${}^-(\frac{7}{15})$, ${}^-(\frac{7}{16})$   45. ${}^-2\frac{1}{3}$, ${}^-2.3$, ${}^-2.13$, ${}^-(\frac{15}{20})$, ${}^-0.7$

PAGE 220   ORAL EXERCISES

1. The opposite of 12   3. Negative five-eighths   5. The opposite of negative one-half   7. The opposite of the opposite of fifteen   9. The opposite of the opposite of negative twelve   11. The opposite of three and one-half   13. 8   15. $\frac{3}{4}$
17. ${}^-2$   19. ${}^-7$   21. 0.8   23. 15   25. True   27. False   29. False

PAGE 221   WRITTEN EXERCISES 9.4

1. 11   3. 22   5. 5.2   7. $\frac{7}{8}$   9. ${}^-25$   11. ${}^-8$   13. ${}^-3\frac{1}{2}$   15. 0   17. ${}^-13$
19. ${}^-3$   21. t   23. 3x   25. ${}^-r$   27. p   29. ${}^-2$   31. 7   33. $\frac{1}{2}$   35. ${}^-4$
37. $\frac{1}{2}$   39. ${}^-(\frac{1}{2})$   41. $\frac{5}{2}$

PAGE 223   ORAL EXERCISES 9.5

1. ${}^-2 > {}^-5$, ${}^-5 < {}^-2$   3. $1 > {}^-7$, ${}^-7 < 1$   5. $7 > 4$, $4 < 7$   7. $5 > 0$, $0 < 5$
9. $0 < 10$, $10 > 0$   11. $7 < 9$, $9 > 7$   13. $5 > {}^-5$, ${}^-5 < 5$   15. ${}^-3\frac{1}{2} < \frac{1}{2}$, $\frac{1}{2} > {}^-3\frac{1}{2}$

PAGE 224   WRITTEN EXERCISES 9.5

1. $3 < 8$; ${}^-3 > {}^-8$   3. ${}^-10 < {}^-3$; $10 > 3$   5. ${}^-7 < 5$; $7 > {}^-5$   7. ${}^-7 < 0$; $7 > 0$
9. $0 < 8$; $0 > {}^-8$   11. ${}^-3\frac{1}{4} < {}^-1\frac{1}{2}$; $3\frac{1}{4} > 1\frac{1}{2}$   13. ${}^-2.7 < 3.3$; $2.7 > {}^-3.3$   15. ${}^-0.66 < \frac{2}{3}$;

$0.66 > {}^-(\frac{2}{3})$   17. ${}^-10 < 3$; $10 > {}^-3$   19. ${}^-11 < {}^-2$; $11 > 2$   21. $15 > {}^-2$, ${}^-2 < 15$

23. $13 > 11$, $11 < 13$   25. ${}^-8 < {}^-1$, ${}^-1 > {}^-8$   27. $0 < 17$, $17 > 0$   29. $5\frac{1}{8} > \frac{19}{4}$,

$\frac{19}{4} < 5\frac{1}{8}$   31. $2.8 \geq {}^-0.7$, ${}^-0.7 \leq 2.8$   33. $5.2 \leq 8.3$, $8.3 \geq 5.2$   35. $5 \geq {}^-7$, ${}^-7 \leq 5$
37. False   39. True   41. True   43. False   45. True   47. 5 is greater
49. $5\frac{1}{8}$ is greater   51. 17 is greater

PAGE 226   ORAL EXERCISES 9.6

1. $x > {}^-(\frac{1}{4})$   3. $x > \frac{1}{2}$   5. $x \geq 10$   7. $x > {}^-10$   9. $x = 5\frac{1}{2}$   11. $x > 8.9$
13. $\{{}^-3\}$   15. $\{{}^-3\}$   17. $\{{}^-3, {}^-2, {}^-1, 0\}$   19. $\{2, 3\}$   21. $\{{}^-3, {}^-2, {}^-1\}$
23. $\{x : x > 8\}$   25. $\{x : x \geq {}^-2.5\}$   27. $\{{}^-19\}$   29. $\{{}^-5\}$

PAGE 227   WRITTEN EXERCISES 9.6

1. $x < {}^-20$, ${}^-20 > x$   3. $x \geq 27$, $27 \leq x$   5. $x > 4.2$, $4.2 < x$   7. $x = {}^-3\frac{3}{4}$
9. $x = \frac{5}{8}$   11. ${}^-12.9 \leq x$, $x \geq {}^-12.9$   13. $x < \frac{15}{8}$, $\frac{15}{8} > x$   15. $x \leq 0$, $0 \geq x$
17. $\{{}^-5, {}^-4, {}^-3, {}^-2, {}^-1, 0\}$   19. $\{{}^-2, {}^-1, 0, 1, 2, 3, 4, 5\}$   21. $\{4, 5\}$
23. $\{3\}$   25. $\{{}^-3\}$   27. $\{0, 1, 2, 3, 4, 5\}$   29. $\{y : y < 6\}$   31. $\{r : r \geq {}^-(\frac{1}{2})\}$

33. $\{w : w > 2.8\}$  35. $\left\{-\left(\frac{28}{15}\right)\right\}$  37. $\{0.9\}$  39. $\{k : k \geq 2.7\}$

PAGE 229   ORAL EXERCISES 9.7
1.  10   3.  $1\frac{3}{4}$   5.  0   7.  14.7   9.  $2\frac{1}{2}$   11.  5   13.  True   15.  True   17.  False

PAGE 229   WRITTEN EXERCISES 9.7
1.  25   3.  99   5.  0   7.  $12\frac{1}{2}$   9.  7.6   11.  8.6   13.  0.9   15.  13   17.  13
19.  ‾8   21.  ‾6   23.  $\{-2, -1, 0, 1, 2\}$   25.  $\{-1, 0, 1\}$   27.  $\{-3, 3\}$
29.  $\{-5, -4, -3, 3, 4, 5\}$   31.  x   33.  y

PAGE 230   CHAPTER REVIEW
1.  $\{-9, -8, -7, \cdots\}$   3.  $\{\cdots, -6, -4, -2\}$   5.  ‾12, ‾9, ‾6, 0, 5, 13
7.  ‾42, ‾28, ‾19, ‾5, 0, 54   9.  A   11.  $\left\{-15, -\left(\frac{15}{3}\right)\right\}$   13.  -2.6   15.  0
17.  ‾2.25   19.  ‾2.625   21.  0.444 $\cdots$   23.  ‾18 < 18, 18 > ‾18   25.  ‾14.5 < ‾12.6,
-12.6 > ‾14.5   27.  $-\left(\frac{10}{13}\right) < -\left(\frac{1}{13}\right), -\left(\frac{1}{13}\right) > -\left(\frac{10}{13}\right)$   29.  $\frac{1}{3}$   31.  g   33.  ‾28 < ‾15,
28 > 15   35.  0.3 < 4.2,  ‾0.3 > ‾4.2   37.  ‾13.5 < ‾9.2, 13.5 > 9.2   39.  $\{2, 3\}$
41.  $\{-3, -2, -1, 0, 1, 2\}$   43.  $\{3\}$   45.  $\{1\}$   47.  $\{-5.6\}$   49.  $\{x : x < 4.2\}$
51.  $\{a : a \leq 1.9\}$   53.  8.6   55.  0   57.  14   59.  23.5   61.  84   63.  ‾10


CHAPTER 10   RATIONAL NUMBERS:   ADDITION


PAGE 236   ORAL EXERCISES 10.1
1.  1   3.  7   5.  ‾3   7.  ‾2   9.  0   11.  ‾6   13.  5   15.  0   17.  ‾12   19.  12
21.  ‾18   23.  ‾17   25.  ‾11   27.  0   29.  ‾24   31.  Ahead of   33.  The size of the
moves.   35.  Negative

PAGE 237   WRITTEN EXERCISES 10.1
1.  ‾2   3.  ‾9   5.  7   7.  0   9.  ‾9   11.  ‾16   13.  ‾5   15.  4   17.  0
19.  ‾24   21.  ‾25   23.  ‾4   25.  ‾6   27.  ‾15   29.  4   31.  ‾3   33.  6   35.  ‾11
37.  11 + (‾15) = ‾4

PAGE 239   ORAL EXERCISES 10.2
For Ex. 1-15, a number and direction are given for each move, followed by the sum of
the moves.   1.  Left 1; right 3; 2   3.  Left 3; left 2; ‾5   5.  Left 6; right 2; ‾4
7.  Left 10, no move; ‾10   9.  Right $4\frac{1}{2}$; left $2\frac{1}{4}$; $2\frac{1}{4}$   11.  Left 1.8; left 3.2; ‾5
13.  Left 3.8; right 1.3; ‾2.5   15.  Right 4.9; left 4.9; 0   17.  (‾6) + 9 = 3
19.  $\left(-2\frac{1}{2}\right) + 5\frac{3}{4} = 3\frac{1}{4}$

PAGE 240   WRITTEN EXERCISES 10.2
For Ex. 1-11, a number and direction are given for each move, followed by the sum of the
moves.  For Ex. 13-29, only the sums are given.   1.  Left 2; left 3; ‾5   3.  Right 2;
right 4; 6   5.  Left 2; right 7; 5   7.  Right 5; left 9; ‾4   9.  No move; left 6; ‾6
11.  Left 4; right 4; 0   13.  3   15.  ‾32   17.  4   19.  ‾1   21.  ‾6   23.  7.4

25. ⁻14.3  27. ⁻1.3  29. 0  31. False  33. False  35. True

PAGE 243  ORAL EXERCISES 10.3
1. ⁻60  3. ⁻10  5. 10  7. 0  9. ⁻500  11. ⁻2  13. ⁻60  15. ⁻0.3
17. 0.15  19. ⁻20.0  21. 5.5  23. 10.6  25. ⁻21.1  27. ⁻117.8  29. 0

PAGE 243  WRITTEN EXERCISES 10.3
1. 300  3. ⁻84  5. ⁻37  7. 24  9. ⁻525  11. 56  13. ⁻154  15. ⁻$16\frac{1}{2}$
17. ⁻$8\frac{3}{4}$  19. ⁻$2\frac{7}{8}$  21. ⁻21.2  23. ⁻16.3  25. 13.5  27. 0  29. 12.38
31. ⁻8.241  33. ⁻25.6  35. 136  37. ⁻19.6  39. 104  41. ⁻32  43. 72
45. 26  47. ⁻72  49. 0  51. True  53. True

PAGE 247  ORAL EXERCISES 10.4
1. 2  3. ⁻9  5. ⁻3  7. 11  9. ⁻4  11. 7  13. 5  15. ⁻30  17. 10

PAGE 247  WRITTEN EXERCISES 10.4
1. ⁻5  3. 2  5. ⁻29  7. ⁻25  9. 2  11. 0  13. ⁻34  15. 33  17. ⁻13
19. 10  21. ⁻4  23. ⁻$11\frac{1}{2}$  25. 7.0  27. ⁻15.3

PAGE 249  ORAL EXERCISES 10.5
1. x + 3  3. x + 5  5. n + (⁻17)  7. r + 3  9. p + (⁻12)  11. q + 3
13. a + 3.5  15. y + $1\frac{1}{4}$  17. x + (⁻5)  19. ⁻12  21. 3  23. 0  25. x + (⁻7)

PAGE 250  WRITTEN EXERCISES 10.5
1. x + 5  3. x + (⁻6)  5. x + (⁻11)  7. x + (⁻61)  9. x + 1.1  11. x + (⁻4.5)
13. x + (⁻8)  15. x + (⁻41)  17. x + $\frac{1}{4}$  19. x + (⁻$9\frac{1}{4}$)  21. x + (⁻7.5)
23. k + (⁻28)  25. x + 0.9  27. x + (⁻86)  29. x + 7  31. x + 40  33. x + 3.4
35. r + s + ⁻($\frac{1}{2}$)  37. x + 7  39. x + 75

PAGE 252  ORAL EXERCISES 10.6
Note: Read -x, -t, -s, -p, -r, etc., as "the opposite of x," "the opposite of t," etc.
Read (⁻4), (⁻6), etc., as "negative 4," "negative 6," etc.  1. (⁻5) + (⁻9)
3. 5 + 8  5. 0.8 + 0.7  7. -x + 3  9. (⁻8.2) + n  11. 12 + r + (-s)
13. -r + 5 + s + t  15. x = 5 + (⁻3)  17. ⁻5 = (⁻3) + x  19. x = 7 + (⁻5)
21. 1 = 7 + x  23. x + (⁻3.8) = ⁻5.2

PAGE 253  WRITTEN EXERCISES 10.6
1. 19 + (⁻12)  3. (⁻12.9) + 6.5  5. 0.6 + 0.7  7. -r + 26  9. m + (⁻19(
11. 17 + (-r) + s  13. 8.2 + (-x) + y  15. ⁻24 + c + 18  17. -r + s + (-t) + (-w)
19. x = 3  21. x = 3  23. x = 3.5  25. x = 99  27. -(-x + 5)
29. -x( + (⁻13) + (-y))  31. -(p + q + 96)  33. -(-x + 5.8 + (⁻6.2) + y)
35. -(k + n + r + q + (-28))

PAGE 256  ORAL EXERCISES 10.7
1. (⁻3.2) + (⁻1.4) = ⁻4.6; drop of 4.6°  3. (⁻$2\frac{3}{4}$) + (⁻$1\frac{1}{2}$) = ⁻$4\frac{1}{4}$; decline of $4\frac{1}{4}$ points

5. ($^-$16) + 13 = $^-$3; loss of 3 yards in 2 plays   7.  15,000 + ($^-$6000) = 9000; profit of $9000 in one year    9.   500 + ($^-$800) = $^-$300; decrease of 300 m in altitude
11.  ($^-$1200) + 800 = $^-$400; decrease in sales of $400   13.  ($^-$15) + ($^-$12) + ($^-$8) = -35; a loss of 35 yd.   15.   6 + ($^-$2) + 3 + ($^-$3) = 4; score of 4 over par in 4 days
17.  15.3 + ($^-$12.8) + ($^-$7.5) = $^-$5.0; ship's movement of 5 kilometers west
19.  $2\frac{1}{4}$ + $1\frac{1}{2}$ + ($^-2\frac{3}{4}$) = 1; gain of 1 point in the price of stock

## PAGE 257  WRITTEN EXERCISES 10.7
1.  350 gain   3.  $33\frac{1}{2}$ or $33.50   5.  3.5 cm deficiency   7.  $9700 decrease
9.  3.5 units over   11.  -x + ($^-$16) = $^-$52; x = 36   13.  -x = ($^-$19.3) + 27.4; x = $^-$8.1
15.  $^-$9°

## PAGE 262  CHAPTER REVIEW
1.  6   3.  $^-$22   5.  0   7.  $^-$17   9.  $350 added to account   For Ex. 11 and 13,
a number and direction are given for each move, followed by the sum of the moves.
For Ex. 15-21, only the sums are given.   11.  Left 4, right 9; 5   13.  Left $2\frac{1}{2}$, left
$1\frac{1}{2}$; $^-$4   15.  $^-$23   17.  27   19.  -($\frac{1}{2}$)   21.  $^-$22.4   23.  $^-$105   25.  13   27.  8.6
29.  $^-$195   31.  $^-$3   33.  $^-$67   35.  -11   37.  -47.3   39.  $^-1\frac{1}{4}$   41.  x + ($^-$7)
43.  x + ($^-$51)   45.  x + ($^-$17.5)   47.  x + 28   49.  x + 9.3   51.  19 + (-t)
53.  13 + r + (-s)   55.  (-k) + t + (-n) + r   57.  Gain of 61 subscriptions

## CHAPTER 11  RATIONAL NUMBERS:  MULTIPLICATION

## PAGE 268  ORAL EXERCISES 11.1
1.  $^-$6   3.  $^-$20   5.  $^-$28   7.  $^-$42   9.  $^-$32   11.  $^-$27   13.  $^-$48   15.  $^-$44
17.  -18   19.  -36   21.  0   23.  0   25.  $^-$4   27.  -8   29.  $^-$8.2   31.  $^-$6.6
33.  -49   35.  0   37.  66   39.  $^-$30   41.  $^-$1200

## PAGE 269  WRITTEN EXERCISES 11.1
1.  -12   3.  -35   5.  $^-$30   7.  $^-$63   9.  $^-$54   11.  $^-$96   13.  $^-$64   15.  $^-$54   17. -7
19.  $^-$14   21.  $^-$5   23.  $^-$6   25.  $^-$15.6   27.  $^-$60.2   29.  -16.8   31.  $^-$0.39
33.  -($\frac{1}{10}$)   35.  0   37.  $^-$420   39.  $^-$638   41.  $^-$3000   43.  $^-$48   45.  -54
47.  $^-$200   49.  $^-$42   51.  True   53.  True   55.  True

## PAGE 272  ORAL EXERCISES 11.2
1.  35   3.  9   5.  45   7.  80   9.  36   11.  18   13.  24   15.  32   17.  6.6
19.  2.7   21.  7   23.  9   25.  $^-$63   27.  $^-$60   29.  3.2   31.  $^-$0.6

## PAGE 272  WRITTEN EXERCISES 11.2
1.  24   3.  24   5.  84   7.  72   9.  128   11.  126   13.  10.8   15.  113.68
17.  $^-$128   19.  1200   21.  $^-$360   23.  0.14   25.  $^-$16   27.  $3\frac{17}{20}$   29.  84   31.  4
33.  72   35.  $^-$56   37.  $^-$36

PAGE 275   ORAL EXERCISES 11.3

1.  12   3.  $^-6$   5.  $^-10$   7.  40   9.  12   11.  $-(\frac{2}{5})$   13.  16   15.  $^-1$   17.  $^-10$
19.  $^-20a$   21.  $^-24t$   23.  $-56y$

PAGE 275   WRITTEN EXERCISES  11.3

1.  $^-42$   3.  $^-48$   5.  90   7.  180   9.  38   11.  30   13.  $^-10$   15.  $^-110$
17.  14.4   19.  0.84   21.  10   23.  $\frac{1}{5}$   25.  $^-7$   27.  $^-240$   29.  24   31.  $^-32n$
33.  $-48k$   35.  $56x$   37.  $^-12y$   39.  $8a$   41.  $^-95t$   43.  $^-1$   45.  $^-5$   47.  $^-9$
49.  $-25$   51.  $^-8$   53.  45   55.  13   57.  51   59.  $^-92$

PAGE 279   ORAL EXERCISES 11.4

1.  $^-2x + (^-10)$   3.  $^-1n + 3$   5.  $^-10x + (^-15)$   7.  $-3r^2 + 6r$   9.  $^-2k^2 + 5k$
11.  $^-5(a + b)$; Negative   13.  $8(k + ^-5)$; Eight times the quantity k plus negative five
15.  $x(r + ^-6)$; x times the quantity r plus negative six   17.  $^-12n(y + x)$; Negative
twelve n times the quantity y plus x   19.  $k(^-2x + 1)$; k times the quantity negative
two x plus one   21.  $3t(-m + n)$; Three t times the quantity negative m plus n
23.  $-40x$   25.  $^-14x^2$   27.  $-6ay^2$   29.  $20y^2 + 15y$

PAGE 280   WRITTEN EXERCISES 11.4

1.  $^-16a + 10$   3.  $15r + 35$   5.  $^-35 + ^-21x$   7.  $3x + ^-1$   9.  $2 + ^-3x$
11.  $^-5x + 2x^2$   13.  $-6a^2 + ^-4a$   15.  $^-6n^2 + 15n$   17.  $2a^2 + ^-a$   19.  $^-7(x + y)$
21.  $(t + s)(-8)$   23.  $^-8.6(r + s)$   25.  $(^-12 + 3y)0.5$   27.  $5r(w + ^-x)$
29.  $a(5x + ^-6y)$   31.  $25(p + -q)$   33.  $5(m + ^-n)$   35.  $3m(-x + y)$   37.  $13a(^-3x + 1)$
39.  $4(x + 5)$   41.  $^-5(r + 3)$   43.  $t(1 + ^-3r)$   45.  $3z(-w + 4)$   47.  $4(2ap + ^-3q)$

PAGE 282   ORAL EXERCISES 11.5

1.  $-y$   3.  $(^-1)t$   5.  x   7.  $^-1(y + ^-3)$   9.  $-x + ^-7$   11.  $-s + 5$   13. $k + ^-10$
15.  $^-1(p + ^-13)$   17.  $-w + x + (-y)$   19.  $-kg$   21.  cd   23.  5mn

PAGE 283   WRITTEN EXERCISES 11.5

1.  $12y$   3.  $2r^2$   5.  $3mnp$   7.  $^-6p^2q^2$   9.  $5p^3t$   11.  $21s^3t$   13.  $6 - a$   15. $4 - x$
17.  $12 + k + t$   19.  $-xy + 2x$   21.  $2ab + ^-10a$   23.  $2am + ^-2an$   25.  $5r^2 + 15r$
27.  $^-8s^2t + ^-4st^2$   29.  $8rp + ^-8rq + 56r$

PAGE 285   ORAL EXERCISES 11.6

1.  $3x$ and $^-4x$   3.  $5m^2n$ and $-m^2n$; mn and $^-4mn$   5.  $-2.3p^2q$ and $-p^2q$   7.  3m
9.  $^-8x^2$   11.  $^-1rs$ or $-rs$   13.  $-3 + 5y$   15.  $^-6a^2b$   17.  $2a^2$   19.  $^-10xy$
21.  $4t^2$   23.  $4x^2 + (^-4x) + (^-3)$   25.  $4ab^2 + 2a^2b$   27.  $5r + 2s + (^-7t)$

PAGE 286   WRITTEN EXERCISES 11.6

1.  $^-7k$   3.  $^-11r$   5.  $^-13.3p$   7.  7rw   9.  $-35a^2$   11.  $18r^2s$   13.  $17y + (^-9)$
15.  $13 + (^-1.3k)$   17.  $3m + 5$   19.  $^-7g$   21.  $^-10.8x^2$   23.  $5.3t + 6.4$
25.  $-9m^2n + (^-3mn^2) + 5mn$   27.  $^-15x + 24y + (-6)$   29.  $4x^2 + (-34x) + 14$
31.  $^-11a + 7b$   33.  $^-7x^2 + (^-7x)$   35.  $15p + (^-11q) + 13$   37.  $4x + 5y + y^2$

1. $x^2 + 6x + 8$   3. $t^2 + (-t) + (^-6)$   5. $r^2 + 4r + (^-21)$   7. $6k^2 + (-k) + (^-1)$
9. $x^2 + 5x + 4$   11. $x^2 + (^-5x) + 6$   13. $x^2 + 13x + 30$   15. $x^2 + (^-8x) + 12$
17. $x^2 + 2x + 1$   19. $x^2 + ^-2x + 1$   21. $a^2 + 10a + 25$   23. $y^2 + ^-10y + 25$

PAGE 290 WRITTEN EXERCISES 11.7

1. $x^2 + 3x + 2$   3. $t^2 + ^-4t + 3$   5. $y^2 + y + ^-2$   7. $n^2 + ^-2n + ^-3$   9. $x^2 + 7x + 10$   11. $a^2 + ^-7a + 10$   13. $k^2 + k + ^-12$   15. $y^2 + ^-3y + ^-10$   17. $2x^2 + 9x + 10$
19. $2x^2 + (-x) + ^-6$   21. $y^2 + 12y + 36$   23. $t^2 + ^-16t + 64$   25. $d^2 + 18d + 81$
27. $w^2 + ^-24w + 144$   29. $4t^2 + 4t + 1$   31. $16m^2 + ^-16m + 4$   33. $6x^2 + 17x + 5$
35. $12x^2 + x + ^-6$   37. $12x^2 + ^-31x + 20$   39. $10x^2 + ^-13x + ^-30$

PAGE 291 CHAPTER REVIEW

1. $^-108$   3. $^-2.08$   5. $^-6$   7. $-3740$   9. $120$   11. $^-27$   13. $35.36$   15. $\frac{1}{3}$
17. $^-540$   19. $-918$   21. $480$   23. $-135k$   25. $36r + 24$   27. $-4s + ^-(\frac{15}{2})$
29. $^-24x^2 + 72x$   31. $^-19(r + s)$   33. $1.8(5t + ^-12)$   35. $12n(a + (-k))$   37. $20n$
39. $^-12abc$   41. $-tr + 10t$   43. $12w^2 + 72w$   45. $5n$   47. $9.4ab$   49. $26pq^2$
51. $r^2 + 8r + 15$   53. $x^2 + ^-3x + ^-40$   55. $x^2 + ^-18x + 81$

CHAPTER 12 RATIONAL NUMBERS: SUBTRACTION AND DIVISION

PAGE 295 ORAL EXERCISES 12.1
1. "14 plus the opposite of 5"   3. "5 plus the opposite of negative 14"   5. "16 plus the opposite of negative 7"   7. "0 plus the opposite of 17"   9. "n plus the opposite of 19"   11. $^-3$   13. $^-15$   15. $16$   17. $^-20$   19. $6$   21. $26$   23. $0$   25. $-5\frac{1}{4}$
27. $^-5.7$   29. $14 + y$

PAGE 296 WRITTEN EXERCISES 12.1
1. $15 + (^-11)$; $4$   3. $19 + (^-26)$; $^-7$   5. $18 + 7$; $25$   7. $24 + 29$; $53$
9. $(^-13) + 5$; $^-8$   11. $(^-9) + 23$; $14$   13. $0 + (^-24)$; $^-24$   15. $0 + 36$; $36$
17. $0.9 + 4.8$; $5.7$   19. $0.24 + (-0.93)$; $-0.69$   21. $(^-13.9) + (^-9.5)$; $-23.4$
23. $52 + k$; $52 + k$   25. $0 + w$; $w$   27. $r + 8.6$; $r + 8.6$   29. $17 - (^-15) = 17 + 15 = 32$   31. $(^-12) - 23 = (^-12) + (^-23) = ^-35$   33. $7 - 16 = 7 + (^-16) = ^-9$
35. $(^-6) - (^-21) = (^-6) + 21 = 15$   37. $(^-18) - 27 = (^-18) + (^-27) = ^-45$

PAGE 298 ORAL EXERCISES 12.2
1. $13$   3. $-20$   5. $24$   7. $-11$   9. $1$   11. $-4.0$   13. $24.2$   15. $0$   17. $-15$
19. $-10$   21. $(-18) - (-37)$   23. $20 - (-16)$

PAGE 299 WRITTEN EXERCISES 12.2
1. $24$   3. $36$   5. $-45$   7. $-9$   9. $-10\frac{1}{4}$   11. $-12$   13. $29$   15. $-9\frac{1}{4}$
17. $-4\frac{1}{4}$   19. $-5.5$   21. $-0.2$   23. $-1.96$   25. $-11$   27. $-20$   29. $-52$
31. $-13.3$   33. $10.2$   35. $(27) - (-16) = (27) + 16 = 43$; he gained 43 more yards.

37. $(-25.8) - (-30.1) = (-25.8) + 30.1 = 4.3$; the record temperature is $4.3^{\circ}$C less.

39. 3 and -3   41. -1 and -13   43. No   45. Commutative Property of Addition

PAGE 302   ORAL EXERCISES 12.3

Note: For all exercises where the answer contains more than one term, only one answer
is given. Other answers, with the terms in different order, may also be correct.
For example, the answer to Exercise 11 could also be x - 7.   1. $x + 2$   3. $3x$
5. $-5x$   7. $x$   9. $-9x$   11. $-7 + x$   13. $3 - 3x$   15. $2 + x$   17. $8 - x$
19. $x + 1$   21. $-3x - 4$   23. $-10r + 3s$   25. $-y^2 - 7$   27. $5g - 6s^2$

PAGE 303   WRITTEN EXERCISES 12.3

1. $5x + 7$   3. $4y$   5. $3a$   7. $-4w$   9. $-n$   11. $x - 5$   13. $-10p + 3$   15. $-6t$
17. $-0.4m - 1.8$   19. $-3a - 11$   21. $3\frac{1}{4}w - 1\frac{1}{4}$   23. $-4.6w$   25. $4x - 10$   27. $2 - r$
29. $-2n + 7$   31. $-2x$   33. $-10.4n^2 - 13.2n - 15.0$   35. $28y - 34z - 28$
37. $20y^2 - 37y + 9$

PAGE 306   ORAL EXERCISES 12.4

1. $r - s - 7$   3. $-6 + m - n$   5. $p - 9 + q$   7. $-2 - x + y$   9. $-a + 2b$
11. $2x - 2y$   13. $10x - 15$   15. $r^2 - 2r$   17. $a - 3$   19. $-8x + 8y$   21. $x^2 - 7x$
23. $-3t - 3$   25. $2x - 2y - 6$   27. $-10r + 15s + 20$

PAGE 307   WRITTEN EXERCISES 12.4

1. $17 - t$   3. $-5r + 3$   5. $-17 - 12y$   7. $6k - 17$   9. $26s - 19$   11. $-1.3a + 2.6$
13. $6\frac{1}{2}m - \frac{1}{4}$   15. $-22y + 1.6$   17. $-5t - 3$   19. $0$   21. $3 - 4x$   23. $-8s^2 + 12$
+ 8s   25. $5r - 40$   27. $56y - 48$   29. $-6a^2 + 21a$   31. $3w - 48$   33. $6x - 4$
35. $-0.35 + 0.65k$   37. $-2r + 3s + 7t$   39. $10x^3 - 20x^2 + 35x$

PAGE 309   ORAL EXERCISES 12.5

1. $\frac{1}{7}$   3. $\frac{5}{2}$   5. $\frac{3}{8}$   7. $-1$   9. $-\frac{2}{3}$   11. $1$   13. $-10$   15. $r$   17. $\frac{b}{a}$

PAGE 310   WRITTEN EXERCISES 12.5

1. $\frac{1}{14}$   3. $-\frac{1}{4}$   5. $3$   7. $-12$   9. $\frac{8}{5}$   11. $-\frac{12}{11}$   13. $\frac{4}{21}$   15. $-\frac{8}{21}$   17. $\frac{10}{7}$
19. $-\frac{10}{41}$   21. $-\frac{1}{2}$   23. $-1$   25. $k$   27. $\frac{2s}{r}$   29. $\frac{5}{3}$   31. $\frac{1}{10}$   33. $-\frac{1}{5}$   35. $4$
37. $-\frac{1}{3}$   39. $-5$   41. $\frac{4}{9}$   43. $-\frac{10}{16}$

PAGE 312   ORAL EXERCISES 12.6

1. $(-7)(\frac{1}{2})$   3. $(-5)(-\frac{1}{6})$   5. $13(-\frac{1}{7})$   7. $(-15)(-\frac{1}{3})$   9. $(-11)(-\frac{1}{5})$   11. $(-12)(\frac{4}{3})$
13. $(-19)(-2)$   15. $25(-\frac{1}{5})$

PAGE 313   WRITTEN EXERCISES 12.6

1. $12(-\frac{1}{5})$   3. $2(-\frac{1}{3})$   5. $(-5)(-\frac{1}{6})$   7. $13(\frac{1}{4})$   9. $(-18)(\frac{1}{9})$   11. $20(-\frac{1}{12})$
13. $(-21)(-\frac{1}{8})$   15. $(-2)(-\frac{1}{19})$   17. $(-8)(-\frac{5}{3})$   19. $(-11)(\frac{3}{2})$   21. $-6$

23. -8    25. 10    27. $-\dfrac{25}{2}$    29. $-\dfrac{27}{6}$    31. -7    33. 3    35. -4    37. 1    39. 12

41. -4    43. 12    45. $-\dfrac{1}{6}$

## PAGE 315   ORAL EXERCISES 12.7

1. $\dfrac{5}{-7}$; $-\dfrac{5}{7}$    3. $\dfrac{-7}{10}$; $\dfrac{7}{-10}$    5. $\dfrac{-t}{5}$; $-\dfrac{t}{5}$    7. $\dfrac{-(w-5)}{6}$; $-\dfrac{w-5}{6}$    9. $\dfrac{-r}{s}$; $-\dfrac{r}{s}$

11. $\dfrac{-(a-b)}{c}$; $\dfrac{a-b}{-c}$    13. $\dfrac{15}{-(r-8)}$; $\dfrac{-15}{r-8}$; $\dfrac{15}{r-8}$    15. $\dfrac{3}{7}$    17. $\dfrac{1}{13}$    19. 4

21. 4    23. $\dfrac{x}{y}$    25. $\dfrac{a}{b}$    27. $\dfrac{x+y}{a}$

## PAGE 316   WRITTEN EXERCISES 12.7

1. $\dfrac{8}{-13}$; $-\dfrac{8}{13}$    3. $\dfrac{-5}{11}$; $-\dfrac{5}{11}$    5. $\dfrac{-17}{18}$; $\dfrac{17}{-18}$    7. $\dfrac{k}{-8}$; $-\dfrac{k}{8}$    9. $\dfrac{-t}{-12}$; $-\dfrac{-t}{12}$; $\dfrac{t}{12}$

11. $\dfrac{x+3}{-5}$; $-\dfrac{x+3}{5}$    13. $\dfrac{-(t+6)}{2}$; $-\dfrac{t+6}{2}$    15. $\dfrac{-r}{s}$; $\dfrac{r}{-s}$    17. $\dfrac{-(n-3)}{2}$; $\dfrac{n-3}{-2}$

19. $\dfrac{-4}{x-2}$; $\dfrac{4}{-(x-2)}$    21. $\dfrac{4}{15}$    23. $\dfrac{2}{11}$    25. $\dfrac{5}{9}$    27. $-\dfrac{a}{b}$    29. $-\dfrac{x+3}{10}$

31. $-\dfrac{a-5}{3}$    33. $-\dfrac{t-4}{9}$    35. $-\dfrac{1}{k-3}$    37. 8    39. $\dfrac{2}{7}$    41. $-\dfrac{2}{11}$    43. $\dfrac{7}{x+y}$

## PAGE 318   ORAL EXERCISES 12.8

1. -6    3. -7    5. -7    7. 8    9. -12    11. 20    13. -10    15. $-\dfrac{1}{3}$    17. $-\dfrac{2}{3}$

19. $-\dfrac{7}{9}$

## PAGE 319   WRITTEN EXERCISES 12.8

1. -8    3. 12    5. -13    7. $-\dfrac{7}{2}$    9. $-\dfrac{23}{3}$    11. $\dfrac{21}{4}$    13. -18    15. -36    17. 28

19. -6    21. -10    23. 35    25. $-\dfrac{1}{5}$    27. $\dfrac{2}{3}$    29. $-\dfrac{2}{3}$    31. -0.3°    33. $-\dfrac{3}{40}$

## PAGE 322   CHAPTER REVIEW

1. 18 + (-25); ⁻7    3. 15 + 8; 23    5. (⁻13) + 18; 5    7. (⁻9) + (⁻24); ⁻33

9. 5.8 + (⁻12.3); ⁻6.5    11. -55    13. 52    15. -38    17. -8    19. -8.0

21. 11r    23. -9w    25. -18n + 17    27. -4x + 8    29. 29 - 4x    31. -6w + 4.9

33. 48 - 28p    35. $x^2 - 4 - 8x$    37. 60n - 48    39. $27t^2 - 72t$    41. $-9r^3 + 21r^2 - 6r$

43. -8    45. $\dfrac{3}{13}$    47. $-\dfrac{10}{53}$    49. $-\dfrac{2}{13}$    51. $-\dfrac{1}{8}$    53. -1    55. $(-13)(\dfrac{1}{19})$

57. $(-5)(-\dfrac{1}{23})$    59. $3r(-\dfrac{4}{3})$    61. -16    63. $\dfrac{25}{4}$    65. -3    67. -36    69. $\dfrac{8}{17}$

71. $\dfrac{3}{16}$    73. $-\dfrac{q-5}{6}$    75. -12    77. -9    79. $\dfrac{1}{6}$    81. -2    83. $-\dfrac{26}{7}$

## PAGE 325   REVIEW EXERCISES FOR CHAPTERS 7-12

1. $\dfrac{7}{16}$    3. $\dfrac{k}{t}$    5. x = 12    7. $y = 5\dfrac{1}{3}$    9. $\dfrac{3}{16} = \dfrac{x}{100}$; $x = 18\dfrac{3}{4}\%$    11. $\dfrac{13}{60} = \dfrac{x}{100}$;

$x = 21\dfrac{2}{3}\%$    13. $\dfrac{40}{100} = \dfrac{t}{92}$; t = 36.8    15. $\dfrac{72}{n} = \dfrac{12}{100}$; n = 600    17. (0.74)t or 0.74t

19. (0.01a)(2400) or 24a    21. 0.1r    23. Discount: $2.80; Net price: $11.20

25. d: number of days; d - 7    27. f: fish Kim's father caught; f + 8:  fish Kim

caught; f + f + 8 = 22; f = 7 fish (father); f + 8 = 15 fish (Kim)    29. x:  length;

x - 8:  width; 2x + 2(x - 8) = 192; x = 52 cm (length); x - 8 = 44 cm (width)

31. s: student tickets sold; 2s + 20: adult tickets sold; 50s + 75(2s + 20) = 81500; s = 400 student tickets; 2s + 20 = 820 adult tickets   33. x: least number; x + 2: next greater number; x + 4: greatest number; x + x + 2 + x + 4 = 189; x = 61; x + 2 = 63; x + 4 = 65   35. $\frac{x}{1,000,000} = \frac{0.00216}{1}$;   x = 2160 cm$^3$   37. 50x: gold; 35x: copper; 15x: silver; 50x + 35x + 15x = 1500; 50x = 750 g(gold); 35x = 525 g (copper); 15x = 225 g (silver)   39. $\{4, 5, 6, \cdots\}$   41. ⁻5.02   43. ⁻4.75   45. 0.1212 $\cdots$   47. 27   49. ⁻12   51. ⁻4 < 11   53. 14.6 > ⁻8.4   55. $\{^-3\}$   57. $\{2, 3\}$   59. 13.8   61. 17   63. 3   65. ⁻32   Note: For Exercises 67 and 69, a number and direction are given for each move, followed by the sum of the moves.   67. Left 4; right 8; 4   69. Left 2; left 4; ⁻6   71. 79   73. ⁻10   75. (⁻29) + x   77. 78 + (⁻x)   79. $1165 profit   81. ⁻20.0   83. ⁻12.4   85. 259.2   87. ⁻4800   89. ⁻48q + ⁻64   91. 7ak + ⁻21bk   93. ⁻14.2w   95. n$^2$ + (⁻n) + (⁻132)   97. 24 + (⁻35); ⁻11   99. (⁻16) + 28; 12   101. 58.0   103. -13k   105. -50t$^2$ + 90t   107. -19   109. $-\frac{8}{57}$   111. -12   113. $5\frac{1}{2}$   115. $\frac{9}{16}$   117. $\frac{1}{6}$   119. -25   121. 18

## CHAPTER 13  RATIONAL NUMBERS:  SOLVING EQUATIONS

**PAGE 331  ORAL EXERCISES 13.1**
1. x + 18 - 18 = 7 - 18   3. x + 5 - 5 = -22 - 5   5. $x - \frac{3}{4} + \frac{3}{4} = -4\frac{1}{2} + \frac{3}{4}$   7. 28 + 17 = -17 + x + 17   9. -12.8 + 3.9 = x - 3.9 + 3.9   11. 15.6 + 0.9 = -0.9 + x + 0.9   13. 43 - x - 43 = 24 - 43   15. -56 - 27 = 27 - x - 27

**PAGE 331  WRITTEN EXERCISES 13.1**
1. 39   3. 9   5. -13   7. -27   9. -4.3   11. $2\frac{1}{2}$   13. -2.5   15. 18   17. 0.9   19. $2\frac{1}{2}$   21. -8   23. 9   25. -20.8   27. 28.2   29. $-\frac{18}{12}$, or $-\frac{3}{2}$   31. x - 8 = -4   33. -x + 12 = -32

**PAGE 333  ORAL EXERCISES 13.2**
1. x + 13   3. x - 8   5. x - 20 (or 1.0x - 20)   7. x - 6   9. x - 4   11. -6 + x = -13   13. -5 = -x - 3   15. -x - 5 = -6   17. -3x - 12 + 4x = -15

**PAGE 333  WRITTEN EXERCISES 13.2**
1. 16   3. 21   5. -5.3   7. 25   9. $-1\frac{3}{4}$   11. 4   13. 17.8   15. 6   17. 36   19. 1.6

**PAGE 335  ORAL EXERCISES 13.3**
1. Subtract 12x or 11x.   3. Add x or 2x.   5. Add $\frac{1}{2}$x or subtract $\frac{1}{2}$x   7. 29; 29; Yes   9. 26; 26; Yes   11. 9; 5; No

**PAGE 335  WRITTEN EXERCISES 13.3**
1. -12   3. -10   5. -17   7. 6.6   9. 16   11. -8   13. -10   15. -15   17. -2   19. 1   21. 8.4

PAGE 337   ORAL EXERCISES 13.4

1. $\frac{12x}{12} = \frac{-48}{12}$   3. $\frac{-6x}{-6} = \frac{42}{-6}$   5. $4(\frac{x}{4}) = 4(-7)$   7. $-7(10) = -7(\frac{x}{-7})$   9. $-3(-\frac{1}{3}x) =$
$-3(5)$   11. $\frac{3}{2}(\frac{2}{3}x) = \frac{3}{2}(-12)$   13. $-\frac{4}{7}(-\frac{7x}{4}) = -\frac{4}{7}(21)$   15. $-\frac{2}{5}(\frac{5}{8}) = -\frac{2}{5}(-\frac{5x}{2})$   17. 2
19. 12   21. $-\frac{9}{2}$ or $-4\frac{1}{2}$

PAGE 338   WRITTEN EXERCISES 13.4

1. 8   3. -7   5. 8   7. -34   9. -114   11. 26.6   13. -12   15. $-4\frac{5}{6}$   17. 28
19. $-\frac{1}{10}$   21. -7.3   23. $-\frac{1}{2}$   25. -4   27. $4\frac{1}{2}$   29. -9

PAGE 341   ORAL EXERCISES 13.5

1. $3x + 2 - 2 = 5 - 2$   3. $4x - 6 + 6 = -19 + 6$   5. $12 - 8 = 8 - 3x - 8$
7. $5.8 - 12.4 = 12.4 - 2x - 12.4$   9. $\frac{x}{3} - 5 + 5 = -19 + 5$   11. $6x + 1.9 - 1.9 =$
$-3.5 - 1.9$   13. $-\frac{3}{5}x - 1\frac{2}{3} + 1\frac{2}{3} = 4\frac{1}{3} + 1\frac{2}{3}$   15. $-3\frac{1}{2} + 8\frac{1}{4} = \frac{x}{-2} - 8\frac{1}{4} + 8\frac{1}{4}$
17. $3x + 6 = -9$   19. $5x - 8 + x = -18$   21. $-23 = -4x + 12 - 7$

PAGE 341   WRITTEN EXERCISES 13.5

1. -5   3. -2   5. -12   7. 42   9. $-1\frac{1}{2}$   11. 3.3   13. 36   15. 35   17. -4.5
19. 3   21. $-2\frac{2}{3}$   23. 7   25. $4\frac{3}{4}$   27. n: greater number; n - 10: lesser number;
n + (n - 10) = -6.  The numbers are 2 and -8.   29. x: width; x + 2: length;
$2x + 2(x + 2) = 44$.  The width is 10 dm; the length is 12 dm.   31. n: greater number;
4 - n: lesser number; $2n - 4(4 - n) = 29$.  The numbers are $7\frac{1}{2}$ and $-3\frac{1}{2}$.   33. n: greater
number; 6 - n: lesser number; $3n = 8 + 2(6 - n)$.  The numbers are 4 and 2.

PAGE 344   ORAL EXERCISES 13.6

1. Add x or 5x.   3. Subtract 3x or add 2x.   5. Subtract x or add 3x.   7. Subtract
20x or 18x.   9. Add 3x or 5x.   11. $-3x = -4x - 12$   13. $-10x + 15 + 3x = 3x$
15. $40 - 15x = -8x + 12$

PAGE 345   WRITTEN EXERCISES 13.6

1. -5   3. 3   5. $-\frac{15}{2}$   7. 15   9. 3   11. $-\frac{11}{2}$   13. $\frac{1}{3}$   15. $-\frac{7}{4}$   17. 3
19. $-\frac{1}{2}$   21. n: greater number; 12 - n: lesser number; $3(12 - n) - 4 = n$.  The
numbers are 8 and 4.   23. x: width of rectangle; x + 5: length of rectangle;
x: length of shortest side; 3x: length of longest side; x + 6: length of third side;
$2x + 2(x + 5) = x + 3x + x + 6$.  The width is 4 cm; the length is 9 cm.  The lengths of
the sides of the triangle are 4 cm, 12 cm, and 10 cm.

PAGE 347   ORAL EXERCISES 13.7

1. -11, 5   3. -2, -13   5. 6   7. 0, $\frac{5}{4}$   9. 5.9, -0.8   11. $-\frac{3}{2}, \frac{1}{5}$
13. $2(x - 2) = 0$   15. $5x(x + 3) = 0$   17. $1.6x(x - 3) = 0$

PAGE 348   WRITTEN EXERCISES 13.7

1. -1, -2   3. 2, -5   5. 3, 2   7. -5, 5   9. $-\frac{1}{2}$, 3   11. -3.5, 1.7   13. 3

15. $-\frac{3}{2}$   17. 1   19. $-\frac{5}{2}$, 5   21. $3x(x-4)=0$; 0, 4   23. $4x(3x-1)=0$; 0, $-\frac{1}{3}$

25. $2.3x(x-4)=0$; 0, 4   27. $\frac{1}{2}x(x-\frac{1}{4})=0$; 0, $\frac{1}{4}$   29. $5x(-3x+4)=0$; 0, $\frac{4}{3}$

PAGE 349   CHAPTER REVIEW

1. 14   3. -44   5. -5.0   7. $1\frac{3}{4}$   9. -6   11. 8   13. 19   15. 55   17. 9

19. 9.3   21. -15   23. $8\frac{1}{4}$   25. $-5\frac{3}{4}$   27. 32.2   29. -14   31. $-\frac{128}{125}$   33. -4

35. -24   37. 16   39. -5   41. $13\frac{1}{2}$   43. n:  unknown number; $5n-8=14-3n$.
The number is $2\frac{3}{4}$.   45. 1.6, 2.9   47. 0, $\frac{3}{4}$


CHAPTER 14   REAL NUMBERS

PAGE 353   ORAL EXERCISES 14.1

1. 64   3. 144   5. $\frac{4}{9}$   7. $\frac{49}{64}$   9. 1.44   11. $\frac{9}{4}$ or $2\frac{1}{4}$   13. 7, -7   15. $\frac{6}{7}$, $-\frac{6}{7}$

17. 0.7, -0.7   19. 0.3, -0.3   21. 1.3, -1.3   23. 10   25. 14   27. $\frac{4}{7}$   29. 1.5

PAGE 354   WRITTEN EXERCISES 14.1

1. 144   3. 100   5. 256   7. 289   9. $\frac{1}{49}$   11. $\frac{4}{81}$   13. $\frac{25}{441}$   15. 3.24

17. 0.0144   19. 0.0064   21. 12, -12   23. 15, -15   25. $\frac{1}{8}$, $-\frac{1}{8}$   27. $\frac{13}{7}$, $-\frac{13}{7}$

29. 0.2, -0.2   31. -1   33. 6   35. -10   37. 0.7   39. $\frac{2}{7}$   41. $-\frac{15}{9}$ or $-\frac{5}{3}$

43. -1.1   45. 0.06   47. No   49. Yes   51. No   53. No


PAGE 356   ORAL EXERCISES 14.2

1. 7   3. 18   5. 36   7. $\frac{1}{2}$   9. $\frac{11}{8}$   Note:  For Exercises 11-29 R. means rational
and Irr. means irrational.   11. R.   13. Irr.   15. R.   17. R.   19. Irr.
21. Irr.   23. R.   25. R.   27. Irr.   29. R.


PAGE 357   WRITTEN EXERCISES 14.2

1. 15   3. 13   5. $\frac{1}{3}$   7. 208   9. 64   Note:  R. means rational; Irr. means
irrational.   11. R.   13. Irr.   15. R.   17. R.   19. R.   21. R.   23. R.
25. Irr.   27. R.   29. R.   31. R.   33. Irr.   35. $4\sqrt{3}$   37. $\sqrt{370}$   39. $7\sqrt{13}$


PAGE 360   ORAL EXERCISES 14.3

1. $\sqrt{12}$   3. $\sqrt{35}$   5. $\sqrt{28}$   7. $\sqrt{90}$   9. $\sqrt{3}\cdot\sqrt{7}$   11. $\sqrt{2}\cdot\sqrt{13}$
13. $\sqrt{11}\cdot\sqrt{3}$   15. $\sqrt{3}\cdot\sqrt{5}$   17. $2\sqrt{7}$   19. $3\sqrt{5}$   21. $6\sqrt{2}$   23. $2\sqrt{13}$


PAGE 360   WRITTEN EXERCISES 14.3

1. $\sqrt{14}$   3. $\sqrt{45}$   5. $\sqrt{56}$   7. $\sqrt{36}$   9. $\sqrt{121}$   11. $\sqrt{24}$   13. $3\sqrt{33}$
15. $5\sqrt{37}$   17. $7\sqrt{7}$   19. 7   21. $3\sqrt{15}$   23. $4\sqrt{26}$   25. $9\sqrt{35}$   27. $2\sqrt{6}$
29. $3\sqrt{5}$   31. $4\sqrt{5}$


PAGE 362   ORAL EXERCISES 14.4

1. $14\sqrt{2}$   3. $3\sqrt{5}$   5. $15\sqrt{11}$   7. $-2\sqrt{15}$   9. $\sqrt{13}$   11. $12\sqrt{2}$   13. $5\sqrt{5}$

15. $-\sqrt{11}$  17. $\sqrt{5}$  19. $7\sqrt{3}$  21. 0

PAGE 363  WRITTEN EXERCISES 14.4
1. $16\sqrt{2}$  3. $14\sqrt{5}$  5. $3\sqrt{6}$  7. $13\sqrt{11}$  9. $-2\sqrt{10}$  11. $8\sqrt{3}$  13. $6\sqrt{6}$
15. $-9\sqrt{10}$  17. $\frac{9}{2}\sqrt{6}$  19. $8\sqrt{2}$  21. $8\sqrt{2}$  23. $\sqrt{6}$  25. $3\sqrt{7}+3\sqrt{3}-3\sqrt{5}$
27. $10\sqrt{2}$

PAGE 365  ORAL EXERCISES 14.5
1. $-20\sqrt{3}$  3. $-70\sqrt{6}$  5. $\sqrt{42}$  7. $-\sqrt{55}$  9. $-12\sqrt{14}$  11. $2\sqrt{3}$  13. 256
15. 19  17. -18  19. 3.162  21. -5.099

PAGE 366  WRITTEN EXERCISES 14.5
1. $-72\sqrt{5}$  3. $-120\sqrt{7}$  5. $18\sqrt{2}$  7. $\sqrt{65}$  9. $-\sqrt{66}$  11. $\sqrt{230}$  13. $-12\sqrt{10}$
15. $-\frac{5}{2}\sqrt{30}$  17. $10\sqrt{6}$  19. $2\sqrt{5}$  21. $-6\sqrt{10}$  23. $10\sqrt{14}$  25. 4.472
27. 7.070  29. 6.928  31. 8.484  33. 10.392  35. 14.140  37. 11.312
39. 5.830  41. 6.246  43. 6.480

PAGE 368  ORAL EXERCISES 14.6
1. $\sqrt{\frac{32}{8}}$; 2  3. $\sqrt{\frac{50}{2}}$; 5  5. $\sqrt{\frac{60}{6}}$; $\sqrt{10}$  7. $\frac{\sqrt{3}}{\sqrt{10}}$  9. $\frac{\sqrt{3}}{\sqrt{19}}$  11. $\frac{\sqrt{21}}{7}$
13. $\frac{\sqrt{15}}{3}$  15. $\frac{\sqrt{3}}{8}$

PAGE 369  WRITTEN EXERCISES 14.6
1. $\sqrt{\frac{28}{7}}$; 2  3. $\sqrt{\frac{45}{5}}$; 3  5. $\sqrt{\frac{125}{5}}$; 5  7. $\sqrt{\frac{98}{2}}$; 7  9. $\sqrt{\frac{60}{10}}$; $\sqrt{6}$  11. $\frac{\sqrt{2}}{\sqrt{9}}$; $\frac{\sqrt{10}}{7}$
13. $\frac{\sqrt{13}}{\sqrt{36}}$; $\frac{\sqrt{5}}{5}$  15. $\frac{\sqrt{29}}{\sqrt{64}}$; $\frac{\sqrt{29}}{8}$  17. $\frac{\sqrt{11}}{\sqrt{64}}$; $\frac{\sqrt{11}}{8}$  19. $\frac{\sqrt{21}}{\sqrt{100}}$; $\frac{\sqrt{21}}{10}$  21. 0.866

23. 0.535  25. 0.258  27. $\frac{\sqrt{30}}{3}$  29. $\frac{\sqrt{42}}{6}$  31. $\frac{\sqrt{26}}{13}$  33. $\frac{\sqrt{22}}{22}$  35. $\frac{3\sqrt{14}}{34}$

PAGE 372  CHAPTER REVIEW
1. -5  3. $\frac{3}{5}$  5. $\frac{1}{3}$  7. -0.4  9. 17  11. $\frac{5}{8}$  13. 1078  15. Irrational
17. Rational  19. Rational  21. Rational  23. $\sqrt{39}$  25. $8\sqrt{11}$  27. 79
29. $5\sqrt{3}$  31. $5\sqrt{2}$  33. $3\sqrt{7}$  35. $6\sqrt{3}$  37. $15\sqrt{5}$  39. $17\sqrt{3}$  41. $-12\sqrt{6}$
43. $-3\sqrt{6}$  45. $-56\sqrt{5}$  47. $4\sqrt{6}$  49. $-48\sqrt{15}$  51. $6\sqrt{15}$
53. $\sqrt{\frac{52}{13}}$; 2  55. $\sqrt{\frac{128}{8}}$; 4  57. $\frac{\sqrt{7}}{\sqrt{36}}$; $\frac{\sqrt{7}}{6}$  59. $\frac{\sqrt{10}}{\sqrt{81}}$; $\frac{\sqrt{10}}{9}$  61. $\frac{\sqrt{65}}{13}$  63. $\frac{\sqrt{110}}{11}$
65. $\frac{4}{3}\sqrt{3}$

CHAPTER 15  RELATIONS AND FUNCTIONS

PAGE 377  ORAL EXERCISES 15.1
Note: For Exercises 1-15, start at the origin and make the moves listed for each point.
1. Right 3; down 6  3. Left 1; down 7  5. Right 8; down 9  7. Left 12; down 20
9. Left 25; up 50  11. Left 15  13. Up 30  15. Right 32; down 32  17. (-3, 1)
30  CHAPTER 15

19. (2, -2)  21. (-2, 2)  23. (5, 3)  25. (0, 3)  27. (-5, -3)  29. (2, 2)
31. (4, 0)

PAGE 378  WRITTEN EXERCISES 15.1
Note: For Exercises 1-23, start at the origin and make the moves listed for each point.
1. Right 4; up 13  3. Left 5; down 12  5. Right 15; down 3  7. Left 30; up 10
9. Left 14  11. Up 11  13. Right 4; up 2  15. Left 3; down 5  17. Right 4;
down 5  19. Left 5; up 4  21. Right 6  23. Down 5  25. (-4, 2)  27. (-3, -2)
29. (0, 4)  31. (4, -2)  33. (2, 0)  35. (2, 3)

PAGE 380  ORAL EXERCISES 15.2

1.
| x | y |
|----|----|
| -5 | -3 |
| -1 | 1 |
| 0 | 2 |
| 4 | 6 |

3.
| x | y |
|----|----|
| -3 | -1 |
| -1 | 3 |
| 0 | 5 |
| $1\frac{1}{2}$ | 8 |

5. Multiply each x value by 2.

PAGE 381  WRITTEN EXERCISES 15.2
Note: For Exercises 1-5 each graph is four points.  1. First point: 3 units left,
2 units up; second: 4 right, 2 down; third: 3 up; fourth: 2 right, 5 up  3. First
point: 2 units right, 2 units down; 2nd: 4 left, 5 down; 3rd: 3 down; 4th: 4 right,
1 down  5. First point: $2\frac{1}{2}$ units right, 3 units up; 2nd: 4 left, $1\frac{1}{2}$ down; 3rd: $3\frac{1}{2}$
down; 4th: $4\frac{1}{2}$ right, $2\frac{1}{2}$ up  7. $\left\{(0, 0), (1\frac{1}{2}, -3), (3, -6), (-4, 8)\right\}$  9. $\left\{(0, -2),\right.$
$(1\frac{1}{2}, 1), (3, 4), (-4, -10)\right\}$  11. $\left\{(0, -1\frac{1}{2}), (1\frac{1}{2}, -\frac{3}{4}), (3, 0), (-4, -3\frac{1}{2})\right\}$

13. Add -2 to each x value.
| x | 5 | 1 | -3 | 0 | 3 | -4 |
|----|----|----|----|----|----|----|
| y | 3 | -1 | -5 | -2 | 1 | -6 |

15. Take the opposite of each x value.
| x | $-1\frac{1}{2}$ | 0 | 3 | -5 | $\frac{3}{4}$ | -1.7 |
|----|----|----|----|----|----|----|
| y | $1\frac{1}{2}$ | 0 | -3 | 5 | $-\frac{3}{4}$ | 1.7 |

17.
| x | 3x - 2 |
|----|----|
| -3 | -11 |
| -1 | -5 |
| 0 | -2 |
| 5 | 13 |

19.
| x | -x + 3 |
|----|----|
| -5 | 8 |
| 0 | 3 |
| 12 | -9 |
| $-3\frac{1}{2}$ | $6\frac{1}{2}$ |

PAGE 383  ORAL EXERCISES 15.3
1. Yes  3. No  5. Yes  7. D = $\left\{1, -3, -1\right\}$; R = $\left\{4, 5, 4\right\}$  9. D = $\left\{\frac{1}{2}, -\frac{1}{4}, 7\right\}$;
R = $\left\{3, 2, \frac{3}{4}\right\}$  11. D = $\left\{0, -1, 3, 5\right\}$; R = $\left\{5, 6, -2, -1\right\}$  13. $\left\{-5, 0, 5, 10\right\}$
15. $\left\{2, 0, -2, -4\right\}$  17. $\left\{-4, -1, 2, 5\right\}$  19. $\left\{-1, 0, 1, 2\right\}$

PAGE 384  WRITTEN EXERCISES 15.3
1. Yes  3. No  5. No  7. $\left\{(0, 1), (-1, -3), (2, 9), (-3, -11)\right\}$  9. $\left\{(0, 3),\right.$
$(2, -1), (-2, 7), (3, -3)\right\}$  11. $\left\{(-5, 3), (2, -4), (0, -2), (\frac{1}{2}, -2\frac{1}{2})\right\}$

13. $D = \{5, 3, 8\}$; $R = \{0, -2, 3\}$  15. $D = \{-1, 5, 0, 2\}$; $R = \{8, 2, -3\}$  17. $D = \{3, 0, -3, 4\}$; $R = \{0, 3, -3\}$  19. $D = \{1, -2, -3, -4\}$; $R = \{2, 3, 4, 0\}$

## PAGE 386   ORAL EXERCISES 15.4

1. -2   3. -1   5. 1   7. 1

9.

| x | y |
|---|---|
| -2 | 0 |
| -1 | 1 |
| 0 | 2 |
| 1 | 3 |
| 2 | 4 |

11.

| x | y |
|---|---|
| -2 | 3 |
| -1 | 2 |
| 0 | 1 |
| 1 | 0 |
| 2 | -1 |

13.

| x | -2 | -1 | 0 | 1 | 2 |
|---|---|---|---|---|---|
| y | -5 | -2 | 1 | 4 | 7 |

## PAGE 387   WRITTEN EXERCISES 15.4

1.

| x | y |
|---|---|
| -4 | -2 |
| -2 | 0 |
| 0 | 2 |
| 2 | 4 |

3.

| x | y |
|---|---|
| -4 | 1 |
| -2 | -1 |
| 0 | -3 |
| 2 | -5 |

5.

| x | y |
|---|---|
| -1 | -5 |
| 0 | -3 |
| 2 | 1 |
| 4 | 5 |

7.

| x | y |
|---|---|
| -4 | -3 |
| -2 | -2 |
| 0 | -1 |
| 2 | 0 |

Note: For Exercises 9-15, each graph is a straight line containing the two points given for each.

9. $(0, 2)$, $(-2, 0)$   11. $(0, -3)$, $(-3, 0)$   13. $(0, -3)$, $(1\frac{1}{2}, 0)$   15. $(0, -1)$, $(2, 0)$   Note: For Exercises 17-23 each graph is a straight line. Four ordered pairs are given for each function.   17. $(-1, 5)(0, 4)(1, 3)(2, 2)$   19. $(2, 3)$, $(1, 1)$, $(0, -1)$, $(-1, -3)$   21. $(-2, 3)$, $(0, 2)$, $(2, 1)$, $(4, 0)$   23. $(-2, -4)$, $(0, -1)$, $(2, 2)$, $(4, 5)$   Note: Exercise 29 is linear. Exercises 25 and 27 are not linear. Four points are given for each graph.   25. $(-1, 1)$, $(0, 0)$, $(1, 1)$, $(2, 4)$   27. $(-2, 1)$, $(-1, 0)$, $(0, 1)$, $(1, 2)$   29. $(-1, 0)$, $(0, 1)$, $(1, 2)$, $(2, 3)$

## PAGE 389   ORAL EXERCISES 15.5

1. -2   3. 10   5. $-\frac{1}{2}$   7. 0.7   9. -8.4   11. -1   13. -4   15. -2   17. $-\frac{1}{2}$

## PAGE 390   WRITTEN EXERCISES 15.5

1. 5   3. -4   5. 0   7. $-\frac{1}{2}$   9. -2.1   11. 6.9   13. 3   15. -10   17. -2
19. $\frac{1}{3}$   21. $-\frac{5}{2}$   23. $-\frac{7}{3}$   Note: For Ex. 25-35, each graph is a straight line. In the ordered pairs, the X intercept is given first, then the Y intercept, and then one other point.   25. $(3, 0)$, $(0, -3)$, $(1, -2)$   27. $(-\frac{5}{2}, 0)$, $(0, \frac{5}{2})$, $(\frac{1}{2}, 3)$
29. $(2, 0)$, $(0, -4)$, $(1, -2)$   31. $(4, 0)$, $(0, -2)$, $(2, -1)$   33. $(2, 0)$, $(0, 3)$, $(-2, 6)$   35. $(2, 0)$, $(0, -6)$, $(1, -3)$   Note: For Ex. 37-45, the X intercept is given first.   37. 2; -2   39. 8; -4   41. $-\frac{5}{2}$; 5   43. $-\frac{9}{4}$; -9   45. -6; 2

## PAGE 392   ORAL EXERCISES 15.6

1. Yes   3. No   5. Yes

## PAGE 392   WRITTEN EXERCISES 15.6

Note: For Exercises 1-7, each graph is two straight lines.

1. Intersection $\{(1\frac{1}{2}, -\frac{1}{2})\}$

| x | y |
|---|---|
| -2 | -4 |
| 0 | -2 |
| 4 | 2 |

| x | y |
|---|---|
| -3 | 4 |
| 0 | 1 |
| 4 | -3 |

3. Intersection $\{(2, 3)\}$

| x | y |
|---|---|
| -2 | -5 |
| 0 | -1 |
| 2 | 3 |

| x | y |
|---|---|
| -4 | -3 |
| -2 | -1 |
| 3 | 4 |

5. Intersection

$\{(-2, 5)\}$

| x | y |
|---|---|
| -2 | 5 |
| 0 | -1 |
| 2 | -7 |

| x | y |
|---|---|
| -1 | 3 |
| 1 | -1 |
| 3 | -5 |

7. Intersection

$\{\ \}$, or $\phi$

| x | y |
|---|---|
| -4 | -4 |
| -2 | -3 |
| 0 | -2 |

| x | y |
|---|---|
| -2 | 0 |
| 0 | 1 |
| 4 | 3 |

## PAGE 393   CHAPTER REVIEW

1. $(-3, 2)$   3. $(3, -1)$   5. $(-3, 0)$   For Ex. 7-11 start at origin and make the moves given for each.   7. 2 left; 3 down   9. 2 right; 4 up   11. 2 up   Note: For Ex. 13-15, each graph is 4 points.   13. First point: 2 units right, 3 units up; 2nd: 4 left, 2 up; 3rd: 3 down; 4th: 2 left, 2 down.   15. First point: $2\frac{1}{2}$ right, $1\frac{1}{2}$ up; 2nd: 3 left, $2\frac{1}{2}$ up; 3rd: $3\frac{1}{2}$ left, 4 down; 4th: $\frac{1}{2}$ left.   17. $\{(0, -5), (-1, -6),$ $(2, -3), (-2, -7)\}$   19. $\{(0, -3), (-1, -4), (2, -1), (-2, -5)\}$   21. Yes   23. D = $\{7, 4, -6\}$; R = $\{-2, 0, 1\}$   25. D = $\{-\frac{1}{2}, 3, 0\}$; R = $\{1, -4\}$   Note: For Ex. 27 and 29, each graph is a straight line. Four ordered pairs are given for each.
27. $\{(0, -2), (-2, 0), (1, -3), (-1, -1)\}$   29. $\{(-2, -1), (0, -2), (2, -3), (4, -4)\}$
31. -6   33. 15   35. 12   37. -6   Note: The graph is a pair of straight lines. Ordered pairs show X and Y intercepts.   39. Intersection: $\{(-2, -5)\}$; $(\frac{1}{2}, 0)$, 0, -1), (3, 0), (0, -3)

## CHAPTER 16   EQUATIONS WITH TWO VARIABLES

### PAGE 397   ORAL EXERCISES 16.1

1. Yes   3. No   5. Yes   7. $y = x - 1$   9. $y = 2x + 5$   11. $y = -2x - 3$   13. Yes

### PAGE 397   WRITTEN EXERCISES 16.1

Note: For Exercises 1-15, each graph is a pair of straight lines. The coordinates of two points are given for each line.   1. $(0, 2)$, $(2, 0)$; $(0, -1)$, $(1, 1)$; Truth set: $\{(1, 1)\}$   3. First equation: $(2, 2)$, $(0, 1)$; Second equation: $(-3, 0)$, $(0, 3)$; Truth set: $\{(-4, -1)\}$   5. First equation: $(-2, 0)$, $(2, 2)$; Second equation: $(0, -2)$, $(-4, 2)$; Truth set: $\{(-2, 0)\}$   7. First equation: $(-1, -2)$, $(1, 2)$; Second equation: $(-3, 1)$, $(3, -1)$; Truth set: $\{(0, 0)\}$   9. First equation: $(-6, 5)$, $(-3, 3)$; Second equation: $(4, 3)$, $(-6, -2)$; Truth set: $\{(0, 1)\}$   11. First equation: $(-1, 0)$, $(1, 4)$; Second equation: $(0, -1)$, $(4, 1)$; Truth set: $\{(-2, -2)\}$   13. First equation: $(-1, 0)$, $(1, -1)$; Second equation: $(0, \frac{3}{2})$, $(-1, 1)$; Truth set: $\{(-2, \frac{1}{2})\}$   15. First equation: $(-4, 5)$, $(-3, 1)$; Second equation: $(-1, 0)$, $(2, 2)$; Truth set: $\{(-2\frac{1}{2}, -1)\}$

### PAGE 400   ORAL EXERCISES 16.2

1. $x = -y + 10$ or $y = -x + 10$   3. $y = -3x + 1$   5. $x = 2y - 7$   7. $y = 3x - 9$
9. $x = 2y - 4$   11. $-2y + 6 + 3y - 1 = 0$   13. $-x - 4x - 6 + 4 = 0$
15. $y - 2 + y - 5 = 0$

### PAGE 400   WRITTEN EXERCISES 16.2

1. $\{(2, -3)\}$   3. $\{(-5, -2)\}$   5. $\{(7, -3)\}$   7. $\{(-7, -18)\}$   9. $\{(\frac{3}{2}, 3)\}$

11. $\{(14, 10)\}$   13. $\left\{(-\frac{1}{4}, \frac{9}{4})\right\}$   15. $\left\{(\frac{3}{2}, 3)\right\}$

PAGE 402   ORAL EXERCISES 16.3

1. $3y - 2 = 0$   3. $5x = 6$   5. $3x = -5$   7. Multiply the first equation by 2.
9. Multiply the second equation by 3.   11. Multiply the first equation by -5 and
the second equation by 2, or multiply the first equation by 5 and the second equation
by -2.   13. $\{(-2, 4)\}$   15. $\left\{(\frac{2}{3}, -3)\right\}$

PAGE 403   WRITTEN EXERCISES 16.3

1. $\{(-1, 2)\}$   3. $\left\{(\frac{1}{3}, 2)\right\}$   5. $\{(0, 1)\}$   7. $\{(-2, -1)\}$   9. $\{(7, 2)\}$   11. $\{(0, 0)\}$
13. $\left\{(-2, \frac{1}{3})\right\}$   15. $\{(-4, 7)\}$   17. $\{(0, -1)\}$   19. $\{(-1, -1)\}$   21. $\left\{(\frac{1}{2}, 1)\right\}$

PAGE 405   ORAL EXERCISES 16.4

1. $y = x + 12$   3. $y = 3x$, $x > 0$; $x = \frac{y}{3}$, $x < 0$   5. $x - y = -3$   7. $x = \frac{y}{3}$, $y > 0$;
$y = \frac{x}{3}$, $y < 0$   9. $y = x + 16$   11. $2x = y + 2$   13. $x - y = -25$   15. $-x = y + 12$

PAGE 406   WRITTEN EXERCISES 16.4

1. x: greater number; y: lesser number; $x + y = 31$; $x - y = 3$; $x = 17$; $y = 14$
3. x: lesser number; y: greater number; $x + y = 5$; $x - y = -2$; $x = 1\frac{1}{2}$; $y = 3\frac{1}{2}$
5. x: one number; y: other number; $x - y = 13$; $x + y = 38$; $x = 25\frac{1}{2}$; $y = 12\frac{1}{2}$
7. x: greater number; y: smaller number; $x - y = 8$; $x + 4 = 2y$; $x = 20$; $y = 12$
9. x: greater number; y: smaller number; $3x = 2y$; $x + y = -20$; $x = -8$; $y = -12$
11. x: smaller number; y: greater number; $2x = y - 18$; $3y = x + 34$; $x = -4$; $y = 10$

PAGE 408   ORAL EXERCISES 16.5

1. $x + y = 21$; $10x + 5y = 230$   3. $x + y = 48$; $5x + 2y = 216$

PAGE 409   WRITTEN EXERCISES 16.5

1. x: number of nickels; y: number of dimes; $x + y = 29$; $5x + 10y = 185$; $x = 17$;
$y = 10$   3. x: boxes of $2.00 cookies; y: boxes of $2.50 cookies; $x + y = 29$;
$200x + 250y = 6800$; $x = 9$; $y = 20$   5. x: number of hot dogs; y: number of hamburgers; $x = y + 4$; $65x + 90y = 1965$; $x = 15$ hot dogs; $y = 11$ hamburgers   7. x:
number of white tickets; y: number of red tickets; $x + y = 260$; $75x + 125y = 29000$;
$x = 70$ white tickets; $y = 190$ red tickets   9. x: number of dimes; $x + 4$: number of
nickels; y: number of quarters; $x + (x + 4) + y = 34$; $10x + 5(x + 4) + 25y = 490$;
$x = 8$ dimes; $x + 4 = 12$ nickels; $y = 14$ quarters

PAGE 411   ORAL EXERCISES 16.6

1. $2x + 2y = 25$   3. $x + 2y = 25$   5. $x = y + 200$   7. $x + y = 37$
9. $3x + 3y = 81$ or $x + y = 27$   11. $92x + 85y = 1225$   13. $x + y = 16$

PAGE 412   WRITTEN EXERCISES 16.6

1. x: width; y: length; $x = y - 5$; $2x + 2y = 54$; $x = 11$ millimeters (width);

y = 16 millimeters (length)   3.  x:  length of each of two sides; y:  length of third
side; 2x + y = 18; y = x + 3; x = 5 meters; y = 8 meters   5.  x:  Jody's age; y:
brother's age; x = 2 + 2y; x - y = 6; x = 10 years (Jody); y = 4 years (brother)
7.  x:  length of each of two sections; y:  length of third section; x = y - 5;
2x + y = 53; x = 16 centimeters; y = 21 centimeters   9.  x:  distance from Dallas to
Houston; y:  distance from Houston to Mexico City; x = y - 850; x + y = 1550; x = 350
kilometers; y = 1200 kilometers   11.  x:  tens digit; y:  ones digit; x + y = 17;
x = y - 1; x = 8; y = 9  The number is 89.

## PAGE 416   CHAPTER REVIEW

Note:  For Exercises 1-15, each graph is a pair of straight lines.  The coordinates of
two points are given for each line.   1.  (-1, 0), (1, 2); (0, -2), (-6, 1); Truth set:
$\{(-2, -1)\}$   3.  (1, 0), (-1, 2); $(-\frac{1}{2}, 0)$, (1, 3); Truth set: $\{(0, 1)\}$   5. $\{(-1, -1)\}$
7. $\{(10, 6)\}$   9. $\{(-2, 0)\}$   11. $\{(-3, 4)\}$   13.  x:  one number; y:  other number;
x + y = 32; x - y = 7; $x = 19\frac{1}{2}$; $y = 12\frac{1}{2}$   15.  x:  greater number; y:  lesser number;
x + y = 52; x = y + 22; x = 37; y = 15   17.  x:  glasses of tea; y:  glasses of
lemonade; x + y = 30; 15x + 20y = 510; x = 18; y = 12   19.  x:  number of nickels;
y:  number of dimes; x + y = 15; 5x + 10y = 120; x = 6 nickels; y = 9 dimes
21.  x:  width; y:  length; 2x + 2y = 28; x = 2y - 10; x = 6 centimeters; y = 8
centimeters   23.  x:  Pat's age; y:  teacher's age; y = x + 29; x + y = 61; x = 16
years (Pat); y = 45 years (teacher)

## CHAPTER 17   MORE ALGEBRAIC FRACTIONS

### PAGE 421   ORAL EXERCISES 17.1

1. $\frac{3}{3}$   3. $\frac{3 \cdot 5}{3 \cdot 5}$ or $\frac{15}{15}$   5. $\frac{3a}{3a}$   7. $\frac{x}{x}$   9. $\frac{4ab}{4ab}$   11. $-\frac{x}{2y}$   13. $\frac{2}{3x}$   15. $\frac{2}{3x}$
17. $\frac{x}{x + 1}$   19. $\frac{x + 1}{x + 1}$   21. $\frac{x}{x - 2}$

### PAGE 422   WRITTEN EXERCISES 17.1

1. $\frac{1}{3}$   3. $\frac{5}{5}$   5. $\frac{5y}{5y}$   7. $\frac{4}{4}$   9. $\frac{3}{4y}$   11. $\frac{x + 2}{x + 2}$   13. $-\frac{x}{y}$   15. $\frac{r}{2t}$   17. $-\frac{5x}{3y}$
19. $-\frac{3a}{7}$   21. $-\frac{1}{2x}$   23. $\frac{4}{7}$   25. $-\frac{x - 1}{2(x + 1)}$   27. $\frac{a}{b}$

### PAGE 425   ORAL EXERCISES 17.2

1. $7 - n$   3. $r - s$   5. $\frac{1}{2} - 3y$   7. 1   9. 1   11. -1   13. $-\frac{1}{4}$   15. 1

### PAGE 425   WRITTEN EXERCISES 17.2

1. $18 - r$   3. $y - 1.9$   5. $6 - 2a$   7. $2y - 3x$   9. 1   11. 1   13. -1   15. 1
17. $-\frac{2}{3}$   19. $\frac{1}{2}$   21. $-\frac{1}{2}$   23. $\frac{2}{3}$   25. $-\frac{2}{3}$   27. $-\frac{1}{2}$   29. $\frac{y}{2}$   31. $\frac{a(5a - b)}{3a(a + 2b)}$

### PAGE 427   ORAL EXERCISES 17.3

1. $-\frac{6}{77}$   3. $-\frac{3a}{5x}$   5. $\frac{10}{xy}$   7. $\frac{15}{2}$   9. $\frac{ax}{by}$   11. $\frac{3}{5}$   13. $-\frac{5}{8}$   15. 1

1. $\frac{6}{55}$  3. $-\frac{2y}{5t}$  5. $\frac{10}{3}$  7. $\frac{3}{2}$  9. $\frac{1}{4}$  11. $-\frac{1}{3}$  13. $-\frac{1}{2x}$  15. $\frac{1}{x}$  17. $\frac{1}{x}$
19. $-\frac{1}{3x}$  21. $\frac{3}{8x}$  23. $-\frac{1}{3}$

PAGE 431  ORAL EXERCISES 17.4

1. $\frac{7}{y}$  3. $\frac{3a}{x}$  5. $-\frac{4}{y}$  7. $\frac{2y}{x-2}$  9. $\frac{x}{t}$  11. $\frac{2t+3}{x+4}$

PAGE 431  WRITTEN EXERCISES 17.4

1. $-\frac{3}{5x}$  3. $\frac{1}{2m}$  5. $\frac{2s}{3t}$  7. $\frac{4x}{5y}$  9. $\frac{6x}{x+7}$  11. $\frac{p}{q+6}$  13. $\frac{2x-5}{x-8}$
15. 1  17. -1  19. $\frac{x+4}{x+2}$  21. 2  23. $\frac{1}{2}$  25. $\frac{x}{2}$

PAGE 433  ORAL EXERCISES 17.5

1. $\frac{1}{4} \cdot \frac{4}{3}$  3. $(-\frac{r}{6}) \cdot (-\frac{2}{s})$  5. $\frac{5t}{t-3} \cdot \frac{4}{t+2}$  7. $\frac{x}{2} \cdot \frac{5}{x-3}$  9. 10  11. 8
13. 12  15. 24y

PAGE 434  WRITTEN EXERCISES 17.5

1. $\frac{3}{5} \cdot (-\frac{8}{7}) = -\frac{24}{35}$  3. $\frac{a}{3} \cdot \frac{9}{2a} = \frac{3}{2}$  5. $(-\frac{a}{5}) \cdot (-\frac{3}{2a}) = \frac{3}{10}$  7. $\frac{5}{x-2} \cdot \frac{x-2}{3} = \frac{5}{3}$
9. $\frac{y+3}{2y} \cdot \frac{y}{y+3} = \frac{1}{2}$  11. $\frac{1}{2}$  13. $\frac{2n}{3+n}$  15. $\frac{15+2x}{4}$  17. $\frac{18+3x}{2}$
19. $\frac{3}{2+8y}$  21. $\frac{12a+9}{-30+2a}$

PAGE 435  CHAPTER REVIEW

1. $-\frac{r}{s}$  3. $\frac{2x}{3y}$  5. $-\frac{3}{4}$  7. -1  9. $\frac{5}{6}$  11. $-\frac{4}{5}$  13. $-\frac{6s}{5}$  15. $-\frac{3}{4}$  17. $-\frac{3}{7}$
19. $-\frac{1}{4x}$  21. $\frac{4q+5}{q+2}$  23. $\frac{5m-2}{m+3}$  25. $-\frac{2a}{3} \cdot \frac{9}{10a}; -\frac{3}{5}$  27. $\frac{4x-3}{3y} \cdot \frac{6}{4x-3}; \frac{2}{y}$
29. $\frac{18+4x}{3-5x}$

CHAPTER 18  POLYNOMIALS

PAGE 439  ORAL EXERCISES 18.1

1. $-2x + 2$  3. $x^2 - 3x + 6$  5. $-2x^2 + x + 7$  7. $3x^2 - \frac{3}{4}$  9. $3x^2 - 2x - 3$

PAGE 439  WRITTEN EXERCISES 18.1

1. $4x - 2$  3. $2x^2 + x + 9$  5. $-5x^2 - 2x - 7$  7. $10x^3 + 2x^2 - x + 1$
9. $4x^2 - 9x - 9$  11. $4x^3 - 4x + 15$  13. $x^4 + 2x^3 - 11$  15. $\frac{3}{4}x^3 + x^2 - 1$
17. $-4.7x^2 + 1.8x + 0.8$  19. $22x^4 + 11x^2 - 7x + 24$  21. $2x^2 + 3x - 3$
23. $7x + 1$  25. $4x^2 - 2x - 3$

PAGE 441  ORAL EXERCISES 18.2

1. 4  3. 5  5. -4  7. 0  9. -24  11. -15

PAGE 441   WRITTEN EXERCISES 18.2

1. 11   3. 10   5. -41   7. -1   9. -5   11. -2   13. 26   15. 53   17. -7
19. 1   21. $-\frac{7}{16}$   23. $-\frac{1}{8}$   25. -0.896   27. 2.168

PAGE 443   ORAL EXERCISES 18.3

1. $7x + 3$   3. $3x^2 + 4x$   5. $5x^2 - 3x + 7$   7. $2x^2 - 4x + 5$   9. $-x^2y + 3xy + 6xy^2$
$- 2y^3$   11. $-2x^2 + 2$   13. $4x^2 + x - 7$   15. $5x^2y - xy + 2$

PAGE 443   WRITTEN EXERCISES 18.3

1. $-2x + 5$   3. $2x^2 - 3$   5. $7x^2 - 3x + 5$   7. $6x^2 - 3x + 3$   9. $8.2x^3 - 5.6x^2$
$- 1.7x - 2.3$   11. $3x^2 + 4x - 2$   13. $2x^3 - 3x^2 + 2x + 7$   15. $2x^2 - 8x + 5$
17. $2x^2y - 3xy^2 - 3xy - 4$   Note: For Exercises 19-29, only the answer is given.
19. $x^3 + 2x + 4$   21. $-2x^3 + x^2 - x + 12$   23. $2x^3 - 3x + 16$   25. $2x^3y^2 + 5x^2y^2$
$+ 5x^2y - 2xy^3 + 5xy - 6$   27. $1.5x^2 - 0.9xy + 3.8xy^2 - 6.3x - 5.8y$
29. $9x^2yz^3 + 9xy^2z - 5xyz^2 + 7xyz + 19xz$

PAGE 446   ORAL EXERCISES 18.4

1. $4x - 7$   3. $-5x^2 - 4x + 2$   5. $2x + 5$   7. $2x^2 + x - 2$

PAGE 446   WRITTEN EXERCISES 18.4

1. $4x - 5$   3. $-x^2 + 7x$   5. $8x^2 - 5x + 10$   7. $-3.5x^2 + 3.7x + 4.6$   9. $2x^2 - 7x$
$+ 11$   11. $-3x^3 - 3x^2 + 3x + 6$   13. $2.8x^2 - 2.7x - 0.6$   15. $-2x^3 - 2x^2 + 2x - 8$
17. $-2x^4 - 3x^3 + 2x^2 + 11x - 21$   19. $3x^2y^2 - 11xy - 7xy^2 - 5xy^3 + 9$

PAGE 448   ORAL EXERCISES 18.5

1. $x^2 + 5x + 6$   3. $x^2 + 3x - 10$   5. $2x^2 - 5x - 3$   7. $x^2 - 6x + 9$   9. $6x^2 - x - 2$
11. $8x^2 - 12x$   13. $-6x^2 + 9x - 12$   15. $x^3 - 8$

PAGE 449   WRITTEN EXERCISES 18.5

1. $x^2 + 3x - 10$   3. $x^2 - 17x + 72$   5. $3x^2 + 7x - 6$   7. $16x^2 - 40x + 25$
9. $9x^2 - 49$   11. $2x^3 - 2x^2 + 3x - 3$   13. $2x^3 - 11x^2 + 8x - 15$   15. $x^3 + 5x^2$
$- 19x + 40$   17. $x^3 + x^2 - x + 15$   19. $-3x^4 - 6x^3 + 2x^2 + 3x - 2$   21. $-2x^4 + 3x^3$
$- 8x^2 + 9x - 6$   23. $x^5 - x^4 - x^3 + x^2 + x - 1$   25. $x^4 + x^3 - 3x^2 + 7x - 6$
27. $-3x^5 - 6x^3 - x^2 + 9x - 3$   29. $2x^5 - 6x^4 - 7x^3 + 4x^2 + 21x + 10$

PAGE 451   ORAL EXERCISES 18.6

1. -5   3. x   5. -2x   7. $-2x + 2$   9. $-x - 8$   11. -9

PAGE 451   WRITTEN EXERCISES 18.6

1. $2x + 3$   3. $-2x + 5$   5. $x - 7$   7. $x^2 - 2x + 3$   9. $x^2 - 4x + 6$   11. $x^2 - 5x - 5$

PAGE 454   CHAPTER REVIEW

1. $-x^2 + 5x + 3$   3. $x^3 + 3x^2 + 5$   5. $-0.4x^2 + 3.6x - 12.6$   7. -55   9. 1
11. -14   13. $3x - 4$   15. $-2x^2 + 6x - 4$   17. $3x^3 - x^2 + 6x + 4$   19. $4x^4 + 3x^3$
$+ x^2 + 3x - 12$   21. $5x^2 - 5x + 15$   23. $-2.1x^3 + 1.8x^2 + 7.8x + 0.9$

25. $20x^4 - 24x^3 - 12x^2 + 17x + 19$   27. $4x^3 - 12x^2 + 19x - 15$
29. $-3x^5 - x^4 - 6x^3 + x^2 + 6$   31. $4x^4 - x^3 + 14x^2 - 3x + 6$   33. $5x + 2$
35. $-3x^2 + x + 2$

PAGE 456   REVIEW EXERCISES FOR CHAPTERS 13-18
1. $x = 46$   3. $x = -4$   5. $x = -15$   7. $x = -18$   9. $x = -4$   11. $x = 4$
13. 8, -11   15. -4   17. $\frac{1}{8}$   19. Irrational   21. Rational   23. $4\sqrt{5}$   25. $3\sqrt{6}$
27. $21\sqrt{3}$   29. $-15\sqrt{15}$   31. $63\sqrt{5}$   33. $\sqrt{\frac{12}{3}}$; 2   35. $\sqrt{\frac{128}{8}}$; 4   Note: For
Exercises 37 and 39, start at the origin and make the moves listed for each point.
37. Right 5; down 3   39. Down 3   41. Add 8 to each x value; 5; 0   43. D =
$\left\{-1, 0, \frac{1}{2}, -10\right\}$; R = $\left\{2, -5, 3, 1\right\}$   Note: For Exercises 45 and 47, each graph is a
straight line containing the points given.   45. (0, 2), (-2, 0)   47. (0, -3),
(-6, 0)   49. 7   51. $-\frac{3}{2}$   53. -5   55. $3\frac{1}{2}$ or $\frac{7}{2}$   Note: For Exercises 57 and 59,
each graph is two straight lines containing the points given.   57. (0, 1), $(-\frac{1}{2}, 0)$;
(0, -2), (-2, 0); Intersection: $\left\{(-1, -1)\right\}$   59. (0, 3), (-3, 0); (0, $\frac{3}{2}$), (3, 0);
Truth set: $\left\{(-1, 2)\right\}$   61. $\left\{(1, 2)\right\}$   63. $\left\{(3, 7)\right\}$   65. x:   smaller number;
y:   greater number; x + 12 = y; x + y = 6; x = -3; y = 9   67. x:   price of hamburger
in cents; y:   price of milk shake in cents; 12x + 9y = 1320; x = 2y; x = 80 cents;
y = 40 cents   69. x:   distance from Chicago to Kansas City; y:   distance from
Kansas City to Denver; x + 227 = y; x + y = 1945; x = 859 km; y = 1086 km
71. $-\frac{6}{7x}$   73. $\frac{3}{4}$   75. -1   77. $-\frac{2}{3}$   79. $\frac{6}{7}$   81. $\frac{13s}{7t}$   83. $-\frac{5}{6}$
85. $2x^3 - 6x^2 + 4$   87. -9   89. $-2x^2 - 6x - 7$   91. $-5x^4 + 5x^3 + x^2 + 5x - 5$
93. $6x^3 - 19x^2 + 19x - 6$   95. $5x + 2$